Student Solutions Manual

Kelli Jade Hammer
Broward Community College

Prealgebra

Fourth Edition

K. Elayn Martin-Gay

PEARSON
Prentice Hall

Upper Saddle River, NJ 07458

Editor-in-Chief: Chris Hoag
Project Manager: Mary Beckwith
Assistant Editor: Christina Simoneau
Supplement Editor: Elizabeth Covello
Assistant Managing Editor: John Matthews
Production Editor: Donna Crilly
Supplement Cover Manager: Paul Gourhan
Supplement Cover Designer: Joanne Alexandris
Manufacturing Buyer: Ilene Kahn

Pearson Prentice Hall
Pearson Education, Inc.
Upper Saddle River, NJ 07458

Printed in the United States of America

10 9 8 7 6 5 4 3 2

ISBN 0-13-144539-1

Pearson Education Ltd., *London*
Pearson Education Australia Pty. Ltd., *Sydney*
Pearson Education Singapore, Pte. Ltd.
Pearson Education North Asia Ltd., *Hong Kong*
Pearson Education Canada, Inc., *Toronto*
Pearson Educación de Mexico, S.A. de C.V.
Pearson Education—Japan, *Tokyo*
Pearson Education Malaysia, Pte. Ltd.

Table of Contents

Chapter 1

Pretest

1. The place value of the 7 in 5732 is hundreds.

2. 23,490 is written as twenty-three thousand, four hundred ninety.

3. $$\begin{array}{r} \scriptstyle 1 \\ 58 \\ +\ 29 \\ \hline 87 \end{array}$$

4. $$\begin{array}{r} 413 \\ \times\ 9 \\ \hline 3717 \end{array}$$

5. $$\begin{array}{r} 857 \\ -\ 231 \\ \hline 626 \end{array}$$

   Check:
   $$\begin{array}{r} 626 \\ +\ 231 \\ \hline 857 \end{array}$$

6. $$\begin{array}{r} 51 \\ -\ 19 \\ \hline 32 \end{array}$$

   Check:
   $$\begin{array}{r} \scriptstyle 1 \\ 32 \\ +\ 19 \\ \hline 51 \end{array}$$

7. To find how many more pages Karen must read, we subtract the number of pages she has read from the number of pages in the book.
   $$\begin{array}{r} 329 \\ -\ 193 \\ \hline 136 \end{array}$$
   Karen has 136 pages left to read.

8. To round 9045 to the nearest 10, observe that the digit in the ones place is 5. Since this digit is at least 5, we need to add 1 to the digit in the tens place. The number 9045, rounded to the nearest ten is 9050.

9. $$\begin{array}{rlr} 382 & \text{rounds to} & 400 \\ 436 & \text{rounds to} & 400 \\ 2084 & \text{rounds to} & 2100 \\ +\ 176 & \text{rounds to} & +\ 200 \\ \hline & & 3100 \end{array}$$
   The estimated sum is 3100.

10. $9(3 + 11) = 9 \cdot 3 + 9 \cdot 11$

11. The perimeter is the sum of the lengths of the sides.
    $$\begin{array}{r} \scriptstyle 1 \\ 8 \\ 11 \\ +\ 6 \\ \hline 25 \end{array}$$
    The perimeter is 25 inches.

12. The area of a rectangle is the product of its length and its width.
    (23 yards)(8 yards) = 184 square yards

13. The total number of seats is the product of the number of rows and the number of seats in each row.
    (32 rows)(18 seats per row) = 576 seats

14. $$\begin{array}{r} 243 \\ 9\overline{)\ 2187} \\ -18 \\ \hline 38 \\ -36 \\ \hline 27 \\ -27 \\ \hline 0 \end{array}$$
    Check: $243 \cdot 9 = 2187$

15. $\frac{5361}{12}$
    $$\begin{array}{r} 446 \text{ R9} \\ 12\overline{)\ 5361} \\ -48 \\ \hline 56 \\ -48 \\ \hline 81 \\ -72 \\ \hline 9 \end{array}$$
    Check: $446 \cdot 12 + 9 = 5361$

16. There are 7 numbers.

$$\begin{array}{r} 29 \\ 36 \\ 84 \\ 41 \\ 6 \\ 12 \\ +\ 65 \\ \hline 273 \end{array} \qquad \text{average} = \frac{273}{7} = 39$$

The average is 39.

17. To find out how much money each nephew is to receive, we divide the total inheritance of \$29,640 by the number of nephews which is 3.

$$\begin{array}{r} 7880 \\ 3\overline{)\ 29,640} \\ -27 \\ \hline 26 \\ -24 \\ \hline 24 \\ -24 \\ \hline 00 \\ -0 \\ \hline 0 \end{array}$$

Each boy receives \$7880.

18. There are 7 factors of 9, so $9 \cdot 9 \cdot 9 \cdot 9 \cdot 9 \cdot 9 \cdot 9 = 9^7$.

19. $7^4 = 7 \cdot 7 \cdot 7 \cdot 7 = 2401$

20. $36 + 18 \div 6 = 36 + 3 = 39$

21.

$$\begin{aligned} \frac{2x^2+3}{y} &= \frac{2(3)^2+3}{7} \\ &= \frac{2(9)+3}{7} \\ &= \frac{18+3}{7} \\ &= \frac{21}{7} \\ &= 3 \end{aligned}$$

22. In words: twice a number and 6
Translate: $2x + 6$

Section 1.1

Exercise Set 1.1

1. Answers may vary.

3. Answers may vary.

5. The video icon tells you that the corresponding exercise may be viewed on the videotape that corresponds to that section.

7. Answers may vary.

9. Answers may vary.

11. Answers may vary.

13. Answers may vary.

15. Yes; answers may vary

17. Answers may vary.

19. Chart will vary.

Section 1.2

Practice Problems

1. The place value of the 7 in 72,589,620 is ten-millions.

2. The place value of the 7 in 67,890 is thousands.

3. The place value of the 7 in 50,722 is hundreds.

4. 395 is written as three hundred ninety-five.

5. 2807 is written as two thousand, eight hundred seven.

6. 321,670,200 is written as three hundred twenty-one million, six hundred seventy thousand, two hundred.

7. Twenty-nine in standard form is 29.

8. Seven hundred ten in standard form is 710.

9. Twenty-six thousand seventy-one in standard form is 26,071.

10. Six thousand, five hundred seven in standard form is 6507.

11. 1,047,608
$= 1{,}000{,}000 + 40{,}000 + 7000 + 600 + 8$

12. **a.** $0 < 19$

b. $18 < 32$

c. $107 > 103$

13. a. Read from left to right across the line marked Russia until the "Gold" column is reached. We find that Russia has won 32 bronze medals.

b. No countries shown have won more than 100 gold medals.

Exercise Set 1.2

1. The place value of the 5 in 352 is tens.

3. The place value of the 5 in 5890 is thousands.

5. The place value of the 5 in 62,500,000 is hundred-thousands.

7. The place value of the 5 in 5,070,099 is millions.

9. 5420 is written as five thousand, four hundred twenty.

11. 26,990 is written as twenty-six thousand, nine hundred ninety.

13. 1,620,000 is written as one million, six hundred twenty thousand.

15. 53,520,170 is written as fifty-three million, five hundred twenty thousand, one hundred seventy.

17. 63,960 is written as sixty-three thousand, nine hundred sixty.

19. 1483 is written as one thousand, four hundred eighty-three.

21. 12,662 is written as twelve thousand, six hundred sixty-two.

23. 13,600,000 is written as thirteen million, six hundred thousand.

25. 3893 is written as three thousand, eight hundred ninety-three.

27. Six thousand, five hundred eight in standard form is 6508.

29. Twenty-nine thousand, nine hundred in standard form is 29,900.

31. Six million, five hundred four thousand, nineteen in standard form is 6,504,019.

33. Three million, fourteen in standard form is 3,000,014.

35. Two hundred twenty miles in standard form is 220.

37. Seven hundred fifty-five in standard form is 755.

39. Seventy-three million, five hundred thousand in standard form is 73,500,000.

41. One thousand eight hundred fifteen in standard form is 1815.

43. One thousand two hundred sixty-two in standard form is 1262.

45. Forty-five thousand in standard form is 45,000.

47. $406 = 400 + 6$

49. $5290 = 5000 + 200 + 90$

51. $62,407 = 60,000 + 2000 + 400 + 7$

53. $30,680 = 30,000 + 600 + 80$

55. $39,680,000 = 30,000,000 + 9,000,000 + 600,000 + 80,000$

57. $1006 = 1000 + 6$

59. $3 < 8$

61. $9 > 0$

63. $6 > 2$

65. $22 > 0$

67. 4000 is written as four thousand.

69. $4145 = 4000 + 100 + 40 + 5$

71. The Nile is the longest river in the world.

73. The Labrador Retriever has the most AKC registrations; one hundred sixty-five thousand, nine hundred seventy-three.

75. The Golden Retriever has more dogs registered than the Chihuahua.

77. The largest number is achieved when the largest number available is used for each place value when reading from left to right. Thus, the largest number possible is 7632.

79. Answers may vary.

81. The town is Canton.

Section 1.3

Practice Problems

1. $$\begin{array}{r} 7235 \\ +\ 542 \\ \hline 7777 \end{array}$$

2. $$\begin{array}{r} {\scriptstyle 11\ 11} \\ 27,364 \\ +\ 92,977 \\ \hline 120,341 \end{array}$$

3. $$\begin{aligned} 11+7+8+9+13 &= 11+9+7+13+8 \\ &= (11+9)+(7+13)+8 \\ &= 20+20+8 \\ &= 40+8 \\ &= 48 \end{aligned}$$

4. $$\begin{array}{r} {\scriptstyle 112} \\ 19 \\ 5042 \\ 638 \\ +\ 526 \\ \hline 6225 \end{array}$$

5. To find the perimeter, add the lengths of the sides.
5 centimeters + 8 centimeters + 10 centimeters + 4 centimeters = 27 centimeters

6. To find the perimeter of the mall, add the lengths of the sides, all three of which have length 532 feet.
$$\begin{array}{r} 532 \\ 532 \\ +\ 532 \\ \hline 1596 \end{array}$$
The perimeter of the building is 1596 feet.

7. The phrase "more than" suggests we add. The addition statement "Texas' pecan production + 15 million pounds = Georgia's pecan production" translates to:

$$\begin{array}{r} 90 \text{ million lbs.} \\ +\ 15 \text{ million lbs.} \\ \hline 105 \text{ million lbs.} \end{array}$$

Georgia produces 105 million lbs. of pecans per year.

8. The number of thimbles that Elham has is the sum of the numbers of different types of thimbles that she has.

	13
glass thimbles	42
steel thimbles	17
porcelain thimbles	37
silver thimbles	9
plastic thimbles	+ 15
total thimbles	120

Elham has 120 thimbles.

Calculator Explorations

1. Press the keys 89 [+] 45 [= or ENTER]. The display will read 134.

2. Press the keys 76 [+] 97 [= or ENTER]. The display will read 173.

3. Press the keys 285 [+] 55 [= or ENTER]. The display will read 340.

4. Press the keys 8773 [+] 652 [= or Enter]. The display will read 9425.

5. Press the keys 985 [+] 1210 [+] 562 [+] 77 [= or ENTER]. The display will read 2834.

6. Press the keys 465 [+] 9888 [+] 620 [+] 1550 [= or Enter]. The display will read 12,523.

Mental Math

1. $5 + 7 = 12$

2. $20 + 30 = 50$

3. $5000 + 4000 = 9000$

4. $4300 + 26 = 4326$

5. $1620 + 0 = 1620$

6. Rearranging will make this easier: $6 + 126 + 4 = 126 + (6 + 4) = 126 + 10 = 136$

Exercise Set 1.3

1. $$\begin{array}{r} 14 \\ +\ 22 \\ \hline 36 \end{array}$$

3. $$\begin{array}{r} 62 \\ +\ 30 \\ \hline 92 \end{array}$$

5. $$\begin{array}{r} 12 \\ 13 \\ +\ 24 \\ \hline 49 \end{array}$$

7. $$\begin{array}{r} 5267 \\ +\ 132 \\ \hline 5399 \end{array}$$

9. $$\begin{array}{r} {\scriptstyle 1\ \ } \\ 53 \\ +\ 64 \\ \hline 117 \end{array}$$

11. $$\begin{array}{r} {\scriptstyle 1\ } \\ 22 \\ +\ 49 \\ \hline 71 \end{array}$$

13. $$\begin{array}{r} {\scriptstyle 11\ } \\ 38 \\ +\ 79 \\ \hline 117 \end{array}$$

15. $$\begin{array}{r} {\scriptstyle 2\ } \\ 8 \\ 9 \\ 2 \\ 5 \\ +\ 1 \\ \hline 25 \end{array}$$

17. $$\begin{array}{r} {\scriptstyle 2\ } \\ 6 \\ 21 \\ 14 \\ 9 \\ +\ 12 \\ \hline 62 \end{array}$$

19. $$\begin{array}{r} {\scriptstyle 22} \\ 81 \\ 17 \\ 23 \\ 79 \\ +\ 12 \\ \hline 212 \end{array}$$

21. $$\begin{array}{r} {\scriptstyle 1\ } \\ 62 \\ 18 \\ +\ 14 \\ \hline 94 \end{array}$$

23. $$\begin{array}{r} {\scriptstyle 1\ \ \ } \\ 40 \\ 800 \\ +\ 70 \\ \hline 910 \end{array}$$

25. $$\begin{array}{r} {\scriptstyle 111\ } \\ 7542 \\ 49 \\ +\ 682 \\ \hline 8273 \end{array}$$

27. $$\begin{array}{r} {\scriptstyle 1\ \ 12} \\ 24 \\ 9006 \\ 489 \\ +\ 2407 \\ \hline 11{,}926 \end{array}$$

29. $$\begin{array}{r} {\scriptstyle 1\ 2\ } \\ 627 \\ 628 \\ +\ 629 \\ \hline 1884 \end{array}$$

31. $$\begin{array}{r} {\scriptstyle 111\ } \\ 6820 \\ 4271 \\ +\ 5626 \\ \hline 16{,}717 \end{array}$$

33. $$\begin{array}{r} {\scriptstyle 111} \\ 507 \\ 593 \\ +\ \ 10 \\ \hline 1110 \end{array}$$

35. $$\begin{array}{r} 4200 \\ 2107 \\ +\ 2692 \\ \hline 8999 \end{array}$$

37. $$\begin{array}{r} {\scriptstyle 11\ 22\ } \\ 49 \\ 628 \\ 5\ 762 \\ +\ 29{,}462 \\ \hline 35{,}901 \end{array}$$

39.
$$\begin{array}{r} \scriptstyle 1\,2\,2\,2\,1 \\ 121{,}742 \\ 57{,}279 \\ 6\,586 \\ +\ 426{,}782 \\ \hline 612{,}389 \end{array}$$

41. $8+3+5+7+5+1 = 8+1+3+7+5+5$
$= 9+10+10$
$= 29$
The perimeter is 29 inches.

43. $8 + 10 + 7 = 8 + 7 + 10 = 15 + 10 = 25$
The perimeter is 25 feet.

45. Opposite sides of a rectangle have the same length.
$4 + 8 + 4 + 8 = 12 + 12 = 24$
The perimeter is 24 inches.

47. All the sides of a square have the same length.
$2 + 2 + 2 + 2 = 4 + 4 = 8$
The perimeter is 8 yards.

49.
$$\begin{array}{r} 3560 \\ +3124 \\ \hline 6684 \end{array}$$
Mount Mitchell is 6684 feet high.

51.
$$\begin{array}{r} \scriptstyle 2\,1\ \ \\ 70 \\ 78 \\ 90 \\ +\ 102 \\ \hline 340 \end{array}$$
He needs 340 feet of wire.

53.
$$\begin{array}{r} \scriptstyle 1\qquad\quad \\ 234{,}500 \\ +29{,}200 \\ \hline 263{,}700 \end{array}$$
There were 263,700 motorcycles shipped.

55.
$$\begin{array}{r} 15{,}000 \\ +13{,}000 \\ \hline 28{,}000 \end{array}$$
The newly combined company had 28,000 employees.

57.
$$\begin{array}{r} \scriptstyle 1\,1\quad \\ 7981 \\ +564 \\ \hline 8545 \end{array}$$
There were 8545 Blockbuster Stores in 2002.

59. Key word: total
$$\begin{array}{rr} \text{upper} & 1430 \\ \text{middle} & 675 \\ +\quad \text{lower} & +\ 320 \\ \hline \text{total height} & 2425 \end{array} \text{ feet}$$

61.
$$\begin{array}{r} 1795 \\ +\ 11{,}460 \\ \hline 13{,}255 \end{array}$$
The total highway mileage in Alaska is 13,255 miles.

63.
$$\begin{array}{r} \scriptstyle 1\quad\ \ \\ 6532 \\ +953 \\ \hline 7485 \end{array}$$
Cats had staged 7485 performances.

65.
$$\begin{array}{r} \scriptstyle 1\,1\quad \\ 9821 \\ +\ 592 \\ \hline 10{,}413 \end{array}$$
There were 10,413 kidney transplants in 2002.

67. Texas has the most Wal-Mart stores.

69.
$$\begin{array}{r} \scriptstyle 1\quad \\ 342 \\ 182 \\ +154 \\ \hline 678 \end{array}$$

71.
$$\begin{array}{r} \scriptstyle 2\,3\ \ \\ 102 \\ 154 \\ 182 \\ 115 \\ 140 \\ 112 \\ 104 \\ 128 \\ 116 \\ +342 \\ \hline 1495 \end{array}$$
The ten stores total 1495.

73. Answers may vary.

75.
$$\begin{array}{r} \scriptstyle 1\,1\ \ 2\ \ 2\,2\ \ 1\quad \\ 78{,}962 \\ 129{,}968{,}350 \\ +\ 36{,}462{,}880 \\ \hline 166{,}510{,}192 \end{array}$$

77. The computation is not correct; answers may vary.

Section 1.4

Practice Problems

1. a. $14 - 9 = 5$ because $5 + 9 = 14$.

b. $9 - 9 = 0$ because $0 + 9 = 9$.

c. $4 - 0 = 4$ because $4 + 0 = 4$.

2. a. $\begin{array}{r} 4689 \\ -\ 253 \\ \hline 4436 \end{array}$

Check: $\begin{array}{r} 4436 \\ +\ 253 \\ \hline 4689 \end{array}$

b. $\begin{array}{r} 981 \\ -\ 630 \\ \hline 351 \end{array}$

Check: $\begin{array}{r} 351 \\ +\ 630 \\ \hline 981 \end{array}$

3. a. $\begin{array}{r} 227 \\ -\ 175 \\ \hline 52 \end{array}$

Check: $\begin{array}{r} {}^{1}\ \ \\ 52 \\ +\ 175 \\ \hline 227 \end{array}$

b. $\begin{array}{r} 1136 \\ -\ 914 \\ \hline 222 \end{array}$

Check: $\begin{array}{r} {}^{1}\ \ \ \\ 222 \\ +\ 914 \\ \hline 1136 \end{array}$

c. $\begin{array}{r} 8627 \\ -\ 4119 \\ \hline 4508 \end{array}$

Check: $\begin{array}{r} {}^{1}\ \ \\ 4508 \\ +\ 4119 \\ \hline 8627 \end{array}$

4. a. $\begin{array}{r} 400 \\ -\ 164 \\ \hline 236 \end{array}$

Check: $\begin{array}{r} {}^{11}\ \\ 236 \\ +\ 164 \\ \hline 400 \end{array}$

b. $\begin{array}{r} 200 \\ -\ 45 \\ \hline 155 \end{array}$

Check: $\begin{array}{r} {}^{11}\ \\ 155 \\ +\ 45 \\ \hline 200 \end{array}$

c. $\begin{array}{r} 1000 \\ -\ 762 \\ \hline 238 \end{array}$

Check: $\begin{array}{r} {}^{11}\ \\ 238 \\ +\ 762 \\ \hline 1000 \end{array}$

5.

radius of Earth	6378
less 2981	− 2981
radius of Mars	3397

The radius of Mars is 3397 kilometers.

6.

original price	92
sale price	− 47
amount taken off	45

$45 was taken off the original price.

7. a. NC-17/X had 0 nominees, which is the least number of Best Picture nominees.

b.

Rated R nominees	52
Rated G nominees	− 2
	50

There were 50 more Best Picture nominees rated R than rated G.

Calculator Explorations

1. Press the keys 865 [-] 95 [= or Enter].
   The display will read 770.

2. Press the keys 76 [-] 27 [= or Enter].
   The display will read 49.

3. Press the keys 147 [-] 38 [= or Enter].
   The display will read 109.

4. Press the keys 366 [-] 87 [= or Enter].
   The display will read 279.

5. Press the keys 9625 [-] 647 [= or Enter].
   The display will read 8978.

6. Press the keys 10,711 [-] 8925 [= or Enter].
   The display will read 1786.

Mental Math

1. $9-2=7$

2. $6-6=0$

3. $5-0=5$

4. $44-22=22$

5. $93-93=0$

6. $700-400=300$

7. $700-300=400$

8. $700-700=0$

9. $600-100=500$

10. $600-0=600$

Exercise Set 1.4

1. $\begin{array}{r} 67 \\ -\ 23 \\ \hline 44 \end{array}$

   Check:
   $\begin{array}{r} 44 \\ +\ 23 \\ \hline 67 \end{array}$

3. $\begin{array}{r} 82 \\ -\ 22 \\ \hline 60 \end{array}$

   Check:
   $\begin{array}{r} 60 \\ +\ 22 \\ \hline 82 \end{array}$

5. $\begin{array}{r} 389 \\ -\ 124 \\ \hline 265 \end{array}$

   Check:
   $\begin{array}{r} 265 \\ +\ 124 \\ \hline 389 \end{array}$

7. $\begin{array}{r} 677 \\ -\ 423 \\ \hline 254 \end{array}$

   Check:
   $\begin{array}{r} 254 \\ +\ 423 \\ \hline 677 \end{array}$

9. $\begin{array}{r} 998 \\ -\ 453 \\ \hline 545 \end{array}$

   Check:
   $\begin{array}{r} 545 \\ +\ 453 \\ \hline 998 \end{array}$

11. $\begin{array}{r} 749 \\ -\ 149 \\ \hline 600 \end{array}$

   Check:
   $\begin{array}{r} 600 \\ +\ 149 \\ \hline 749 \end{array}$

13. $\begin{array}{r} 62 \\ -\ 37 \\ \hline 25 \end{array}$

   Check:
   $\begin{array}{r} \scriptstyle 1 \\ 25 \\ +\ 37 \\ \hline 62 \end{array}$

15. $$\begin{array}{r} 70 \\ -\ 25 \\ \hline 45 \end{array}$$

Check: $$\begin{array}{r} {\scriptstyle 1} \\ 45 \\ +\ 25 \\ \hline 70 \end{array}$$

17. $$\begin{array}{r} 938 \\ -\ 792 \\ \hline 146 \end{array}$$

Check: $$\begin{array}{r} {\scriptstyle 1} \\ 146 \\ +\ 792 \\ \hline 938 \end{array}$$

19. $$\begin{array}{r} 922 \\ -\ 634 \\ \hline 288 \end{array}$$

Check: $$\begin{array}{r} {\scriptstyle 11} \\ 288 \\ +\ 634 \\ \hline 922 \end{array}$$

21. $$\begin{array}{r} 600 \\ -\ 432 \\ \hline 168 \end{array}$$

Check: $$\begin{array}{r} {\scriptstyle 11} \\ 168 \\ +\ 432 \\ \hline 600 \end{array}$$

23. $$\begin{array}{r} 42 \\ -\ 36 \\ \hline 6 \end{array}$$

Check: $$\begin{array}{r} {\scriptstyle 1} \\ 6 \\ +\ 36 \\ \hline 42 \end{array}$$

25. $$\begin{array}{r} 923 \\ -\ 476 \\ \hline 447 \end{array}$$

Check: $$\begin{array}{r} {\scriptstyle 11} \\ 447 \\ +\ 476 \\ \hline 923 \end{array}$$

27. $$\begin{array}{r} 6283 \\ -\ 560 \\ \hline 5723 \end{array}$$

Check: $$\begin{array}{r} {\scriptstyle 1} \\ 5723 \\ +\ 560 \\ \hline 6283 \end{array}$$

29. $$\begin{array}{r} 533 \\ -\ 29 \\ \hline 504 \end{array}$$

Check: $$\begin{array}{r} {\scriptstyle 1} \\ 504 \\ +\ 29 \\ \hline 533 \end{array}$$

31. $$\begin{array}{r} 200 \\ -\ 111 \\ \hline 89 \end{array}$$

Check: $$\begin{array}{r} {\scriptstyle 11} \\ 89 \\ +\ 111 \\ \hline 200 \end{array}$$

33. $$\begin{array}{r} 1983 \\ -\ 1904 \\ \hline 79 \end{array}$$

Check: $$\begin{array}{r} {\scriptstyle 1} \\ 79 \\ +\ 1904 \\ \hline 1983 \end{array}$$

35. $$\begin{array}{r} 56,422 \\ -\ 16,508 \\ \hline 39,914 \end{array}$$

Check: $$\begin{array}{r} {\scriptstyle 111} \\ 39,914 \\ +\ 16,508 \\ \hline 56,422 \end{array}$$

37. $$\begin{array}{r} 50,000 \\ -\ 17,289 \\ \hline 32,711 \end{array}$$

Check: $$\begin{array}{r} {\scriptstyle 1111} \\ 32,711 \\ +\ 17,289 \\ \hline 50,000 \end{array}$$

39. $\begin{array}{r} 7020 \\ -\ 1979 \\ \hline 5041 \end{array}$

Check:
$\begin{array}{r} {}^{1\,1\,1} \\ 5041 \\ +\ 1979 \\ \hline 7020 \end{array}$

41. $\begin{array}{r} 51,111 \\ -\ 19,898 \\ \hline 31,213 \end{array}$

Check:
$\begin{array}{r} {}^{11\ 11} \\ 31,213 \\ +\ 19,898 \\ \hline 51,111 \end{array}$

43. $\begin{array}{r} 9 \\ -\ 5 \\ \hline 4 \end{array}$

Check:
$\begin{array}{r} 4 \\ +\ 5 \\ \hline 9 \end{array}$

45. $\begin{array}{r} 41 \\ -\ 21 \\ \hline 20 \end{array}$

Check:
$\begin{array}{r} 20 \\ +\ 21 \\ \hline 41 \end{array}$

47. $\begin{array}{r} 63 \\ -\ 56 \\ \hline 7 \end{array}$

Check:
$\begin{array}{r} {}^{1} \\ 7 \\ +\ 56 \\ \hline 63 \end{array}$

49. $\begin{array}{r} 108 \\ -36 \\ \hline 72 \end{array}$

Check:
$\begin{array}{r} 72 \\ +36 \\ \hline 108 \end{array}$

51. $\begin{array}{r} 100 \\ -12 \\ \hline 88 \end{array}$

Check:
$\begin{array}{r} {}^{1} \\ 88 \\ +12 \\ \hline 100 \end{array}$

53. $\begin{array}{r} 503 \\ -\ 239 \\ \hline 264 \end{array}$

Dyllis must read 264 more pages.

55. $\begin{array}{r} 25 \text{ million sq km} \\ -21 \text{ million sq km} \\ \hline 4 \text{ million sq km} \end{array}$

The hole in the Earth's ozone has grown by 4 million square kilometers.

57. $\begin{array}{r} 20,320 \\ -\ 14,255 \\ \hline 6\ 065 \end{array}$

Mt. McKinley is 6065 feet higher than Long's Peak.

59. We need to find the total amount of the checks.

$\begin{array}{r} {}^{1} \\ 27 \\ 101 \\ +\ 236 \\ \hline 364 \end{array}$

The checks total \$364.

$\begin{array}{r} 539 \\ -\ 364 \\ \hline 175 \end{array}$

Buhler will have \$175 left in his account.

61. $\begin{array}{r} 645 \\ -\ 287 \\ \hline 358 \end{array}$

The distance between Hays and Denver is 358 miles.

63. $\begin{array}{r} 971 \\ -732 \\ \hline 239 \end{array}$

Pat will have \$239 left in his savings account.

65. $\begin{array}{r} 2380 \\ -2207 \\ \hline 173 \end{array}$

Stackhouse scored 173 more points than Iverson.

67. $\begin{array}{r} 38,803 \\ -1768 \\ \hline 37,035 \end{array}$

There were 37,035 boxers registered with the AKC in 2001.

69. The total number of votes cast for Jo was:

$\begin{array}{r} {}^{1\,2\,1} \\ 276 \\ 362 \\ 201 \\ +179 \\ \hline 1018 \end{array}$

The total number of votes cast for Trudy was:

$\begin{array}{r} {}^{2\,1} \\ 295 \\ 122 \\ 312 \\ +182 \\ \hline 911 \end{array}$

Since more votes were cast for Jo than for Trudy, Jo won the election.

$\begin{array}{r} 1018 \\ -911 \\ \hline 107 \end{array}$

Jo won by 107 votes.

71. $\begin{array}{r} 15,982,378 \\ -12,937,926 \\ \hline 3,044,452 \end{array}$

Florida's population increased by 3,044,452 people.

73. $\begin{array}{r} 100,000 \\ -94,080 \\ \hline 5920 \end{array}$

The Dole Plantation maze is 5920 square feet larger.

75. $\begin{array}{r} 28,547 \\ -26,372 \\ \hline 2175 \end{array}$

The Lake Pontchartrain Bridge is 2175 feet longer.

77. Atlanta, Hartsfield International is busiest.

79. $\begin{array}{r} 67,448 \\ -61,606 \\ \hline 5842 \end{array}$

Chicago O'Hare International Airport has 5842 thousand more passenger arrivals and departures.

81. General Motors Corp. spent more than \$3 billion on advertising.

83. $\begin{array}{r} 3,374,400,000 \\ -1,985,300,000 \\ \hline 1,389,100,000 \end{array}$

Daimler Chrysler spent \$1,389,100,000 less on advertising.

85. $\begin{array}{r} 3,374,400,000 \\ 2,540,600,000 \\ 2,408,200,000 \\ 2,210,400,000 \\ 2,189,500,000 \\ 1,985,300,000 \\ 1,885,300,000 \\ 1,815,700,000 \\ 1,757,300,000 \\ +1,618,100,000 \\ \hline 21,784,800,000 \end{array}$

These ten companies spent a total of \$21,784,800,000 on advertising.

87. $\begin{array}{r} 5269 \\ -2385 \\ \hline 2884 \end{array}$

89. Answers may vary.

Section 1.5

Practice Problems

1. a. To round 46 to the nearest ten, observe that the digit in the ones place is 6. Since this digit is at least 5, we need to add 1 to the digit in the tens place. The number 46 rounded to the nearest ten is 50.

   b. To round 731 to the nearest ten, observe that the digit in the ones place is 1. Since this digit is less than 5, we do not add 1 to the digit in the tens place. The number 731 rounded to the nearest ten is 730.

   c. To round 125 to the nearest ten, observe that the digit in the ones place is 5. Since this digit is at least 5, we need to add 1 to the digit in the tens place. The number 125 rounded to the nearest ten is 130.

2. **a.** To round 56,702 to the nearest thousand, observe that the digit in the hundreds place is 7. Since this digit is at least 5, we need to add 1 to the digit in the thousands place. The number 56,702 rounded to the nearest thousand is 57,000.

   b. To round 7444 to the nearest thousand, observe that the digit in the hundreds place is 4. Since this digit is less than 5, we do not add 1 to the digit in the thousands place. The number 7444 rounded to the nearest thousand is 7000.

   c. To round 291,500 to the nearest thousand, observe that the digit in the hundreds place is 5. Since this digit at least 5, we need to add 1 to the digit in the thousands place. The number 291,500 rounded to the nearest thousand is 292,000.

3. **a.** To round 2777 to the nearest hundred, observe that the digit in the tens place is 7. Since this digit is at least 5, we need to add 1 to the digit in the hundreds place. The number 2777 rounded to the nearest hundred is 2800.

   b. To round 38,152 to the nearest hundred, observe that the digit in the tens place is 5. Since this digit is at least 5, we need to add 1 to the digit in the hundreds place. The number 38,152 rounded to the nearest hundred is 38,200.

   c. To round 762,955 to the nearest hundred, observe that the digit in the tens place is 5. Since this digit is at least 5, we need to add 1 to the digit in the hundreds place. The number 762,955 rounded to the nearest hundred is 763,000.

4.
$$\begin{array}{rlr} 79 & \text{rounds to} & 80 \\ 35 & \text{rounds to} & 40 \\ 42 & \text{rounds to} & 40 \\ 21 & \text{rounds to} & 20 \\ \underline{+\ 98} & \text{rounds to} & \underline{+\ 100} \\ & & 280 \end{array}$$

   The estimated sum is 280. (The exact sum is 275.)

5.
$$\begin{array}{rlr} 4725 & \text{rounds to} & 5000 \\ \underline{-\ 2879} & \text{rounds to} & \underline{-\ 3000} \\ & & 2000 \end{array}$$

   The estimated difference is 2000. (The exact difference is 1846.)

6.
$$\begin{array}{rlr} 11 & \text{rounds to} & 10 \\ 16 & \text{rounds to} & 20 \\ 19 & \text{rounds to} & 20 \\ \underline{+\ 31} & \text{rounds to} & \underline{+\ 30} \\ & & 80 \end{array}$$

   It is approximately 80 miles from Grove to Hays. (The exact distance is 77 miles.)

7.
$$\begin{array}{rlr} 120,624 & \text{rounds to} & 120,000 \\ 22,866 & \text{rounds to} & 20,000 \\ \underline{+\ 45,970} & \text{rounds to} & \underline{+\ 50,000} \\ & & 190,000 \end{array}$$

   The approximate number of cases reported was 190,000.

Exercise Set 1.5

1. To round 632 to the nearest ten, observe that the digit in the ones place is 2. Since this digit is less than 5, we do not add 1 to the digit in the tens place. The number 632 rounded to the nearest ten is 630.

3. To round 635 to the nearest ten, observe that the digit in the ones place is 5. Since this digit is at least 5, we need to add 1 to the digit in the tens place. The number 635 rounded to the nearest ten is 640.

5. To round 792 to the nearest ten, observe that the digit in the ones place is 2. Since this digit is less than 5, we do not add 1 to the digit in the tens place. The number 792 rounded to the nearest ten is 790.

7. To round 395 to the nearest ten, observe that the digit in the ones place is 5. Since this digit is at least 5, we need to add 1 to the digit in the tens place. The number 395 rounded to the nearest ten is 400.

9. To round 1096 to the nearest ten, observe that the digit in the ones place is 6. Since this digit is at least 5, we need to add 1 to the digit in the tens place. The number 1096 rounded to the nearest ten is 1100.

11. To round 42,682 to the nearest thousand, observe that the digit in the hundreds place is 6. Since this digit is at least 5, we need to add 1 to the digit in the thousands place. The number 42,682 rounded to the nearest thousand is 43,000.

13. To round 248,695 to the nearest hundred, observe that the digit in the tens place is 9. Since this digit is at least 5, we need to add 1 to the digit in the hundreds place. The number 248,695 rounded to the nearest hundred is 248,700.

15. To round 36,499 to the nearest thousand, observe that the digit in the hundreds place is 4. Since this digit is less than 5, we do not add 1 to the digit in the thousands place. The number 36,499 rounded to the nearest thousand is 36,000.

17. To round 99,995 to the nearest ten, observe that the digit in the ones place is 5. Since this digit is at least 5, we need to add 1 to the digit in the tens place. The number 99,995 rounded to the nearest ten is 100,000.

19. To round 59,725,642 to the nearest ten-million, observe that the digit in the millions place is 9. Since this digit is at least 5, we need to add 1 to the digit in the ten-millions place. The number 59,725,642 rounded to the nearest ten-million is 60,000,000.

		Ten	Hundred	Thousand
21.	5281	5280	5300	5000
23.	9444	9440	9400	9000
25.	14,876	14,880	14,900	15,000

27. To round 11,331 to the nearest thousand, observe that the digit in the hundreds place is 3. Since this digit is less than 5, we do not add 1 to the digit in the thousands place. The number 11,331 rounded to the nearest thousand is 11,000.

29. To round 38,387 to the nearest thousand, observe that the digit in the hundreds place is 3. Since this digit is less than 5, we do not add 1 to the digit in the thousands place. The number 38,387 rounded to the nearest thousand is 38,000.

31. Since the digit in the millions place is at least 5, we add 1 to the digit in the ten-millions place. The number 116,856,000 rounded to the nearest ten-million is 120,000,000.

33. Since the digit in the hundreds place is less than 5, we do not add 1 to the digit in the thousands place. 18,188 rounds to 18,000.

35.
$$\begin{array}{rlr} 29 & \text{rounds to} & 30 \\ 35 & \text{rounds to} & 40 \\ 42 & \text{rounds to} & 40 \\ \underline{+\ 16} & \text{rounds to} & \underline{+\ 20} \\ & & 130 \end{array}$$

The estimated sum is 130.

37.
$$\begin{array}{rlr} 649 & \text{rounds to} & 650 \\ \underline{-\ 272} & \text{rounds to} & \underline{-\ 270} \\ & & 380 \end{array}$$

The estimated difference is 380.

39.
$$\begin{array}{rlr} 1812 & \text{rounds to} & 1800 \\ 1776 & \text{rounds to} & 1800 \\ \underline{+\ 1945} & \text{rounds to} & \underline{+\ 1900} \\ & & 5500 \end{array}$$

The estimated sum is 5500.

41.
$$\begin{array}{rlr} 1774 & \text{rounds to} & 1800 \\ \underline{-\ 1492} & \text{rounds to} & \underline{-\ 1500} \\ & & 300 \end{array}$$

The estimated difference is 300.

43.
$$\begin{array}{rlr} 2995 & \text{rounds to} & 3000 \\ 1649 & \text{rounds to} & 1600 \\ \underline{+\ 3940} & \text{rounds to} & \underline{+\ 3900} \\ & & 8500 \end{array}$$

The estimated sum is 8500.

45. $362 + 419$ is approximately
$360 + 420 = 780$.
The answer of 781 is correct.

47. $432 + 679 + 198$ is approximately
$400 + 700 + 200 = 1300$.
The answer of 1139 is incorrect.

49. $7806 + 5150$ is approximately
$7800 + 5200 = 13,000$.
The answer of 12,956 is correct.

51. $31,439 + 18,781$ is approximately
$31,000 + 19,000 = 50,000$.
The answer is 50,220 is correct.

53.
$$\begin{array}{rlr} 799 & \text{rounds to} & 800 \\ 1299 & \text{rounds to} & 1300 \\ \underline{+\ 999} & \text{rounds to} & \underline{+\ 1000} \\ & & 3100 \end{array}$$

The total cost is approximately \$3100.

55.
$$\begin{array}{rlr} 19 & \text{rounds to} & 20 \\ 27 & \text{rounds to} & 30 \\ \underline{+\ 34} & \text{rounds to} & \underline{+\ 30} \\ & & 80 \end{array}$$

The distance from Stockton to LaCrosse is approximately 80 miles.

57.
$$\begin{array}{rlr} 20,320 & \text{rounds to} & 20,000 \\ \underline{-14,410} & \text{rounds to} & \underline{-14,000} \\ & & 6000 \end{array}$$

The difference in elevation is approximately 6,000 feet.

59.
$$\begin{array}{rlr} 2,896,016 & \text{rounds to} & 2,900,000 \\ \underline{-1,517,550} & \text{rounds to} & \underline{-1,500,000} \\ & & 1,400,000 \end{array}$$

Chicago's population is larger by approximately 1,400,000 people.

61.
$$\begin{array}{rlr} 41,126,233 & \text{rounds to} & 41,000,000 \\ \underline{-\ 27,174,898} & \text{rounds to} & \underline{-\ 27,000,000} \\ & & 14,000,000 \end{array}$$

Johnson won the election by approximately 14,000,000 votes.

63.
$$\begin{array}{rlr} 905,235 & \text{rounds to} & 905,000 \\ \underline{-750,695} & \text{rounds to} & \underline{-751,000} \\ & & 154,000 \end{array}$$

The Head Start enrollment increased by approximately 154,000 children.

65.
$$\begin{array}{rlr} 3274 & \text{rounds to} & 3300 \\ \underline{-2159} & \text{rounds to} & \underline{-2200} \\ & & 1100 \end{array}$$

The difference in diameter is approximately 1100 miles.

67. 3,374,400,000 rounds to 3,400,000,000. General Motors Corp. spent approximately \$3,400,000,000 on advertising.

69. 2,210,400,000 rounds to 2,000,000,000. PepsiCo spent approximately \$2,000,000,000 on advertising.

71. The smallest possible number that rounds to 8600 is 8550.

73. The largest possible number that rounds to 1,500,000 is 1,549,999.

75.
$$\begin{array}{rlr} 7693 & \text{rounds to} & 7700 \\ 8203 & \text{rounds to} & 8200 \\ \underline{+5950} & \text{rounds to} & \underline{+6000} \\ & & 21{,}900 \end{array}$$

The perimeter is approximately 21,900 miles.

Section 1.6

Practice Problems

1. a. $3 \times 0 = 0$

b. $4(1) = 4$

c. $(0)(34) = 0$

d. $1 \cdot 76 = 76$

2. a. $5(2 + 3) = 5 \cdot 2 + 5 \cdot 3$

b. $9(8 + 7) = 9 \cdot 8 + 9 \cdot 7$

c. $3(6 + 1) = 3 \cdot 6 + 3 \cdot 1$

3. a.
$$\begin{array}{r} \scriptstyle 2 \\ 36 \\ \times\ 4 \\ \hline 144 \end{array}$$

b.
$$\begin{array}{r} \scriptstyle 1 \\ 92 \\ \times\ 9 \\ \hline 828 \end{array}$$

4. a.
$$\begin{array}{r} 594 \\ \times\ 72 \\ \hline 1\,188 \\ 41{,}580 \\ \hline 42{,}768 \end{array}$$

b.
$$\begin{array}{r} 306 \\ \times\ 81 \\ \hline 306 \\ 24{,}480 \\ \hline 24{,}786 \end{array}$$

5. a.
$$\begin{array}{r} 726 \\ \times\ 142 \\ \hline 1\,452 \\ 29{,}040 \\ 72{,}600 \\ \hline 103{,}092 \end{array}$$

b.
$$\begin{array}{r} 4 \\ \times\ 288 \\ \hline 32 \\ 320 \\ 800 \\ \hline 1152 \end{array}$$

6.
$$\begin{array}{r} 360 \\ \times\ 280 \\ \hline 0 \\ 28{,}800 \\ 72{,}000 \\ \hline 100{,}800 \end{array}$$

The area is 100,800 square miles.

7.
$$\begin{array}{r} 240 \\ \times\ 15 \\ \hline 1200 \\ 2400 \\ \hline 3600 \end{array}$$

The printer can print 3600 characters in 15 seconds.

8. The cost of 4 plain shirts is $4 \cdot 6 = \$24$.
The cost of 5 striped shirts is $5 \cdot 7 = \$35$.
The total cost is $24 + 35 = \$59$.

9.
$$\begin{array}{rlr} 259 & \text{rounds to} & 300 \\ \underline{\times\ 195} & \text{rounds to} & \underline{\times\ 200} \\ & & 60{,}000 \end{array}$$

There are approximately 60,000 words on 195 pages.

Calculator Explorations

1. Press the keys 72 [×] 48 [= or ENTER].
The display will read 3456.

2. Press the keys 81 [×] 92 [= or ENTER].
The display will read 7452.

3. Press the keys 163 [×] 94 [= or ENTER].
The display will read 15,322.

4. Press the keys 285 [×] 144 [= or ENTER].
The display will read 41,040.

5 Press the keys 983 [×] 277 [= or ENTER].
The display will read 272,291.

6. Press the keys 1562 [×] 843 [= or ENTER].
The display will read 1,316,766.

Mental Math

1. $1 \cdot 24 = 24$

2. $55 \cdot 1 = 55$

3. $0 \cdot 19 = 0$

4. $27 \cdot 0 = 0$

5. $8 \cdot 0 \cdot 9 = 0$

6. $7 \cdot 6 \cdot 0 = 0$

7. $87 \cdot 1 = 87$

8. $1 \cdot 41 = 41$

Exercise Set 1.6

1. $4(3+9) = 4 \cdot 3 + 4 \cdot 9$

3. $2(4+6) = 2 \cdot 4 + 2 \cdot 6$

5. $10(11+7) = 10 \cdot 11 + 10 \cdot 7$

7. $$\begin{array}{r} 42 \\ \times\ 6 \\ \hline 252 \end{array}$$

9. $$\begin{array}{r} 624 \\ \times\ 3 \\ \hline 1872 \end{array}$$

11. $$\begin{array}{r} 277 \\ \times\ 6 \\ \hline 1662 \end{array}$$

13. $$\begin{array}{r} 1062 \\ \times\ 5 \\ \hline 5310 \end{array}$$

15. $$\begin{array}{r} 298 \\ \times\ 14 \\ \hline 1192 \\ 2980 \\ \hline 4172 \end{array}$$

17. $$\begin{array}{r} 231 \\ \times\ 47 \\ \hline 1\ 617 \\ 9\ 240 \\ \hline 10,857 \end{array}$$

19. $$\begin{array}{r} 809 \\ \times\ 14 \\ \hline 3236 \\ 8090 \\ \hline 11,326 \end{array}$$

21. $$\begin{array}{r} 620 \\ \times\ 40 \\ \hline 0 \\ 24,800 \\ \hline 24,800 \end{array}$$

23. $(998)(12)(0) = 0$

25. $(590)(1)(10) = 5900$

27. $$\begin{array}{r} 1\ 234 \\ \times\ 48 \\ \hline 9\ 872 \\ 49,360 \\ \hline 59,232 \end{array}$$

29. $$\begin{array}{r} 609 \\ \times\ 234 \\ \hline 2\ 436 \\ 18,270 \\ 121,800 \\ \hline 142,506 \end{array}$$

31. $$\begin{array}{r} 5621 \\ \times\ 324 \\ \hline 22,484 \\ 112,420 \\ 1,686,300 \\ \hline 1,821,204 \end{array}$$

33. $$\begin{array}{r} 1941 \\ \times\ 235 \\ \hline 9\ 705 \\ 58,230 \\ 388,200 \\ \hline 456,135 \end{array}$$

35. $\begin{array}{r} 589 \\ \times\ 110 \\ \hline 0 \\ 5\,890 \\ 58{,}900 \\ \hline 64{,}790 \end{array}$

37. $\begin{array}{r} 964 \\ \times\ 207 \\ \hline 6748 \\ 00 \\ 192{,}800 \\ \hline 199{,}548 \end{array}$

39. $\begin{array}{rlr} 576 & \text{rounds to} & 600 \\ \times\ 354 & \text{rounds to} & \times\ 400 \\ \cline{3-3} & & 240{,}000 \end{array}$

576×354 is approximately 240,000.

41. $\begin{array}{rlr} 604 & \text{rounds to} & 600 \\ \times\ 451 & \text{rounds to} & \times\ 500 \\ \cline{3-3} & & 300{,}000 \end{array}$

604×451 is approximately 300,000.

43. $\begin{array}{rlr} 872 & \text{rounds to} & 870 \\ \times\ 27 & \text{rounds to} & \times\ 30 \\ \cline{3-3} & & 26{,}100 \end{array}$

872×27 is approximately 26,100

45. $\begin{array}{rlr} 36 & \text{rounds to} & 40 \\ \times\ 87 & \text{rounds to} & \times\ 90 \\ \cline{3-3} & & 3600 \end{array}$

36×87 is approximately 3600.

47. $\begin{aligned} \text{Area} &= \text{length} \cdot \text{width} \\ &= (9 \text{ meters})(7 \text{ meters}) \\ &= 63 \text{ square meters} \end{aligned}$

The area is 63 square meters.

49. $\begin{aligned} \text{Area} &= \text{length} \cdot \text{width} \\ &= (30 \text{ feet})(13 \text{ feet}) \\ &= 390 \text{ square feet} \end{aligned}$

The area is 390 square feet.

51. $\begin{array}{r} 125 \\ \times\ 3 \\ \hline 375 \end{array}$

There are 375 calories in 3 tablespoons of olive oil.

53. $\begin{array}{r} 54 \\ \times\ 35 \\ \hline 270 \\ 1620 \\ \hline 1890 \end{array}$

The books cost a total of \$1890.

55. $\begin{array}{r} 12 \\ \times\ 8 \\ \hline 96 \end{array}$

$2 \times 96 = 192$
There are 192 cans in a case.

57. $\begin{array}{r} 90 \\ \times\ 110 \\ \hline 0 \\ 900 \\ 9000 \\ \hline 9900 \end{array}$

The area of the plot is 9900 square feet.

59. $\begin{array}{r} 350 \\ \times\ 160 \\ \hline 0 \\ 21{,}000 \\ 35{,}000 \\ \hline 56{,}000 \end{array}$

The lobby's area is 56,000 square feet.

61. $\begin{array}{r} 62 \\ \times\ 94 \\ \hline 248 \\ 5580 \\ \hline 5828 \end{array}$

The screen contains a total of 5828 pixels.

63. $\begin{array}{r} 80 \\ \times\ 25 \\ \hline 400 \\ 1600 \\ \hline 2000 \end{array}$

There are 2000 characters in 25 lines.

65. $\begin{array}{r} 160 \\ \times\ 8 \\ \hline 1280 \end{array}$

There are 1280 calories in 8 ounces of peanuts.

67. $\begin{array}{r} 7927 \\ \times\ 9 \\ \hline 71,343 \end{array}$

Saturn has a diameter of 71,343 miles.

69. $7 \times 2 = 14$ windows
$4 \times 2 = 8$ windows
$14 + 8 = 22$ windows

$\begin{array}{r} 22 \\ \times\ 23 \\ \hline 66 \\ 440 \\ \hline 506 \end{array}$

The building has a total of 506 windows.

71. $\begin{array}{r} 700,000 \\ \times\ 31 \\ \hline 700,000 \\ 21,000,000 \\ \hline 21,700,000 \end{array}$

21,700,000 quarts of milk would be used in March.

73. $\begin{array}{rcr} 905,235 & \text{rounds to} & 905,000 \\ \times\ 6,633 & \text{rounds to} & \times\ 7000 \\ \hline & & 6,335,000,000 \end{array}$

The total cost of the Head Start program is approximately $6,335,000,000.

75. $5 \times 10 = 50$
50 students chose grapes as their favorite fruit.

77. The apple (chosen by $9 \times 10 = 90$ students) and the orange (chosen by $7 \times 10 = 70$ students) were the most popular.

79. The result of multiplying 3 by the digit in the first blank is a number ending in 6. Only 2 works. The result of multiplying the digit in the second blank by 42 is 378, so the digit in the second blank is 9.

$\begin{array}{r} 4\underline{2} \\ \times\ \underline{9}3 \\ \hline 126 \\ 3780 \\ \hline 3906 \end{array}$

81. Answers may vary.

83. $61 \times 3 = 183$
$640 \times 2 = 1280$

$\begin{array}{r} 183 \\ 1280 \\ +\ 475 \\ \hline 1938 \end{array}$

Kobe Bryant scored 1938 points in the 2000-2001 season.

Section 1.7

Practice Problems

1. a. $8\overline{)48}$ = 6 because $6 \cdot 8 = 48$.

b. $35 \div 5 = 7$, because $7 \cdot 5 = 35$.

c. $\frac{49}{7} = 7$, because $7 \cdot 7 = 49$.

2. a. $\frac{8}{8} = 1$, because $1 \cdot 8 = 8$.

b. $3 \div 1 = 3$, because $3 \cdot 1 = 3$.

c. $1\overline{)12}$ = 12, because $12 \cdot 1 = 12$.

d. $2 \div 1 = 2$, because $2 \cdot 1 = 2$.

e. $\frac{5}{1} = 5$, because $5 \cdot 1 = 5$.

3. a. $\frac{0}{7} = 0$, because $0 \cdot 7 = 0$.

b. $5\overline{)0}$ = 0, because $0 \cdot 5 = 0$.

c. $9 \div 0$ is undefined, because any number multiplied by 0 is 0 and not 9.

d. $0 \div 6 = 0$, because $0 \cdot 6 = 0$.

4. a. $\begin{array}{r} 897 \\ 6\overline{)\ 5382} \\ -48 \\ \hline 58 \\ -54 \\ \hline 42 \\ -42 \\ \hline 0 \end{array}$

Check: $897 \cdot 6 = 5382$

b.
$$\begin{array}{r} 553 \\ 4\overline{)\,2212} \\ \underline{-20} \\ 21 \\ \underline{-20} \\ 12 \\ \underline{-12} \\ 0 \end{array}$$

Check: 553 · 4 = 2212

5. a.
$$\begin{array}{r} 799 \\ 3\overline{)\,2397} \\ \underline{-21} \\ 29 \\ \underline{-27} \\ 27 \\ \underline{-27} \\ 0 \end{array}$$

Check: 799 · 3 = 2397

b.
$$\begin{array}{r} 360 \\ 7\overline{)\,2520} \\ \underline{-21} \\ 42 \\ \underline{-42} \\ 00 \\ \underline{-0} \\ 0 \end{array}$$

Check: 360 · 7 = 2520

6. a.
$$\begin{array}{r} 189 \text{ R } 4 \\ 5\overline{)\,949} \\ \underline{-5} \\ 44 \\ \underline{-40} \\ 49 \\ \underline{-45} \\ 4 \end{array}$$

Check: 189 · 5 + 4 = 949

b.
$$\begin{array}{r} 733 \text{ R } 1 \\ 6\overline{)\,4399} \\ \underline{-42} \\ 19 \\ \underline{-18} \\ 19 \\ \underline{-18} \\ 1 \end{array}$$

Check: 733 · 6 + 1 = 4399

7. a.
$$\begin{array}{r} 8168 \text{ R } 1 \\ 5\overline{)\,40841} \\ \underline{-40} \\ 08 \\ \underline{-5} \\ 34 \\ \underline{-30} \\ 41 \\ \underline{-40} \\ 1 \end{array}$$

Check: 8168 · 5 + 1 = 40,841

b.
$$\begin{array}{r} 3204 \text{ R } 2 \\ 7\overline{)\,22430} \\ \underline{-21} \\ 14 \\ \underline{-14} \\ 03 \\ \underline{-0} \\ 30 \\ \underline{-28} \\ 2 \end{array}$$

Check: 3204 · 7 + 2 = 22,430

8.
$$\begin{array}{r} 302 \text{ R } 2 \\ 19\overline{)\,5740} \\ \underline{-57} \\ 04 \\ \underline{-0} \\ 40 \\ \underline{-38} \\ 2 \end{array}$$

Check: 302 · 19 + 2 = 5740

9.
$$\begin{array}{r} 67 \text{ R } 40 \\ 247\overline{)\,16589} \\ \underline{-1482} \\ 1769 \\ \underline{-1729} \\ 40 \end{array}$$

Check: 67 · 247 + 40 = 16,589

10.
$$\begin{array}{r} 40 \\ 3\overline{)\,120} \\ \underline{-12} \\ 00 \\ \underline{-0} \\ 0 \end{array}$$

Each person got 40 diskettes.

11.
$$\begin{array}{r} 32 \text{ R } 3 \\ 6\overline{)\,195} \\ \underline{-18} \\ 15 \\ \underline{-12} \\ 3 \end{array}$$

195 sandwiches yield 32 full packages, with 3 sandwiches left over.

12.
$$\begin{array}{r} 20 \text{ R } 17 \\ 24\overline{)\ 497} \\ \underline{-48} \\ 17 \\ \underline{-0} \\ 17 \end{array}$$

20 full boxes will be shipped, with 17 calculators left over.

13. Add the scores, then divide by 7, the number of scores.

$$\begin{array}{r} 5 \\ 7 \\ 20 \\ 6 \\ 9 \\ 3 \\ \underline{+\ 48} \\ 98 \end{array} \qquad \begin{array}{r} 14 \\ 7\overline{)\ 98} \\ \underline{-7} \\ 28 \\ \underline{-28} \\ 0 \end{array}$$

The average elapsed time is 14 minutes.

Calculator Explorations

1. Press the keys 848 [÷] 16 [= or ENTER]. The display will read 53.
2. Press the keys 8564 [÷] 12 [= or ENTER]. The display will read 47.
3. Press the keys 5890 [÷] 95 [= or ENTER]. The display will read 62.
4. Press the keys 1053 [÷] 27 [= or ENTER]. The display will read 39.
5. Press the keys 32,886 [÷] 126 [= or ENTER]. The display will read 261.
6. Press the keys 143,088 [÷] 264 [= or ENTER]. The display will read 542.
7. Press the keys 0 [÷] 315 [= or ENTER]. The display will read 0.
8. Press the keys 315 [÷] 0 [= or ENTER]. The display will read *Error.*

Mental Math

1. $40 \div 8 = 5$
2. $72 \div 9 = 8$
3. $45 \div 5 = 9$
4. $24 \div 3 = 8$
5. $0 \div 5 = 0$
6. $0 \div 8 = 0$
7. $9 \div 1 = 9$
8. $12 \div 1 = 12$
9. $\frac{16}{16} = 1$
10. $\frac{49}{49} = 1$
11. $\frac{25}{5} = 5$
12. $\frac{45}{9} = 5$
13. $6 \div 0$ is undefined
14. $\frac{12}{0}$ is undefined
15. $7 \div 1 = 7$
16. $6 \div 6 = 1$
17. $0 \div 4 = 0$
18. $7 \div 0$ is undefined
19. $16 \div 2 = 8$
20. $18 \div 3 = 6$

Exercise Set 1.7

1.
$$\begin{array}{r} 12 \\ 9\overline{)108} \\ \underline{-9} \\ 18 \\ \underline{-18} \\ 0 \end{array}$$

Check: $12 \cdot 9 = 108$

3.
$$\begin{array}{r} 37 \\ 6\overline{)\ 222} \\ \underline{-18} \\ 42 \\ \underline{-42} \\ 0 \end{array}$$

Check: $37 \cdot 6 = 222$

5.
$$\begin{array}{r} 338 \\ 3\overline{)1014} \\ \underline{-9} \\ 11 \\ \underline{-9} \\ 24 \\ \underline{-24} \\ 0 \end{array}$$

Check: $338 \cdot 3 = 1014$

7.
$$\begin{array}{r} 16 \text{ R } 2 \\ 6\overline{)\;98} \\ \underline{-6} \\ 38 \\ \underline{-36} \\ 2 \end{array}$$

Check: $16 \cdot 6 + 2 = 98$

9.
$$\begin{array}{r} 563 \text{ R } 1 \\ 2\overline{)\;1127} \\ \underline{-10} \\ 12 \\ \underline{-12} \\ 07 \\ \underline{-6} \\ 1 \end{array}$$

Check: $563 \cdot 2 + 1 = 1127$

11.
$$\begin{array}{r} 37 \text{ R } 1 \\ 5\overline{)\;186} \\ \underline{-15} \\ 36 \\ \underline{-35} \\ 1 \end{array}$$

Check: $37 \cdot 5 + 1 = 186$

13.
$$\begin{array}{r} 265 \text{ R } 1 \\ 8\overline{)\;2121} \\ \underline{-16} \\ 52 \\ \underline{-48} \\ 41 \\ \underline{-40} \\ 1 \end{array}$$

Check: $265 \cdot 8 + 1 = 2121$

15.
$$\begin{array}{r} 49 \\ 23\overline{)1127} \\ \underline{-92} \\ 207 \\ \underline{-207} \\ 0 \end{array}$$

Check: $49 \cdot 23 = 1127$

17.
$$\begin{array}{r} 13 \\ 55\overline{)\;715} \\ \underline{-55} \\ 165 \\ \underline{-165} \\ 0 \end{array}$$

Check: $13 \cdot 55 = 715$

19.
$$\begin{array}{r} 97 \text{ R } 40 \\ 97\overline{)\;9449} \\ \underline{-873} \\ 719 \\ \underline{-679} \\ 40 \end{array}$$

Check: $97 \cdot 97 + 40 = 9449$

21.
$$\begin{array}{r} 206 \\ 18\overline{)\;3708} \\ \underline{-36} \\ 10 \\ \underline{-0} \\ 108 \\ \underline{-108} \\ 0 \end{array}$$

Check: $206 \cdot 18 = 3708$

23.
$$\begin{array}{r} 506 \\ 13\overline{)\;6578} \\ \underline{-65} \\ 07 \\ \underline{-0} \\ 78 \\ \underline{-78} \\ 0 \end{array}$$

Check: $506 \cdot 13 = 6578$

25.
$$\begin{array}{r} 202 \text{ R } 7 \\ 46\overline{)\;9299} \\ \underline{-92} \\ 09 \\ \underline{-0} \\ 99 \\ \underline{-92} \\ 7 \end{array}$$

Check: $202 \cdot 46 + 7 = 9299$

27.
$$\begin{array}{r} 45 \\ 236\overline{)10620} \\ \underline{-944} \\ 1180 \\ \underline{-1180} \\ 0 \end{array}$$

Check: $45 \cdot 236 = 10620$

29.
$$
\begin{array}{r}
98 \text{ R } 100 \\
103\overline{)10194} \\
\underline{-927} \\
924 \\
\underline{-824} \\
100
\end{array}
$$

Check: $98 \cdot 103 + 100 = 10{,}194$

31.
$$
\begin{array}{r}
202 \text{ R } 15 \\
102\overline{)20619} \\
\underline{-204} \\
21 \\
\underline{-0} \\
219 \\
\underline{-204} \\
15
\end{array}
$$

Check: $202 \cdot 102 + 15 = 20{,}619$

33.
$$
\begin{array}{r}
202 \\
223\overline{)45046} \\
\underline{-446} \\
44 \\
\underline{-0} \\
446 \\
\underline{-446} \\
0
\end{array}
$$

Check: $202 \cdot 223 = 45{,}046$

35.
$$
\begin{array}{r}
58 \\
85\overline{)4930} \\
\underline{-425} \\
680 \\
\underline{-680} \\
0
\end{array}
$$

There are 58 students in the group.

37.
$$
\begin{array}{r}
252000 \\
21\overline{)5292000} \\
\underline{-42} \\
109 \\
\underline{-105} \\
42 \\
\underline{-42} \\
00 \\
\underline{-0} \\
00 \\
\underline{-0} \\
00 \\
\underline{-0} \\
0
\end{array}
$$

Each person receives \$252,000.

39.
$$
\begin{array}{r}
415 \\
14\overline{)5810} \\
\underline{-56} \\
21 \\
\underline{-14} \\
70 \\
\underline{-70} \\
0
\end{array}
$$

The truck hauls 415 bushels each trip.

41.
$$
\begin{array}{r}
88 \text{ R } 1 \\
3\overline{)265} \\
\underline{-24} \\
25 \\
\underline{-24} \\
1
\end{array}
$$

There are 89 bridges in 265 miles.

43.
$$
\begin{array}{r}
23 \text{ R } 1 \\
8\overline{)185} \\
\underline{-16} \\
25 \\
\underline{-24} \\
1
\end{array}
$$

She has enough for 22 students, with another student's worth plus one more foot, or $8 + 1 = 9$ feet extra.

45.
$$
\begin{array}{r}
24 \\
6\overline{)144} \\
\underline{-12} \\
24 \\
\underline{-24} \\
0
\end{array}
$$

He scored 24 touchdowns during 2002.

47.
$$
\begin{array}{r}
1760 \\
3\overline{)5280} \\
\underline{-3} \\
22 \\
\underline{-21} \\
18 \\
\underline{-18} \\
00 \\
\underline{-0} \\
0
\end{array}
$$

There are 1760 yards in 1 mile.

49. There are six numbers.

$$\begin{array}{r} 14 \\ 22 \\ 45 \\ 18 \\ 30 \\ +\ 27 \\ \hline 156 \end{array} \qquad \begin{array}{r} 26 \\ 6\overline{)\ 156} \\ \underline{-12} \\ 36 \\ \underline{-36} \\ 0 \end{array}$$

$$\text{Average} = \frac{156}{6} = 26$$

51. There are four numbers.

$$\begin{array}{r} 204 \\ 968 \\ 552 \\ +\ 268 \\ \hline 1992 \end{array} \qquad \begin{array}{r} 498 \\ 4\overline{)\ 1992} \\ \underline{-16} \\ 39 \\ \underline{-36} \\ 32 \\ \underline{-32} \\ 0 \end{array}$$

$$\text{Average} = \frac{1992}{4} = 498$$

53. There are five numbers.

$$\begin{array}{r} 86 \\ 79 \\ 81 \\ 69 \\ +\ 80 \\ \hline 395 \end{array} \qquad \begin{array}{r} 79 \\ 5\overline{)\ 395} \\ \underline{-35} \\ 45 \\ \underline{-45} \\ 0 \end{array}$$

$$\text{Average} = \frac{395}{5} = 79$$

55. Add those month's temperatures, then divide by 3, the number of temperatures.

$$\begin{array}{r} 18 \\ 12 \\ +\ 18 \\ \hline 48 \end{array} \qquad \begin{array}{r} 16 \\ 3\overline{)\ 48} \\ \underline{-3} \\ 18 \\ \underline{-18} \\ 0 \end{array}$$

The average temperature is $\frac{48}{3} = 16$ degrees.

57. Add the 2 greatest amounts, then divide by 2.

$$\begin{array}{r} 3,374,400,000 \\ +2,540,600,000 \\ \hline 5,915,000,000 \end{array}$$

$$\begin{array}{r} 2957500000 \\ 2\overline{)\ 5915000000} \\ \underline{-4} \\ 19 \\ \underline{-18} \\ 11 \\ \underline{-10} \\ 15 \\ \underline{-14} \\ 10 \\ \underline{-10} \\ 00 \\ \underline{-0} \\ 00 \\ \underline{-0} \\ 00 \\ \underline{-0} \\ 00 \\ \underline{-0} \\ 00 \\ \underline{-0} \\ 0 \end{array}$$

The average amount spent by the top two companies is \$2,957,500,000.

59. Increases, because 71 lies below the average, which is 83.

61. No, because all the numbers are greater than 86.

Integrated Review

1.

$$\begin{array}{r} {\scriptstyle 11} \\ 23 \\ 46 \\ +\ 79 \\ \hline 148 \end{array}$$

2.

$$\begin{array}{r} 7006 \\ -\ 451 \\ \hline 6555 \end{array}$$

3.

$$\begin{array}{r} 36 \\ \times\ 45 \\ \hline 180 \\ 1440 \\ \hline 1620 \end{array}$$

4.
$$\begin{array}{r} 562 \\ 8\overline{)\,4496} \\ \underline{-40} \\ 49 \\ \underline{-48} \\ 16 \\ \underline{-16} \\ 0 \end{array}$$

5. $1 \cdot 79 = 79$

6. $\frac{36}{0}$ is undefined.

7. $9 \div 1 = 9$

8. $9 \div 9 = 1$

9. $0 \cdot 13 = 0$

10. $7 \cdot 0 \cdot 8 = 0$

11. $0 \div 2 = 0$

12. $12 \div 4 = 3$

13.
$$\begin{array}{r} 4219 \\ \underline{-\,1786} \\ 2433 \end{array}$$

14.
$$\begin{array}{r} {\scriptstyle 2\,2\,1\,\,} \\ 1861 \\ 7965 \\ 199 \\ \underline{+\,2870} \\ 12,895 \end{array}$$

15.
$$\begin{array}{r} 213\ \text{R } 3 \\ 5\overline{)\,1068} \\ \underline{-10} \\ 06 \\ \underline{-5} \\ 18 \\ \underline{-15} \\ 3 \end{array}$$

16.
$$\begin{array}{r} 1259 \\ \underline{\times\ 63} \\ 3\,777 \\ \underline{75,540} \\ 79,317 \end{array}$$

17. $3 \cdot 9 = 27$

18. $45 \div 5 = 9$

19.
$$\begin{array}{r} 207 \\ \underline{-\ 69} \\ 138 \end{array}$$

20.
$$\begin{array}{r} {\scriptstyle 1\,\,\,} \\ 207 \\ \underline{+\ 69} \\ 276 \end{array}$$

21.
$$\begin{array}{r} 1099\ \text{R2} \\ 7\overline{)\,7695} \\ \underline{-\,7} \\ 06 \\ \underline{-\,0} \\ 69 \\ \underline{-\,63} \\ 65 \\ \underline{-\,63} \\ 2 \end{array}$$

22.
$$\begin{array}{r} 111\ \text{R } 1 \\ 9\overline{)\,1000} \\ \underline{-\,9} \\ 10 \\ \underline{-\,9} \\ 10 \\ \underline{-\,9} \\ 1 \end{array}$$

23.
$$\begin{array}{r} 663\ \text{R } 6 \\ 32\overline{)\,21222} \\ \underline{-192} \\ 202 \\ \underline{-192} \\ 102 \\ \underline{-96} \\ 6 \end{array}$$

24.
$$\begin{array}{r} 1076\ \text{R } 60 \\ 65\overline{)\,70000} \\ \underline{-65} \\ 50 \\ \underline{-0} \\ 500 \\ \underline{-455} \\ 450 \\ \underline{-390} \\ 60 \end{array}$$

25.
$$\begin{array}{r} 4000 \\ \underline{-2976} \\ 1024 \end{array}$$

26. $\begin{array}{r} 10{,}000 \\ -\ \ 101 \\ \hline 9{,}899 \end{array}$

27. $\begin{array}{r} 303 \\ \times\ 101 \\ \hline 303 \\ 00 \\ 30{,}300 \\ \hline 30{,}603 \end{array}$

28. $\begin{array}{r} 475 \\ \times\ 100 \\ \hline 47{,}500 \end{array}$

29. $\begin{array}{r} 0 \\ 7\overline{)\ 0} \\ -0 \\ \hline 0 \end{array}$

30. 14 ÷ 0 is undefined because 0 times any number is 0, and not 14.

31. $\begin{array}{r} 0 \\ 6\overline{)\ 0} \\ -0 \\ \hline 0 \end{array}$

32. $\begin{array}{r} 0 \\ 105\overline{)\ 0} \\ -0 \\ \hline 0 \end{array}$

33. $\begin{array}{r} 100 \\ -14 \\ \hline 86 \end{array}$

34. $\begin{array}{r} 43 \\ -21 \\ \hline 22 \end{array}$

		Tens	Hundreds	Thousands
35.	8625	8630	8600	9000
36.	1553	1550	1600	2000
37.	10,901	10,900	10,900	11,000
38.	432,198	432,200	432,200	432,000

39. A square has all equal sides. Therefore, if one side is 5 feet, each side is 5 feet.

40. Opposite sides of a rectangle have the same length. To find the perimeter add the length of all the sides. 14 + 14 + 7 + 7 = 42 inches. To find the area, multiply length times width. 14 × 7 = 98 square inches.

41. Add up the length of all the sides. 11 + 7 + 8 = 26 miles.

42. Find the length of the missing sides by looking at the sides directly across from the sides that have no stated value. The bottom side of the figure is 6 meters (3 + 3). The right side of the figure is 7 meters (3 + 4). Add up all the sides. 3 + 7 + 6 + 3 + 3 + 4 = 26 meters.

43. $\begin{array}{r} 1933 \\ +2054 \\ \hline 3987 \end{array}$

The northern boundary of the United States is 3987 miles.

44. $\begin{array}{r} 14 \\ +29 \\ \hline 43 \end{array}$

It takes 43 muscles to frown.

45. $\begin{array}{r} 206\ \text{R}\ 12 \\ 48\overline{)\ 9900} \\ -96 \\ \hline 30 \\ -0 \\ \hline 300 \\ -288 \\ \hline 12 \end{array}$

206 cases can be filled with 12 cans left over. Yes, there are enough cases to fill a 200 case order.

46.
$$\begin{array}{r} 540 \\ \times\ \ 33 \\ \hline 1620 \\ 16200 \\ \hline 17{,}820 \end{array}$$

The video players cost a total of \$17,820.

Section 1.8

Practice Problems

1. $2 \cdot 2 \cdot 2 = 2^3$

2. $3 \cdot 3 = 3^2$

3. $10 \cdot 10 \cdot 10 \cdot 10 \cdot 10 \cdot 10 = 10^6$

4. $5 \cdot 5 \cdot 4 \cdot 4 \cdot 4 = (5 \cdot 5)(4 \cdot 4 \cdot 4) = 5^2 \cdot 4^3$

5. $2^3 = 2 \cdot 2 \cdot 2 = 8$

6. $5^2 = 5 \cdot 5 = 25$

7. $10^1 = 10$

8. $4 \cdot 5^2 = 4(5 \cdot 5) = 4 \cdot 25 = 100$

9. $16 \div 4 - 2 = 4 - 2$
   $= 2$

10. $18 \div 3^2 \cdot 2^2 = 18 \div 9 \cdot 4$
    $= 2 \cdot 4$
    $= 8$

11. $(9-8)^3 + 3 \cdot 2^4 = 1^3 + 3 \cdot 2^4$
    $= 1 + 3 \cdot 16$
    $= 1 + 48$
    $= 49$

12. $24 \div [20 - (3 \cdot 4)] + 2^3 - 5$
    $= 24 \div [20 - 12] + 2^3 - 5$
    $= 24 \div 8 + 8 - 5$
    $= 3 + 8 - 5$
    $= 6$

13. $\dfrac{60 - 5^2 + 1}{3(1+1)} = \dfrac{60 - 25 + 1}{3(2)}$
    $= \dfrac{36}{6}$
    $= 6$

14. Area of a square = $(\text{side})^2$
    $= (11 \text{ centimeters})^2$
    $= 121$ square centimeters

Calculator Explorations

1. Press the keys 3 [y^x] 6 [= or ENTER]. The display will read 729.

2. Press the keys 5 [y^x] 6 [= or ENTER]. The display will read 15,625.

3. Press the keys 4 [y^x] 5 [= or ENTER]. The display will read 1024.

4. Press the keys 7 [y^x] 6 [= or ENTER]. The display will read 117,649.

5. Press the keys 2 [y^x] 11 [= or ENTER]. The display will read 2048.

6. Press the keys 6 [y^x] 8 [= or ENTER]. The display will read 1,679,616.

7. Press the keys 7 [y^x] 4 [+] 5 [y^x] 3 [= or ENTER]. The display will read 2526.

8. Press the keys 12 $\boxed{y^x}$ 4 $\boxed{-}$ 8 $\boxed{y^x}$ 4 $\boxed{= \text{ or ENTER}}$. The display will read 16,640.

9. Press the keys 63 $\boxed{\times}$ 75 $\boxed{-}$ 43 $\boxed{\times}$ 10 $\boxed{= \text{ or ENTER}}$. The display will read 4295.

10. Press the keys 8 $\boxed{\times}$ 22 $\boxed{+}$ 7 $\boxed{\times}$ 16 $\boxed{= \text{ or ENTER}}$. The display will read 288.

11. Press the keys 4 $\boxed{\times}$ $\boxed{(}$ 15 $\boxed{\div}$ 3 $\boxed{+}$ 2 $\boxed{)}$ $\boxed{-}$ 10 $\boxed{\times}$ 2 $\boxed{= \text{ or ENTER}}$. The display will read 8.

12. Press the keys 155 $\boxed{-}$ 2 $\boxed{\times}$ $\boxed{(}$ 17 $\boxed{+}$ 3 $\boxed{)}$ $\boxed{+}$ 185 $\boxed{= \text{ or ENTER}}$. The display will read 300.

Exercise Set 1.8

1. $3 \cdot 3 \cdot 3 \cdot 3 = 3^4$

3. $7 \cdot 7 \cdot 7 \cdot 7 \cdot 7 \cdot 7 \cdot 7 \cdot 7 = 7^8$

5. $12 \cdot 12 \cdot 12 = 12^3$

7. $6 \cdot 6 \cdot 5 \cdot 5 \cdot 5 = (6 \cdot 6)(5 \cdot 5 \cdot 5) = 6^2 \cdot 5^3$

9. $9 \cdot 9 \cdot 9 \cdot 8 = (9 \cdot 9 \cdot 9)8 = 9^3 \cdot 8$

11. $3 \cdot 2 \cdot 2 \cdot 2 \cdot 2 \cdot 2 = 3(2 \cdot 2 \cdot 2 \cdot 2 \cdot 2) = 3 \cdot 2^5$

13. $3 \cdot 2 \cdot 2 \cdot 5 \cdot 5 \cdot 5 = 3(2 \cdot 2)(5 \cdot 5 \cdot 5) = 3 \cdot 2^2 \cdot 5^3$

15. $5^2 = 5 \cdot 5 = 25$

17. $5^3 = 5 \cdot 5 \cdot 5 = 125$

19. $2^6 = 2 \cdot 2 \cdot 2 \cdot 2 \cdot 2 \cdot 2 = 64$

21. $2^{10} = 2 \cdot 2 \cdot 2 \cdot 2 \cdot 2 \cdot 2 \cdot 2 \cdot 2 \cdot 2 \cdot 2 = 1024$

23. $7^1 = 7$

25. $3^5 = 3 \cdot 3 \cdot 3 \cdot 3 \cdot 3 = 243$

27. $2^8 = 2 \cdot 2 \cdot 2 \cdot 2 \cdot 2 \cdot 2 \cdot 2 \cdot 2 = 256$

29. $4^3 = 4 \cdot 4 \cdot 4 = 64$

31. $9^2 = 9 \cdot 9 = 81$

33. $9^3 = 9 \cdot 9 \cdot 9 = 729$

35. $10^2 = 10 \cdot 10 = 100$

37. $10^4 = 10 \cdot 10 \cdot 10 \cdot 10 = 10{,}000$

39. $10^1 = 10$

41. $1920^1 = 1920$

43. $3^6 = 3 \cdot 3 \cdot 3 \cdot 3 \cdot 3 \cdot 3 = 729$

45.
$$\begin{aligned} 15 + 3 \cdot 2 &= 15 + 6 \\ &= 21 \end{aligned}$$

47.
$$\begin{aligned} 20 - 4 \cdot 3 &= 20 - 12 \\ &= 8 \end{aligned}$$

49.
$$\begin{aligned} 5 \cdot 9 - 16 &= 45 - 16 \\ &= 29 \end{aligned}$$

51.
$$\begin{aligned} 28 \div 4 - 3 &= 7 - 3 \\ &= 4 \end{aligned}$$

53.
$$\begin{aligned} 14 + \frac{24}{8} &= 14 + 3 \\ &= 17 \end{aligned}$$

55.
$$\begin{aligned} 6 \cdot 5 + 8 \cdot 2 &= 30 + 8 \cdot 2 \\ &= 30 + 16 \\ &= 46 \end{aligned}$$

57.
$$\begin{aligned} 0 \div 6 + 4 \cdot 7 &= 0 + 4 \cdot 7 \\ &= 0 + 28 \\ &= 28 \end{aligned}$$

59.
$$\begin{aligned} 6 + 8 \div 2 &= 6 + 4 \\ &= 10 \end{aligned}$$

61. $(6+8)\div 2 = 14\div 2$
$= 7$

63. $\left(6^2-4\right)\div 8 = (36-4)\div 8$
$= 32\div 8$
$= 4$

65. $\left(3+5^2\right)\div 2 = (3+25)\div 2$
$= 28\div 2$
$= 14$

67. $6^2\cdot(10-8) = 36\cdot(10-8)$
$= 36\cdot 2$
$= 72$

69. $\frac{18+6}{2^4-4} = \frac{24}{16-4}$
$= \frac{24}{12}$
$= 2$

71. $(2+5)\cdot(8-3) = 7\cdot(8-3)$
$= 7\cdot 5$
$= 35$

73. $\frac{7(9-6)+3}{3^2-3} = \frac{7\cdot 3+3}{9-3}$
$= \frac{21+3}{6}$
$= \frac{24}{6}$
$= 4$

75. $5 \div 0 + 24$ is undefined because $5 \div 0$ is undefined.

77. $3^4-[35-(12-6)] = 3^4-[35-6]$
$= 81-29$
$= 52$

79. $(7\cdot 5)+[9\div(3\div 3)] = (7\cdot 5)+[9\div 1]$
$= 35+9$
$= 44$

81. $8\cdot[4+(6-1)\cdot 2]-50\cdot 2$
$= 8\cdot[4+5\cdot 2]-50\cdot 2$
$= 8\cdot[4+10]-100$
$= 8\cdot 14-100$
$= 112-100$
$= 12$

83. $7^2-\left\{18-[40\div(4\cdot 2)+2]+5^2\right\}$
$= 7^2-\left\{18-[40\div 8+2]+5^2\right\}$
$= 49-\{18-[5+2]+25\}$
$= 49-\{18-7+25\}$
$= 49-36$
$= 13$

85. Area of a square = $(\text{side})^2$
= $(20\text{ miles})^2$
= 400 square miles

87. Area of a square = $(\text{side})^2$
= $(8\text{ centimeters})^2$
= 64 square centimeters

89. Area of base = $(\text{side})^2$
= $(100\text{ meters})^2$
= 10,000 square meters

91. $(2+3)\cdot 6-2 = 5\cdot 6-2$
$= 30-2$
$= 28$

93. $24\div(3\cdot 2)+2\cdot 5 = 24\div 6+2\cdot 5$
$= 4+10$
$= 14$

95. Missing side lengths are 60 – 40 = 20 feet and 30 – 12 = 18 feet.
Perimeter of one home = 12 + 60 + 30 + 40 + 18 + 20 = 180 feet.
Total perimeter = $7\times 180 = 1260$ feet.

97. $\left(7+2^4\right)^5-\left(3^5-2^4\right)^2$
$= (7+16)^5-\left(3^5-2^4\right)^2$
$= 23^5-(243-16)^2$
$= 6{,}436{,}343-227^2$
$= 6{,}436{,}343-51{,}529$
$= 6{,}384{,}814$

Section 1.9

Practice Problems

1. Replace x with 5 in the expression $x-2$.
$x-2 = 5-2 = 3$

2. $y(x-3) = 7(3-3)$
$= 7(0)$
$= 0$

3. $\frac{y+6}{x} = \frac{8+6}{2}$
$= \frac{14}{2}$
$= 7$

4. $25 - z^3 + 1 = 25 - (2)^3 + 1$
$= 25 - 8 + 1$
$= 18$

5. $\frac{5(F-32)}{9} = \frac{5(41-32)}{9}$
$= \frac{5(9)}{9}$
$= 5$

6. a. In words: twice a number
Translate: $2 \cdot x$ or $2x$

b. In words: 8 increased by a number
Translate: $x + 8$

c. In words: 10 minus a number
Translate: $10 - x$

d. In words: 10 subtracted from a number
Translate: $x - 10$

e. In words: the quotient of 6 and a number
Translate: $6 \div x$ or $\frac{6}{x}$

Exercise Set 1.9

1. $3 + 2z = 3 + 2(3)$
$= 3 + 6$
$= 9$

3. $6xz - 5x = 6(2)(3) - 5(2)$
$= 36 - 10$
$= 26$

5. $z - x + y = 3 - 2 + 5$
$= 6$

7. $3x - z = 3 \cdot 2 - 3$
$= 6 - 3$
$= 3$

9. $y^3 - 4x = 5^3 - 4(2)$
$= 125 - 4(2)$
$= 125 - 8$
$= 117$

11. $2xy^2 - 6 = 2(2)(5)^2 - 6$
$= 2(2)(25) - 6$
$= 100 - 6$
$= 94$

13. $8 - (y - x) = 8 - (5 - 2)$
$= 8 - 3$
$= 5$

15. $y^4 + (z - x) = 5^4 + (3 - 2)$
$= 5^4 + 1$
$= 625 + 1$
$= 626$

17. $\frac{6xy}{z} = \frac{6 \cdot 2 \cdot 5}{3}$
$= \frac{60}{3}$
$= 20$

19. $\frac{2y-2}{x} = \frac{2 \cdot 5 - 2}{2}$
$= \frac{10-2}{2}$
$= \frac{8}{2}$
$= 4$

21. $\frac{x+2y}{z} = \frac{2+2 \cdot 5}{3}$
$= \frac{2+10}{3}$
$= \frac{12}{3}$
$= 4$

23. $\frac{5x}{y} - \frac{10}{y} = \frac{5 \cdot 2}{5} - \frac{10}{5}$
$= \frac{10}{5} - \frac{10}{5}$
$= 0$

25. $2y^2 - 4y + 3 = 2 \cdot 5^2 - 4 \cdot 5 + 3$
$= 2 \cdot 25 - 4 \cdot 5 + 3$
$= 50 - 20 + 3$
$= 33$

27. $(3y - 2x)^2 = (3 \cdot 5 - 2 \cdot 2)^2$
$= (15 - 4)^2$
$= (11)^2$
$= 121$

29. $(xy+1)^2 = (2\cdot 5+1)^2$
$= (10+1)^2$
$= (11)^2$
$= 121$

31. $2y(4z-x) = 2\cdot 5(4\cdot 3-2)$
$= 2\cdot 5(12-2)$
$= 2\cdot 5(10)$
$= 10(10)$
$= 100$

33. $xy(5+z-x) = 2\cdot 5(5+3-2)$
$= 2\cdot 5(8-2)$
$= 2\cdot 5(6)$
$= 10(6)$
$= 60$

35. $\dfrac{7x+2y}{3x} = \dfrac{7\cdot 2+2\cdot 5}{3\cdot 2}$
$= \dfrac{14+10}{6}$
$= \dfrac{24}{6}$
$= 4$

37.

t	1	2	3	4
$16t^2$	$16(1)^2$	$16(2)^2$	$16(3)^2$	$16(4)^2$
	$16\cdot 1$	$16\cdot 4$	$16\cdot 9$	$16\cdot 16$
	16	64	144	256

39. $x+5$

41. $x+8$

43. $20-x$

45. $512x$

47. $x \div 2$ or $\dfrac{x}{2}$

49. $5x+(17+x)$

51. $5x$

53. $11-x$

55. $x-5$

57. $6 \div x$ or $\dfrac{6}{x}$

59. $50-8x$

61. $x^4 - y^2 = (23)^4 - (72)^2$ Substitute
$= 279,841 - 5184$ Exponentiate
$= 274,657$ Subtract

63. $x^2 + 5y - 112$
$= (23)^2 + 5(72) - 112$ Substitute
$= 529 + 360 - 112$ Exponentiate
$= 777$ Add and subtract

65. Compare expressions:
$\dfrac{x}{3} = \left(\dfrac{1}{3}\right)x$
$\left(\dfrac{1}{3}\right)x < 2x < 5x$
$5x$ is the largest.

67.

t	1	2	3	4
$16t^2$	16	64	144	256

As t gets larger, $16t^2$ gets larger.

Chapter 1 Review

1. $5\underline{4}80$
↓
hundreds

2. $\underline{4}6,200,120$
↓
ten millions

3. 5480 = five thousand, four hundred eighty

4. 46,200,120 = forty-six million, two hundred thousand, one hundred twenty

5. 6279 = 6000 + 200 + 70 + 9

6. 403,225,000 = 400,000,000 + 3,000,000 + 200,000 + 20,000 + 5000

7. Fifty-nine thousand, eight hundred = 59,800

8. Six billion, three hundred four million = 6,304,000,000

9. In 1990, Houston had a population of 1,630,553 people.

10. In 1980, Los Angeles had a population of 2,968,528 people.

11. $$\begin{array}{r} 1,321,045 \\ -789,704 \\ \hline 531,341 \end{array}$$

The population of Phoenix increased by 531,341 people from 1980 to 2000.

12. $$\begin{array}{r} 1,027,974 \\ -\ 951,270 \\ \hline 76,704 \end{array}$$

The population of Detroit decreased by 76,704 people from 1990 to 2000.

13. $7+6=13$

14. $8+9=17$

15. $3+0=3$

16. $0+10=10$

17. $$\begin{array}{r} {\scriptstyle 1}\ \ \\ 25 \\ 8 \\ +\ 5 \\ \hline 38 \end{array}$$

18. $$\begin{array}{r} 27 \\ +41 \\ \hline 68 \end{array}$$

19. $$\begin{array}{r} 32 \\ +24 \\ \hline 56 \end{array}$$

20. $$\begin{array}{r} {\scriptstyle 1}\ \ \\ 19 \\ +21 \\ \hline 40 \end{array}$$

21. $$\begin{array}{r} {\scriptstyle 1\,1}\ \ \\ 47 \\ +63 \\ \hline 110 \end{array}$$

22. $$\begin{array}{r} {\scriptstyle 1\,1}\ \ \\ 77 \\ +43 \\ \hline 120 \end{array}$$

23. $$\begin{array}{r} {\scriptstyle 1\,1}\ \ \\ 567 \\ +383 \\ \hline 950 \end{array}$$

24. $$\begin{array}{r} {\scriptstyle 1\,1\,1}\ \ \\ 463 \\ +787 \\ \hline 1250 \end{array}$$

25. $$\begin{array}{r} {\scriptstyle 1\,2\,1}\ \ \\ 591 \\ 623 \\ +497 \\ \hline 1711 \end{array}$$

26. $$\begin{array}{r} {\scriptstyle 1\,1\,1}\ \ \\ 5982 \\ 1647 \\ +2238 \\ \hline 9867 \end{array}$$

27. $$\begin{array}{r} {\scriptstyle 1\ \ 1}\ \ \\ 714 \\ +7318 \\ \hline 8032 \end{array}$$

The total distance from Chicago to New Delhi via New York City is 8032 miles.

28. $$\begin{array}{r} {\scriptstyle 1\,1\,1\ \ 1}\ \ \\ 62,589 \\ 65,340 \\ +\ 69,770 \\ \hline 197,699 \end{array}$$

Sean Cruise's total earnings during the three years is $197,699.

29. $$\begin{array}{r} {\scriptstyle 2}\ \ \\ 50 \\ 72 \\ 72 \\ +82 \\ \hline 276 \end{array}$$

The perimeter is 276 feet.

30. $$\begin{array}{r} 11 \\ 20 \\ +35 \\ \hline 66 \end{array}$$

The perimeter is 66 kilometers.

31. $$\begin{array}{r} 42 \\ -9 \\ \hline 33 \end{array}$$

Check:

$$\begin{array}{r} {\scriptstyle 1}\ \ \\ 33 \\ +9 \\ \hline 42 \end{array}$$

32. $$\begin{array}{r} 67 \\ -24 \\ \hline 43 \end{array}$$

Check:

$$\begin{array}{r} 43 \\ +24 \\ \hline 67 \end{array}$$

33. $$\begin{array}{r} 93 \\ -\ 79 \\ \hline 14 \end{array}$$

Check:
$$\begin{array}{r} \scriptstyle 1 \\ 14 \\ +\ 79 \\ \hline 93 \end{array}$$

34. $$\begin{array}{r} 60 \\ -\ 27 \\ \hline 33 \end{array}$$

Check:
$$\begin{array}{r} \scriptstyle 1 \\ 33 \\ +\ 27 \\ \hline 60 \end{array}$$

35. $$\begin{array}{r} 599 \\ -\ 237 \\ \hline 362 \end{array}$$

Check:
$$\begin{array}{r} 362 \\ +\ 237 \\ \hline 599 \end{array}$$

36. $$\begin{array}{r} 462 \\ -\ 397 \\ \hline 65 \end{array}$$

Check:
$$\begin{array}{r} \scriptstyle 11 \\ 65 \\ +\ 397 \\ \hline 462 \end{array}$$

37. $$\begin{array}{r} 583 \\ -\ 279 \\ \hline 304 \end{array}$$

Check:
$$\begin{array}{r} \scriptstyle 1 \\ 304 \\ +\ 279 \\ \hline 583 \end{array}$$

38. $$\begin{array}{r} 600 \\ -\ 124 \\ \hline 476 \end{array}$$

Check:
$$\begin{array}{r} \scriptstyle 11 \\ 476 \\ +\ 124 \\ \hline 600 \end{array}$$

39. $$\begin{array}{r} 4000 \\ -\ 1886 \\ \hline 2114 \end{array}$$

Check:
$$\begin{array}{r} \scriptstyle 111 \\ 2114 \\ +\ 1886 \\ \hline 4000 \end{array}$$

40. $$\begin{array}{r} 4268 \\ -\ 3947 \\ \hline 321 \end{array}$$

Check:
$$\begin{array}{r} \scriptstyle 1 \\ 321 \\ +\ 3947 \\ \hline 4268 \end{array}$$

41. $$\begin{array}{r} 712 \\ -\ 315 \\ \hline 397 \end{array}$$

Check:
$$\begin{array}{r} \scriptstyle 11 \\ 397 \\ +\ 315 \\ \hline 712 \end{array}$$

Bob Roma has 397 pages left.

42. $$\begin{array}{r} 18,425 \\ -\ 1\ 599 \\ \hline 16,826 \end{array} \qquad \begin{array}{r} 16,826 \\ -\ 1\ 200 \\ \hline 15,626 \end{array}$$

Check:
$$\begin{array}{r} \scriptstyle 1\ \ 11 \\ 15,626 \\ 1\ 200 \\ +\ \ 1\ 599 \\ \hline 18,425 \end{array}$$

Shelly Winters paid \$15,626 for the car.

43. During May, when it was \$100.

44. During August, when it was \$490.

45. During April and May.

46. During July, August, and September.

47. To round 93 to the nearest ten, observe that the digit in the ones place is 3. Since this digit is less than 5, we do not add 1 to the digit in the tens place. The number 93 rounded to the nearest ten is 90.

48. To round 45 to the nearest ten, observe that the digit in the ones place is 5. Since this digit is at least 5, we need to add 1 to the digit in the tens place. The number 45 rounded to the nearest ten is 50.

49. To round 467 to the nearest ten, observe that the digit in the ones place is 7. Since this digit is at least 5, we need to add 1 to the digit in the tens place. The number 467 rounded to the nearest ten is 470.

50. To round 493 to the nearest hundred, observe that the digit in the tens place is 9. Since this digit is at least 5, we need to add 1 to the digit in the hundreds place. The number 493 rounded to the nearest hundred it 500.

51. To round 4832 to the nearest hundred, observe that the digit in the tens place is 3. Since this digit is less than 5, we do not add 1 to the digit in the hundreds place. The number 4832 rounded to the nearest hundred is 4800.

52. To round 57,534 to the nearest thousand, observe that the digit in the hundreds place is 5. Since this digit is at least 5, we need to add 1 to the digit in the thousands place. The number 57,534 rounded to the nearest thousand is 58,000.

53. To round 49,683,712 to the nearest million, observe that the digit in the hundred-thousands place is 6. Since this digit is at least 5, we need to add 1 to the digit in the millions place. The number 49,683,712 rounded to the nearest million is 50,000,000.

54. To round 768,542 to the nearest hundred-thousand, observe that the digit in the ten-thousands place is 6. Since this digit is at least 5, we need to add 1 to the digit in the hundred-thousands place. The number 768,542 rounded to the nearest hundred-thousand is 800,000.

55.

4892	rounds to	4900
647	rounds to	600
+ 1867	rounds to	+ 1900
		7400

4892 + 647 + 1867 is approximately 7400.

56.

5925	rounds to	5900
− 1787	rounds to	− 1800
		4100

5925 − 1787 is approximately 4100.

57. When rounding to the nearest million, 68,490,000 rounds to 68,000,000.

58. When rounding to the nearest thousand, 679,967 rounds to 680,000.

59. $6 \cdot 7 = 42$

60. $8 \cdot 3 = 24$

61. $5(0) = 0$

62. $0(9) = 0$

63.
$$\begin{array}{r} 47 \\ \times\ 30 \\ \hline 0 \\ 1410 \\ \hline 1410 \end{array}$$

64.
$$\begin{array}{r} 69 \\ \times\ 42 \\ \hline 138 \\ 2760 \\ \hline 2898 \end{array}$$

65.
$$\begin{aligned} 20(8)(5) &= 20 \cdot 40 \\ &= 800 \end{aligned}$$

66.
$$\begin{aligned} 25(9 \times 4) &= 25 \cdot 36 \\ &= 900 \end{aligned}$$

67.
$$\begin{array}{r} 48 \\ \times\ 77 \\ \hline 336 \\ 3360 \\ \hline 3696 \end{array}$$

68.
$$\begin{array}{r} 77 \\ \times\ 22 \\ \hline 154 \\ 1540 \\ \hline 1694 \end{array}$$

69. $49 \cdot 49 \cdot 0 = 0$, because anything times zero is zero.

70. $62 \cdot 88 \cdot 0 = 0$, because anything times zero is zero.

71.
$$\begin{array}{r} 586 \\ \times\ 29 \\ \hline 5\,274 \\ 11,720 \\ \hline 16,994 \end{array}$$

72.
$$\begin{array}{r} 242 \\ \times\ 37 \\ \hline 1694 \\ 7260 \\ \hline 8954 \end{array}$$

73.
$$\begin{array}{r} 642 \\ \times\ 177 \\ \hline 4\ 494 \\ 44{,}940 \\ 64{,}200 \\ \hline 113{,}634 \end{array}$$

74.
$$\begin{array}{r} 347 \\ \times\ 129 \\ \hline 3\ 123 \\ 6\ 940 \\ 34{,}700 \\ \hline 44{,}763 \end{array}$$

75.
$$\begin{array}{r} 1026 \\ \times\ \ 401 \\ \hline 1\ 026 \\ 00 \\ 410{,}400 \\ \hline 411{,}426 \end{array}$$

76.
$$\begin{array}{r} 2107 \\ \times\ 302 \\ \hline 4\ 214 \\ 00 \\ 632{,}100 \\ \hline 636{,}314 \end{array}$$

77.
$$\begin{array}{rlr} 49 & \text{rounds to} & 50 \\ \times\ 32 & \text{rounds to} & \times\ 30 \\ \cline{1-1}\cline{3-3} & & 1500 \end{array}$$

$49 \cdot 32$ is approximately 1500.

78.
$$\begin{array}{rlr} 586 & \text{rounds to} & 600 \\ \times\ 357 & \text{rounds to} & \times\ 400 \\ \cline{1-1}\cline{3-3} & & 240{,}000 \end{array}$$

$586 \cdot 357$ is approximately 240,000.

79.
$$\begin{array}{rlr} 5231 & \text{rounds to} & 5200 \\ \times\ 243 & \text{rounds to} & \times\ 200 \\ \cline{1-1}\cline{3-3} & & 1{,}040{,}000 \end{array}$$

$5231 \cdot 243$ is approximately 1,040,000.

80.
$$\begin{array}{rlr} 7836 & \text{rounds to} & 7800 \\ \times\ 912 & \text{rounds to} & \times\ 900 \\ \cline{1-1}\cline{3-3} & & 7{,}020{,}000 \end{array}$$

$7836 \cdot 912$ is approximately 7,020,000.

81. $8 \times 3 = 24$

There are 24 grams of fat in 3 ounces of Swiss cheese.

82.
$$\begin{array}{r} 5283 \\ \times\ 927 \\ \hline 36{,}981 \\ 105{,}660 \\ 4{,}754{,}700 \\ \hline 4{,}897{,}341 \end{array}$$

The tuition collected totaled $4,897,341.

83.
$$\begin{array}{r} 12 \\ \times\ 5 \\ \hline 60 \end{array}$$

The area is 60 square miles.

84.
$$\begin{array}{r} 20 \\ \times\ 25 \\ \hline 100 \\ 400 \\ \hline 500 \end{array}$$

The area is 500 square centimeters.

85.
$$\begin{array}{r} 3 \\ 6\overline{)\ 18} \\ -18 \\ \hline 0 \end{array}$$

Check: $3 \cdot 6 = 18$

86.
$$\begin{array}{r} 4 \\ 9\overline{)\ 36} \\ -36 \\ \hline 0 \end{array}$$

Check: $4 \cdot 9 = 36$

87.
$$\begin{array}{r} 6 \\ 7\overline{)\ 42} \\ -42 \\ \hline 0 \end{array}$$

Check: $6 \cdot 7 = 42$

88.
$$\begin{array}{r} 5 \\ 5\overline{)\ 25} \\ -25 \\ \hline 0 \end{array}$$

Check: $5 \cdot 5 = 25$

89.
$$\begin{array}{r} 5\ \text{R}\ 2 \\ 5\overline{)\ 27} \\ -25 \\ \hline 2 \end{array}$$

Check: $5 \cdot 5 + 2 = 27$

90.
$$\begin{array}{r} 4\ \text{R}\ 2 \\ 4\overline{)\ 18} \\ -16 \\ \hline 2 \end{array}$$

Check: $4 \cdot 4 + 2 = 18$

91. $16 \div 0$ is undefined

92. $0 \div 8 = 0$
Check: $0 \cdot 8 = 0$

93. $9 \div 9 = 1$
Check: $9 \cdot 1 = 9$

94. $10 \div 1 = 10$
Check: $10 \cdot 1 = 10$

95. $918 \div 0$ is undefined

96. $0 \div 668 = 0$
Check: $668 \cdot 0 = 0$

97.
$$\begin{array}{r} 15 \\ 5\overline{)\;75} \\ -5 \\ \hline 25 \\ -25 \\ \hline 0 \end{array}$$

Check: $15 \cdot 5 = 75$

98.
$$\begin{array}{r} 19\text{ R }7 \\ 8\overline{)159} \\ -8 \\ \hline 79 \\ -72 \\ \hline 7 \end{array}$$

Check: $19 \cdot 8 + 7 = 159$

99.
$$\begin{array}{r} 24\text{ R }2 \\ 26\overline{)\;626} \\ -52 \\ \hline 106 \\ -104 \\ \hline 2 \end{array}$$

Check: $24 \cdot 26 + 2 = 626$

100.
$$\begin{array}{r} 56 \\ 6\overline{)\;336} \\ -30 \\ \hline 36 \\ -36 \\ \hline 0 \end{array}$$

Check: $56 \cdot 6 = 336$

101.
$$\begin{array}{r} 1\text{ R }17 \\ 32\overline{)\;49} \\ -32 \\ \hline 17 \end{array}$$

Check: $1 \cdot 32 + 17 = 49$

102.
$$\begin{array}{r} 35\text{ R }15 \\ 19\overline{)\;680} \\ -57 \\ \hline 110 \\ -95 \\ \hline 15 \end{array}$$

Check: $35 \cdot 19 + 15 = 680$

103.
$$\begin{array}{r} 500 \\ 20\overline{)\;10000} \\ -100 \\ \hline 00 \\ -0 \\ \hline 00 \\ -0 \\ \hline 0 \end{array}$$

Check: $500 \cdot 20 = 10{,}000$

104.
$$\begin{array}{r} 21\text{ R }6 \\ 43\overline{)\;909} \\ -86 \\ \hline 49 \\ -43 \\ \hline 6 \end{array}$$

Check: $21 \cdot 43 + 6 = 909$

105.
$$\begin{array}{r} 506 \\ 47\overline{)\;23782} \\ -235 \\ \hline 28 \\ -0 \\ \hline 282 \\ -282 \\ \hline 0 \end{array}$$

Check: $506 \cdot 47 = 23{,}782$

106.
$$\begin{array}{r} 16 \\ 30\overline{)\;480} \\ -30 \\ \hline 180 \\ -180 \\ \hline 0 \end{array}$$

Check: $16 \cdot 30 = 480$

107.
$$\begin{array}{r} 199\text{ R }8 \\ 16\overline{)\;3192} \\ -16 \\ \hline 159 \\ -144 \\ \hline 152 \\ -144 \\ \hline 8 \end{array}$$

Check: $199 \cdot 16 + 8 = 3192$

108.
$$\begin{array}{r} 200 \\ 25\overline{)\ 5000} \\ \underline{-50} \\ 00 \\ \underline{-0} \\ 00 \\ \underline{-0} \\ 0 \end{array}$$

Check: $200 \cdot 25 = 5000$

109.
$$\begin{array}{r} 458 \\ 12\overline{)\ 5496} \\ \underline{-48} \\ 69 \\ \underline{-60} \\ 96 \\ \underline{-96} \\ 0 \end{array}$$

Check: $458 \cdot 12 = 5496$
There are 458 feet in 5496 inches.

110. Add the numbers, then divide by four.
$$\begin{array}{r} 76 \\ 49 \\ 32 \\ \underline{+\ 47} \\ 204 \end{array} \qquad \begin{array}{r} 51 \\ 4\overline{)\ 204} \\ \underline{-20} \\ 04 \\ \underline{-4} \\ 0 \end{array}$$

The average is $\frac{204}{4} = 51$.

111. $7 \cdot 7 \cdot 7 \cdot 7 = 7^4$

112. $3 \cdot 3 \cdot 3 = 3^3$

113. $4 \cdot 2 \cdot 2 \cdot 2 = 4 \cdot 2^3$

114. $5 \cdot 5 \cdot 7 \cdot 7 \cdot 7 = 5^2 \cdot 7^3$

115. $7^2 = 7 \cdot 7 = 49$

116. $2^6 = 2 \cdot 2 \cdot 2 \cdot 2 \cdot 2 \cdot 2 = 64$

117. $5^3 \cdot 3^2 = 5 \cdot 5 \cdot 5 \cdot 3 \cdot 3 = 1125$

118. $4^1 \cdot 10^2 \cdot 7^2 = 4 \cdot 10 \cdot 10 \cdot 7 \cdot 7 = 19{,}600$

119.
$$\begin{aligned} 18 \div 3 + 7 &= 6 + 7 \\ &= 13 \end{aligned}$$

120.
$$\begin{aligned} 12 - 8 \div 4 &= 12 - 2 \\ &= 10 \end{aligned}$$

121.
$$\begin{aligned} \frac{6^2 - 3}{3^2 + 2} &= \frac{36 - 3}{9 + 2} \\ &= \frac{33}{11} \\ &= 3 \end{aligned}$$

122.
$$\begin{aligned} \frac{16 - 8}{2^3} &= \frac{8}{8} \\ &= 1 \end{aligned}$$

123.
$$\begin{aligned} 2 + 3[1 + (20 - 17) \cdot 3] &= 2 + 3[1 + 3 \cdot 3] \\ &= 2 + 3[1 + 9] \\ &= 2 + 3[10] \\ &= 2 + 30 \\ &= 32 \end{aligned}$$

124.
$$\begin{aligned} &21 - \left[2^4 - (7 - 5) - 10\right] + 8 \cdot 2 \\ &= 21 - \left[2^4 - 2 - 10\right] + 8 \cdot 2 \\ &= 21 - [16 - 2 - 10] + 16 \\ &= 21 - 4 + 16 \\ &= 33 \end{aligned}$$

125.
$$\begin{aligned} \text{Area} &= (\text{side})^2 \\ &= (7 \text{ meters})^2 \\ &= 49 \text{ square meters} \end{aligned}$$

126.
$$\begin{aligned} \text{Area} &= (\text{side})^2 \\ &= (3 \text{ inches})^2 \\ &= 9 \text{ square inches} \end{aligned}$$

127. $\frac{2 \cdot 5}{2} = \frac{10}{2} = 5$

128 $4(5) - 3 = 20 - 3 = 17$

129. $\frac{5 + 7}{0} = \frac{12}{0}$ is undefined

130. $\frac{0}{5(5)} = 0$

131. $5^3 - 2 \cdot 2 = 125 - 4 = 121$

132. $\frac{7 + 5}{3(2)} = \frac{12}{6} = 2$

133. $(0 + 2)^2 = 2^2 = 4$

134. $\frac{100}{5}+\frac{0}{3}=20+0=20$

135. $x-5$

136. $x+7$

137. $10 \div (x+1)$

138. $5(x+3)$

139.

x	0	1	2	3
$8x^2$	$8(0)^2$	$8(1)^2$	$8(2)^2$	$8(3)^2$
	0	8	32	72

Chapter 1 Test

1. $59+82=141$

2. $600-487=113$

3.
$$\begin{array}{r} 496 \\ \times\ \ 30 \\ \hline 000 \\ 1488\ \\ \hline 14,880 \end{array}$$

4.
$$\begin{array}{r} 766 \text{ R } 42 \\ 69\overline{)\ 52896} \\ -483 \\ \hline 459 \\ -414 \\ \hline 456 \\ -414 \\ \hline 42 \end{array}$$

$$\begin{array}{r} 7666 \\ \times\ \ 69 \\ \hline 52854 \\ +\ \ 42 \\ \hline 52896 \end{array}$$

5. $2^3 \cdot 5^2 = 8 \cdot 25 = 200$

6. $6^1 \cdot 2^3 = 6 \cdot 2 \cdot 2 \cdot 2 = 48$

7. $98 \div 1 = 98$

8. $0 \div 49 = 0$

9. $62 \div 0$ is undefined.

10. $(2^4-5)=(16-5)\cdot 3$
$=11\cdot 3$
$=33$

11. $16+9 \div 3 \cdot 4 - 7 = 16+12-7=21$

12. $2[(6-4)^2+(22-19)^2]+10$
$=2[2^2+3^2]+10$
$=2[4+9]+10$
$=2(13)+10$
$=26+10$
$=36$

13. 52,369 rounded to the nearest thousand is 52,000.

14.
$$\begin{array}{r} 6289 \\ 5403 \\ +\ 1957 \\ \hline \end{array} \qquad \begin{array}{r} 6300 \\ 5400 \\ +\ 2000 \\ \hline 13,700 \end{array}$$

15.
$$\begin{array}{r} 4267 \\ -2738 \\ \hline \end{array} \qquad \begin{array}{r} 4300 \\ -\ 2700 \\ \hline 1600 \end{array}$$

16.
$$\begin{array}{r} \$17 \\ 29\overline{)\ 493} \\ -29 \\ \hline 203 \\ -203 \\ \hline 0 \end{array}$$

$$\begin{array}{r} 17 \\ \times\ 29 \\ \hline \$493 \end{array}$$

17.
$$\begin{array}{r} 17 \\ \times\ 7 \\ \hline \$119 \end{array}$$

18.
$$\begin{array}{r} 725 \\ -\ 599 \\ \hline \$126 \end{array}$$ more expensive

19.
$$\begin{array}{r} 11 \\ -\ 4 \\ \hline 7 \end{array}$$
7 billion more tablets per year are taken for heart disease.

20.
$$\begin{array}{r} 34,000 \\ \times \quad\quad 5 \\ \hline 170,000 \end{array}$$
During a five-day work week the FBI receives over 170,000 fingerprint cards.

21. $5[(2)^3 - 2] = 5[8 - 2] = 5 \cdot 6 = 30$

22. $\dfrac{3(7) - 5}{2(8)} = \dfrac{21 - 5}{16} = 1$

23. **a.** $17x$

b. $20 - 2x$

24. Perimeter
= length + width + length + width
= 20 yards + 10 yards + 20 yards + 10 yards
= 60 yards

Area = length · width
= (20 yards)(10 yards)
= 200 square yards

25. Area = $(\text{side})^2 = (5 \text{ cm})^2 = 25$ sq cm
Perimeter = 4(side) = 4(5 cm) = 20 cm

26. Cast Away earned $233,630,478 in 2000.

27.
$$\begin{array}{r} 215,397,307 \\ -\ 171,383,253 \\ \hline 44,014,054 \end{array}$$

In 2000, Mission Impossible 2 earned $44,014,054 more than the Matrix did in 1999.

28.
$$\begin{array}{r} 431,065,444 \\ -\ 260,031,035 \\ \hline 171,034,439 \end{array}$$

The top-grossing movie in 1999 earned $171,034,439 more than the top-grossing movie in 2000.

Chapter 2

Pretest

1. If 0 represents the line of scrimmage, a loss of 22 yards is –22.

2. 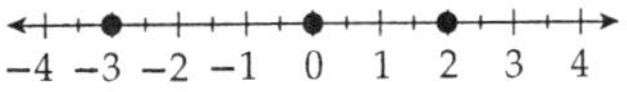

3. $-31 > -36$

4. $|-8| = 8$, because –8 is 8 units from 0.

5. The opposite of –12 is –(–12) = 12.

6. $-19 + 8$
We are adding two numbers with different signs.
$|-19| = 19$, $|8| = 8$
$19 - 8 = 11$
–19 has the larger absolute value and its sign is –.
$-19 + 8 = -11$

7. $x + y = -6 + (-11)$
We are adding two numbers with the same sign.
$|-6| = 6$, $|-11| = 11$
$6 + 11 = 17$
Their common sign is negative, so the sum is negative.
$-6 + (-11) = -17$

8. $-9 + 5 + 7 = -4 + 7 = 3$
The temperature was 3°F at 9 a.m.

9. $-9 - (-14) = -9 + 14 = 5$

10. $$\begin{aligned} 4 - 6 - (-2) + 8 &= 4 + (-6) + 2 + 8 \\ &= -2 + 2 + 8 \\ &= 0 + 8 \\ &= 8 \end{aligned}$$

11. $m - n = -5 - 10 = -5 + (-10) = -15$

12. $$\begin{aligned} 88 + 35 - 72 - 55 &= 88 + 35 + (-72) + (-55) \\ &= 123 + (-72) + (-55) \\ &= 51 + (-55) \\ &= -4 \end{aligned}$$

13. $(-8)(13) = -104$

14. $\dfrac{-36}{-4} = 9$

15. $\dfrac{x}{y} = \dfrac{-96}{-2} = 48$

16. $xy = 4 \cdot (-5) = -20$

17. $(-20) \cdot 3 = -60$

18. $-5^2 = -(5)(5) = -25$

19. $\dfrac{9-17}{-6+2} = \dfrac{9+(-17)}{-6+2} = \dfrac{-8}{-4} = 2$

20. $$\begin{aligned} (-2) \cdot |-7| - (-6) &= (-2) \cdot 7 + 6 \\ &= -14 + 6 \\ &= -8 \end{aligned}$$

21. $$\begin{aligned} x - y^2 &= 2 - (-6)^2 \\ &= 2 - 36 \\ &= 2 + (-36) \\ &= -34 \end{aligned}$$

22. Add the integers, then divide by 5 (the number of integers).

$$\frac{-17+10+(-9)+5+(-19)}{5} = \frac{-30}{5} = -6$$

Section 2.1

Practice Problems

1. a. If 0 represents the surface of the earth, then 800 feet below the surface can be represented by –800 feet.

   b. If 0 represents a balance of \$0, then \$2 million loss can be represented by –2 million dollars.

2. 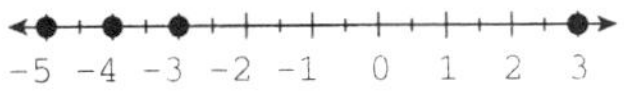

3. a. 0 is to the right of –3, so $0 > -3$.

   b. –5 is to the left of 5, so $-5 < 5$.

   c. –8 is to the right of –12, so $-8 > -12$.

4. a. $|-4| = 4$, because –4 is 4 units from 0.

   b. $|2| = 2$, because 2 is 2 units from 0.

   c. $|-8| = 8$, because 8 is 8 units from 0.

5. a. The opposite of 7 is –7.

   b. The opposite of –17 is –(–17) or 17.

6. a. $-|-2| = -2$

b. $-|5| = -5$

c. $-(-11) = 11$

7. Substitute x with -9.
$-|-9| = -9$

8. Venus has the highest temperature. It is $867°$F.

Exercise Set 2.1

1. If 0 represents ground level, then 1445 feet underground is –1445.

3. If 0 represents sea level, then 14,433 feet above sea level is +14,494.

5. Above 0 is + 118.

7. If 0 represents sea level, then 11,730 feet below sea level is – 11,730.

9. A net loss is – 1683 million.

11. Joe, below sea level, is at –135. Sara, below sea level, is at – 157. Sara is deeper in the water.

13. A loss is – 81.

15. 

17. 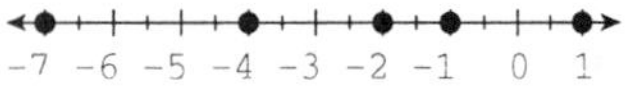

19. 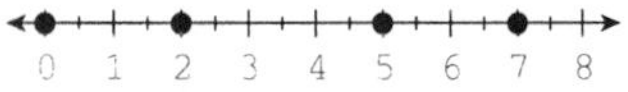

21. 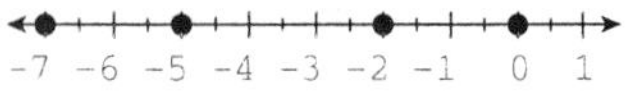

23. $4 > 0$

25. $-7 < -5$

27. $-30 > -35$

29. $-26 < 26$

31. $|5| = 5$, because 5 is 5 units from 0.

33. $|-8| = 8$, because –8 is 8 units from 0.

35. $|0| = 0$, because 0 is 0 units from 0.

37. $|-5| = 5$, because –5 is 5 units from 0.

39. The opposite of 5 is –5.

41. The opposite of –4 is $-(-4) = 4$.

43. The opposite of 23 is –23.

45. The opposite of –10 is $-(-10) = 10$.

47. $|-7| = 7$, because –7 is 7 units from 0.

49. $-|20| = -20$
The opposite of the absolute value of 20 is the opposite of 20.

51. $-|-3| = -3$
The opposite of the absolute value of –3 is the opposite of 3.

53. $-(-8) = 8$
The opposite of negative 8 is 8.

55. $|-14| = 14$, because –14 is 14 units from 0.

57. $-(-29) = 29$
The opposite of negative 29 is 29.

59. $|-(-8)| = |8| = 8$

61. $-|-3| = -3$

63. $|-23| = 23$

65. $-|4| = -4$

67. $-3 > -5$

69. $|-9| \ ? \ |-14|$
$9 \ ? \ 14$
$9 < 14$

71. $|-33| \ ? \ -(-33)$
$33 \ ? \ 33$
$33 = 33$

73. $-|-10| \ ? \ -(-10)$
$-10 \ ? \ 10$
$-10 < 10$

75. $0 \ ? \ -9$
$0 > -9$

77. $|0| \ ? \ |-9|$
$0 \ ? \ 9$
$0 < 9$

79. $-|-2| \ ? -|-10|$
$-2 > -10$

81. $-(-12) \ ? -(-18)$
$12 < 18$

83. $2^2 = 4$
$-|3| = -3$
$-(-5) = 5$
$-|-8| = -8$
$-8, -3, 4, 5$ or $-|-8|, -|3|, 2^2, -(-5)$

85. $|-1| = 1$
$-|-6| = -6$
$-(-6) = 6$
$-|1| = -1$
$-6, -1, 1, 6$ or $-|-6|, -|1|, |-1|, -(-6)$

87. $-(-2) = 2$
$5^2 = 25$
$-10 = -10$
$-|-9| = -9$
$|-12| = 12$
$-10, -9, 2, 12, 25$ or $-10, -|-9|, -(-2), |-12|, 5^2$

89. Maracaibo Lake is at 0, which is sea level.

91. Eyre Lake, at 52 feet below sea level, has the second lowest elevation.

93. Earth, with an average temperature of 56° F, is closest to 0° F.

95. Saturn, with an average temperature of −218° F, is closest to −200° F.

97. $0 + 13 = 13$

99.
$$\begin{array}{r} 15 \\ +\ 20 \\ \hline 35 \end{array}$$

101.
$$\begin{array}{r} 47 \\ 236 \\ +\ 77 \\ \hline 360 \end{array}$$

103. $-12 < -8$
D

105. $-(-|-5|) = -(-5) = 5$

107. False; consider $-1 > -2$.

109. True; consider the values on a number line.

111. False; consider $a = -3$, then $-a = -(-3) = 3$.

113. Answers will vary.

Section 2.2

Practice Problems

1. $5 + (-1) = 4$

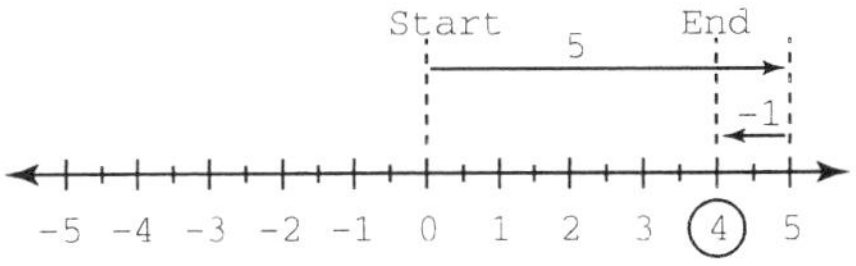

2. $-6 + (-2) = -8$

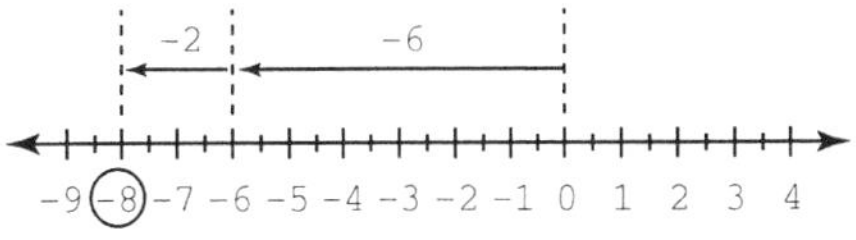

3. $-8 + 3 = -5$

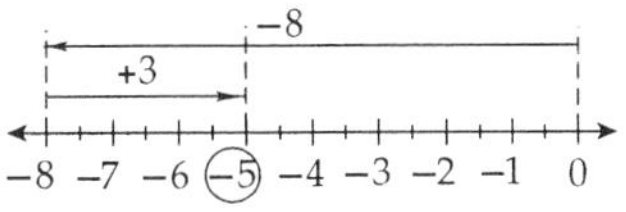

4. $|-3| = 3$, $|-9| = 9$, and $3 + 9 = 12$
Their common sign is negative, so the sum is negative.
$(-3) + (-9) = -12$

5. $-12 + (-3) = -15$

6. $9 + 5 = 14$

7. $|-3| = 3$, $|9| = 9$, and $9 - 3 = 6$
9 has the larger absolute value and its sign is an understood +: $-3 + 9 = 6$.

8. $|2| = 2$, $|-8| = 8$, and $8 - 2 = 6$
−8 has the larger absolute value and its sign is −:
$2 + (-8) = -6$

9. $-46 + 20 = -26$

10. $8 + (-6) = 2$

11. $-2 + 0 = -2$

12. $15 + (-15) = 0$

13. $-80 + 80 = 0$

14. $8+(-3)+(-13) = 5+(-13)$
$= -8$

15. $5+(-3)+12+(-14) = 2+12+(-14)$
$= 14+(-14)$
$= 0$

16. $x + y = -4 + 1 = -3$

17. $x + y = -11 + (-6) = 17$

18. $-8 + 4 + 7 = 3$
The temperature at 8 a.m. was 3° Fahrenheit.

Calculator Explorations

The following may vary depending on your calculator.

1. Press the keys 256 [+/–] [+] 97 [= or ENTER].
The display will read – 159.

2. Press the keys 811 [+] 1058 [+/–] [= or ENTER].
The display will read – 247.

3. Press the keys 6 [×] 15 [+] 46 [+/–] [= or ENTER]. The display will read 44.

4. 129 [+/–] [+] 10 [×] 48 [= or ENTER].
The display will read 351.

5. 108650 [+/–] [+] 786205 [+/–] [= or ENTER].
The display will read –894,855.

6. 196662 [+/–] [+] 129856 [+/–] [= or ENTER].
The display will read –326,518.

Mental Math

1. $5 + 0 = 5$

2. $(-2) + 0 = -2$

3. $0 + (-35) = -35$

4. $0 + 3 = 3$

5. $-12 + 12 = 0$

6. $48 + (-48) = 0$

7. $28 + (-28) = 0$

8. $-9 + 9 = 0$

Exercise Set 2.2

1. $-1 + (-6) = -7$

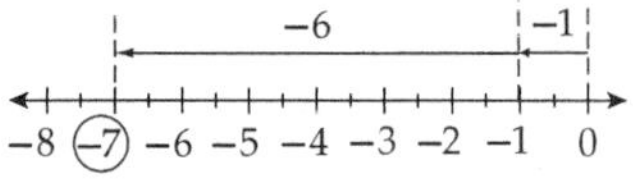

3. $-4 + 7 = 3$

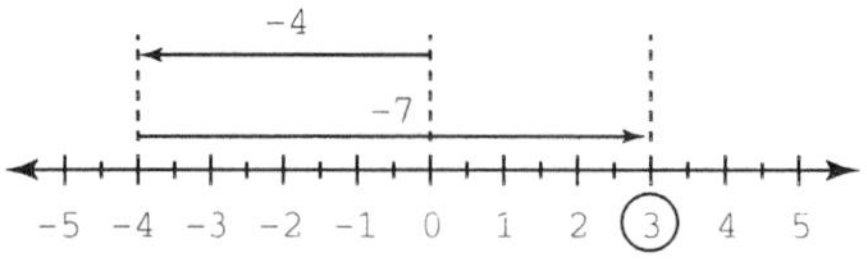

5. $-13 + 7 = -6$

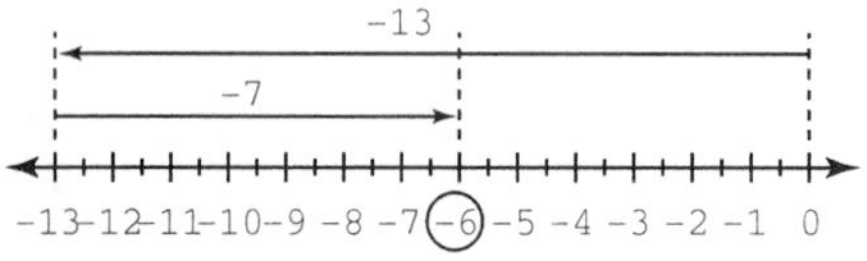

7. $|23| + |12| = 35$
Common sign is positive, so answer is +35.

9. $|-6| + |-2| = 8$
Common sign is negative, so answer is –8.

11. $|-43| - |43| = 0$
Sign does not matter.

13. $|6| - |-2| = 4$
$6 > 2$ so answer is +4.

15. $|8| - |-6| = 2$
$8 > 6$ so answer is +2.

17. $|-5| - |3| = 2$
$5 > 3$ so answer is –2.

19. $|-2| + |-7| = 9$
Common sign is negative, so answer is –9.

21. $|-12| + |-12| = 24$
Common sign is negative, so answer is –24.

23. $|-25| + |-32| = 57$
Common sign is negative, so answer is –57.

25. $|-123| + |-100| = 223$
Common sign is negative, so answer is –223.

27. $|7| - |-7| = 0$
Sign does not matter.

29. $|12| - |-5| = 7$
12 > 5, so answer is +7.

31. $|-6| - |3| = 3$
6 > 3, so answer is –3.

33. $|-12| - |3| = 9$
12 > 3, so answer is –9.

35. $|56| - |-26| = 30$
56 > 26, so answer is +30.

37. $|57| - |-37| = 20$
57 > 37, so answer is +20.

39. $|93| - |-42| = 51$
93 > 42, so answer is +51.

41. $|-67| - |34| = 33$
67 > 34, so answer is –33.

43. $|-144| - |124| = 20$
144 > 124, so answer is –20.

45. $|-82| + |-43| = 125$
Common sign is negative, so –125.

47. $-4 + 2 + (-5)$ add from left to right
$= -2 + (-5)$
$= -7$

49. $-52 + (-77) + (-117)$ add from left to right
$= -129 + (-117)$ add from left to right
$= -246$

51. $12 + (-4) + (-4) + 12$ add from left to right
$= 8 + (-4) + 12$ add from left to right
$= 4 + 12$
$= 16$

53. $(-10) + 14 + 25 + (-16)$add from left to right
$= 4 + 25 + (-16)$ add from left to right
$= 29 + (-16)$
$= 13$

55. $-8 + (-14) + (-11)$ add from left to right
$= -22 + (-11)$ add from left to right
$= -33$

57. $|-26| - |5| = 21$
26 > 5, so answer is – 21.

59. $5 + (-1) + 17$ add from left to right
$= 4 + 17$ add from left to right
$= 21$

61. $-14 + (-31) = -45$

63. $13 + 14 + (-18)$ add from left to right
$= 27 + (-18)$ add from left to right
$= 9$

65. $-87 + 87 = 0$

67. $-3 + (-8) + 12 + (-1)$ add from left to right
$= -11 + 12 + (-1)$ add from left to right
$= 1 + (-1)$
$= 0$

69. $0 + (-103) = -103$

71. $x + y$ substitute values
$= (-2) + 3$ add from left to right
$= 1$

73. $x + y$ substitute values
$= (-20) + (-50)$ add from left to right
$= -70$

75. $x + y$ substitute values
$= 3 + (-30)$ add from left to right
$= -27$

77. The net income for Gateway Inc. in 2000 was \$236,630,000.

79. $-1,031,062 + (-297,718) = -1,328,780,000$
The total net income for 2001 and 2002 was $-\$1,328,780,000$.

81. $-10 + 12 = 2$
The temperature at 11 p.m. was 2°C.

83. $75,083 + (-10,412) + (-1,786) + 96,398$
$= 64,671 + (-1,786) + 96,398$
$= 62,885 + 96,398$
$= 159,283$
The net income is \$159,283.

85. Team 1 Total $= -2 + (-13) + 20 + 2$
$= 7$
Team 2 Total $= 5 + 11 + (-7) + (-3)$
$= 6$
7 > 6 so the winning team is Team 1.

87. $-66 + 26 = -40$
Kansas's record low is - 40° F.

89. $-230+(-370)+(-346)$
$=-600+(-346)$
$=-946$
The total U.S. trade balance is $-\$946$ billion.

91. $44-0=44$

93. $52-52=0$

95. $87-59=28$

97. $-8602+(-1056)=-9658$

99. $-|-56|+|-56|=-56+56=0$

101. True; add any two negative numbers on a number line to verify.

103. False; consider $5+(-1)=4$.

105. Answers will vary.

Section 2.3

Practice Problems

1. $12-7=12+(-7)=5$

2. $-6-4=-6+(-4)=-10$

3. $11-(-14)=11+14=25$

4. $-9-(-1)=-9+1=-8$

5. $5-9=5+(-9)=-4$

6. $-12-4=-12+(-4)=-16$

7. $-2-(-7)=-2+7=5$

8. $-10-5=-10+(-5)=-15$

9. $-4-3-7-(-5)=-4+(-3)+(-7)+5$
$=-7+(-7)+5$
$=-14+5$
$=-9$

10. $3+(-5)-6-(-4)=3+(-5)+(-6)+4$
$=-2+(-6)+4$
$=-8+4$
$=-4$

11. $x-y=-2-14=-2+(-14)=-16$

12. $y-z=-3-(-4)=-3+4=1$

13. $29{,}028-(-1312)$
$=29{,}028+1312$
$=30{,}340$
Mount Everest is 30,340 feet higher than the Dead Sea.

Exercise Set 2.3

1. $5-5=5+(-5)=0$

3. $8-3=8+(-3)=5$

5. $3-8=3+(-8)=-5$

7. $7-(-7)=7+(7)=14$

9. $-5-(-8)=-5+(8)=3$

11. $-14-4=-14+(-4)=-18$

13. $2-16=2+(-16)=-14$

15. $-10-(-10)=-10+10=0$

17. $-15-(-15)=-15+15=0$

19. $3-7=3+(-7)=-4$

21. $30-45=30+(-45)=-15$

23. $-4-10=-4+(-10)=-14$

25. $-230-0=-230+0=-230$

27. $4-(-6)=4+6=10$

29. $-7-(-3)=-7+3=-4$

31. $-16-(-23)=-16+23=7$

33. $-20-18=-20+(-18)=-38$

35. $-20-(-3)=-20+(3)=-17$

37. $2-(-11)=2+(11)=13$

39. $7-3-2=7+(-3)+(-2)$
$=4+(-2)$
$=2$

41. $12-5-7=12+(-5)+(-7)$
$=7+(-7)$
$=0$

43. $-5-8-(-12)=-5+(-8)+12$
$=-13+12$
$=-1$

45. $-10+(-5)-12=-10+(-5)+(-12)$
$=-15+(-12)$
$=-27$

47. $12-(-34)+(-6)=12+34+(-6)$
$=46+(-6)$
$=40$

49. $-(-6)-12+(-16)=6+(-12)+(-16)$
$=-6+(-16)$
$=-22$

51. $-9-(-12)+(-7)-4=-9+12+(-7)+(-4)$
$=3+(-7)+(-4)$
$=-4+(-4)$
$=-8$

53. $-3+4-(-23)-10=-3+4+23+(-10)$
$=1+23+(-10)$
$=24+(-10)$
$=14$

55. $x-y$
$=(-3)-(5)$ show substitution exactly
$=-3+(-5)$ change subtraction to addition
$=-8$

57. $x-y$
$=6-(-30)$ show substitution exactly
$=6+(30)$ change subtraction to addition
$=36$

59. $x-y$
$=(-4)-(-4)$ show substitution exactly
$=-4+(4)$ change subtraction to addition
$=0$

61. $x-y$
$=(1)-(-18)$ show substitution exactly
$=1+(18)$ change subtraction to addition
$=19$

63. $59-(-369)=59+369=428$
The difference in temperature is 428 degrees.

65. $-330-(-369)=-330+369=39$
The difference in temperature is 39 degrees.

67. To find how many degrees warmer, subtract the coldest temperature from the warmest temperature.
$136-(-129)=136+129=265$
136°F is 265°F warmer than −129°F.

69. Subtract check amounts from the checking account, and add the deposit.
$125-117+45-69$
$=125+(-117)+45+(-69)$
$=8+45+(-69)$
$=53+(-69)$
$=-16$
Aaron has overdrawn his checking account by $16.

71. $-6+(-3)+4+(-7)$ add from left to right
$=-9+4+(-7)$ add from left to right
$=-5+(-7)$
$=-12$°C

73. $-282-(-436)=-282+436=154$
The difference in elevation is 154 feet.

75. $-436-(-505)=-436+505=69$
The difference in elevation is 69 feet.

77. $600-(-52)=600+52=652$ feet

79. $144-0=144$ feet

81. $663-912=663+(-912)=-249$
The U.S. trade balance in 1998 was −$249 billion.

83. $436\cdot 0=0$

85. $436\cdot 1=436$

87.
$$\begin{array}{r} 23 \\ \times\ 46 \\ \hline 138 \\ +\ 92 \\ \hline 1058 \end{array}$$

89. $5^2-6\cdot 2+8=25-6\cdot 2+8$
$=25-12+8$
$=13+8$
$=21$

91. $x-y-z$ show substitution exactly
$=(-4)-(3)-(15)$ change subtraction to addition
$=-4+(-3)+(-15)$ add left to right
$=-7+(-15)$
$=-22$

93. $a+b-c$ show substitution exactly
$=(-16)+(14)-(-22)$ change subtraction to addition
$=-16+14+22$ add from left to right
$=-2+22$
$=20$

95. $|-3|-|-7|=3-7=3+(-7)=-4$

97. $|-6|-|6|=6-6=6+(-6)=0$

99. $-8067-1129=-8067+(-1129)=-9196$

101. False. $|-8-3|=|-8+(-3)|=|-11|=11$

103. Answers may vary.

Integrated Review

1. If 0 represents an elevation of 0 feet, then 29,028 feet above sea level is 29,028.

2. If 0 represents an elevation of 0 feet, then 35,840 feet below sea level is –35,840.

3. If 0 represents sea level, then 7 miles below sea level is – 7.

4.

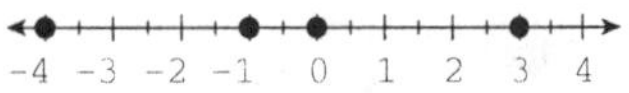

5. 0 is to the right of –3, so $0 > -3$.

6. –15 is to the left of –5, so $-15 < -5$.

7. –1 is to the left of 1, so $-1 < 1$.

8. –2 is to the right of –7, so $-2 > -7$.

9. $|-1|=1$, because –1 is 1 unit from 0.

10. $-|-4|=-4$

11. $|-8|=8$, because –8 is 8 units from 0.

12. $-(-5) = 5$

13. The opposite of 6 is –6.

14. The opposite of –3 is $-(-3) = 3$.

15. The opposite of 89 is –89.

16. The opposite of 0 is 0.

17. $-7 + 12 = 5$

18. $-9 + (-11) = -20$

19. $25 + (-35) = -10$

20. $1 - 3 = 1 + (-3) = -2$

21. $26 - (-26) = 26 + 26 = 52$

22. $-2 - 1 = -2 + (-1) = -3$

23. $-18 - (-102) = -18 + 102 = 84$

24. $-8 + (-6) + 20 = -14 + 20 = 6$

25. $-11 - 7 - (-19) = -11 + (-7) + 19$
$= -18 + 19 = 1$

26. $-4+(-8)-16-(-9)=-4+(-8)+(-16)+9$
$=-12+(-16)+9$
$=-28+9$
$=-19$

27. $26 - 14 = 26 + (-14) = 12$

28. $-12 - (-8) = -12 + 8 = -4$

29. $|18|>0, |-3|>0, |-21|>0$
$18>0, 3>0, 21>0$
b, c, d

30. $|0|>-5, |3|>-5, |-1|>-5, |-1000|>-5$
$0>-5, 3-5, 1-5, 1000-5$
a, b, c, d

31. $-1 + 11 = 10$

32. $-1 - 11 = -1 + (-11) = -12$

33. $11 - (-1) = 11 + 1 = 12$

34. $11 + (-1) = 10$

Section 2.4

Practice Problems

1. $-2 \cdot 6 = -12$

2. $-4(-3) = 12$

3. $0 \cdot (-10) = 0$

4. $5(-15) = -75$

5. $7(-2)(-4) = -14(-4) = 56$

6. $(-5)(-6)(-1) = 30(-1) = -30$

7. $(-2)(-5)(-6)(-1) = 10(-6)(-1)$
$= -60(-1)$
$= 60$

8. $(-3)^4 = (-3)(-3)(-3)(-3)$
$= 9(-3)(-3)$
$= -27(-3)$
$= 81$

9. $-9^2 = -(9 \cdot 9) = -81$

10. $\frac{28}{-7} = -4$

11. $-18 \div (-2) = 9$

12. $\frac{-60}{10} = -6$

13. $\frac{-1}{0}$ is undefined because there is no number that gives a product of -1 when multiplied by 0.

14. $\frac{0}{-2} = 0$ because $0 \cdot (-2) = 0$.

15. $xy = 5(-9) = -45$

16. $\frac{x}{y} = \frac{-9}{-3} = 3$

17. $4(-12) = -48$
The card player's total score was -48.

Exercise Set 2.4

1. $-2(-3) = 6$

3. $-4(9) = -36$

5. $8(-8) = -64$

7. $0(-14) = 0$

9. $6(-4)(2) = -24(2) = -48$

11. $-1(-2)(-4) = 2(-4) = -8$

13. $-4(4)(-5) = -16(-5) = 80$

15. $10(-5)(0) = -50(0) = 0$

17. $-5(3)(-1)(-1)$
$= -15(-1)(-1)$
$= 15(-1)$
$= -15$

19. $-2^2 = -(2)(2) = -4$

21. $(-3)^3 = (-3)(-3)(-3) = 9(-3) = -27$

23. $-5^2 = -(5)(5) = -25$

25. $(-2)^3 = (-2)(-2)(-2) = 4(-2) = -8$

27. $-24 \div 6 = -4$

29. $\frac{-30}{6} = -5$

31. $\frac{-88}{-11} = 8$

33. $\frac{0}{14} = 0$

35. $\frac{2}{0}$ is undefined.

37. $\frac{39}{-3} = -13$

39. $-12(0) = 0$

41. $-4(3) = -12$

43. $-9 \cdot 6 = -54$

45. $-7(-6) = 42$

47. $-3(-4)(-2) = 12(-2) = -24$

49. $(-4)^2 = (-4)(-4) = 16$

51. $-\frac{10}{5} = -2$

53. $-\frac{56}{8} = -7$

55. $-12 \div 3 = -4$

57. $4(-4)(-3) = -16(-3) = 48$

59. $-30(6)(-2)(-3) = -180(-2)(-3)$
$= 360(-3)$
$= -1080$

61. $3 \cdot (-2) \cdot 0 = (-6) \cdot 0 = 0$

63. $\frac{100}{-20} = -5$

65. $240 \div (-40) = -6$

67. $\frac{-12}{-4} = 3$

69. $-1^4 = -(1)(1)(1)(1) = -1$

71. $(-3)^5 = (-3)(-3)(-3)(-3)(-3)$
$= 9 \cdot (-3)(-3)(-3)$
$= (-27)(-3)(-3)$
$= 81 \cdot (-3)$
$= -243$

73. $-2(3)(5)(-6) = (-6)(5)(-6)$
$= (-30)(-6)$
$= 180$

75. $(-1)^{32} = (-1)(-1)\cdots(-1)$ 32 factors
$= (-1)(-1)(-1)(-1)\cdots(-1)$ 30 factors
$= (1)(-1)(-1)\cdots(-1)$ 30 factors
$= (-1)(-1)\cdots(-1)$ 30 factors
Repeating the pattern 15 more times, we find that $(-1)^{32} = 1$.

77. $-2(-2)(-5) = 4(-5) = -20$

79.
$$\begin{array}{r} 42 \\ \times\ 23 \\ \hline 126 \\ 840 \\ \hline 966 \end{array}$$
$-42 \cdot 23 = -966$

81.
$$\begin{array}{r} 25 \\ \times\ 82 \\ \hline 50 \\ 2000 \\ \hline 2050 \end{array}$$
$25 \cdot (-82) = -2050$

83. $a \cdot b = (-4) \cdot (7)$ substitute
$= -28$

85. $a \cdot b = (3) \cdot (-2)$ substitute
$= -6$

87. $a \cdot b = (-5) \cdot (-5)$ substitute
$= 25$

89. $\frac{x}{y}$
$= \frac{5}{-5}$ show substitution exactly
$= -1$

91. $\frac{x}{y}$
$= \frac{-12}{0}$ show substitution exactly
undefined division by zero

93. $\frac{x}{y}$
$= \frac{-36}{-6}$ show substitution exactly
$= 6$

95. $x \cdot y$
$= (-4)(-2)$ show substitution exactly
$= 8$
$\frac{x}{y}$
$= \frac{-4}{-2}$ show substitution exactly
$= 2$

97. $x \cdot y$
$= (0)(-6)$ show substitution exactly
$= 0$ multiplication property of zero
$\frac{x}{y}$
$= \frac{0}{-6}$ show substitution exactly
$= 0$ zero division property

99. $3(-70) = -210$
The melting point of nitrogen is $-210°$ C.

101. $-3(63) = -189$
The melting point of argon is $-189°$ C.

103. $(-4)(3) = -12$
A loss of 12 yards

105. $5(-20) = -100$
He is at a depth of 100 feet.

107. $-2420 \cdot 3 = -7260$
Kmart's income would be –$7260 million.

109. **a.** $192 - 27 = 165$
There was a change of 165 condors.

b. 1987 to 2002 is 15 years.
$\frac{165}{15} = 11$
There was a change of 11 condors per year.

111. $\frac{-4+(-2)+1+1}{4}=\frac{-4}{4}=-1$

His average score per round was −1.

113. $(3\cdot 5)^2=(3\cdot 5)(3\cdot 5)=(15)(15)=225$

115. $90+12^2-5^3=90+12\cdot 12-5\cdot 5\cdot 5$
$=90+144-125$
$=109$

117. $12\div 4-2+7=3-2+7=8$

119. true; product of two different signs is negative.

121. true; product of two same signs is positive.

123. positive; product of an even number of negatives is positive.

125. negative; product of an odd number of negatives is negative.

127. $(-5)^{17}, (-2)^{17}, (-2)^{12}, (-5)^{12}$

129. a. $2131-2190=-59$
There was a change of −59 radio stations.

b. $4(-59)=-236$
The change will be −236 radio stations.

c. 2006 is 4 years from 2002.
$2131-236=1895$
There will be 1895 radio stations in 2006.

131. Answers may vary.

133. $87^2-(-12)^5=7569-(-248{,}832)$
$=7569+248{,}832$
$=256{,}401$

Section 2.5

Practice Problems

1. $(-2)^4=(-2)(-2)(-2)(-2)$
$=4(-2)(-2)$
$=-8(-2)$
$=16$

2. $-2^4=-(2)(2)(2)(2)$
$=-4(2)(2)$
$=-8(2)$
$=-16$

3. $3\cdot 6^2=3\cdot(6\cdot 6)=3\cdot 36=108$

4. $\frac{25}{5(-1)}=\frac{25}{-5}=-5$

5. $\frac{-18+6}{-3-1}=\frac{-12}{-4}=3$

6. $-20+2\cdot 7+4=-20+14+4$
$=-6+4$
$=-2$

7. $-2^3+(-4)^2+1^5=-8+16+1$
$=8+1$
$=9$

8. $2(2-8)+(-12)-3=2(-6)+(-12)-3$
$=-12+(-12)-3$
$=-24-3$
$=-27$

9. $(-5)\cdot|-4|+(-3)+2^3=-5\cdot 4+(-3)+2^3$
$=-5\cdot 4+(-3)+8$
$=-20+(-3)+8$
$=-23+8$
$=-15$

10. $4(-6)\div\left[3(5-7)^2\right]=4(-6)\div\left[3(-2)^2\right]$
$=4(-6)\div[3\cdot(4)]$
$=4(-6)\div(12)$
$=-24\div 12$
$=-2$

11. $x^2=(-12)^2=(-12)(-12)=144$
$-x^2=-(-12)^2=-(-12)(-12)=-144$

12. $5y^2=5(3)^2=5(9)=45$
$5y^2=5(-3)^2=5(9)=45$

13. $x^2+y=(-5)^2+(-2)=25+(-2)=23$

14. $4-x^2=4-(-9)^2=4-81=-77$

15. Add temperature and divide by 7 (the number of months).

$\frac{15+(-1)+(-11)+(-14)+(-16)+(-14)+(-1)}{7}$

$=\frac{-42}{7}=-6$

The average temperature from Oct. through April is −6° F.

Calculator Explorations

The answers may vary depending on what type of calculator you have.

1. Press the keys [( ] 120 [+/−] [−] 360 [ )] [÷] 10 [+/−] [= or ENTER].
The display will read 48.

2. Press the keys 4750 [÷] [( ] 2 [+/−] [+] 17 [+/−] [ )] [= or ENTER].
The display will read – 250.

3. Press the keys [( ] 316 [+/−] [+] 458 [+/−] [ )] [÷] [( ] 28 [+] 25 [+/−] [ )] [= or ENTER].
The display will read – 258.

4. Press the keys [( ] 234 [+/−] [+] 86 [ )] [÷] [( ] 18 [+/−] [+] 16 [ )] [= or ENTER].
The display will read 74.

Mental Math

1. -3^2 base: 3; exponent: 2

2. $(-3)^2$ base: –3; exponent: 2

3. $4 \cdot 2^3$ base: 2; exponent: 3

4. $9 \cdot 5^6$ base: 5; exponent: 6

5. $(-7)^5$ base: –7; exponent: 5

6. -9^4 base: –9; exponent: 4

7. $5^7 \cdot 10$ base: 5; exponent: 7

8. $2^8 \cdot 11$ base: 2; exponent: 8

Exercise Set 2.5

1. $(-4)^3 = (-4)(-4)(-4) = 16(-4) = -64$

3. $-4^3 = -(4)(4)(4) = -64$

5. $6 \cdot 2^2 = 6 \cdot 4 = 24$

7. $-1(-2) + 1$ multiply before adding
$= 2 + 1$
$= 3$

9. $9 - 12 - 4$ change to addition
$= 9 + (-12) + (-4)$ add from left to right
$= -3 + (-4)$
$= -7$

11. $4 + 3(-6)$ multiply before adding
$= 4 + (-18)$
$= -14$

13. $5(-9) + 2$ multiply before adding
$= -45 + 2$
$= -43$

15. $(-10) + 4 \div 2$ divide before adding
$= (-10) + 2$
$= -8$

17. $6 + 7 \cdot 3 - 40 = 6 + 21 - 40$
$= 27 - 40$
$= -13$

19. $\frac{16-13}{-3}$ simplify numerator
$= \frac{3}{-3}$
$= -1$

21. $\frac{24}{10+(-4)}$ simplify the bottom of the fraction bar first
$= \frac{24}{6}$
$= 4$

23. $5(-3) - (-12)$ multiply before adding
$= -15 - (-12)$ change to addition
$= -15 + 12$
$= -3$

25. $(-19) - 12(3)$ multiply before adding
$= (-19) - 36$ change to addition
$= (-19) + (-36)$
$= -55$

27. $-8 + 4^2$ exponents first
$= -8 + 16$
$= 8$

29. $(8 + (-4))^2$ grouping symbols first
$= [4]^2$
$= 16$

31. $8 \cdot 6 - 3 \cdot 5 + (-20) = 48 - 15 + (-20)$
$= 33 + (-20)$
$= 13$

33. $16-(-3)^4$ exponents first
$= 16-(81)$ change to addition
$= 16+(-81)$
$= -65$

35. $|5+3|\cdot 2^3$ grouping symbols first
$= |8|\cdot 2^3$ exponents before multiplication
$= 8\cdot 8$
$= 64$

37. $7\cdot 8^2+4$ exponents first
$= 7\cdot 64+4$ multiply before adding
$= 448+4$
$= 452$

39. $5^3-(4-2^3)$ exponents inside grouping symbols first
$= 5^3-(4-8)$ grouping symbols next
$= 5^3-(-4)$ exponents before subtraction
$= 125-(-4)$ change subtraction to addition
$= 125+4$
$= 129$

41. $|3-12|\div 3$
$= |-9|\div 3$
$= 9\div 3$
$= 3$

43. $-(-2)^2 = -4$

45. $(5-9)^2\div(4-2)^2$ grouping symbols first
$= (-4)^2\div(2)^2$ exponents next
$= 16\div 4$
$= 4$

47. $|8-24|\cdot(-2)\div(-2)$ grouping symbol first
$= |-16|\cdot(-2)\div(-2)$ absolute value
$= 16\cdot(-2)\div(-2)$ multiply and divide from left to right
$= -32\div(-2)$
$= 16$

49. $(-12-20)\div 16-25$ grouping symbols first
$= (-32)\div 16-25$ divide
$= -2-25$
$= -27$

51. $5(5-2)+(-5)^2-6$ grouping symbols first
$= 5(3)+5^2-6$ exponents next
$= 5(3)+25-6$ multiply before adding
$= 15+25-6$
$= 34$

53. $(2-7)\cdot(6-19)$ grouping symbols first
$= (-5)\cdot(-13)$
$= 65$

55. $2-7\cdot 6-19$ multiply
$= 2-42-19$ subtract from left to right
$= -59$

57. $(-36\div 6)-(4\div 4)$ divide
$= -6-1$
$= -7$

59. -5^2-6^2 exponents first (watch the signs)
$= -25-36$
$= -61$

61. $(-5)^2-6^2$ exponents first (watch the signs)
$= 25-36$
$= -11$

63. $(10-4^2)^2 = (10-16)^2$
$= (-6)^2$
$= (-6)(-6)$
$= 36$

65. $2(8-10)^2-5(1-6)^2$
$= 2(-2)^2-5(-5)^2$
$= 2(-2)(-2)-5(-5)(-5)$
$= 2(-2)(-2)+(-5)(-5)(-5)$
$= (-4)(-2)+(25)(-5)$
$= 8+(-125)$
$= -117$

67. $3(-10)\div(5(-3)-7(-2))$
$= 3(-10)\div(5(-3)+(-7)(-2))$
$= 3(-10)\div(-15+14)$
$= 3(-10)\div(-1)$
$= -30\div -1$
$= 30$

69. $\dfrac{(-7)(-3)-(4)(3)}{3[7\div(3-10)]}=\dfrac{(-7)(-3)+(-4)(3)}{3(7\div(3+(-10)))}$
$=\dfrac{21+(-12)}{3(7\div(-7))}$
$=\dfrac{9}{3(-1)}$
$=\dfrac{9}{-3}$
$=-3$

71. $-5[4+5(-3+5)]+11$
$=-5[4+5(2)]+11$
$=-5[4+10]+11$
$=-5[14]+11$
$=-70+11$
$=-59$

73. $x+y+z$ show substitution exactly
$=(-2)+4+(-1)$ add from left to right
$=2+(-1)$
$=1$

75. $2x-3y-4z=2(-2)-3(4)-4(-1)$
$=-4-12+4$
$=-16+4$
$=-12$

77. x^2-y show substitution exactly
$=(-2)^2-4$ exponents first
$=4-4$
$=0$

79. $\dfrac{5y}{z}$ show substitution exactly
$=\dfrac{5\cdot 4}{-1}$ simplify numerator
$=\dfrac{20}{-1}$
$=-20$

81. $x^2=(-3)^2=9$

83. $-z^2=-(-4)^2=-16$

85. $10-(-3)^2=10-9=1$

87. $2x^3-z=2(-3)^2-(-4)$
$=2(-27)-(-4)$
$=-54+4$
$=-50$

89. $\dfrac{-10+8+(-4)+2+7+(-5)+(-12)}{7}$
$=\dfrac{-14}{7}=-2$

91. $\dfrac{-17+(-26)+(-20)+(-13)}{4}$
$=\dfrac{-76}{4}=-19$

93. $15-(-13)=15+13=28$
The difference between the highest and lowest score is 28 points.

95. $\dfrac{-13+(-2)+0+5+7+15)}{6}$
$=\dfrac{12}{6}=2$

97. No; answers may vary.

99. $45\cdot 90=4050$

101. $90-45=45$

103. $p=4(8)=32$ in.

105. $p=2(9)+2(6)$
$=18+12$
$=30$ feet

107. $2\cdot(7-5)\cdot 3=2\cdot(2)\cdot 3=4\cdot 3=12$

109. $-6\cdot(10-4)=-6\cdot 6=-36$

111. $(-12)^4=(-12)(-12)(-12)(-12)$
$=144(-12)(-12)$
$=-1728(-12)$
$=20,736$

113. x^3-y^2
$=21^3-(-19)^2$ substitute
$=21\cdot 21\cdot 21-(-19)(-19)$
$=21\cdot 21\cdot 21+(19)(-19)$
$=441\cdot 21+(-361)$
$=9261+(-361)$
$=8900$

115. $(xy+z)^x$
$=[2\cdot(-5)+7]^2$ substitute
$=(-3)^2$
$=(-3)(-3)$
$=9$

117. Answers may vary.

Chapter 2 Review

1. 1435 feet down in a mine is represented as −1435.

2. 7562 meters above sea level is represented as 7562.

3. 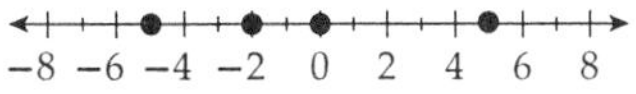

4. 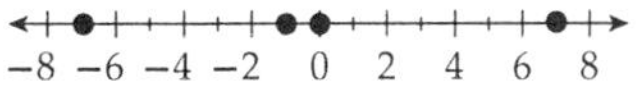

5. $|-12| = 12$

6. $|0| = 0$

7. $-|6| = -6$

8. $-(-9) = 9$

9. $-|-9| = -0$

10. $-(-2) = 2$

11. $-18 > -20$

12. $-5 < 5$

13. $123 > -198$

14. $8 - 12 = -4 > -16$

15. $-(-12) = 12$

16. $-(-(-3)) = -3$

17. False

18. True

19. True

20. True

21. $5 + (-3) = 2$

22. $18 + (-4) = 14$

23. $-12 + 16 = 4$

24. $-23 + 40 = 17$

25. $-8 + (-15) = -23$

26. $-5 + (-17) = -22$

27. $-24 + 3 = -21$

28. $-89 + 19 = -70$

29. $15 + (-15) = 0$

30. $-24 + 24 = 0$

31. $-43 + (-108) = -151$

32. $-100 + (-506) = -606$

33. $-0 + (-5) + (-7) = -14 + (-7) = -21$
Annik Sorenstam's total score was −21.

34. $-1 + 3 + (-5) + 3 = 2 + (-5) + 3 = -3 + 3 = 0$
Joanne Morley's total score was 0.

35. $-15 - 5 = -20$
The temperature was −20°C at 6 a.m.

36. $-127 + (-23) = -150$
The divers current depth is −150 feet.

37. $-56 + 155 = 99$
The high temperature for London is 99° F.

38. $-13 + 125 = 112$
The high temperature for Los Angeles is 112° F.

39. $12 - 4 = 12 + (-4) = 8$

40. $-12 - 4 = -12 + (-4) = -16$

41. $8 - 19 = 8 + (-19) = -11$

42. $-8 - 19 = -8 + (-19) = -27$

43. $7 - (-13) = 7 + 13 = 20$

44. $-6 - (-14) = -6 + 14 = 8$

45. $16 - 16 = 16 + (-16) = 0$

46. $-16 - 16 = -16 + (-16) = -32$

47. $-12 - (-12) = -12 + 12 = 0$

48. $|-5| - |-12| = 5 - 12 = 5 + (-12) = -7$

49. $-(-5) - 12 + (-3) = 5 + (-12) + (-3) = -10$

50.
$$\begin{aligned} -8 + |-12| - 10 - |-3| &= -8 + 12 + (-10) - 3 \\ &= -8 + 12 + (-10) + (-3) \\ &= 4 + (-10) + (-3) \\ &= -6 + (-3) \\ &= -9 \end{aligned}$$

51. $142-125+43-85=142+(-125)+43+(-85)$
$=17+43+(-85)$
$=60+(-85)$
$=-25$
The balance of his account represented as an integer is –25.

52. $600-(-92)=600+92=692$ feet

53. $32-35=32+(-35)=-3$
The low temperature for ReyKjavik is –3° F.

54. $10-14=10+(-4)=-4$
The low temperature for Berlin is –4° F.

55. $|-5|-|-6|=5-6$
$5-6=5-6$ True

56. $|-5-(-6)|=5+6$
$|-5+6|=11$
$|1|=11$
$1=11$ False

57. True

58. True

59. $(-3)\cdot(-7)=21$

60. $(-6)\cdot(3)=-18$

61. $-4\cdot 16=-64$

62. $(-5)\cdot(-12)=60$

63. $(-5)^2=(-5)(-5)=25$

64. $(-1)^5=(-1)(-1)(-1)(-1)(-1)=-1$

65. $12(-3)(0)=0$

66. $-1(6)(2)(-2)=-6(2)(-2)=-12(-2)=24$

67. $-15\div 3=-5$

68. $\frac{-24}{-8}=3$

69. $0\div(-3)=0$

70. $\frac{-46}{0}$ is undefined.

71. $\frac{100}{-5}=-20$

72. $\frac{-72}{8}=-9$

73. $\frac{-38}{-1}=38$

74. $\frac{45}{-9}=-5$

75. $-5(2)=-10$
The team lost 10 yards.

76. $-50(4)=-200$
The bettor lost $200.

77. $3(-9)=-27$
The low temperature for Bucharest is –27° F.

78. $30\div(-10)=-3$
The low temperature for Geneva is –3° F.

79. $-56\div(-2)=28$
The low temperature for Capetown is 28° F.

80. $2(-13)=-26$
The low temperature for Stockholm is –26° F.

81. $(-7)^2=(-7)(-7)=49$

82. $-7^2=-(7)(7)=-49$

83. $-2^5=-(2)(2)(2)(2)(2)=-32$

84. $(-2)^5=(-2)(-2)(-2)(-2)(-2)=-32$

85. $5-8+3=0$

86. $-3+12+(-7)-10=-3+12+(-7)+(-10)$
$=-8$

87. $-10+3\cdot(-2)=-10+(-6)=-16$

88. $5-10\cdot(-3)=5-(-30)=5+30=35$

89. $16\cdot(-2)+4=-32+4=-28$

90. $3\cdot(-12)-8=-36+(-8)=-44$

91. $5+6\div(-3)=5-2=3$

92. $-6+(-10)\div(-2)=-6+5=-1$

93. $16+(-3)\cdot 12\div 4=16+(-36)\div 4$
$=16+(-9)$
$=7$

94. $(-12)+25\cdot 1\div(-5)=(-12)+25\div(-5)$
$=(-12)+(-5)$
$=-17$

95. $4^3-(8-3)^2=4^3-5^2=64-25=39$

96. $4^3-90=64+(-90)=-26$

97. $-(-4)\cdot|-3|-5=4\cdot 3-5$
$=12-5$
$=12+(-5)$
$=7$

98. $|5-1|^2\cdot(-5)=|4|^2\cdot(-5)$
$=4^2\cdot(-5)$
$=16\cdot(-5)$
$=-80$

99. $\dfrac{(-4)(-3)-(-2)(-1)}{-10+5}=\dfrac{12-2}{-10+5}$
$=\dfrac{12+(-2)}{-10+5}$
$=\dfrac{10}{-5}$
$=-2$

100. $\dfrac{4(12-18)}{-10\div(-2-3)}=\dfrac{4[12+(-18)]}{-10\div[-2+(-3)]}$
$=\dfrac{4(-6)}{-10\div(-5)}$
$=\dfrac{-24}{2}$
$=-12$

101. $\dfrac{-18+25+(-30)+7+0+(-2)}{6}=\dfrac{-18}{6}=-3$

102. $\dfrac{-45+(-40)+(-30)+(-25)}{4}=\dfrac{-140}{4}=-35$

103. $2(-2)-1=-4-1=-5$

104. $1^2+(-2)^2=1+4=5$

105. $\dfrac{3(-2)}{6}=\dfrac{-6}{6}=-1$

106. $\dfrac{5(1)-(-2)}{-1}=\dfrac{5+2}{-1}=\dfrac{7}{-1}=-7$

107. $x^2=(-2)^2=4$

108. $-x^2=-(-2)^2=-4$

109. $7-x^2=7-(-2)^2$
$=7-4$
$=3$

110. $100-x^3=100-(-2)^3$
$=100-(-8)$
$=100+8$
$=108$

Chapter 2 Test

1. $-5+8=3$

2. $18-24=18+(-24)=-6$

3. $5\cdot(-20)=-100$

4. $(-16)\div(-4)=4$

5. $(-18)+(-12)=-30$

6. $-7-(-19)=-7+19=12$

7. $(-5)\cdot(-13)=65$

8. $\dfrac{-25}{-5}=5$

9. $|-25|+(-13)=25+(-13)=12$

10. $14-|-20|=14-20$
$=14+(-20)$
$=-6$

11. $|5|\cdot|-10|=5\cdot 10=50$

12. $\dfrac{|-10|}{-|-5|}=\dfrac{10}{-5}=-2$

13. $(-8)+9\div(-3)=-8+(-3)=-11$

14. $-7+(-32)-12+5=-7+(-32)+(-12)+5$
$=-51+5$
$=-46$

15. $(-5)^3-24\div(-3)=(-125)-24\div(-3)$
$=(-125)-(-8)$
$=-125+8$
$=-117$

16. $(5-9)^2 \cdot (8-2)^3 = (-4)^2 \cdot (6)^3$
$= 16 \cdot 216$
$= 3456$

17. $-(-7)^2 \div 7 \cdot (-4) = -49 \div 7 \cdot (-4)$
$= -7 \cdot (-4)$
$= 28$

18. $3-(8-2)^3 = 3-(6)^3 = 3-216 = -213$

19. $-6 + (-15) \div (-3) = -6 + 5 = -1$

20. $\frac{4}{2} - \frac{8^2}{16} = \frac{4}{2} - \frac{64}{16} = 2 - 4 = -2$

21. $\frac{(-3)(-2)+12}{-1(-4-5)} = \frac{6+12}{-1(-9)} = \frac{18}{9} = 2$

22. $\frac{|25-30|^2}{2(-6)+7} = \frac{|-5|^2}{2(-6)+7}$
$= \frac{5^2}{-12+7}$
$= \frac{25}{-5}$
$= -5$

23. $5(-8) - [6 - (2-4)] + (12-16)^2$
$= 5(-8) - [6 - (-2)] + (-4)^2$
$= 5(-8) - [6+2] + (-4)^2$
$= 5(-8) - 8 + (-4)^2$
$= 5(-8) - 8 + 16$
$= -40 - 8 + 16$
$= -48 + 16$
$= -32$

24. $-2^3 - 2^2 = -8 - 4 = -12$

25. $3(0) + (-3) = 0 + (-3) = -3$

26. $|-3| + |0| + |2| = 3 + 0 + 2 = 5$

27. $\frac{3(2)}{2(-3)} = \frac{6}{-6} = -1$

26. $5 - (-3) = 5 + 3 = 8$

27. $14,893 - 147 = 14,893 + (-147) = 14,746$
His final elevation is 14,746 feet.

28. $2(-3)^3 = 2(-27) = -54$

29. $10 - (-3)^2 = 10 - 9 = 1$

30. $7(0) + 3(-3) - 4(2) = 0 + (-9) - 8$
$= -9 - 8$
$= -17$

31. Sea level is 0. Each descent is –22.
4(-22) = –88
Her elevation is 88 feet below sea level.

32. $129 - 79 - 40 + 35 = 50 - 40 + 35$
$= 10 + 35$
$= 45$
His new balance is $45.

33. 6288 – (–25,354) = 6288 + 25,354 = 31,642
The difference in elevation is 31,642 feet.

34. 1495 + (–5315) = –3820
The elevation of the lake's deepest point is –3820 feet or 3820 feet below sea level.

35. $\frac{-12 + (-13) + 0 + 9}{4} = \frac{-16}{4} = -4$

Chapter 2 Cumulative Review

1. 4 is in the ten-thousands place.

2. 4 is in the hundreds place.

3. 4 is in the tens place.

4. 4 is in the thousands place.

5. 4 is in the millions place.

6. 4 is in the hundreds-thousands place.

7. $5 < 50$
$101 > 0$
$29 > 27$

8. $12 < 4$
$13 > 31$
$82 > 79$

9.
$$\begin{array}{r} \scriptstyle 2 \\ 13 \\ 2 \\ 7 \\ 8 \\ +9 \\ \hline 39 \end{array}$$

10. $\begin{array}{r} \overset{1}{11} \\ 3 \\ 9 \\ +16 \\ \hline 39 \end{array}$

11. $\begin{array}{r} 7826 \\ -505 \\ \hline 7321 \end{array}$

Check: $\begin{array}{r} 7321 \\ +505 \\ \hline 7826 \end{array}$

12. $\begin{array}{r} 3285 \\ -272 \\ \hline 3013 \end{array}$

Check: $\begin{array}{r} 3013 \\ +272 \\ \hline 3285 \end{array}$

13. $6052 - 3612 = 2440$
The radius of Mercury is 2440 km.

14. $762 - 237 = 525$
C.J. will have $525 in her account.

15. To round 568 to the nearest ten, observe that the digit in the ones place is at least 5. Therefore we need to add 1 to the digit in the tens place. 568 rounded to the nearest ten is 570.

16. To round 468 to the nearest hundred, observe that the digit in the tens place is at last 5. Therefore we need to add 1 to the digit in the hundreds place. 568 rounded to the nearest hundred is 600.

17. 4725 rounds to 4700
2879 rounds to $\begin{array}{r} -2900 \\ \hline 1800 \end{array}$

18. 8394 rounds to 8000
2913 rounds to $\begin{array}{r} -3000 \\ \hline 5000 \end{array}$

19.
a. $3(4+5) = 3\cdot 4 + 3\cdot 5$
b. $10(6+8) = 10\cdot 6 + 10\cdot 8$
c. $2(7+3) = 2\cdot 7 + 2\cdot 3$

20.
a. $5(2+12) = 5\cdot 2 + 5\cdot 12$
b. $9(3+6) = 9\cdot 3 + 9\cdot 6$
c. $4(8+1) = 4\cdot 8 + 4\cdot 1$

21. $\begin{array}{r} 631 \\ \times\ 125 \\ \hline 3155 \\ 12,620 \\ 63,100 \\ \hline 78,875 \end{array}$

22. $\begin{array}{r} 299 \\ \times\ 104 \\ \hline 1196 \\ 00 \\ 29,900 \\ 31,096 \end{array}$

23. $42 \div 7 = 6$
Check: $6\cdot 7 = 42$

$\frac{81}{9} = 9$
Check: $9\cdot 9 = 81$

$\begin{array}{r} 6 \\ 4\overline{)\ 24} \\ -24 \\ \hline 0 \end{array}$

Check: $6\cdot 4 = 24$

24. $\frac{35}{5} = 7$
Check: $7\cdot 5 = 35$

$64 \div 8 = 8$
Check: $8\cdot 8 = 64$

$\begin{array}{r} 12 \\ 4\overline{)\ 48} \\ -4 \\ \hline 08 \\ -\ 8 \\ \hline 0 \end{array}$

Check: $12\cdot 4 = 48$

25. $\begin{array}{r} 741 \\ 5\overline{)\ 3705} \\ -35 \\ \hline 20 \\ -\ 20 \\ \hline 05 \\ -\ 5 \\ \hline 0 \end{array}$

Check: $741\cdot 5 = 3705$

26. $$\begin{array}{r} 456 \\ 8\overline{)\ 3648} \\ -32 \\ \hline 44 \\ -\ 40 \\ \hline 48 \\ -48 \\ \hline 0 \end{array}$$

Check: $456 \cdot 8 = 3648$

27. $$\begin{array}{r} 6 \text{ R } 2 \\ 9\overline{)\ 56} \\ -54 \\ \hline 2 \end{array}$$

Because there is a remainder of 2, six boxes would not be enough. They would need 7 boxes to send all 56 pairs.

28. $324 \div 36 = 9$
Each ticket cost $9.

29. $8^2 = 8 \cdot 8 = 64$

30. $5^3 = 5 \cdot 5 \cdot 5 = 25 \cdot 5 = 125$

31. $7^1 = 7$

32. $4^1 = 4$

33. $5 \cdot 6^2 = 5 \cdot 36 = 180$

34. $2^3 \cdot 7 = 8 \cdot 7 = 56$

35. $$\begin{aligned} \frac{7 - 2 \cdot 3 + 3^2}{2^2 + 1} &= \frac{7 - 2 \cdot 3 + 9}{4 + 1} \\ &= \frac{7 - 6 + 9}{4 + 1} \\ &= \frac{1 + 9}{4 + 1} \\ &= \frac{10}{5} \\ &= 2 \end{aligned}$$

36. $$\begin{aligned} \frac{6^2 + 4 \cdot 4 + 2^3}{37 - 5^2} &= \frac{36 + 4 \cdot 4 + 8}{37 - 25} \\ &= \frac{36 + 16 + 8}{37 - 25} \\ &= \frac{52 + 8}{37 - 25} \\ &= \frac{60}{12} \\ &= 5 \end{aligned}$$

37. $8 + 7 = 15$

38. $5 + 9 = 14$

39. **a.** $|-2| = 2$

b. $|5| = 5$

c. $|0| = 0$

40. $|4| = 4$
$|-7| = 7$

41. $-2 + 5 = 3$

42. $8 + (-3) = 5$

43. $8 - (-6) = 8 + 6 = 14$

44. $-2 - (-7) = -2 + 7 = 5$

45. $-7 \cdot 3 = -21$

46. $5(-2) = -10$

47. $0 \cdot (-4) = 0$

48. $-6 \cdot 9 = = 54$

49. $$\begin{aligned} 3(4 - 7) + (-2) - 5 &= 3(-3) + (-2) - 5 \\ &= -9 + (-2) - 5 \\ &= -11 - 5 \\ &= -16 \end{aligned}$$

50. $$\begin{aligned} 4 - 8(7 - 3) - (-1) &= 4 - 8(4) - (-1) \\ &= 4 - 32 - (-1) \\ &= -28 - (-1) \\ &= -28 + 1 \\ &= -27 \end{aligned}$$

Chapter 3

Pretest

1. $9x - 4 + 6x + 8 = 9x + 6x - 4 + 8$
$= (9 + 6)x + 4$
$= 15x + 4$

2. $3(2x - 1) - (x - 8)$
$= 3(2x - 1) + (-1)(x - 8)$
$= 3 \cdot 2x - 3 \cdot 1 + (-1)(x) + (-1)(-8)$
$= 6x - 3 - x + 8$
$= 6x - x - 3 + 8$
$= 5x + 5$

3. $8(7b) = (8 \cdot 7)b$
$= 56b$

4. $-5(2y - 7) = -5 \cdot 2y + (-5)(-7)$
$= -10y + 35$

5. perimeter $= 4a + 17 + 9a$
$= 13a + 17$
The perimeter is $(13a + 17)$ inches.

6. area = length · width
$= (4x - 1) \cdot 3$
$= 3(4x - 1)$
$= 3 \cdot 4x - 3 \cdot 1$
$= 12x - 3$
The area is $(12x - 3)$ square feet.

7. $2y - 3 = -5$
$2(-4) - 3 = -5$
$-8 - 3 = -5$
$-11 = -5$ False
No, –4 is not a solution.

8. $-7 = x + 5$
$-7 - 5 = x + 5 - 5$
$-12 = x$

9. $9n + 3 - 8n = 8 - 14$
$n + 3 = -6$
$n + 3 - 3 = -6 - 3$
$n = -9$

10. $-6x = 42$
$\frac{-6x}{-6} = \frac{42}{-6}$
$x = -7$

11. $2m - 9m = -77$
$-7m = -77$
$\frac{-7m}{-7} = \frac{-77}{-7}$
$m = 11$

12. $2(x - 12)$

13. $3x$

14. $18 - 3x = -9$
$18 - 3x - 18 = -9 - 18$
$-3x = -27$
$\frac{-3x}{-3} = \frac{-27}{-3}$
$x = 9$

15. $8a - 5 = 2a + 7$
$8a - 5 + 5 = 2a + 7 + 5$
$8a = 2a + 12$
$8a - 2a = 2a + 12 - 2a$
$6a = 12$
$\frac{6a}{6} = \frac{12}{6}$
$a = 2$

16. $4(x + 1) = 9x - 1$
$4x + 4 = 9x - 1$
$4x + 4 - 4 = 9x - 1 - 4$
$4x = 9x - 5$
$4x - 9x = 9x - 5 - 9x$
$-5x = -5$
$\frac{-5x}{-5} = \frac{-5}{-5}$
$x = 1$

17. $-2(3x + 4) - 10 = 0$
$-2.3x + (-2)(4) - 10 = 0$
$-6x - 8 - 10 = 0$
$-6x - 18 = 0$
$-6x - 18 + 18 = 0 + 18$
$-6x = 18$
$\frac{-6x}{-6} = \frac{18}{-6}$
$x = -3$

18. $\frac{54}{-6} = -9$

19. $x - 5 = 12$

20. $68 = 9x + 5$
$68 - 5 = 9x + 5 - 5$
$63 = 9x$
$\frac{63}{9} = \frac{9x}{9}$
$7 = x$

Section 3.1

Practice Problems

1. a. $8m - 11m = (8 - 11)m$
$= -3m$

b. $5a + a = 5a + 1a$
$= (5 + 1)a$
$= 6a$

c. $-y^2 + 3y^2 + 7 = -1y^2 + 3y^2 + 7$
$= (-1 + 3)y^2 + 7$
$= 2y^2 + 7$

2. $8m + 5 + m - 4 = 8m + 5 + m + (-4)$
$= 8m + m + 5 + (-4)$
$= (8 + 1)m + 5 + (-4)$
$= 9m + 1$

3. $7y + 11y - 8 = 18y - 8$

4. $2y - 6 + y + 7 = 2y + y - 6 + 7$
$= 3y + 1$

5. $-9y + 2 - 4y - 8x + 12 - x$
$= -9y + 2 + (-4y) + (-8x) + 12 + (-x)$
$= -9y + (-4y) + (-8x) + (-x) + 2 + 12$
$= -13y - 9x + 14$

6. $7(8a) = (7 \cdot 8)a$
$= 56a$

7. $-5(9x) = (-5 \cdot 9)x$
$= -45x$

8. $7(y + 2) = 7 \cdot y + 7 \cdot 2$
$= 7y + 14$

9. $4(7a - 5) = 4 \cdot 7a + 4 \cdot (-5)$
$= 28a - 20$

10. $6(5 - y) = 6 \cdot 5 - 6 \cdot y = 30 - 6y$

11. $5(y - 3) - 8 + y = 5 \cdot y - 5 \cdot 3 - 8 + y$
$= 5y - 15 - 8 + y$
$= 6y - 23$

12. $5(2x - 3) + 7(x - 1)$
$= 5 \cdot 2x - 5 \cdot 3 + 7 \cdot x - 7 \cdot 1$
$= 10x - 15 + 7x - 7$
$= 10x + (-15) + 7x + (-7)$
$= 17x - 22$

13. $-(y + 1) + 3y - 12 = -1(y + 1) + 3y + (-12)$
$= -1 \cdot y + (-1)(1) + 3y + (-12)$
$= -y + (-1) + 3y + (-12)$
$= 2y - 13$

14. Find the sum of the lengths of the sides. A square has 4 sides of equal length.
perimeter $= 2x + 2x + 2x + 2x$
$= 8x$
The perimeter is $8x$ centimeters.

15. $A = \text{length} \cdot \text{width}$
$= (12y + 9) \cdot 3$
$= 3(12y + 9)$
$= 3 \cdot 12y + 3 \cdot 9$
$= 36y + 27$
The area is $(36y + 27)$ square yards.

Mental Math

1. The numerical coefficient of $5y$ is 5.
2. The numerical coefficient of $-2z$ is -2.
3. The numerical coefficient of z is 1.
4. The numerical coefficient of $3xy^2$ is 3.
5. The numerical coefficient of $11a$ is 11.
6. The numerical coefficient of $-x$ is -1.

Exercise Set 3.1

1. $3x + 5x = (3 + 5)x = 8x$

3. $5n - 9n = (5 - 9)n = -4n$

5. $4c + c - 7c = (4 + 1 - 7)c = -2c$

7. $5x - 7x + x - 3x = (5 - 7 + 1 - 3)x = -4x$

9. $4a + 3a + 6a - 8 = (4 + 3 + 6)a - 8 = 13a - 8$

11. $6(5x) = (6 \cdot 5)x = 30x$

13. $-2(11y) = (-2 \cdot 11)y = -22y$

15. $12(6a) = (12 \cdot 6)a = 72a$

17. $2(y + 2) = 2 \cdot y + 2 \cdot 2 = 2y + 4$

19. $5(a-8) = 5 \cdot a + 5 \cdot (-8) = 5a - 40$

21. $-4(3x+7) = -4 \cdot 3x + (-4) \cdot 7$
$= -12x - 28$

23. $2(x+4)+7 = 2 \cdot x + 2 \cdot 4 + 7$
$= 2x + 8 + 7$
$= 2x + 15$

25. $-4(6n-5)+3n = -4 \cdot 6n + (-4) \cdot (-5) + 3n$
$= -24n + 20 + 3n$
$= -21n + 20$

27. $5(3c-1)+8 = 5 \cdot 3c - 5 \cdot 1 + 8$
$= 15c - 5 + 8$
$= 15c + 3$

29. $3 + 6(w+2) + w = 3 + 6 \cdot w + 6 \cdot 2 + w$
$= 3 + 6w + 12 + w$
$= 6w + w + 3 + 12$
$= 7w + 15$

31. $2(3x+1) + 5(x-2)$
$= 2(3x) + 2(1) + 5(x) - 5(2)$
$= 6x + 2 + 5x - 10$
$= 6x + 5x + 2 + (-10)$
$= 11x - 8$

33. $-(5x-1) - 10 = -1(5x-1) - 10$
$= -1 \cdot 5x + (-1) \cdot (-1) - 10$
$= -5x + 1 - 10$
$= -5x - 9$

35. $18y - 20y = (18-20)y = -2y$

37. $z - 8z = (1-8)z = -7z$

39. $9d - 3c - d = 9d - d - 3c = 8d - 3c$

41. $2y - 6 + 4y - 8 = 2y + 4y - 6 - 8$
$= 6y - 14$

43. $5q + p - 6q - p = p - p + 5q - 6q$
$= -q$

45. $2(x+1) + 20 = 2 \cdot x + 2 \cdot 1 + 20$
$= 2x + 2 + 20$
$= 2x + 22$

47. $5(x-7) - 8x = 5 \cdot x - 5 \cdot 7 - 8x$
$= 5x - 35 - 8x$
$= 5x - 8x - 35$
$= -3x - 35$

49. $-5(z+3) + 2z = -5 \cdot z + (-5) \cdot 3 + 2z$
$= -5z - 15 + 2z$
$= -5z + 2z - 15$
$= -3z - 15$

51. $8 - x + 4x - 2 - 9x$
$= -x + 4x - 9x + 8 - 2$
$= -6x + 6$

53. $-7(x+5) + 5(2x+1)$
$= -7 \cdot x + (-7) \cdot 5 + 5 \cdot 2x + 5 \cdot 1$
$= -7x - 35 + 10x + 5$
$= -7x + 10x - 35 + 5$
$= 3x - 30$

55. $3r - 5r + 8 + r = 3r - 5r + r + 8$
$= -r + 8$

57. $-3(n-1) - 4n = -3 \cdot n - (-3) \cdot 1 - 4n$
$= -3n + 3 - 4n$
$= -3n - 4n + 3$
$= -7n + 3$

59. $4(z-3) + 5z - 2 = 4 \cdot z - 4 \cdot 3 + 5z - 2$
$= 4z - 12 + 5z - 2$
$= 4z + 5z - 12 - 2$
$= 9z - 14$

61. $6(2x-1) - 12x = 6 \cdot 2x - 6 \cdot 1 - 12x$
$= 12x - 6 - 12x$
$= 12x - 12x - 6$
$= -6$

63. $-(4x-5) + 5 = -1(4x-5) + 5$
$= -1 \cdot 4x - (-1) \cdot 5 + 5$
$= -4x + 5 + 5$
$= -4x + 10$

65. $-(4xy-10) + 2(3xy+5)$
$= -1(4xy-10) + 2 \cdot 3xy + 2 \cdot 5$
$= -1 \cdot 4xy - (-1) \cdot 10 + 6xy + 10$
$= -4xy + 10 + 6xy + 10$
$= -4xy + 6xy + 10 + 10$
$= 2xy + 20$

67. $3a + 4(a+3) = 3a + 4 \cdot a + 4 \cdot 3$
$= 3a + 4a + 12$
$= 7a + 12$

69. $5y - 2(y-1) + 3 = 5y - 2y - 2(-1) + 3$
$= 3y + 2 + 3$
$= 3y + 5$

71. There are five sides, each of length $-5x + 11$ inches, so the perimeter is:
$$5(-5x+11) = 5(-5x)+5(11) = -(25x+55) \text{ inches}$$

73. $5y + 16 + 3y + 4y + 2y + 6$
$= 5y + 3y + 4y + 2y + 16 + 6$
$= (14y + 22)$ meters

75. There are three sides of length $2a$ feet, two sides of length 6 feet, and one side of length $5a$ feet, so the perimeter is:
$$3(2a)+2\cdot 6+5a = 6a+12+5a = 6a+5a+12 = (11a+12) \text{ feet}$$

77. $\text{Area} = (\text{side})^2$
$= (4z)^2$
$= (4z)(4z)$
$= (4)(4)(z)(z)$
$= 16z^2$ square centimeters

79. $A = \text{length}\cdot\text{width}$
$= 20(5x-7)$
$= 100x - 140$
$= (100x-140)$ square inches

81. $-13 + 10 = -3$

83. $-4 - (-12) = -4 + 12 = 8$

85. $-4 + 4 = 0$

87. $9684q - 686 - 4860q + 12{,}960$
$= (9684 - 4860)q + (12{,}960 - 686)$
$= 4824q + 12{,}274$

89. Answers may vary.

91. Add the areas of the two rectangles.
Area = (length) · (width)
$\begin{pmatrix}\text{Area of left}\\ \text{rectangle}\end{pmatrix} + \begin{pmatrix}\text{Area of right}\\ \text{rectangle}\end{pmatrix}$
$= 7(2x + 1) + 3(2x + 3)$
$= 7(2x) + 7(1) + 3(2x) + 3(3)$
$= 14x + 7 + 6x + 9$
$= (14 + 6)x + 16$
$= (20x + 16)$
The area is $(20x + 16)$ square miles.

93. Answers will vary.

Section 3.2

Practice Problems

1.
$$\begin{aligned} 3(y-6) &= 6 \\ 3(4-6) &= 6 \\ 3(-2) &= 6 \\ -6 &= 6 \quad \text{False} \end{aligned}$$
Since $-6 = 6$ is false, 4 is not a solution of the equation.

2.
$$\begin{aligned} -4x-3 &= 5 \\ -4(-2)-3 &= 5 \\ 8-3 &= 5 \\ 5 &= 5 \quad \text{True} \end{aligned}$$
Since $5 = 5$ is true, -2 is a solution of the equation.

3.
$$\begin{aligned} y-5 &= -3 \\ y-5+5 &= -3+5 \\ y &= 2 \end{aligned}$$

4.
$$\begin{aligned} z+9 &= 1 \\ z+9-9 &= 1-9 \\ z &= -8 \end{aligned}$$

5.
$$\begin{aligned} 10x &= -2+9x \\ 10x-9x &= -2+9x-9x \\ 1x &= -2 \text{ or } x = -2 \end{aligned}$$

6.
$$\begin{aligned} x+6 &= 1-3 \\ x+6 &= -2 \\ x+6-6 &= -2-6 \\ x &= -8 \end{aligned}$$

7.
$$\begin{aligned} -6y-1+7y &= 17 \\ y-1 &= 17 \\ y-1+1 &= 17+1 \\ y &= 18 \end{aligned}$$

8.
$$\begin{aligned} 13x &= 4(3x-1) \\ 13x &= 4\cdot 3x - 4\cdot 1 \\ 13x &= 12x-4 \\ 13x-12x &= 12x-4-12x \\ 1x &= -4 \text{ or } x = -4 \end{aligned}$$

Exercise Set 3.2

1.
$$\begin{aligned} x-8 &= 2 \\ 10-8 &= 2 \\ 2 &= 2 \quad \text{True} \end{aligned}$$
Yes, 10 is a solution.

3. $z+8=14$
$6+8=14$
$14=14$ True
Yes, 6 is a solution.

5. $x+12=7$
$-5+12=7$
$7=7$ True
Yes, –5 is a solution.

7. $7f=64-f$
$7(8)=64-8$
$56=64-8$
$56=56$ True
Yes, 8 is a solution.

9. $h-8=-8$
$0-8=-8$
$-8=-8$ True
Yes, 0 is a solution.

11. $4c+2-3c=-1+6$
$4(3)+2-3(3)=5$
$12+2-9=5$
$14-9=5$
$5=5$ True
Yes, 3 is a solution.

13. $a+5=23$
$a+5-5=23-5$
$a=18$
Check: $a+5=23$
$18+5=23$
$23=23$ True
The solution is 18.

15. $d-9=17$
$d-9+9=17+9$
$d=26$
Check: $d-9=17$
$26-9=17$
$17=17$ True
The solution is 26.

17. $7=y-2$
$7+2=y-2+2$
$9=y$
Check: $7=y-2$
$7=9-2$
$7=7$ True
The solution is 9.

19. $-12=x+4$
$-12-4=x+4-4$
$-16=x$
Check: $-12=x+4$
$-12=-16+4$
$-12=-12$ True
The solution is –16.

21. $3x=2x+11$
$3x-2x=2x+11-2x$
$x=11$
Check: $3x=2x+11$
$3(11)=2(11)+11$
$33=22+11$
$33=33$ True
The solution is 11.

23. $-4+y=2y$
$-4+y-y=2y-y$
$-4=y$
Check: $-4+y=2y$
$-4+(-4)=2(-4)$
$-8=-8$ True
The solution is –4.

25. $x-3=-1+4$
$x-3=3$
$x-3+3=3+3$
$x=6$
Check: $x-3=-1+4$
$6-3=-1+4$
$3=3$ True
The solution is 6.

27. $y+1=-3+4$
$y+1=1$
$y+1-1=1-1$
$y=0$
Check: $y+1=-3+4$
$0+1=-3+4$
$1=1$ True
The solution is 0.

29. $-7+10=m-5$
$3=m-5$
$3+5=m-5+5$
$8=m$
Check: $-7+10=m-5$
$-7+10=8-5$
$3=3$ True
The solution is 8.

31. $-2-3=-4+x$
$-5=-4+x$
$-5+4=-4+x+4$
$-1=x$
Check: $-2-3=-4+x$
$-2-3=-4+(-1)$
$-5=-5$ True
The solution is −1.

33. $2(5x-3)=11x$
$2\cdot 5x-2\cdot 3=11x$
$10x-6=11x$
$10x-6-10x=11x-10x$
$-6=x$
Check: $2(5x-3)=11x$
$2(5\cdot(-6)-3)=11\cdot(-6)$
$2(-30-3)=-66$
$2(-33)=-66$
$-66=-66$ True
The solution is −6.

35. $3y=2(y+12)$
$3y=2\cdot y+2\cdot 12$
$3y=2y+24$
$3y-2y=2y+24-2y$
$y=24$
Check: $3y=2(y+12)$
$3\cdot 24=2(24+12)$
$72=2(36)$
$72=72$ True
The solution is 24.

37. $-8x+4+9x=-1+7$
$x+4=6$
$x+4-4=6-4$
$x=2$
Check: $-8x+4+9x=-1+7$
$-8(2)+4+9(2)=-1+7$
$-16+4+18=6$
$6=6$ True
The solution is 2.

39. $2-2=5x-4x$
$0=x$
Check: $2-2=5x-4x$
$2-2=5(0)-4(0)$
$0=0-0$
$0=0$ True
The solution is 0.

41. $7x+14-6x=-4-10$
$x+14=-14$
$x+14-14=-14-14$
$x=-28$
Check: $7x+14-6x=-4-10$
$7(-28)+14-6(-28)=-4-10$
$-196+14+168=-14$
$-14=-14$ True
The solution is −28.

43. $57=y-16$
$57+16=y-16+16$
$73=y$

45. $67=z+67$
$67+(-67)=z+67+(-67)$
$0=z$

47. $x+5=4-3$
$x+5=1$
$x+5+(-5)=1+(-5)$
$x=-4$

49. $z-23=-88$
$z-23+23=-88+23$
$z=-65$

51. $7a+7-6a=20$
$a+7=20$
$a+7+(-7)=20+(-7)$
$a=13$

53. $-12+x=-15$
$-12+x+12=-15+12$
$x=-3$

55. $-8-9=3x+5-2x$
$-17=x+5$
$-17-5=x+5-5$
$-22=x$

57. $8(3x-2)=25x$
$8\cdot 3x-8\cdot 2=25x$
$24x-16=25x$
$24x-16-24x=25x-24x$
$-16=x$

59. $7x+7-6x=10$
$x+7=10$
$x+7+(-7)=10+(-7)$
$x=3$

69. $\frac{-3}{-3}=1$

71. Answers may vary.

73. No; answers may vary.

75. $$\begin{aligned} x-76,862&=86,102\\ x-76,862+76,862&=86,102+76,862\\ x&=162,964 \end{aligned}$$

77. $$\begin{aligned} 5^3&=x+4^4\\ 125&=x+16\\ 125-16&=x+16-16 \end{aligned}$$

79. $$\begin{aligned} |-13|+3^2&=100y-|-20|-99y\\ 13+3^2&=100y-20-99y\\ 13+9&=y-20\\ 22&=y-20\\ 22+20&=y-20+22\\ 42&=y \end{aligned}$$

81. $$\begin{aligned} T&=P+R\\ 5560&=P+1933\\ 5560-1933&=P+1933-1933\\ 3627&=P \end{aligned}$$
The total passing yardage was 3627 yards.

83. $$\begin{aligned} I&=R-E\\ 6671&=R-213,141\\ 6671+213,141&=R-213,141+213,141\\ 219,812&=R \end{aligned}$$
The total revenues were $219,812 million.

Section 3.3

Practice Problems

1. $$\begin{aligned} \frac{x}{-4}&=7\\ -4\cdot\frac{x}{-4}&=7\cdot(-4)\\ \frac{-4}{-4}x&=7\cdot(-4)\\ 1x&=-28 \quad or \quad x=-28 \end{aligned}$$

2. $$\begin{aligned} 3y&=-18\\ \frac{3y}{3}&=\frac{-18}{3}\\ \frac{3}{3}\cdot y&=\frac{-18}{3}\\ 1y&=-6 \text{ or } y=-6 \end{aligned}$$

3. $$\begin{aligned} -16&=8x\\ \frac{-16}{8}&=\frac{8x}{8}\\ \frac{-16}{8}&=\frac{8}{8}\cdot x\\ -2&=x \text{ or } x=-2 \end{aligned}$$

4. $$\begin{aligned} -3y&=-27\\ \frac{-3y}{-3}&=\frac{-27}{-3}\\ \frac{-3}{-3}\cdot y&=\frac{-27}{-3}\\ y&=9 \end{aligned}$$

5. $$\begin{aligned} 10&=2m-4m\\ 10&=-2m\\ \frac{10}{-2}&=\frac{-2m}{-2}\\ -5&=m \text{ or } m=-5 \end{aligned}$$

6. $$\begin{aligned} -8+6&=-a\\ -2&=-a\\ \frac{-2}{-1}&=\frac{-1a}{-1}\\ 2&=a \end{aligned}$$

7. $$\begin{aligned} -4-10&=4y+3y\\ -14&=7y\\ \frac{-14}{7}&=\frac{7y}{7}\\ -2&=y \end{aligned}$$

8. **a.** The sum of –3 and a number is –3 + x.

b. – 5 decreased by a number is – 5 – x..

c. Three times a number is $3x$.

d. A number subtracted from 83 is 83 – x..

e. The quotient of a number and 4 is $\frac{x}{4}$.

9. **a.** The product of 5 and a number is $5x$. The product of 5 and a number decreased by 25 is $5x - 25$.

b. The sum of a number and 3 is $x + 3$. Twice the sum of a number and 3 is $2(x + 3)$.

c. Twice a number is $2x$. The quotient of 39 and twice a number is $\frac{39}{2x}$.

Exercise Set 3.3

1. $5x = 20$
$\frac{5x}{5} = \frac{20}{5}$ divide by 5
$x = 4$

3. $-3z = 12$
$\frac{-3z}{-3} = \frac{12}{-3}$ divide by -3
$z = -4$

5. $\frac{x}{7} = 1$
$7 \cdot \frac{x}{7} = 1 \cdot 7$
$x = 7$

7. $\frac{z}{-9} = 9$
$-9 \cdot \frac{z}{-9} = 9(-9)$
$z = -81$

9. $4y = 0$
$\frac{4y}{4} = \frac{0}{4}$ divide by 4
$y = 0$

11. $2z = -34$
$\frac{2z}{2} = \frac{-34}{2}$ divide by 2
$z = -17$

13. $\frac{x}{-8} = -4$
$-8 \cdot \frac{x}{-8} = -4(-8)$
$x = 32$

15. $\frac{y}{-20} = 3$
$-20 \cdot \frac{y}{-20} = 3(-20)$
$y = -60$

17. $-3x = -15$
$\frac{-3x}{-3} = \frac{-15}{-3}$ divide by -3
$x = 5$

19. $\frac{x}{-17} = 0$
$-17 \cdot \frac{x}{-17} = 0(-17)$
$x = 0$

21. $2w - 12w = 40$ combine like terms
$-10w = 40$
$\frac{-10w}{-10} = \frac{40}{-10}$ divide by -10
$w = -4$

23. $16 = 10t - 8t$ combine like terms
$16 = 2t$
$\frac{16}{2} = \frac{2t}{2}$ divide by 2
$8 = t$

25. $2z = 12 - 14$ combine like terms
$2z = -2$
$\frac{2z}{2} = \frac{-2}{2}$ divide by 2
$z = -1$

27. $4 - 10 = \frac{z}{-3}$
$-6 = \frac{z}{-3}$
$-3(-6) = \frac{z}{-3}(-3)$
$18 = z$

29. $-3x - 3x = 50 - 2$ combine like terms
$-6x = 48$
$\frac{6x}{-6} = \frac{48}{-6}$ divide by -6
$x = -8$

31. $\frac{x}{5} = -26 + 16$
$\frac{x}{5} = -10$
$5 \cdot \frac{x}{5} = -10 \cdot 5$
$x = -50$

33. $-10x = 10$
$\frac{-10x}{-10} = \frac{10}{-10}$ divide by -10
$x = -1$

31.
$$\frac{x}{5} = -26 + 16$$
$$\frac{x}{5} = -10$$
$$5 \cdot \frac{x}{5} = -10 \cdot 5$$
$$x = -50$$

33.
$$-10x = 10$$
$$\frac{-10x}{-10} = \frac{10}{-10} \quad \text{divide by } -10$$
$$x = -1$$

35.
$$5x = -35$$
$$\frac{5x}{5} = \frac{-35}{5} \quad \text{divide by } 5$$
$$x = -7$$

37.
$$0 = 3x$$
$$\frac{0}{3} = \frac{3x}{3} \quad \text{divide by } 3$$
$$0 = x$$

39.
$$24 = t + 3t \quad \text{combine like terms}$$
$$24 = 4t$$
$$\frac{24}{4} = \frac{4t}{4} \quad \text{divide by } 4$$
$$6 = t$$

41.
$$10z - 3z = -63 \quad \text{combine like terms}$$
$$7z = -63$$
$$\frac{7z}{7} = \frac{-63}{7} \quad \text{divide by } 7$$
$$z = -9$$

43.
$$3z - 10z = -63 \quad \text{combine like terms}$$
$$-7z = -63$$
$$\frac{-7z}{-7} = \frac{-63}{-7} \quad \text{divide by } -7$$
$$z = 9$$

45.
$$12 = 13y - 10y \quad \text{combine like terms}$$
$$12 = 3y$$
$$\frac{12}{3} = \frac{3y}{3} \quad \text{divide by } 3$$
$$4 = y$$

47.
$$-4x = 20 - (-4) \quad \text{combine like terms}$$
$$-4x = 20 + 4$$
$$-4x = 24$$
$$\frac{-4x}{-4} = \frac{24}{-4} \quad \text{divide by } -4$$
$$x = -6$$

49.
$$18 - 11 = \frac{x}{-5}$$
$$7 = \frac{x}{-5}$$
$$-5 \cdot 7 = \frac{x}{-5} \cdot -5$$
$$-35 = x$$

51.
$$-20 - (-50) = \frac{x}{9}$$
$$-20 + 50 = \frac{x}{9}$$
$$30 = \frac{x}{9}$$
$$9 \cdot 30 = \frac{x}{9} \cdot 9$$
$$270 = x$$

53.
$$10p - 11p = 25 \quad \text{combine like terms}$$
$$-1p = 25$$
$$\frac{-1p}{-1} = \frac{25}{-1} \quad \text{divide by } -1$$
$$p = -25$$

55.
$$6x - x = 4 - 14 \quad \text{combine like terms}$$
$$5x = -10$$
$$\frac{5x}{5} = \frac{-10}{5} \quad \text{divide by } 5$$
$$x = -2$$

57.
$$10 = 7t - 12t \quad \text{combine like terms}$$
$$10 = -5t$$
$$\frac{10}{-5} = \frac{-5t}{-5} \quad \text{divide by } -5$$
$$-2 = t$$

59.
$$5 - 5 = 3x + 2x \quad \text{combine like terms}$$
$$0 = 5x$$
$$\frac{0}{5} = \frac{5x}{5} \quad \text{divide by } 5$$
$$0 = x$$

61.
$$4r - 9r = -20 \quad \text{combine like terms}$$
$$-5r = -20$$
$$\frac{-5r}{-5} = \frac{-20}{-5} \quad \text{divide by } -5$$
$$r = 4$$

63. $\frac{x}{-4} = -1-(-8)$

$\frac{x}{-4} = -1+8$

$\frac{x}{-4} = 7$

$-4 \cdot \frac{x}{-4} = 7(-4)$

$x = -28$

65. $3w - 12w = -27$ combine like terms

$-9w = -27$

$\frac{-9w}{-9} = \frac{-27}{-9}$ divide by -9

$w = 3$

67. $-36 = 9u - 10u$ combine like terms

$-36 = -1u$

$\frac{-36}{-1} = \frac{-1u}{-1}$ divide by -1

$36 = u$

69. $23x - 25x = 7 - 9$ combine like terms

$-2x = -2$

$\frac{-2x}{-2} = \frac{-2}{-2}$ divide by -2

$x = 1$

71. Let x represent a number. The sum of –7 and a number is $-7 + x$.

73. Let x represent a number. The product of –11 and a number is $-11x$.

75. Let x represent a number. A number divided by –12 is $\frac{x}{-12}$ or $-\frac{x}{12}$.

77. Let x represent a number. Eleven subtracted from a number is $x - 11$.

79. Let x represent a number. 7 times a number is $7x$. Thus, negative ten decreased by 7 times a number is $-10 - 7x$.

81. Let x represent a number. The product of –13 and a number is $-13x$.

83. Let x represent a number. The quotient of seventeen and a number is $\frac{17}{x}$. Thus,the quotient of seventeen and a number increased by –15 is $\frac{17}{x} + (-15)$.

85. Let x represent a number. The product of 4 and a number is $4x$. Thus, seven added to the product of 4 and a number is $4x + 7$.

87. Let x represent a number. Twice a number is $2x$. Thus, twice a number, decreased by 17 is $2x -$ 17.

89. Let x represent a number. The sum of a number and 15 is $x + 15$. Thus, the product of –6 and the sum of a number and 15 is $-6(x + 15)$.

91. Let x represent a number. The product of a number and –5 is $-5x$. Thus, the quotient of 45 and the product of a number and –5 is $\frac{45}{-5x}$.

93. $3x + 10 = 3(-5) + 10 = -15 + 10 = -5$

95. $\frac{x-5}{2} = \frac{-5-5}{2} = \frac{-10}{2} = -5$

97. $\frac{3x+4}{x+4} = \frac{3(-5)+4}{-5+4} = \frac{-15+4}{-1} = \frac{-11}{-1} = 11$

99. Answers may vary.

101. $-25x = 900$

$\frac{-25x}{-25} = \frac{900}{-25}$

$x = -36$

103. $\frac{y}{72} = -86-(-1029)$

$\frac{y}{72} = -86+1029$

$\frac{y}{72} = 943$

$72 \cdot \frac{y}{72} = 943 \cdot 72$

$y = 67,896$

105.
$$\frac{x}{-2} = 5^2 - |-10| - (-9)$$
$$\frac{x}{-2} = 25 - 10 + 9$$
$$\frac{x}{-2} = 24$$
$$-2 \cdot \frac{x}{-2} = 24(-2)$$
$$x = 48$$

107.
$$d = r \cdot t$$
$$780 = 65t$$
$$\frac{780}{65} = \frac{65t}{65}$$
$$12 = t$$
It will take 12 hours.

109.
$$d = r \cdot t$$
$$232 = r \cdot 4$$
$$\frac{232}{4} = \frac{r \cdot 4}{4}$$
$$58 = r$$
The driver should drive at 58 miles per hour

Integrated Review

1. $7x + x = 7x + 1x$
$= (7 + 1)x$
$= 8x$

2. $6y - 10y = (6 - 10)y$
$= -4y$

3. $2a + 5a - 9a - 2 = (2 + 5 - 9)a - 2$
$= -2a - 2$

4. $6a - 12 - a - 14 = 6a - a - 12 - 14$
$= (6 - 1)a - 12 - 14$
$= 5a - 26$

5. $-2(4x + 7) = -2 \cdot 4x + (-2)(7) = -8x - 14$

6. $-3(2x - 10) = -3(2x) + (-3)(-10)$
$= -6x + 30$

7. $5(y + 2) - 20 = 5 \cdot y + 5 \cdot 2 - 20$
$= 5y + 10 - 20$
$= 5y - 10$

8. $12x + 3(x - 6) - 13 = 12x + 3 \cdot x + 3(-6) - 13$
$= 12x + 3x - 18 - 13$
$= 15x - 31$

9. $A = \text{length} \cdot \text{width}$
$= (4x - 2) \cdot 3$
$= 3(4x - 2)$
$= 3 \cdot 4x - 3 \cdot 2$
$= 12x - 6$
The area is $(12x - 6)$ square meters.

10. $P = a + b + c$
$= x + 7 + (x + 2)$
$= x + 7 + 1(x + 2)$
$= x + 7 + 1 \cdot x + 1 \cdot 2)$
$= x + 7 + x + 2$
$= x + x + 7 + 2$
$= 2x + 9$
The perimeter is $(2x + 9)$ feet.

11.
$$x + 7 = 20$$
$$x + 7 - 7 = 20 - 7$$
$$x = 13$$
Check: $x + 7 = 20$
$13 + 7 = 20$
$20 = 20$ True
The solution is 13.

12.
$$-11 = x - 2$$
$$-11 + 2 = x - 2 + 2$$
$$-9 = x$$
Check: $-11 = x - 2$
$-11 = -9 - 2$
$-11 = -11$ True
The solution is –9.

13.
$$11x = 55$$
$$\frac{11x}{11} = \frac{55}{11}$$
$$x = 5$$
Check: $11x = 55$
$11(5) = 55$
$55 = 55$ True
The solution is 5.

14.
$$-7y = 0$$
$$\frac{-7y}{-7} = \frac{0}{-7}$$
$$y = 0$$
Check: $-7y = 0$
$-7(0) = 0$
$0 = 0$ True
The solution is 0.

15.
$$\frac{x}{-3} = -13$$
$$-3 \cdot \frac{x}{-3} = -13 \cdot (-3)$$
$$x = 39$$

16.
$$\frac{z}{-5} = -11$$
$$-5 \cdot \frac{z}{-5} = -11 \cdot (-5)$$
$$x = 55$$

17.
$$12 = 11x - 14x$$
$$12 = -3x$$
$$\frac{12}{-3} = \frac{-3x}{-3}$$
$$-4 = x$$

Check:
$$12 = 11x - 14x$$
$$12 = 11(-4) - 14(-4)$$
$$12 = -44 - (-56)$$
$$12 = -44 + 56$$
$$12 = 12 \text{ True}$$

The solution is –4.

18.
$$8y + 7y = -45$$
$$15y = -45$$
$$\frac{15y}{15} = \frac{-45}{15}$$
$$y = -3$$

Check:
$$8y + 7y = -45$$
$$8(-3) + 7(-3) = -45$$
$$-24 + (-21) = -45$$
$$-45 = -45 \text{ True}$$

The solution is –3.

19.
$$-3x = -15$$
$$\frac{-3x}{-3} = \frac{-15}{-3}$$
$$x = 5$$

Check:
$$-3x = -15$$
$$-3(5) = -15$$
$$-15 = -15 \text{ True}$$

The solution is 5.

20.
$$-2m = -1.6$$
$$\frac{-2m}{-2} = \frac{-16}{-2}$$
$$m = 8$$

Check:
$$-2m = -16$$
$$-2(8) = -16$$
$$-16 = -16 \text{ True}$$

The solution is 8.

21.
$$x - 12 = -45 + 23$$
$$x - 12 = -22$$
$$x - 12 + 12 = -22 + 12$$
$$x = -1$$

Check:
$$x - 12 = -45 + 23$$
$$-10 - 12 = -45 + 23$$
$$-22 = -22 \text{ True}$$

The solution is –10.

22.
$$6 - (-5) = x + 5$$
$$6 + 5 = x + 5$$
$$11 = x + 5$$
$$11 - 5 = x + 5 - 5$$
$$6 = x$$

Check:
$$6 - (-5) = x + 5$$
$$6 - (-5) = 6 + 5$$
$$6 + 5 = 11$$
$$11 = 11 \text{ True}$$

The solution is 6.

23.
$$6(3x - 4) = 19x$$
$$6 \cdot 3x - 6 \cdot 4 = 19x$$
$$18x - 24 = 19x$$
$$18x - 24 - 18x = 19x - 18x$$
$$-24 = x$$

Check:
$$6(3x - 4) = 19x$$
$$6(3(-24) - 4) = 19(-24)$$
$$6(-72 - 4) = -456$$
$$6(-76) = -456$$
$$-456 = -456 \text{ True}$$

The solution is –24.

24.
$$25x = 6(4x - 9)$$
$$25x = 6 \cdot 4x + 6(-9)$$
$$25x = 24x - 54$$
$$25x - 24x = 24x - 54 - 24x$$
$$x = -54$$

Check:
$$25x = 6(4x - 9)$$
$$25(054) = 6[4(-54) - 9]$$
$$-1350 = 6(-216 - 9)$$
$$-1350 = 6(-225)$$
$$-1350 = -1350 \text{ True}$$

The solution is – 54.

25.
$$-36x - 10 + 37x = -12 - (-14)$$
$$-36x + 37x - 10 = -12 + 14$$
$$x - 10 = 2$$
$$x - 10 + 1- = 2 + 10$$
$$x = 12$$

27.
$$\frac{x}{13} = -1 - (-3)$$
$$\frac{x}{13} = -1 + 3$$
$$\frac{x}{13} = 2$$
$$13 \cdot \frac{x}{13} = 2 \cdot 13$$
$$x = 26$$
Check: $\frac{x}{13} = -1 - (-3)$
$$\frac{26}{13} = -1 - (-3)$$
$$2 = -1 + 3$$
$$2 = 2 \text{ True}$$
The solution is 26.

28.
$$\frac{y}{4} = 7 - 10$$
$$\frac{y}{4} = -3$$
$$4 \cdot \frac{y}{4} = -3 \cdot 4$$
$$y = -12$$
Check: $\frac{y}{4} = 7 - 10$
$$\frac{12}{4} = 7 - 10$$
$$-3 = -3 \text{ True}$$
The solution is –12.

29.
$$-8z - 2z = 26 - (-4)$$
$$-10z = 26 + 4$$
$$-10z = 30$$
$$\frac{-10z}{-10} = \frac{30}{-10}$$
$$z = -3$$
Check: $-8z - 2z = 26 - (-4)$
$$-8(-3) - 2(-3) = 26 - (-4)$$
$$24 + 6 = 26 + 4$$
$$30 = 30 \text{ True}$$
The solution is –3.

30.
$$-12 + (-13) = 5x - 10x$$
$$-25 = -5x$$
$$\frac{-25}{-5} = \frac{-5x}{-5}$$
$$5 = x$$
Check: $-12 + (-13) = 5x - 10x$
$$-12 + (-13) = 5(5) - 10(5)$$
$$-25 = 25 - 50$$
$$-25 = -25 \text{ True}$$
The solution is 5.

31. The difference of a number and 10 is $x - 10$.

32. The sum of – 20 and a number is $-20 + x$.

33. The product of ten and a number is $10x$.

34. The quotient of ten and a number is $\frac{10}{x}$ or $10 \div x$.

35. The product of –2 and a number is $-2x$. Five added to the product of –2 and a number is $-2x + 5$.

36. The difference of a number and 1 is $x - 1$. The product of – 4 and the difference of a number and 1 is $-4(x - 1)$.

Section 3.4

Practice Problems

1.
$$5y + 2 = 17$$
$$5y + 2 - 2 = 17 - 2$$
$$5y = 15$$
$$\frac{5y}{5} = \frac{15}{5}$$
$$y = 3$$

2.
$$45 = -10 - y$$
$$45 + 10 = -10 - y + 10$$
$$55 = -1y$$
$$\frac{55}{-1} = \frac{-1y}{-1}$$
$$-55 = y$$

3.
$$7x + 12 = 3x - 4$$
$$7x + 12 - 12 = 3x - 4 - 12$$
$$7x = 3x - 16$$
$$7x - 3x = 3x - 16 - 3x$$
$$4x = -16$$
$$\frac{4x}{4} = \frac{-16}{4}$$
$$x = -4$$

4.
$$6(a - 5) = 4(a + 1)$$
$$6a - 30 = 4a + 4$$
$$6a - 30 - 4a = 4a + 4 - 4a$$
$$2a - 30 = 4$$
$$2a - 30 + 30 = 4 + 30$$
$$2a = 34$$
$$\frac{2a}{2} = \frac{34}{2}$$
$$a = 17$$

5.
$$4(x + 3) = 12$$
$$4x + 12 = 12$$
$$4x + 12 - 12 = 12 - 12$$
$$4x = 0$$
$$\frac{4x}{4} = \frac{0}{4}$$
$$x = 0$$

6. a. $110 - 80 = 30$

b. $3(-9 + 11) = 6$

c. $\frac{2(12)}{-6} = -4$

4.
$$\begin{aligned} 6(a-5) &= 4(a+1) \\ 6a-30 &= 4a+4 \\ 6a-30-4a &= 4a+4-4a \\ 2a-30 &= 4 \\ 2a-30+30 &= 4+30 \\ 2a &= 34 \\ \frac{2a}{2} &= \frac{34}{2} \\ a &= 17 \end{aligned}$$

5.
$$\begin{aligned} 4(x+3) &= 12 \\ 4x+12 &= 12 \\ 4x+12-12 &= 12-12 \\ 4x &= 0 \\ \frac{4x}{4} &= \frac{0}{4} \\ x &= 0 \end{aligned}$$

6. a. $110-80=30$

b. $3(-9+11)=6$

c. $\frac{2(12)}{-6}=-4$

Calculator Explorations

The following answers may vary depending on what type of calculator you have.

1. $76(12-25) = -988$

   Press the keys 76 [×] [(] 12 – 25 [)] [= or ENTER]. The display will read 988.

   Yes

2. $-47(35)+862 = -783$

   Press the keys 47 [+/–] [×] 35 [+] 862 [= or ENTER]. The display will read –783.

   Yes

3. $-170+562 = 3(-170)+900$

   Press the keys 170 [+/–] [+] 562 [= or ENTER]. The display will read 391.

   Press the keys 3 [×] 170 [+/–] [+] 900 [= or ENTER]. The display will read 390.

   $391 \neq 390.$

   No

4. $55(-18+10) = 75(-18)+910$

   Press the keys 55 [(] 18 [+/–] [+] 10 [)] [= or ENTER]. The display will read – 440.

   Press the keys 75 [×] 18 [+/–] [+] 910 [= or ENTER]. The display will read – 440.

   $-440 = -440.$

   Yes

5. $29(-21)-1034 = 619-210-362$

   Press the keys 29 [×] 21 [+/–] [–] 1034 [= or ENTER]. The display will read –1643.

   Press the keys 61 [×] 21 [+/–] [–] 362 [= or ENTER]. The display will read –1643.

   $-1643 = -1643$

   Yes

6. $-38(25)+205 = 25(25)+120$

   Press the keys 38 [+/–] [×] 25 [+] 205 [= or ENTER]. The display will read –745.

   Press the keys 25 [×] 25 [+] 120 [= or ENTER]. The display will read 745.

   $-745 \neq 745$

   No

Exercise Set 3.4

1.
$$\begin{aligned} 2x-6&=0\\ 2x-6+6&=0+6\\ 2x&=6\\ \frac{2x}{2}&=\frac{6}{2}\\ x&=3 \end{aligned}$$

3.
$$\begin{aligned} \frac{n}{3}+10&=0\\ \frac{n}{5}+10-10&=0-10\\ \frac{n}{5}&=-10\\ 5\cdot\frac{n}{5}&=-10\cdot 5\\ n&=-50 \end{aligned}$$

5.
$$\begin{aligned} 6-n&=10\\ 6-n-6&=10-6\\ -n&=4\\ \frac{-n}{-1}&=\frac{4}{-1}\\ n&=-4 \end{aligned}$$

7.
$$\begin{aligned} 10x+15&=6x+3\\ 10x+15-15&=6x+3-15\\ 10x&=6x-12\\ 10x-6x&=6x-12-6x\\ 4x&=-12\\ \frac{4x}{4}&=\frac{-12}{4}\\ x&=-3 \end{aligned}$$

9.
$$\begin{aligned} 3x-7&=4x+5\\ 3x-7+7&=4x+5+7\\ 3x&=4x+12\\ 3x-4x&=4x+12-4x\\ -x&=12\\ \frac{-x}{-1}&=\frac{12}{-1}\\ x&=-12 \end{aligned}$$

11.
$$\begin{aligned} 3(x-1)&=12\\ 3x-3&=12\\ 3x-3+3&=12+3\\ 3x&=15\\ \frac{3x}{3}&=\frac{15}{3}\\ x&=5 \end{aligned}$$

13.
$$\begin{aligned} -2(y+4)&=2\\ -2y-8&=2\\ -2y-8+8&=2+8\\ -2y&=10\\ \frac{-2y}{-2}&=\frac{10}{-2}\\ y&=-5 \end{aligned}$$

15.
$$\begin{aligned} 35&=17+3(x-2)\\ 35&=17+3x-6\\ 35&=11+3x\\ 35-11&=11+3x-11\\ 24&=3x\\ \frac{24}{3}&=\frac{3x}{3}\\ 8&=x \end{aligned}$$

17.
$$\begin{aligned} 8-t&=3\\ 8-t-8&=3-8\\ -t&=-5\\ \frac{-t}{-1}&=\frac{-5}{-1}\\ t&=5 \end{aligned}$$

19.
$$\begin{aligned} 0&=4x-4\\ 0+4&=4x-4+4\\ 4&=4x\\ \frac{4}{4}&=\frac{4x}{4}\\ 1&=x \end{aligned}$$

21.
$$\begin{aligned} \frac{x}{-2}-8&=0\\ \frac{x}{-2}-8+8&=0+8\\ \frac{x}{-2}&=8\\ -2\cdot\frac{x}{-2}&=8(-2)\\ x&=-16 \end{aligned}$$

23.
$$\begin{aligned}7 &= 4c-1\\ 7+1 &= 4c-1+1\\ 8 &= 4c\\ \frac{8}{4} &= \frac{4c}{4}\\ 2 &= c\end{aligned}$$

25.
$$\begin{aligned}3r+4 &= 19\\ 3r+4-4 &= 19-4\\ 3r &= 15\\ \frac{3r}{3} &= \frac{15}{3}\\ r &= 5\end{aligned}$$

27.
$$\begin{aligned}2x-1 &= -7\\ 2x-1+1 &= -7+1\\ 2x &= -6\\ \frac{2x}{2} &= \frac{-6}{2}\\ x &= -3\end{aligned}$$

29.
$$\begin{aligned}2 &= 3z-4\\ 2+4 &= 3z-4+4\\ 6 &= 3z\\ \frac{6}{3} &= \frac{3z}{3}\\ 2 &= z\end{aligned}$$

31.
$$\begin{aligned}5x-2 &= -12\\ 5x-2+2 &= -12+2\\ 5x &= -10\\ \frac{5x}{5} &= \frac{-10}{5}\\ x &= -2\end{aligned}$$

33.
$$\begin{aligned}-7c+1 &= -20\\ -7c+1-1 &= -20-1\\ -7c &= -21\\ \frac{-7c}{-7} &= \frac{-21}{-7}\\ c &= 3\end{aligned}$$

35.
$$\begin{aligned}9 &= \frac{x}{2}-15\\ 9+15 &= \frac{x}{2}-15+15\\ 24 &= \frac{x}{2}\\ 2\cdot 24 &= \frac{x}{2}\cdot 2\\ 48 &= x\end{aligned}$$

37.
$$\begin{aligned}8m+79 &= -1\\ 8m+79-79 &= -1-79\\ 8m &= -80\\ \frac{8m}{8} &= \frac{-80}{8}\\ m &= -10\end{aligned}$$

39.
$$\begin{aligned}10+4v &= -6\\ 10+4v-10 &= -6-10\\ 4v &= -16\\ \frac{4v}{4} &= \frac{-16}{4}\\ v &= -4\end{aligned}$$

41.
$$\begin{aligned}-5 &= -13-8k\\ -5+13 &= -13-8k+13\\ 8 &= -8k\\ \frac{8}{-8} &= \frac{-8k}{-8}\\ -1 &= k\end{aligned}$$

43.
$$\begin{aligned}4x+3 &= 2x+11\\ 4x+3-3 &= 2x+11-3\\ 4x &= 2x+8\\ 4x-2x &= 2x+8-2x\\ 2x &= 8\\ \frac{2x}{2} &= \frac{8}{2}\\ x &= 4\end{aligned}$$

45.
$$\begin{aligned}-2y-10 &= 5y+18\\ -2y-10+10 &= 5y+18+10\\ -2y &= 5y+28\\ -2y-5y &= 5y+28-5y\\ -7y &= 28\\ \frac{-7y}{-7} &= \frac{28}{-7}\\ y &= -4\end{aligned}$$

47.
$$\begin{aligned}-8n+1 &= -6n-5\\ -8n+1-1 &= -6n-5-1\\ -8n &= -6n-6\\ -8n+6n &= -6n-6+6n\\ -2n &= -6\\ \frac{-2n}{-2} &= \frac{-6}{-2}\\ n &= 3\end{aligned}$$

49.
$$\begin{aligned} 9-3x &= 14+2x \\ 9-3x-9 &= 14+2x-9 \\ -3x &= 5+2x \\ -3x-2x &= 5+2x-2x \\ -5x &= 5 \\ \frac{-5x}{-5} &= \frac{5}{-5} \\ x &= -1 \end{aligned}$$

51.
$$\begin{aligned} 2(y-3) &= y-6 \\ 2y-6 &= y-6 \\ 2y-6+6 &= y-6+6 \\ 2y &= y \\ 2y-y &= y-y \\ y &= 0 \end{aligned}$$

53.
$$\begin{aligned} 2t-1 &= 3(t+7) \\ 2t-1 &= 3t+21 \\ 2t-1+1 &= 3t+21+1 \\ 2t &= 3t+22 \\ 2t-3t &= 3t+22-3t \\ -1t &= 22 \\ \frac{-t}{-1} &= \frac{22}{-1} \\ t &= -22 \end{aligned}$$

55.
$$\begin{aligned} 3(5c-1)-2 &= 13c+3 \\ 15c-3-2 &= 13c+3 \\ 15c-5 &= 13c+3 \\ 15c-5+5 &= 13c+3+5 \\ 15c &= 13c+8 \\ 15c-13c &= 13c+8-13c \\ 2c &= 8 \\ \frac{2c}{2} &= \frac{8}{2} \\ c &= 4 \end{aligned}$$

57.
$$\begin{aligned} 10+5(z-2) &= 4z+1 \\ 10+5z-10 &= 4z+1 \\ 5z &= 4z+1 \\ 5z-4z &= 4z+1-4z \\ z &= 1 \end{aligned}$$

59.
$$\begin{aligned} 7(6+w) &= 6(2+w) \\ 42+7w &= 12+6w \\ 42+7w-6w &= 12+6w-6w \\ 42+w &= 12 \\ 42+w-42 &= 12-42 \\ w &= -30 \end{aligned}$$

61. The sum of –42 and 16 is –26 translates to $-42 + 16 = -26$.

63. The product of –5 and –29 gives 145 translates to $-5(-29) = 145$.

65. Three times the difference of –14 and 2 amounts to –48 translates to $3(-14-2) = -48$.

67. The quotient of 100 and twice 50 is equal to 1 translates to $\frac{100}{2(50)} = 1$.

69. 2002 shows the greatest increase in the number of electronically filed returns.

71. $73 - 35 = 38$
From 2000 to 2007 the number of electronically filed returns is expected to increase by 38 million.

73. $x^3 - 2xy$ substitute $x = 3$, $y = -1$
$$\begin{aligned} &= 3^3 - 2(3)(-1) \\ &= 27-(-6) \\ &= 27+6 \\ &= 33 \end{aligned}$$

75. $y^5 - 4x^2$ substitute $x = 3$, $y = -1$
$$\begin{aligned} &= (-1)^5 - 4(3)^2 \\ &= (-1)(-1)(-1)(-1)(-1) - 4(3)(3) \\ &= -1-36 \\ &= -37 \end{aligned}$$

77. $(2x-y)^2$ substitute $x = 3$, $y = -1$
$$\begin{aligned} &= [2(3)-(-1)]^2 \\ &= (6+1)^2 \\ &= (7)^2 \\ &= 49 \end{aligned}$$

79. $4xy + 6y^2$ substitute $x = 3$, $y = -1$
$$\begin{aligned} &= 4(3)(-1) + 6(-1)^2 \\ &= -12+6\cdot 1 \\ &= -12+6 \\ &= -6 \end{aligned}$$

81.
$$\begin{aligned} (-8)^2 + 3x &= 5x + 4^3 \\ 64+3x &= 5x+64 \\ 64+3x-5x &= 5x+64-5x \\ 64-2x &= 64 \\ 64-2x-64 &= 64-64 \\ -2x &= 0 \\ \frac{-2x}{-2} &= \frac{0}{-2} \\ x &= 0 \end{aligned}$$

c. Ten subtracted from a number is $x - 10$. Ten subtracted from a number amounts to –23 is $x - 10 = -23$.

d. Five times a number is $5x$. Five times a number added to 7 is equal to –8 is $7 + 5x = -8$.

e. The sum of a number and 4 is $x + 4$. The quotient of 6 and the sum of a number and 4 gives 1 is $\frac{6}{x+4} = 1$.

2. Let x = the unknown number.

$$x+2=3x+6$$
$$x+2-2=3x+6-2$$
$$x=3x+4$$
$$x-3x=3x+4-3x$$
$$-2x=4$$
$$\frac{-2x}{-2}=\frac{4}{-2}$$
$$x=-2$$

The unknown number is –2.

3. Let x = the number of delegates the U.S. sent. Then, $x - 19$ = the number of delegates Japan sent.

$$x+x-19=121$$
$$2x-19=121$$
$$2x-19+19=121+19$$
$$2x=140$$
$$\frac{2x}{2}=\frac{140}{2}$$
$$x=70$$

The United States sent 70 delegates.

4. Let x = the amount son receives.
Then $2x$ = the amount husband receives.

$$x+2x=21,000$$
$$3x=21,000$$
$$\frac{3x}{3}=\frac{21,000}{3}$$
$$x=7000$$
$$2x=2\cdot 7000$$
$$2x=14,000$$

Her son receives \$7000 and her husband receives \$14,000.

Exercise Set 3.5

1. A number added to –5 is –7 translates to $-5 + x = -7$.

3. Three times a number yields 27 translates to $3x = 27$.

5. A number subtracted from –20 amounts to 104 translates to $-20 - x = 104$.

7. Twice the sum of a number and –1 is equal to 50 translates to $2[x + (-1)] = 50$.

9.
$$3x+9=33$$
$$3x=24$$
$$x=8$$

11.
$$9x=54$$
$$x=6$$

13.
$$3+4+x=16$$
$$7+x=16$$
$$x=9$$

15.
$$72=24+8x$$
$$48=8x$$
$$6=x$$

17.
$$x-3=45-x$$
$$2x=48$$
$$x=24$$

19.
$$3(x-5)=9$$
$$3x-15=9$$
$$3x=24$$
$$x=8$$

21.
$$8-x=\frac{15}{5}$$
$$8-x=3$$
$$-x=-5$$
$$x=5$$

23.
$$3x+13=3+5x$$
$$10=2x$$
$$5=x$$

25.
$$5x-40=x+8$$
$$4x=48$$
$$x=12$$

27.
$$x-3=\frac{10}{5}$$
$$x-3=2$$
$$x=5$$

29. Let x = Gore's votes. Then$x + 5$ = Bush's votes

$$x+x+5=527$$
$$2x+5=527$$
$$2x+5-5=527-5$$
$$2x=522$$
$$x=261$$

Gore had 261 electoral votes, and Bush had 261 +5 = 266 electoral votes.

31. Let x = Kelp growth. Then $2x$ = bamboo growth.
$x+2x=54$
$3x=54$
$x=18$
Kelp can grow 18 inches in one day, and bamboo can grow $2\cdot 18=36$ inches in one day.

33. Let x = the number of U.S. universities. Then x +2649=the number of universities in India.
$x+x+2649=14,165$
$2x+2649=14,165$
$2x=11,516$
$x=5758$
The U.S. has 5758 universities, and India has 5758 + 2649 = 8407 universities.

35. Let x = the cost of the Game Cube. Then $3x$ = the cost of the games.
$x+3x=600$
$4x=600$
$x=150$
The Game Cube costs \$150, and the games cost 3(150) = \$450.

37. Let x = the capacity of Neyland Stadium. Then x + 4647 = the capacity of Michigan Stadium.
$x+x+4647=210,355$
$2x+4647=210,355$
$2x=205,708$
$x=102,854$
Neyland Stadium has a capacity of 102,854 and Michigan Stadium has a capacity of 102,854 + 4647 = 107,501.

39. Let x = the native American population of Washington state. Then $3x$ = the native American population of California.
$x+3x=412$
$4x=412$
$x=103$
The native American population of Washington state is 103 thousand. The native American population of California is 3 · 103 = 309 thousand.

41. Let x = the points scored by the Sooners. Then x + 12 = the points scored by the Huskies.
$x+x+12=152$
$2x+12=152$
$2x=140$
$x=70$
The Huskies scored 70 + 12 = 82 points during the game.

43. Let x = the amount of food a finch eats. Then x + 5 = the amount of food a crow eats.
$x+x+5=13$
$2x+5=13$
$2x=8$
$x=4$
The finch eats 4 oz of food a day, and the crow eats 4 + 5 = 9 oz of food a day.

45. To round 586 to the nearest ten, observe that the digit in the ones place is 6. Since this digit is at least 5, we need to add 1 to the digit in the tens place. The number 586 rounded to the nearest ten is 590.

47. To round 1026 to the nearest hundred, observe that the digit in the tens place is 2. Since this digit is less than 5, we do not add 1 to the digit in the hundreds place. The number 1026 rounded to the nearest hundred is 1000.

49. To round 2986 to the nearest thousand observe that the digit in the hundreds place is 9. Since this digit is at least 5, we add 1 to the digit in the thousands place. The number 2986 rounded to the nearest thousand is 3000.

51. Answers may vary.

53. $P=A+C$
$165,000=156,750+C$
$8250=C$
The agent's commission will be \$8250.

55. $P=C+M$
$12=7+M$
$12-7=7+M-7$
$5=M$
The markup of the cat food is \$5.

Chapter 3 Review

1. $3y+7y-15=10y-15$

2. $2y-10-8y=-6y-10$

3. $8a+a-7-15a=-6a-7$

4. $y+3-9y-1=-8y+2$

5. $2(x+5)=2x+10$

6. $-3(y+8)=-3y-24$

7. $7x+3(x-4)+x=7x+3x-12+x$
$=11x-12$

8. $-(3m+2)-m-10=-1\cdot 3m+(-1)(2)-m-10$
$=-3m-2-m-10$
$=-4m-12$

9. $3(5a-2)-20a+10=15a-6-20a+10$
$=-5a+4$

10. $6y+3+2(3y-6)=6y+3+6y-12$
$=12y-9$

11. $P=3+2x+3+2x$
$=4x+6$
The perimeter is $(4x+6)$ yards.

12. $P=5y+5y+5y+5y=20y$
The perimeter is $20y$ meters.

13. $A=3(2x-1)=6x-3$
The area is $(6x-3)$ square yards.

14. $A=10(x-2)+7(5x+4)$
$=10x-20+35x+28$
$=45x+8$
The area is $(45x+8)$ square centimeters.

15. $85(7068x-108)+42x$
$=600{,}780x-9180+42x$
$=600{,}822x-9180$

16. $-4268y+120(63y-32)$
$=-4268y+7560y-3840$
$=3292y-3840$

17. $5(2-4)\ 0\ -10$
$5(-2)\ 0\ -10$
$-10=-10$ True
Yes, it is a solution.

18. $6(0)+2\ 0\ 23+4(0)$
$0+2\ 0\ 23+0$
$2=23$ False
No, it is not a solution.

19. $z-5=-7$
$z-5+5=-7+5$
$z=-2$

20. $3x+10=4x$
$3x+10-3x=4x-3x$
$10=x$

21. $n+18=10-(-2)$
$n+18=10+2$
$n+18=12$
$n+18-18=12-18$
$n=-6$

22. $c-5=-13+7$
$c-5=-6$
$c-5+5=-6+5$
$c=-1$

23. $7x+5-6x=-20$
$x+5=-20$
$x+5-5=-20-5$
$x=-25$

24. $17x=2(8x-4)$
$17x=2\cdot 8x-2\cdot 4$
$17x=16x-8$
$17x-16x=16x-8-16x$
$x=-8$

25. $-3y=-21$
$\frac{-3y}{-3}=\frac{-21}{-3}$
$y=7$

26. $-8x=72$
$\frac{-8x}{-8}=\frac{72}{-8}$
$x=-9$

27. $-5n=-5$
$\frac{-5n}{-5}=\frac{-5}{-5}$
$n=1$

28. $-3a=15$
$\frac{-3a}{-3}=\frac{15}{-3}$
$a=-5$

29. $\frac{x}{-6}=2$
$-6\cdot\frac{x}{16}=2\cdot(-6)$
$x=-12$

30. $\frac{y}{-15}=-3$
$-15\cdot\frac{y}{-15}=-3\cdot(-15)$
$y=45$

31. $-5t+32+4t=32$
$-t+32=32$
$-t+32-32=32-32$
$-t=0$
$t=0$

32. $3z + 72 - 2z = -56$
$z + 72 = -56$
$z + 72 - 72 = -56 - 72$
$z = -128$

33. $\frac{z}{4} = -8 - (-6)$
$\frac{z}{4} = -8 + 6$
$\frac{z}{4} = -2$
$4 \cdot \frac{z}{4} = -2 \cdot 4$
$z = -8$

34. $-1 + (-8) = \frac{x}{5}$
$-9 = \frac{x}{5}$
$-9 \cdot 5 = \frac{x}{5} \cdot 5$
$-45 = x$

35. $6y - 7y = 100 - 105$
$-y = -5$
$\frac{-1y}{1} = \frac{-5}{-1}$
$y = 5$

36. $19x - 16x = 45 - 60$
$3x = -15$
$\frac{3x}{3} = \frac{-15}{3}$
$x = -5$

37. The product of –5 and a number is $-5x$.

38. Three subtracted from a number is $x - 3$.

39. The sum of –5 and a number is $-5 + x$.

40. The quotient of –2 and a number is $\frac{-2}{x}$.

41. Twice a number is $2x$. Eleven added to twice a number is $2x + 11$.

42. The product of –5 and a number is $-5x$. The product of –5 and a number, decreased by 50 is $-5x - 50$.

43. The sum of a number and 6 is $x + 6$. The quotient of 70 and the sum of a number and 6 is $\frac{70}{x+6}$.

44. The difference of a number and 13 is $x - 13$. Twice the difference of a number and 13 is $2(x - 13)$.

45. $3x - 4 = 11$
$3x - 4 + 4 = 11 + 4$
$3x = 15$
$\frac{3x}{3} = \frac{15}{3}$
$x = 5$

46. $6y + 1 = 73$
$6y + 1 - 1 = 73 - 1$
$6y = 72$
$\frac{6y}{6} = \frac{72}{6}$
$y = 12$

47. $14 - y = -3$
$14 - y - 14 = -3 - 14$
$-y = -17$
$\frac{-y}{-1} = \frac{-17}{-1}$
$y = 17$

48. $7 - z = 0$
$7 - z + z = 0 + z$
$7 = z$

49. $4z - z = -6$
$3z = -6$
$\frac{3z}{3} = \frac{-6}{3}$
$z = -2$

50. $t - 9t = -64$
$-8t = -64$
$\frac{-8t}{-8} = \frac{-64}{-8}$
$t = 8$

51. $2x + 5 = 7x - 100$
$2x + 5 - 7x = 7x - 100 - 7x$
$-5x + 5 = -100$
$-5x + 5 - 5 = -100 - 5$
$-5x = -105$
$\frac{-5x}{-5} = \frac{-105}{5}$
$x = 21$

52. $-6x - 4 = x + 66$
$-6x - 4 - x = x + 66 - x$
$-7x - 4 = 66$
$-7x - 4 + 4 = 66 + 4$
$-7x = 70$
$\frac{-7x}{7} = \frac{70}{-7}$
$x = -10$

53.
$$\begin{aligned}2x+7&=6x-1\\2x+7-7&=6x-1-7\\2x&=6x-8\\2x-6x&=6x-8-6x\\-4x&=-8\\\frac{-4x}{-4}&=\frac{-8}{-4}\\x&=2\end{aligned}$$

54.
$$\begin{aligned}5x-18&=-4x\\5x-18+18&=-4x+18\\5x&=-4x+18\\5x+4x&=-4x+18+4x\\9x&=18\\\frac{9x}{9}&=\frac{18}{9}\\x&=2\end{aligned}$$

55.
$$\begin{aligned}\frac{x}{9}+3&=0\\\frac{x}{9}+3-3&=0-3\\\frac{x}{9}&=-3\\9\cdot\frac{x}{9}&=-3\cdot 9\\x&=-27\end{aligned}$$

56.
$$\begin{aligned}\frac{z}{-2}-11&=0\\\frac{z}{-2}-11+11&=0+11\\\frac{z}{-2}&=11\\-2\cdot\frac{z}{-2}&=11\cdot(-2)\\z&=-22\end{aligned}$$

57.
$$\begin{aligned}5(n-3)&=7+3n\\5n-15&=7+3n\\5n-15+15&=7+3n+15\\5n&=22+3n\\5n-3n&=22+3n-3n\\2n&=22\\\frac{2n}{2}&=\frac{22}{2}\\n&=11\end{aligned}$$

58.
$$\begin{aligned}7(2+x)&=4x-1\\14+7x&=4x-1\\14+7x-14&=4x-1-14\\7x&=4x-15\\7x-4x&=4x-15-4x\\3x&=-15\\\frac{3x}{3}&=\frac{-15}{3}\\x&=-5\end{aligned}$$

59. $20-(-8)=28$

60. $5(2+(-6))=-20$

61. $\frac{-75}{5+20}=-3$

62. $-2-19=-21$

63. $2x-8=40$

64. $\frac{x}{2}-12=10$

65. $x-3=x\div 4$ or $x-3=\frac{x}{4}$

66. $6x=x+2$

67.
$$\begin{aligned}40-5x&=3x\\40-5x+5x&=3x+5x\\40&=8x\\\frac{40}{8}&=\frac{8x}{8}\\5&=x\end{aligned}$$

68.
$$\begin{aligned}3x&=2(x-8)\\3x&=2x-16\\3x-2x&=2x-16-2x\\x&=-16\end{aligned}$$

69. Let I = votes recieved by the Independent candidate.
$I+272$ = votes received by the Democratic candidate.
$18,500-14,000=4500$ votes
$$\begin{aligned}I+(I+272)&=4500\\2I+272&=4500\\2I+272-272&=4500-272\\2I&=4228\\\frac{2I}{2}&=\frac{4228}{2}\\I&=2114\end{aligned}$$
$I+272=2114+272=2386$
The Democratic candidate received 2386 votes.

70. Let x = the number of video tapes. Then $2x$ = the number of DVDs.

$$x + 2x = 126$$
$$3x = 126$$
$$\frac{3x}{3} = \frac{126}{3}$$
$$x = 42$$

The number of DVDs = $2x = 2(42) = 84$.
Rajiv has 84 DVDs.

Chapter 3 Test

1. $7x - 5 - 12x + 10 = -5x + 5$

2. $-2(3y + 7) = -6y - 14$

3. $-(3z+2) - 5z - 18 = -1 \cdot 3z - 1 \cdot 2 - 5z - 18$
$= -3z - 2 - 5z - 18$
$= -8z - 20$

4. $P = a + b + c$
$= 5x + 5 + 5x + 5 + 5x + 5$
$= 15x + 15$
The perimeter is $(15x + 15)$ inches.

5. $A = LW$
$= 4(3x - 1)$
$= 12x - 4$
The area is $(12x - 4)$ square meters.

6.
$$9x = -90$$
$$\frac{9x}{9} = \frac{-90}{9}$$
$$x = -10$$

8.
$$12 = y - 3y$$
$$12 = -2y$$
$$\frac{12}{-2} = \frac{-2y}{-2}$$
$$-6 = y$$

9.
$$\frac{x}{2} = -5 - (-2)$$
$$\frac{x}{2} = -5 + 2$$
$$\frac{x}{2} = -3$$
$$2 \cdot \frac{x}{2} = -3 \cdot 2$$
$$x = -6$$

10.
$$5 + 4z = 37$$
$$5 + 4z - 5 = 37 - 5$$
$$4z = 32$$
$$\frac{4z}{4} = \frac{32}{4}$$
$$z = 8$$

11.
$$5x + 12 - 4x - 14 = 22$$
$$x - 2 = 22$$
$$x - 2 + 2 = 22 + 2$$
$$x = 24$$

12.
$$-4x + 7 = 15$$
$$-4x + 7 - 7 = 15 - 7$$
$$-4x = 8$$
$$\frac{-4x}{-4} = \frac{8}{-4}$$
$$x = -2$$

13.
$$2(x - 6) = 0$$
$$2x - 12 = 0$$
$$2x - 12 + 12 = 0 + 12$$
$$2x = 12$$
$$\frac{2x}{2} = \frac{12}{2}$$
$$x = 6$$

14.
$$5x - 2 = x - 10$$
$$5x - 2 + 2 = x - 10 + 2$$
$$5x = x - 8$$
$$5x - x = x - 8 - x$$
$$4x = -8$$
$$\frac{4x}{4} = \frac{-8}{4}$$
$$x = -2$$

15.
$$4(5x + 3) = 2(7x + 6)$$
$$20x + 12 = 14x + 12$$
$$20x + 12 - 12 = 14x + 12 - 12$$
$$20x = 14x$$
$$20x - 14x = 14x - 14x$$
$$6x = 0$$
$$\frac{6x}{6} = \frac{0}{6}$$
$$x = 0$$

16. a. $-23 + x$

b. $-2 - 3x$

17. a. $2 \cdot 5 + (-15) = -5$

b. $3x + 6 = -30$

18. $$\begin{aligned} 3x - 5x &= 4 \\ -2x &= 4 \\ \frac{-2x}{-2} &= \frac{4}{-2} \\ x &= -2 \end{aligned}$$

19. Let x = the number of free throws Maria made.
Then $2x$ = the number of free throws Paula made.
$$\begin{aligned} 2x + x &= 12 \\ 3x &= 12 \\ \frac{3x}{3} &= \frac{12}{3} \\ x &= 4 \end{aligned}$$
Paula's throws $= 2x = 2 \cdot 4 = 8$, so Paula made 8 free throws.

20. Let x = the number of women entered in the race. Then $x + 112$ = the number of men entered in the space.
$$\begin{aligned} x + (x + 112) &= 600 \\ 2x + 112 &= 600 \\ 2x + 112 - 112 &= 600 - 112 \\ 2x &= 488 \\ x &= 244 \end{aligned}$$
244 women entered the race.

Chapter 3 Cumulative Review

1. One hundred six million, fifty-two thousand, four hundred forty-seven.

2. Two hundred seventy-two thousand, four.

3. P = 3 + 1 + 3 + 2 + 4 = 13
Perimeter is 13 inches.

4. P = 6 + 3 + 6 + 3 = 18
Perimeter is 18 inches.

5. $$\begin{array}{r} 900 \\ -174 \\ \hline 726 \end{array}$$
Check: $$\begin{array}{r} 726 \\ +174 \\ \hline 900 \end{array}$$

6. $$\begin{array}{r} 17,801 \\ -8216 \\ \hline 9,585 \end{array}$$
Check: $$\begin{array}{r} 9585 \\ +8216 \\ \hline 17,801 \end{array}$$

7. Since there is an 8 in the tens place, 248,982 rounded to the nearest hundred is 249,000.

8. Since there is a 4 in the hundreds place, 844,497 rounded to the nearest thousand is 844,000.

9. $$\begin{array}{r} 25 \\ \times 8 \\ \hline 200 \end{array}$$

10. $$\begin{array}{r} 395 \\ \times 74 \\ \hline 1580 \\ 27,650 \\ \hline 29,230 \end{array}$$

11. $$\begin{array}{r} 208 \\ 9\overline{)\,1872} \\ -18 \\ \hline 07 \\ -\;0 \\ \hline 72 \\ -72 \\ \hline 0 \end{array}$$
Check: $208 \cdot 9 = 1872$

12. $$\begin{array}{r} 86 \\ 46\overline{)\,3956} \\ -368 \\ \hline 276 \\ -276 \\ \hline 0 \end{array}$$
Check: $86 \cdot 46 = 3956$

13. $$\begin{aligned} 2 \cdot 4 - 3 \div 3 &= 8 - 3 \div 3 \\ &= 8 - 1 \\ &= 7 \end{aligned}$$

14. $$\begin{aligned} 8 \cdot 4 + 9 \div 3 &= 32 + 9 \div 3 \\ &= 32 + 3 \\ &= 35 \end{aligned}$$

15. $$\begin{aligned} 5^2 + 4 - 3 &= 25 + 4 - 3 \\ &= 29 - 3 \\ &= 26 \end{aligned}$$

16. $$\begin{aligned} 2(2)^2 + 5 - 3 &= 2(4) + 5 - 3 \\ &= 8 + 5 - 3 \\ &= 13 - 3 \\ &= 10 \end{aligned}$$

17. **a.** $-7 < 7$
b. $0 > -4$
c. $-9 > -11$

18. **a.** $-14 < 0$
b. $8 > -8$

19. $5 + (-2) = 3$

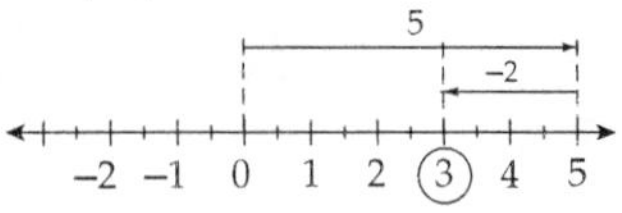

20. $-3 + (-4) = -7$

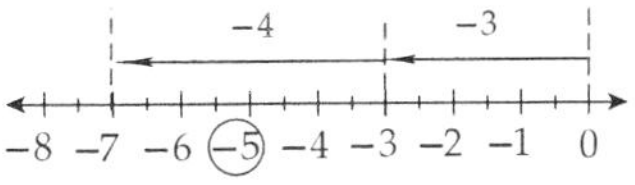

21. $-5 + (-1) = -6$

22. $3 + (-7) = -4$

23. $2 + 6 = 8$

24. $21 + 15 + (-19) = 36 + (v19) = 17$

25. $-4 - 10 = -4 + (-10) = -14$

26. $-2 - 3 = -2 + (v3) = -5$

27. $6 - (-5) = 6 + 5 = 11$

28. $19 - (-10) = 19 + 10 = 29$

29. $-11 - (-7) = -11 + 7 = -4$

30. $-16 - (-13) = -16 + 13 = -3$

31. $\frac{-12}{6} = -2$

32. $\frac{-30}{-5} = 6$

33. $-20 \div (-4) = 5$

34. $26 \div (-2) = -13$

35. $\frac{48}{-3} = -16$

36. $\frac{-120}{12} = -10$

37. $(-3)^2 = (-3)(-3) = 9$

38. $-2^5 = -(2)(2)(2)(2)(2) = -32$

39. $-3^2 = -(3)(3) = -9$

40. $(-5)^2 = (-5)(-5) = 25$

41.
$$\begin{aligned} 2y - 6 + 4y + 8 &= 2y + 4y - 6 + 8 \\ &= (2 + 4)y - 6 + 8 \\ &= 6y + 2 \end{aligned}$$

42.
$$\begin{aligned} 6x + 2 - 3x + 7 &= 6x - 3x + 2 + 7 \\ &= (6 - 3)x + 2 + 7 \\ &= 3x + 9 \end{aligned}$$

43.
$$\begin{aligned} 3(-1) + 1 &= 3 \\ -3 + 1 &= 3 \\ -2 &= 3 \quad \text{False} \end{aligned}$$
-1 is not a solution

44.
$$\begin{aligned} 5(2) - 3 &= 7 \\ 10 - 3 &= 7 \\ 7 &= 7 \quad \text{True} \end{aligned}$$
2 is the solution

45.
$$\begin{aligned} -12x &= -36 \\ \frac{-12x}{-12} &= \frac{-36}{-12} \\ x &= 3 \end{aligned}$$

46.
$$\begin{aligned} 7y - 4y &= 15 \\ 3y &= 15 \\ \frac{3y}{3} &= \frac{15}{3} \\ y &= 5 \end{aligned}$$

47.
$$\begin{aligned} 2x - 6 &= 18 \\ 2x - 6 + 6 &= 18 + 6 \\ 2x &= 24 \\ \frac{2x}{2} &= \frac{24}{2} \\ x &= 12 \end{aligned}$$

48.
$$\begin{aligned} 3a + 5 &= -1 \\ 3a + 5 - 5 &= -1 - 5 \\ 3a &= -6 \\ \frac{3a}{3} &= \frac{-6}{3} \\ a &= -2 \end{aligned}$$

49. Let x = the cost of the software. Let $4x$ = the cost of the computer system.
$$\begin{aligned} x + 4x &= 2100 \\ 5x &= 2100 \\ \frac{5x}{5} &= \frac{2100}{5} \\ x &= 420 \end{aligned}$$
The cost of the software is \$420. The cost of the computer system is $4x = 4(420) = \$1680$.

50. Let x = a number.
$$\begin{aligned} 2x + 4 &= 3x - 7 \\ 2x + 4 - 3x &= 3x - 7 - 3x \\ -x + 4 &= -7 \\ -x + 4 - 4 &= -7 - 4 \\ -x &= -11 \\ \frac{-1x}{-1} &= \frac{-11}{-1} \\ x &= 11 \end{aligned}$$
Rose's number is 11.

Chapter 4

Pretest

1. The figure has 8 equal parts. Three parts are shaded. The fraction that is shaded is $\frac{3}{8}$.

2. $\frac{5}{6}=\frac{5}{6}\cdot 1=\frac{5}{6}\cdot\frac{3}{3}=\frac{5\cdot 3}{6\cdot 3}=\frac{15}{18}$

3. $\frac{0}{-4}=0\div -4=0$

4. $140=2\cdot 70$
$=2\cdot 2\cdot 35$
$=2\cdot 2\cdot 5\cdot 7$ or $2^2\cdot 5\cdot 7$

5. $\frac{30}{54}=\frac{6\cdot 5}{6\cdot 9}=\frac{5}{9}$

6. $\frac{\text{Number of milligrams} \rightarrow}{\text{Number of milligrams in a gram} \rightarrow}\frac{450}{1000}$
$=\frac{5\cdot 9\cdot 10}{5\cdot 2\cdot 10\cdot 10}=\frac{9}{20}$

7. $\frac{3}{4}\cdot\frac{24}{15}=\frac{3\cdot 24}{4\cdot 15}=\frac{3\cdot 6\cdot 4}{4\cdot 3\cdot 5}=\frac{6}{5}$

8. $\frac{5x}{7}\div 10x=\frac{5x}{7}\cdot\frac{1}{10x}$
$=\frac{5x\cdot 1}{7\cdot 10x}$
$=\frac{5x}{7\cdot 5x\cdot 2x}$
$=\frac{1}{14x}$

9. $\frac{8}{11}-\frac{3}{11}=\frac{8-3}{11}=\frac{5}{11}$

10. $-\frac{3}{10}+\frac{2}{10}=\frac{-3+2}{10}=\frac{-1}{10}=-\frac{1}{10}$

11. $\left(-\frac{2}{3}\right)^3=\left(-\frac{2}{3}\right)\left(-\frac{2}{3}\right)\left(-\frac{2}{3}\right)$
$=-\frac{2\cdot 2\cdot 2}{3\cdot 3\cdot 3}$
$=-\frac{8}{27}$

12. $x\div y=\frac{2}{9}\div -\frac{2}{3}$
$=\frac{2}{9}\cdot -\frac{3}{2}$
$=-\frac{2\cdot 3}{9\cdot 2}$
$=-\frac{2\cdot 3}{3\cdot 3\cdot 2}$
$=-\frac{1}{3}$

13. $\frac{5}{9}+\frac{1}{12}=\frac{5}{9}\cdot 1+\frac{1}{12}\cdot 1$
$=\frac{5}{9}\cdot\frac{4}{4}+\frac{1}{12}\cdot\frac{3}{3}$
$=\frac{5\cdot 4}{9\cdot 4}+\frac{1\cdot 3}{12\cdot 3}$
$=\frac{20}{36}+\frac{3}{36}$
$=\frac{20+3}{36}$
$=\frac{23}{36}$

14. $x-y=-\frac{3}{14}-\left(-\frac{2}{7}\right)$
$=-\frac{3}{14}+\frac{2}{7}$
$=-\frac{3}{14}+\frac{2}{7}\cdot 1$
$=-\frac{3}{14}+\frac{2}{7}\cdot\frac{2}{2}$
$=-\frac{3}{14}+\frac{2\cdot 2}{7\cdot 2}$
$=-\frac{3}{14}+\frac{4}{14}$
$=\frac{-3+4}{14}$
$=\frac{1}{14}$

15. $\dfrac{\frac{x}{3}}{\frac{7}{9}} = \dfrac{x}{3} \div \dfrac{7}{9}$

$= \dfrac{x}{3} \cdot \dfrac{9}{7}$

$= \dfrac{x \cdot 9}{3 \cdot 7}$

$= \dfrac{x \cdot 3 \cdot 3}{3 \cdot 7}$

$= \dfrac{3x}{7}$

16. $\left(\dfrac{2}{5}\right)^2 - 2 = \left(\dfrac{2}{5}\right)\left(\dfrac{2}{5}\right) - 2$

$= \dfrac{2 \cdot 2}{5 \cdot 5} - 2 \cdot 1$

$= \dfrac{4}{25} - 2 \cdot \dfrac{25}{25}$

$= \dfrac{4}{25} - \dfrac{50}{25}$

$= \dfrac{4 - 50}{25}$

$= \dfrac{-46}{25}$

$= -\dfrac{46}{25}$

17. $\dfrac{x}{4} + 3 = \dfrac{1}{8}$

$8\left(\dfrac{x}{4} + 3\right) = 8 \cdot \dfrac{1}{8}$

$8 \cdot \dfrac{x}{4} + 8 \cdot 3 = 1$

$2x + 24 = 1$

$2x + 24 - 24 = 1 - 24$

$2x = -23$

$\dfrac{2x}{2} = \dfrac{-23}{2}$

$x = -\dfrac{23}{2}$

18. $2\dfrac{3}{5} = \dfrac{5 \cdot 2 + 3}{5} = \dfrac{10 + 3}{5} = \dfrac{13}{5}$

19. $3\dfrac{1}{5} \cdot 2\dfrac{3}{4} = \dfrac{5 \cdot 3 + 1}{5} \cdot \dfrac{4 \cdot 2 + 3}{4}$

$= \dfrac{15 + 1}{5} \cdot \dfrac{8 + 3}{4}$

$= \dfrac{16}{5} \cdot \dfrac{11}{4}$

$= \dfrac{16 \cdot 11}{5 \cdot 4}$

$= \dfrac{4 \cdot 4 \cdot 11}{5 \cdot 4}$

$= \dfrac{44}{5}$

20.

$$\begin{array}{rcrcr} 5\dfrac{2}{3} & = & 5\dfrac{2 \cdot 2}{3 \cdot 2} & = & 5\dfrac{4}{6} \\ +\ 4\dfrac{1}{6} & = & +\ 4\dfrac{1}{6} & = & +\ 4\dfrac{1}{6} \\ \hline & & & & 9\dfrac{5}{6} \end{array}$$

Section 4.1

Practice Problems

1. $\dfrac{9}{2}$ ← numerator (9) ← denominator (2)

2. $\dfrac{10y}{17}$ ← numerator (10y) ← denominator (17)

3. 3 out of 8 equal parts are shaded: $\dfrac{3}{8}$.

4. 1 out of 6 equal parts is shaded: $\dfrac{1}{6}$.

5. 

6. 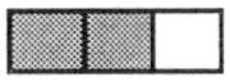

7. Each part is $\dfrac{1}{3}$, and there are 8 parts shaded, or $\dfrac{8}{3}$.

8. Each part is $\dfrac{1}{4}$, and there are 5 parts shaded, or $\dfrac{5}{4}$.

9. 7 out of 9 planets: $\frac{7}{9}$.

10. a.

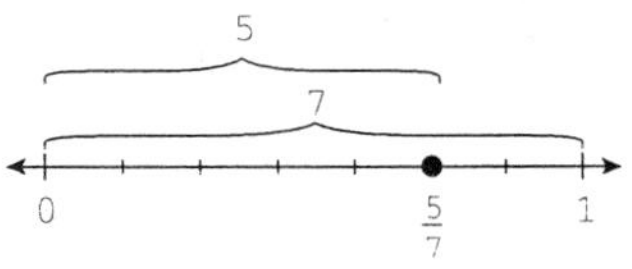

b.

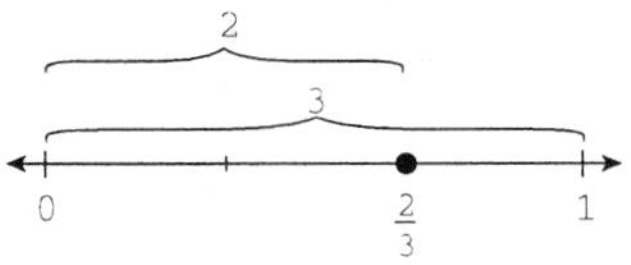

c.

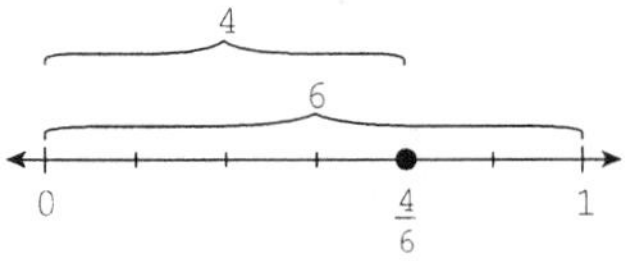

11. a.

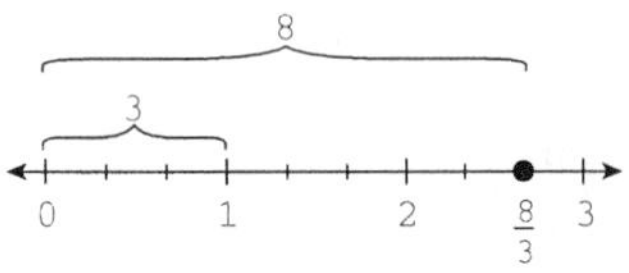

b.

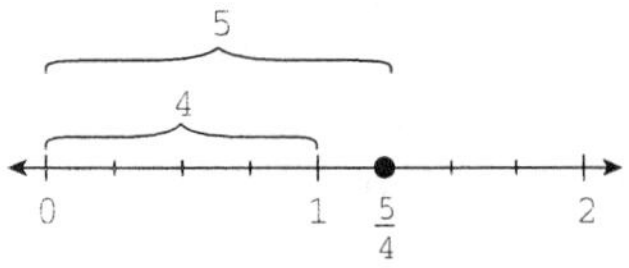

c.

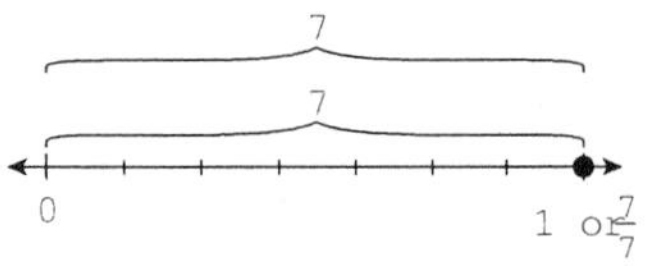

12. $\frac{9}{9} = 9 \div 9 = 1$

13. $\frac{-6}{-6} = -6 \div -6 = 1$

14. $\frac{0}{-1} = 0 \div (-1) = 0$

15. $\frac{4}{1} = 4 \div 1 = 4$

16. $\frac{-13}{0}$ is undefined

17. $\frac{-13}{1} = -13 \div 1 = -13$

18. Since $4 \cdot 5 = 20$, we multiply the numerator and denominator of $\frac{1}{4}$ by 5.

$\frac{1}{4} = \frac{1 \cdot 5}{4 \cdot 5} = \frac{5}{20}$

Then $\frac{1}{4}$ is equivalent to $\frac{5}{20}$.

19. Since $7 \cdot 6 = 42$, we multiply the numerator and denominator of $\frac{3x}{7}$ by 6.

$\frac{3x}{7} = \frac{3x \cdot 6}{7 \cdot 6} = \frac{18x}{42}$

Then $\frac{3x}{7}$ is equivalent to $\frac{18x}{42}$.

20. Recall that $4 = \frac{4}{1}$ and $1 \cdot 6 = 6$.

$\frac{4}{1} = \frac{4 \cdot 6}{1 \cdot 6} = \frac{24}{6}$

21. $4x \cdot 5 = 20x$. Multiply the numerator and denominator by 5.

$\frac{9}{4x} = \frac{9 \cdot 5}{4x \cdot 5} = \frac{45}{20x}$

Mental Math

1. $\frac{1}{2}$ ← numerator (1), ← denominator (2)

2. $\frac{1}{4}$ ← numerator (1), ← denomiantor (4)

3. $\frac{10}{3}$ ← numerator (10), ← denominator (3)

4. $\frac{53}{21}$ ← numerator (53), ← denominator (21)

5. $\frac{3z}{7}$ ← numerator (3z), ← denominator (7)

6. $\frac{11x}{15}$ ← numerator (11x), ← denominator (15)

Exercise Set 4.1

1. 1 out of 3 equal parts is shaded: $\frac{1}{3}$.

3. 4 out of 7 equal parts are shaded: $\frac{4}{7}$

5. 7 out of 12 equal parts are shaded: $\frac{7}{12}$.

7. 3 out of 7 equal parts are shaded: $\frac{3}{7}$.

9. 7 out of 8 equal parts are shaded: $\frac{4}{9}$.

11. 5 out of 8 pieces are gone: $\frac{7}{8}$.

13. 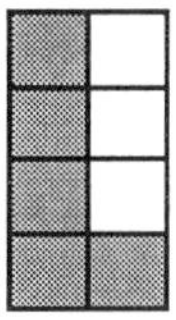

15. 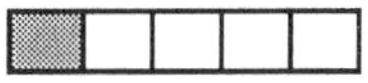

17. 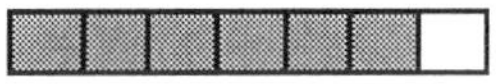

19. 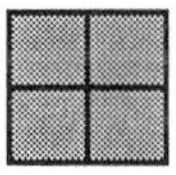

21. $\frac{11}{4}$

23. $\frac{11}{3}$

25. $\frac{3}{2}$

27. $\frac{4}{3}$

29. $\frac{17}{6}$

31. $\frac{14}{9}$

33. Freshmen $\rightarrow$ 42
Students $\rightarrow$ 131
Thus, $\frac{42}{131}$ of the students are freshmen.

35. $131 - 42 = 89$ non-freshmen
Non - freshmen $\rightarrow$ 89
Students $\rightarrow$ 131
Thus, $\frac{89}{131}$ of the students are not freshmen.

37. Injury - related visits $\rightarrow$ 4
Total vists $\rightarrow$ 10
Thus, $\frac{4}{10}$ of the visits are injury-related.

39.
Born in Virginia $\rightarrow$ 8
U.S. Presidents $\rightarrow$ 43
Thus, $\frac{8}{43}$ of the presidents were born in Virginia.

41. Gigabytes currently used $\rightarrow$ 17
Gigabytes on hard drive $\rightarrow$ 32
Thus, $\frac{17}{32}$ of the hard drive is being used.

43. Number of days $\rightarrow$ 11
Days in March $\rightarrow$ 31
Thus, 11 days represents $\frac{11}{31}$ of the month.

45. Number of sophomores $\rightarrow$ 10
Number of students $\rightarrow$ 31
Thus, the sophomores are $\frac{10}{31}$ of the class.

47. **a.** Number of legal states $\rightarrow$ 40
Number of states $\rightarrow$ 50
Thus, consumer fireworks are legal in $\frac{40}{50}$ of the states.

b. $50 - 40 = 10$
Consumer fireworks are illegal in 10 states.

c. Number of illegal states → 10
Number of states → 50

Thus, consumer fireworks are illegal in $\frac{10}{50}$ of the states.

49. To graph $\frac{1}{4}$ on a number line, divide the distance from 0 to 1 into 4 equal parts. Then start at 0 and count over 1 part.

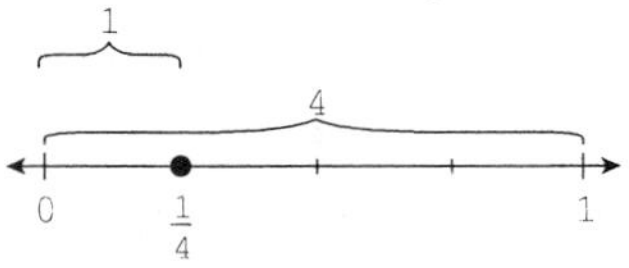

51. To graph $\frac{4}{7}$ on a number line, divide the distance from 0 to 1 into 7 equal parts. Then start at 0 and count over 4 parts.

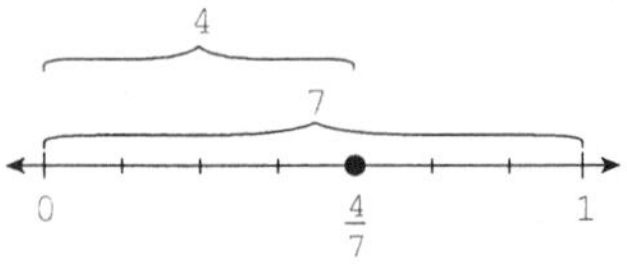

53. To graph $\frac{8}{5}$ on a number line, divide the distance from 0 to 1 into 5 equal parts and divide the distance from 1 to 2 into 5 equal parts. Then start at 0 and count over 8 parts.

55. To graph $\frac{7}{3}$ on a number line, divide the distances from 0 to 1, 1 to 2, and 2 to 3 into 3 equal parts. Then start at 0 and count over 7 parts.

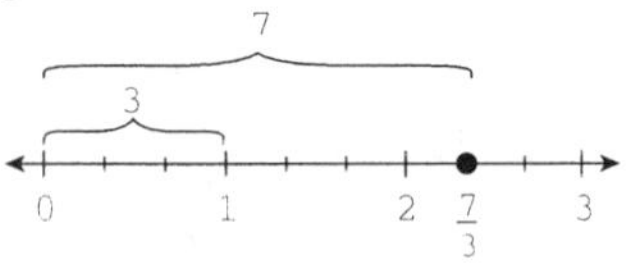

57. To graph $\frac{3}{8}$ on a number line, divide the distance from 0 to 1 into 8 equal parts. Then start at 0 and count over 3 parts.

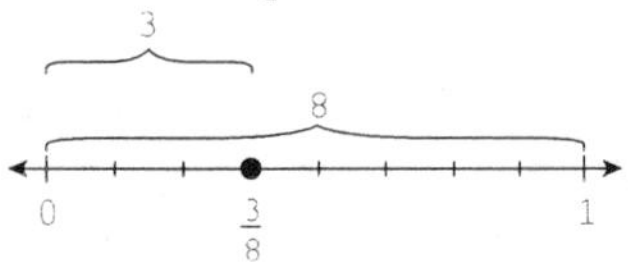

59. $\frac{12}{12} = 12 \div 12 = 1$

61. $\frac{-5}{1} = -5 \div 1 = -5$

63. $\frac{0}{-2} = 0 \div -2 = 0$

65. $\frac{-8}{-8} = -8 \div (-8) = 1$

67. $\frac{-9}{0}$ is undefined.

69. $\frac{3}{1} = 3 \div 1 = 3$

71. $\frac{4}{7} = \frac{?}{35}$

$\frac{4 \cdot 5}{7 \cdot 5} = \frac{20}{35}$

73. $\frac{2}{3} = \frac{?}{21}$

$\frac{2 \cdot 7}{3 \cdot 7} = \frac{14}{21}$

75. $\frac{2y}{5} = \frac{?}{25}$

$\frac{2y \cdot 5}{5 \cdot 5} = \frac{10y}{25}$

77. $\frac{1}{2} = \frac{?}{30}$

$\frac{1 \cdot 15}{2 \cdot 15} = \frac{15}{30}$

79. $\frac{10}{7x} = \frac{?}{21x}$

$\frac{10 \cdot 3}{7x \cdot 3} = \frac{30}{21x}$

81. $2 = \frac{?}{5}$

$\frac{2}{1} = \frac{?}{5}$

$\frac{2 \cdot 5}{1 \cdot 5} = \frac{10}{5}$

83. $\frac{3}{4} = \frac{?}{12}$

$\frac{3 \cdot 3}{4 \cdot 3} = \frac{9}{12}$

85. $\frac{2y}{3} = \frac{?}{12}$

$\frac{2y \cdot 4}{3 \cdot 4} = \frac{8y}{12}$

87. $\frac{1}{2} = \frac{?}{12}$

$\frac{1 \cdot 6}{2 \cdot 6} = \frac{6}{12}$

89. $\frac{4}{3} = \frac{?}{36x}$

$\frac{4 \cdot 12x}{3 \cdot 12x} = \frac{48x}{36x}$

91. $\frac{5}{9} = \frac{?}{36x}$

$\frac{5 \cdot 4x}{9 \cdot 4x} = \frac{20x}{36x}$

93. $1 = \frac{?}{36x}$

$\frac{1}{1} = \frac{?}{36x}$

$\frac{1 \cdot 36x}{1 \cdot 36x} = \frac{36x}{36x}$

95. Denmark: $\frac{13 \cdot 4}{25 \cdot 4} = \frac{52}{100}$

Finland: $\frac{39 \cdot 2}{50 \cdot 2} = \frac{78}{100}$

Israel: $\frac{87}{100}$

Italy: $\frac{21 \cdot 4}{25 \cdot 4} = \frac{84}{100}$

Japan: $\frac{59}{100}$

Norway: $\frac{83}{100}$

Singapore: $\frac{67}{100}$

South Korea: $\frac{6 \cdot 10}{10 \cdot 10} = \frac{60}{100}$

Sweden: $\frac{79}{100}$

United States: $\frac{9 \cdot 5}{20 \cdot 5} = \frac{45}{100}$

97. The smallest numerator of all the fractions with a denominator of 100 is 45, which is the United States.

99. $3^2 = 3 \cdot 3 = 9$

101. $5^3 = 5 \cdot 5 \cdot 5 = 125$

103. $7^2 = 7 \cdot 7 = 49$

105. $2^3 \cdot 3 = 2 \cdot 2 \cdot 2 \cdot 3 = 24$

107.
$$\begin{array}{r} 232 \\ 9\overline{)2088} \\ \underline{18} \\ 28 \\ \underline{27} \\ 18 \\ \underline{18} \\ 0 \end{array}$$

$\frac{2}{9} = \frac{2 \cdot 232}{2 \cdot 232} = \frac{464}{2088}$

109. Answers may vary.

111. Total affiliates = 1651 + 634 = 2285

$\frac{1651}{2285}$ of Habitat for Humanity's affiliates are in the U.S.

113. Total number of Wendy's Corporation restaurants = 6253 + 2348 + 14 + 26 + 210 = 8851.

$\frac{6253}{8851}$ of the restaurants are actually Wendy's.

Section 4.2

Practice Problems

1.

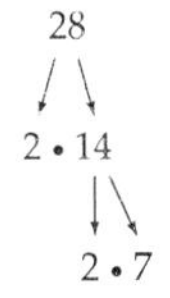

$28 = 2 \cdot 2 \cdot 7 \cdot 5$ or $2^2 \cdot 7$

2.
60
6 • 10
2 • 3 • 2 • 5

$60 = 2 \cdot 2 \cdot 3 \cdot 5$ or $2^2 \cdot 3 \cdot 5$

3.
297
9 • 33
3 • 3 • 3 • 11

$297 = 3 \cdot 3 \cdot 3 \cdot 11$ or $3^3 \cdot 11$

4. $\frac{30}{45} = \frac{2 \cdot 3 \cdot 5}{3 \cdot 3 \cdot 5} = \frac{2}{3}$

5. $\frac{39}{51} = \frac{3 \cdot 13}{3 \cdot 17} = \frac{13}{17}$

6. $\frac{45}{105y} = \frac{3 \cdot 3 \cdot 5}{3 \cdot 5 \cdot 7 \cdot y} = \frac{3}{7y}$

7. $\frac{9a}{50a} = \frac{3 \cdot 3 \cdot a}{2 \cdot 5 \cdot 5 \cdot a} = \frac{9}{50}$

8. $\frac{38}{4} = \frac{2 \cdot 19}{2 \cdot 2} = \frac{19}{2}$

9. $\frac{7a^3}{56a^2} = \frac{7 \cdot a \cdot a \cdot a}{2 \cdot 2 \cdot 2 \cdot 7 \cdot a \cdot a} = \frac{a}{8}$

10. $\frac{12}{80} = \frac{2 \cdot 2 \cdot 3}{2 \cdot 2 \cdot 2 \cdot 2 \cdot 5} = \frac{3}{2 \cdot 2 \cdot 5} = \frac{3}{20}$

Calculator Explorations

The keys pressed may vary depending on what type of calculator you have.

1. Press the keys 128 [$a^b/_c$] 224 [= or ENTER].

The display will read $\frac{4}{7}$.

2. Press the keys 231 [$a^b/_c$] 396 [= or ENTER].

The display will read $\frac{7}{12}$.

3. Press the keys 340 [$a^b/_c$] 459 [= or ENTER].

The display will read $\frac{20}{27}$.

4. Press the keys 999 [$a^b/_c$] 1350 [= or ENTER].

The display will read $\frac{37}{50}$.

5. Press the keys 810 [$a^b/_c$] 432 [= or ENTER].

The display will read $\frac{15}{8}$.

6. Press the keys 315 [$a^b/_c$] 225 [= or ENTER].

The display will read $\frac{7}{5}$.

7. Press the keys 243 [$a^b/_c$] 54 [= or ENTER].

The display will read $\frac{9}{2}$.

8. Press the keys 689 [$a^b/_c$] 455 [= or ENTER].

The display will read $\frac{53}{35}$.

Mental Math

1. Yes, we know that 2430 is divisible by 2 because its ones digit is 0.
Yes, we know that 2430 is divisible by 3 because the sum of its digits, $2 + 4 + 3 + 0 = 9$, is divisible by 3.
Yes, we know that 2430 is divisible by 5 because its ones digit is 0.

2. $15 = 3 \cdot 5$

3. $10 = 2 \cdot 5$

4. $6 = 2 \cdot 3$

5. $21 = 3 \cdot 7$

6. $4 = 2 \cdot 2$ or 2^2

7. $9 = 3 \cdot 3 = 3^2$

8. $14 = 2 \cdot 7$

Exercise Set 4.2

1. $20 = 2 \cdot 10$

$2 \cdot 2 \cdot 5 = 2^2 \cdot 5$

3. $48 = 6 \cdot 8$

$2 \cdot 3 \cdot 2 \cdot 4$

$2 \cdot 3 \cdot 2 \cdot 2 \cdot 2 = 2^4 \cdot 3$

5. $45 = 9 \cdot 5$

$3 \cdot 3 \cdot 5$ or $3^2 \cdot 5$

7. $240 = 2 \cdot 120$

$2 \cdot 2 \cdot 60$

$2 \cdot 2 \cdot 2 \cdot 30$

$2 \cdot 2 \cdot 2 \cdot 2 \cdot 15$

$2 \cdot 2 \cdot 2 \cdot 2 \cdot 3 \cdot 5 = 2^4 \cdot 3 \cdot 5$

9. $\frac{3}{12} = \frac{3}{3 \cdot 4} = \frac{1}{4}$

11. $\frac{7x}{35} = \frac{7 \cdot x}{7 \cdot 5} = \frac{x}{5}$

13. $\frac{14}{16} = \frac{2 \cdot 7}{2 \cdot 8} = \frac{7}{8}$

15. $\frac{24a}{30a} = \frac{2 \cdot 2 \cdot 2 \cdot 3 \cdot a}{2 \cdot 3 \cdot 5 \cdot a} = \frac{4}{5}$

17. $\frac{35}{42} = \frac{7 \cdot 5}{7 \cdot 2 \cdot 3} = \frac{5}{6}$

19. $\frac{30x^2}{36x} = \frac{2 \cdot 3 \cdot 5 \cdot x \cdot x}{2 \cdot 2 \cdot 3 \cdot 3 \cdot x} = \frac{5x}{6}$

21. $\frac{16}{24} = \frac{2 \cdot 2 \cdot 2 \cdot 2}{2 \cdot 2 \cdot 2 \cdot 3} = \frac{2}{3}$

23. $\frac{45xz}{60z} = \frac{3 \cdot 3 \cdot 5 \cdot x \cdot z}{2 \cdot 2 \cdot 3 \cdot 5 \cdot z} = \frac{3x}{4}$

25. $\frac{39ab}{26a^2} = \frac{3 \cdot 13 \cdot a \cdot b}{2 \cdot 13 \cdot a \cdot a} = \frac{3b}{2a}$

27. $\frac{63}{72} = \frac{3 \cdot 3 \cdot 7}{2 \cdot 2 \cdot 2 \cdot 3 \cdot 3} = \frac{7}{8}$

29. $\frac{21}{49} = \frac{3 \cdot 7}{7 \cdot 7} = \frac{3}{7}$

31. $\frac{24y}{40} = \frac{2 \cdot 2 \cdot 2 \cdot 3 \cdot y}{2 \cdot 2 \cdot 2 \cdot 5} = \frac{3y}{5}$

33. $\frac{36z}{63z} = \frac{3 \cdot 3 \cdot 2 \cdot 2 \cdot z}{3 \cdot 3 \cdot 7 \cdot z} = \frac{4}{7}$

35. $\frac{72x^3y^2}{90xy} = \frac{2 \cdot 2 \cdot 2 \cdot 3 \cdot 3 \cdot x \cdot x \cdot x \cdot y \cdot y}{2 \cdot 3 \cdot 3 \cdot 5 \cdot x \cdot y}$

$= \frac{4x^2y}{5}$

37. $\frac{12}{15} = \frac{2 \cdot 2 \cdot 3}{3 \cdot 5} = \frac{4}{5}$

39. $\frac{25x^2}{40x} = \frac{5 \cdot 5 \cdot x \cdot x}{2 \cdot 2 \cdot 2 \cdot 5 \cdot x} = \frac{5x}{8}$

41. $\frac{27xy}{90y} = \frac{3 \cdot 3 \cdot 3 \cdot x \cdot y}{2 \cdot 3 \cdot 3 \cdot 5 \cdot y} = \frac{3x}{10}$

43. $\frac{36a^3bc^2}{24ab^4c^2} = \frac{2 \cdot 2 \cdot 3 \cdot 3 \cdot a \cdot a \cdot a \cdot b \cdot c \cdot c}{2 \cdot 2 \cdot 2 \cdot 3 \cdot a \cdot b \cdot b \cdot b \cdot b \cdot c \cdot c}$

$= \frac{3a^2}{2b^3}$

45. $\frac{40xy}{64xyz} = \frac{2 \cdot 2 \cdot 2 \cdot 5 \cdot x \cdot y}{2 \cdot 2 \cdot 2 \cdot 2 \cdot 2 \cdot 2 \cdot x \cdot y \cdot z}$

$= \frac{5}{8z}$

47. $\frac{6 \text{ hours}}{8 \text{ hours}} = \frac{2 \cdot 3}{2 \cdot 2 \cdot 2} = \frac{3}{2 \cdot 2} = \frac{3}{4}$

6 hours represents $\frac{3}{4}$ of a work shift.

49. $\frac{2640 \text{ feet}}{5280 \text{ feet}} = \frac{2 \cdot 2 \cdot 2 \cdot 2 \cdot 3 \cdot 5 \cdot 11}{2 \cdot 2 \cdot 2 \cdot 2 \cdot 2 \cdot 3 \cdot 5 \cdot 11} = \frac{1}{2}$

2640 feet represents $\frac{1}{2}$ mile

51. $\frac{261}{414} = \frac{3 \cdot 3 \cdot 29}{2 \cdot 3 \cdot 3 \cdot 23} = \frac{29}{46}$

$\frac{29}{46}$ of individuals who have flown in space were Americans.

53. $16{,}000 - 8800 = 7200$

Number of male students $\rightarrow$ $\frac{7200}{16{,}000}$
Number of students $\rightarrow$

$$\frac{7200}{16{,}000} = \frac{9 \cdot 800}{20 \cdot 800} = \frac{9}{20}$$

$\frac{9}{20}$ of the students are male.

55. a. $\frac{16}{50} = \frac{2 \cdot 2 \cdot 2 \cdot 2}{2 \cdot 5 \cdot 5} = \frac{8}{25}$

$\frac{8}{25}$ of states have at least one Ritz-Carlton.

b. $50 - 16 = 34$
34 states have no Ritz-Carlton.

c. $\frac{34}{50} = \frac{2 \cdot 7}{2 \cdot 25} = \frac{17}{25}$

$\frac{17}{25}$ of states have no Ritz-Carlton.

57. $\frac{10}{24} = \frac{2 \cdot 5}{2 \cdot 2 \cdot 2 \cdot 3} = \frac{5}{12}$

$\frac{5}{12}$ of the width is concrete.

59. Education is $\frac{1}{10}$.

61. Answers will vary.

63. $\frac{x^3}{9} = \frac{(-3)^3}{9} = \frac{(-3)(-3)(-3)}{9} = \frac{-27}{9} = -3$

65. $2y = 2(-7) = -14$

67. $3z - y = 3(2) - 6 = 6 - 6 = 0$

69.
$$\begin{aligned} a^2 + 2b + 3 &= 4^2 + 2(5) + 3 \\ &= 16 + 10 + 3 \\ &= 29 \end{aligned}$$

71. d

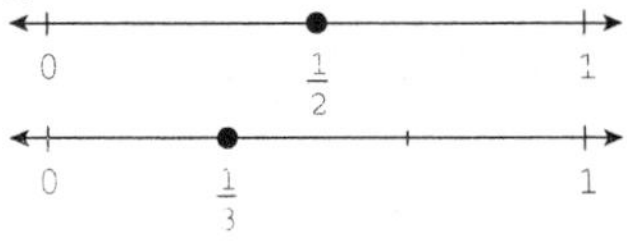

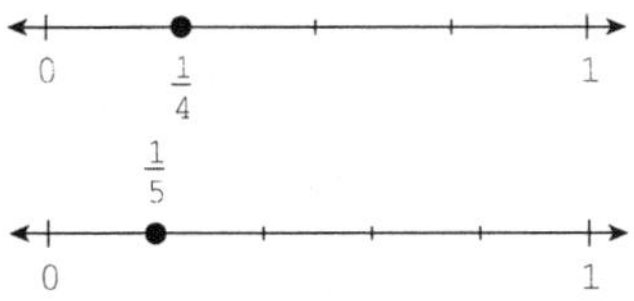

73. False, $\frac{14}{42} = \frac{2 \cdot 7}{2 \cdot 3 \cdot 7} = \frac{1}{3}$

75. True

77. $\frac{372}{620} = \frac{2 \cdot 2 \cdot 3 \cdot 31}{2 \cdot 2 \cdot 5 \cdot 31} = \frac{3}{5}$

79. $\frac{36}{100} = \frac{2 \cdot 2 \cdot 3 \cdot 3}{2 \cdot 2 \cdot 5 \cdot 5} = \frac{3 \cdot 3}{5 \cdot 5} = \frac{9}{25}$

$\frac{9}{25}$ of the donors have A Rh-positive blood type.

81. $3 + 1 = 4$

$\frac{4}{100} = \frac{2 \cdot 2}{2 \cdot 2 \cdot 5 \cdot 5} = \frac{1}{5 \cdot 5} = \frac{1}{25}$

$\frac{1}{25}$ of the donors have AB blood type (either Rh-positive or Rh-negative).

83. $7 + 6 + 1 + 1 = 15$

$\frac{15}{100} = \frac{3 \cdot 5}{2 \cdot 2 \cdot 5 \cdot 5} = \frac{3}{20}$

$\frac{3}{20}$ of the donors have the negative Rh factor.

85. 105, 900, 2235, and 1470 are divisible by 3 because the sum of their digits are divisible by 3. 105, 900, 235, and 1470 are also divisible by 5 because their last digit is either 0 or 5.

87. 15; answers may vary.

Section 4.3

Practice Problems

1. $\frac{3}{8} \cdot \frac{5}{7} = \frac{3 \cdot 5}{8 \cdot 7} = \frac{15}{56}$

2. $\frac{1}{3} \cdot \frac{1}{6} = \frac{1 \cdot 1}{3 \cdot 6} = \frac{1}{18}$

3. $\frac{6}{11} \cdot \frac{5}{8} = \frac{6 \cdot 5}{11 \cdot 8} = \frac{2 \cdot 3 \cdot 5}{11 \cdot 2 \cdot 4} = \frac{3 \cdot 5}{11 \cdot 4} = \frac{15}{44}$

4. $\frac{4}{15} \cdot \frac{3}{8} = \frac{4 \cdot 3}{15 \cdot 8} = \frac{4 \cdot 3}{3 \cdot 5 \cdot 4 \cdot 2} = \frac{1 \cdot 1}{5 \cdot 2} = \frac{1}{10}$

5. $\frac{1}{22}\cdot\left(-\frac{11}{28}\right)=-\frac{1\cdot 11}{22\cdot 28}=-\frac{1\cdot 11}{2\cdot 11\cdot 28}=-\frac{1}{56}$

6. $\frac{9}{5}\cdot\frac{20}{12}=\frac{3\cdot 3\cdot 4\cdot 5}{5\cdot 3\cdot 4}=\frac{3}{1}=3$

7. $\frac{2}{3}\cdot\frac{3y}{2}=\frac{2\cdot 3\cdot y}{3\cdot 2}=\frac{y}{1}=y$

8. $\frac{a^3}{b^2}\cdot\frac{b}{a^2}=\frac{a^3\cdot b}{b^2\cdot a^2}=\frac{a\cdot a\cdot a\cdot b}{b\cdot b\cdot a\cdot a}=\frac{a}{b}$

9. a. $\left(\frac{3}{4}\right)^3=\frac{3}{4}\cdot\frac{3}{4}\cdot\frac{3}{4}=\frac{3\cdot 3\cdot 3}{4\cdot 4\cdot 4}=\frac{27}{64}$

b. $\left(-\frac{4}{5}\right)^2=\left(-\frac{4}{5}\right)\left(-\frac{4}{5}\right)=\frac{4\cdot 4}{5\cdot 5}=\frac{16}{25}$

10. $\frac{3}{2}\div\frac{14}{5}=\frac{3}{2}\cdot\frac{5}{14}=\frac{3\cdot 5}{2\cdot 14}=\frac{15}{28}$

11. $\frac{4}{9}\div\frac{1}{2}=\frac{4}{9}\cdot\frac{2}{1}=\frac{4\cdot 2}{9\cdot 1}=\frac{8}{9}$

12. $\frac{10}{4}\div\frac{2}{9}=\frac{10}{4}\cdot\frac{9}{2}=\frac{2\cdot 5\cdot 9}{4\cdot 2}=\frac{45}{4}$

13. $\frac{3y}{4}\div 5y^3=\frac{3y}{4}\cdot\frac{1}{5y^3}=\frac{3\cdot y\cdot 1}{4\cdot 5\cdot y\cdot y\cdot y}=\frac{3}{20y^2}$

14. $\left(-\frac{2}{3}\cdot\frac{9}{14}\right)\div\frac{7}{15}=\left(-\frac{2\cdot 3\cdot 3}{3\cdot 2\cdot 7}\right)\div\frac{7}{15}=\left(-\frac{3}{7}\right)\div\frac{7}{15}$
$=-\frac{3}{7}\cdot\frac{15}{7}=-\frac{45}{49}$

15. a. $xy=\left(-\frac{3}{4}\right)\cdot\frac{9}{2}=-\frac{3\cdot 9}{4\cdot 2}=-\frac{27}{8}$

b. $x\div y=-\frac{3}{4}\div\frac{9}{2}=-\frac{3}{4}\cdot\frac{2}{9}=-\frac{3\cdot 2}{2\cdot 2\cdot 3\cdot 3}$
$=-\frac{1}{6}$

16. $2x=-\frac{9}{4}$

$2\cdot -\frac{9}{8}=-\frac{9}{4}$

$-\frac{2\cdot 9}{2\cdot 4}=-\frac{9}{4}$

$-\frac{9}{4}=-\frac{9}{4}$ True.

The statement is true, so $-\frac{9}{8}$ is a solution.

17. $\frac{1}{3}\cdot 20{,}439=\frac{1}{3}\cdot\frac{20{,}439}{1}$
$=\frac{1\cdot 20{,}439}{3\cdot 1}$
$=\frac{1\cdot 3\cdot 6813}{3\cdot 1}$
$=\frac{1\cdot 6813}{1}$
$=\frac{6813}{1}$
$=6813$

6813 species are at risk.

Mental Math

1. $\frac{1}{3}\cdot\frac{2}{5}=\frac{2}{15}$

2. $\frac{2}{3}\cdot\frac{4}{7}=\frac{8}{21}$

3. $\frac{6}{5}\cdot\frac{1}{7}=\frac{6}{35}$

4. $\frac{7}{3}\cdot\frac{2}{3}=\frac{14}{9}$

5. $\frac{3}{1}\cdot\frac{3}{8}=\frac{9}{8}$

6. $\frac{2}{1}\cdot\frac{7}{11}=\frac{14}{11}$

Exercise Set 4.3

1. $\frac{7}{8}\cdot\frac{2}{3}=\frac{7\cdot 2}{8\cdot 3}=\frac{7\cdot 2}{2\cdot 2\cdot 2\cdot 3}=\frac{7}{2\cdot 2\cdot 3}=\frac{7}{12}$

3. $-\frac{2}{7}\cdot\frac{5}{8}=-\frac{2\cdot 5}{7\cdot 8}=-\frac{2\cdot 5}{7\cdot 2\cdot 2\cdot 2}=-\frac{5}{28}$

5. $-\frac{1}{2}\cdot -\frac{2}{15}=\frac{1\cdot 2}{2\cdot 15}=\frac{1}{15}$

7. $\frac{18x}{20}\cdot\frac{36}{99}=\frac{18\cdot x\cdot 36}{20\cdot 99}$
$=\frac{9\cdot 2\cdot x\cdot 4\cdot 9}{4\cdot 5\cdot 9\cdot 11}$
$=\frac{2\cdot x\cdot 9}{5\cdot 11}=\frac{18x}{55}$

9. $3a^2\cdot\frac{1}{4}=\frac{3\cdot a^2\cdot 1}{4}=\frac{3a^2}{4}$

11. $\frac{x^3}{y^3}\cdot\frac{y^2}{x}=\frac{x^2\cdot x\cdot y^2}{y^2\cdot y\cdot x}=\frac{x^2}{y}$

13. $\left(\frac{1}{5}\right)^3=\frac{1}{5}\cdot\frac{1}{5}\cdot\frac{1}{5}=\frac{1\cdot 1\cdot 1}{5\cdot 5\cdot 5}=\frac{1}{125}$

15. $\left(-\frac{2}{3}\right)^2=\left(-\frac{2}{3}\right)\cdot\left(-\frac{2}{3}\right)=\frac{2\cdot 2}{3\cdot 3}=\frac{4}{9}$

17. $\left(-\frac{2}{3}\right)^3\cdot\frac{1}{2}=\left(-\frac{2}{3}\right)\cdot\left(-\frac{2}{3}\right)\cdot\left(-\frac{2}{3}\right)\cdot\left(\frac{1}{2}\right)$
$=-\frac{2\cdot 2\cdot 2\cdot 1}{3\cdot 3\cdot 3\cdot 2}$
$=-\frac{4}{27}$

19. $\frac{2}{3}\div\frac{5}{6}=\frac{2}{3}\cdot\frac{6}{5}=\frac{2\cdot 2\cdot 3}{3\cdot 5}=\frac{4}{5}$

21. $-\frac{6}{15}\div\frac{12}{5}=-\frac{6}{15}\cdot\frac{5}{12}$
$=-\frac{6\cdot 5}{3\cdot 5\cdot 2\cdot 6}$
$=-\frac{1}{6}$

23. $\frac{8}{9}\div\frac{x}{2}=\frac{8}{9}\cdot\frac{2}{x}=\frac{2\cdot 2\cdot 2\cdot 2}{3\cdot 3\cdot x}=\frac{16}{9x}$

25. $\frac{11y}{20}\div\frac{3}{11}=\frac{11y}{20}\cdot\frac{11}{3}=\frac{11\cdot y\cdot 11}{2\cdot 2\cdot 5\cdot 3}=\frac{121y}{60}$

27. $-\frac{2}{3}\div 4=-\frac{2}{3}\cdot\frac{1}{4}=-\frac{2\cdot 1}{3\cdot 2\cdot 2}=-\frac{1}{6}$

29. $\frac{1}{5x}\div\frac{5}{x^2}=\frac{1}{5x}\cdot\frac{x^2}{5}=\frac{x\cdot x}{5\cdot x\cdot 5}=\frac{x}{25}$

31. $\frac{2}{3}\cdot\frac{5}{9}=\frac{2\cdot 5}{3\cdot 3\cdot 3}=\frac{10}{27}$

33. $\frac{3x}{7}\div\frac{5}{6x}=\frac{3x}{7}\cdot\frac{6x}{5}=\frac{3\cdot x\cdot 2\cdot 3\cdot x}{7\cdot 5}=\frac{18x^2}{35}$

35. $-\frac{5}{28}\cdot\frac{35}{25}=-\frac{5\cdot 5\cdot 7}{2\cdot 2\cdot 7\cdot 5\cdot 5}=-\frac{1}{4}$

37. $-\frac{3}{5}\div-\frac{4}{5}=\left(-\frac{3}{5}\right)\cdot\left(-\frac{5}{4}\right)=\frac{3\cdot 5}{5\cdot 2\cdot 2}=\frac{3}{4}$

39. $\left(-\frac{3}{4}\right)^2=\left(-\frac{3}{4}\right)\cdot\left(-\frac{3}{4}\right)=\frac{3\cdot 3}{2\cdot 2\cdot 2\cdot 2}=\frac{9}{16}$

41. $\frac{x^2}{y}\cdot\frac{y^3}{x}=\frac{x\cdot x\cdot y\cdot y^2}{y\cdot x}=\frac{x\cdot y^2}{1}=xy^2$

43. $7\div\frac{2}{11}=\frac{7}{1}\cdot\frac{11}{2}=\frac{7\cdot 11}{1\cdot 2}=\frac{77}{2}$

45. $-3x\div\frac{x^2}{12}=-\frac{3x}{1}\cdot\frac{12}{x^2}=-\frac{3\cdot x\cdot 12}{1\cdot x\cdot x}=-\frac{36}{x}$

47. $\left(\frac{2}{7}\div\frac{7}{2}\right)\cdot\frac{3}{4}=\frac{2}{7}\cdot\frac{2}{7}\cdot\frac{3}{4}=\frac{2\cdot 2\cdot 3}{7\cdot 7\cdot 2\cdot 2}=\frac{3}{49}$

49. $-\frac{19}{63y}\cdot 9y^2=-\frac{19}{63y}\cdot\frac{9y^2}{1}$
$=\frac{-19\cdot 9\cdot y\cdot y}{7\cdot 9\cdot y\cdot 1}$
$=-\frac{19y}{7}$

51. $-\frac{2}{3}\cdot-\frac{6}{11}=\frac{2\cdot 2\cdot 3}{3\cdot 11}=\frac{4}{11}$

53. $\frac{4}{8}\div\frac{3}{16}=\frac{4}{8}\cdot\frac{16}{3}=\frac{4\cdot 8\cdot 2}{8\cdot 3}=\frac{8}{3}$

55. $\frac{21x^2}{10y}\div\frac{14x}{25y}=\frac{21x^2}{10y}\cdot\frac{25y}{14x}$
$=\frac{3\cdot 7\cdot x\cdot x\cdot 5\cdot 5\cdot y}{2\cdot 5\cdot y\cdot 2\cdot 7\cdot x}$
$=\frac{3\cdot x\cdot 5}{2\cdot 2}$
$=\frac{15x}{4}$

57. $\left(1\div\frac{3}{4}\right)\cdot\frac{2}{3}=\frac{1}{1}\cdot\frac{4}{3}\cdot\frac{2}{3}=\frac{1\cdot 2\cdot 2\cdot 2}{1\cdot 3\cdot 3}=\frac{8}{9}$

59. $\frac{a^3}{2} \div 30a^3 = \frac{a^3}{2} \cdot \frac{1}{30a^3}$
$= \frac{a^3}{2 \cdot 30 \cdot a^3}$
$= \frac{1}{60}$

61. $\frac{ab^2}{c} \cdot \frac{c}{ab} = \frac{a \cdot b \cdot b \cdot c}{c \cdot a \cdot b} = \frac{b}{1} = b$

63. $\left(\frac{1}{2} \cdot \frac{2}{3}\right) \div \frac{5}{6} = \left(\frac{1 \cdot 2}{2 \cdot 3}\right) \cdot \frac{6}{5}$
$= \frac{1}{3} \cdot \frac{6}{5}$
$= \frac{1 \cdot 2 \cdot 3}{3 \cdot 5}$
$= \frac{2}{5}$

65. $-\frac{4}{7} \div \left(\frac{4}{5} \cdot \frac{3}{7}\right) = -\frac{4}{7} \div \left(\frac{2 \cdot 2 \cdot 3}{5 \cdot 7}\right)$
$= -\frac{4}{7} \cdot \frac{5 \cdot 7}{2 \cdot 2 \cdot 3}$
$= -\frac{4 \cdot 5 \cdot 7}{7 \cdot 4 \cdot 3}$
$= -\frac{5}{3}$

67. a. $xy = \frac{2}{5} \cdot \frac{5}{6} = \frac{2 \cdot 5}{5 \cdot 2 \cdot 3} = \frac{1}{3}$

b. $x \div y = \frac{2}{5} \div \frac{5}{6} = \frac{2}{5} \cdot \frac{6}{5} = \frac{2 \cdot 2 \cdot 3}{5 \cdot 5} = \frac{12}{25}$

69. $xy = -\frac{4}{5} \cdot \frac{9}{11} = -\frac{2 \cdot 2 \cdot 3 \cdot 3}{5 \cdot 11} = -\frac{36}{55}$
$x \div y = -\frac{4}{5} \div \frac{9}{11}$
$= -\frac{4}{5} \cdot \frac{11}{9}$
$= -\frac{2 \cdot 2 \cdot 11}{5 \cdot 3 \cdot 3}$
$= -\frac{44}{45}$

71. $3x = -\frac{5}{6}$
$3\left(-\frac{5}{18}\right) = -\frac{5}{6}$ replace x with $-\frac{5}{18}$
$-\frac{3 \cdot 5}{2 \cdot 3 \cdot 3} = -\frac{5}{6}$
$-\frac{5}{2 \cdot 3} = -\frac{5}{6}$
$-\frac{5}{6} = -\frac{5}{6}$ True
Yes, it is a solution.

73. $-\frac{1}{2}z = \frac{1}{10}$
$-\frac{1}{2} \cdot \frac{2}{5} = \frac{1}{10}$ replace z with $\frac{2}{5}$
$-\frac{1 \cdot 2}{2 \cdot 5} = \frac{1}{10}$
$-\frac{1}{5} = \frac{1}{10}$ False
No, it is not a solution.

75. $\frac{5}{6}(36) = \frac{5 \cdot 6 \cdot 6}{6 \cdot 1} = \frac{30}{1}$
30 gallons are normally in the vat.

77. $\frac{2}{3} \cdot 2757 = \frac{2 \cdot 3 \cdot 919}{3} = 1838$
The sale price of the cruise is \$1838

79. $\frac{1}{2} \cdot \frac{3}{8} = \frac{3}{16}$
The radius is $\frac{3}{16}$ in.

81. $\frac{2}{5} \cdot 2170 = \frac{2 \cdot 5 \cdot 434}{5} = 868$
He has hiked 868 miles.

83. $\frac{7}{10} \cdot 31{,}050 = \frac{7 \cdot 10 \cdot 3{,}105}{10} = 21{,}735$
21,735 tornadoes occurred during that time.

85. Let x = size of Jorge's wrist
(wrist size)
= (fraction of waist) · (waist size)

$$x = \frac{1}{4} \cdot \frac{34}{1} = \frac{1 \cdot 2 \cdot 17}{2 \cdot 2 \cdot 1} = \frac{17}{2}$$

Jorge's wrist is about $\frac{17}{2}$ inches.

87. $9 \cdot \frac{1}{3} = \frac{9}{1} \cdot \frac{1}{3} = \frac{3 \cdot 3}{3} = 3$
3 feet of the 9-foot post should be buried.

89. $2 \div \frac{1}{12} = 2 \cdot 12 = 24$
There are 24 doses available.

91. $\frac{5}{14} \cdot \frac{1}{5} = \frac{5 \cdot 1}{14 \cdot 5} = \frac{1}{14}$
The area is $\frac{1}{14}$ square foot.

93. $90 = 2 \cdot 3 \cdot 3 \cdot 5$ or $2 \cdot 3^2 \cdot 5$

95. $65 = 5 \cdot 13$

97. $126 = 2 \cdot 3 \cdot 3 \cdot 7$ or $2 \cdot 3^2 \cdot 7$

99. $10,300,000 \cdot \frac{7}{10} = 7,210,000$ households

101. Answers may vary.

103. $5144 \div \frac{1}{3} = 5144 \cdot 3 = 15,432$
There are 15,432 flowering plant species that are native to the United States.

105.
$$\frac{42}{25} \cdot \frac{125}{36} \div \frac{7}{6} = \frac{6 \cdot 7 \cdot 5 \cdot 5 \cdot 5}{5 \cdot 5 \cdot 6 \cdot 6} \div \frac{7}{6} = \frac{35}{6} \cdot \frac{6}{7} = \frac{5 \cdot 7 \cdot 6}{6 \cdot 7} = 5$$

Section 4.4

Practice Problems

1. $\frac{5}{9} + \frac{2}{9} = \frac{5+2}{9} = \frac{7}{9}$

2. $\frac{5}{8} + \frac{1}{8} = \frac{5+1}{8} = \frac{6}{8} = \frac{3 \cdot 2}{4 \cdot 2} = \frac{3}{4}$

3. $\frac{10}{11} + \frac{1}{11} + \frac{7}{11} = \frac{10+1+7}{11} = \frac{18}{11}$

4. $\frac{7}{12} - \frac{2}{12} = \frac{7-2}{12} = \frac{5}{12}$

5. $\frac{9}{10} - \frac{1}{10} = \frac{9-1}{10} = \frac{8}{10} = \frac{4 \cdot 2}{5 \cdot 2} = \frac{4}{5}$

6. $-\frac{8}{5} + \frac{4}{5} = \frac{-8+4}{5} = \frac{-4}{5}$ or $-\frac{4}{5}$

7. $\frac{2}{5} - \frac{3y}{5} = \frac{2-3y}{5}$

8. $\frac{4}{11} - \frac{6}{11} - \frac{3}{11} = \frac{4-6-3}{11} = \frac{-5}{11}$ or $-\frac{5}{11}$.

9. $x + y = -\frac{10}{12} + \frac{5}{12} = \frac{-10+5}{12} = \frac{-5}{12}$ or $-\frac{5}{12}$

10. Solve: $\frac{7}{10} = x - \frac{1}{10}$

$$\frac{7}{10} + \frac{1}{10} = x - \frac{1}{10} + \frac{1}{10}$$
$$\frac{8}{10} = x$$
$$\frac{4}{5} = x$$

11. $\frac{3}{4} + \frac{1}{4} = \frac{3+1}{4} = \frac{4}{4} = 1$
She practiced 1 hour.

12. 9 laps on Monday =
$\frac{1}{8} + \frac{1}{8} + \frac{1}{8} + \frac{1}{8} + \frac{1}{8} + \frac{1}{8} + \frac{1}{8} + \frac{1}{8} + \frac{1}{8}$ miles
3 laps on Wednesday = $\frac{1}{8} + \frac{1}{8} + \frac{1}{8} = \frac{3}{8}$ miles
$\frac{9}{8} - \frac{3}{8} = \frac{9-3}{8} = \frac{6}{8} = \frac{2 \cdot 3}{2 \cdot 4} = \frac{3}{4}$ miles
He went $\frac{3}{4}$ mile farther on Monday.

13. Since 15 is not divisible by 12, we check multiples of 15.
$2 \cdot 15 = 30$
30 is not divisible by 12.
$3 \cdot 15 = 45$
45 is not divisible by 12.
$4 \cdot 15 = 60$
60 is divisible by 12.
60 is the LCD.

14. $14 = 2 \cdot 7$
$35 = 5 \cdot 7$
$\text{LCD} = 2 \cdot 5 \cdot 7 = 70$

15. $4 = 2 \cdot 2$
$15 = 3 \cdot 5$
$10 = 2 \cdot 5$
$\text{LCD} = 2 \cdot 2 \cdot 3 \cdot 5 = 60$

16. $y = y$
$11 = 11$
$\text{LCD} = 11 \cdot y = 11y$

Mental Math

1. Since $\frac{7}{8}$ and $\frac{7}{10}$ have different denominators, they are unlike fractions.

2. Since $\frac{2}{3}$ and $\frac{2}{9}$ have different denominators, they are unlike fractions.

3. Since $\frac{9}{10}$ and $\frac{1}{10}$ have the same denominator, they are like fractions.

4. Since $\frac{8}{11}$ and $\frac{2}{11}$ have the same denominator, they are like fractions.

5. Since $\frac{2}{31}$, $\frac{30}{31}$, and $\frac{19}{31}$ have the same denominator, they are like fractions.

6. Since $\frac{3}{10}$, $\frac{3}{11}$, and $\frac{3}{13}$ have different denominators, they are unlike fractions.

7. Since $\frac{5}{12}$, $\frac{7}{12}$, and $\frac{12}{11}$ have different denominators, they are unlike fractions.

8. Since $\frac{1}{5}$, $\frac{2}{5}$, and $\frac{4}{5}$ have the same denominator, they are like fractions.

9. $\frac{3}{7} + \frac{2}{7} = \frac{3+2}{7} = \frac{5}{7}$

10. $\frac{5}{9} + \frac{2}{9} = \frac{5+2}{9}$
$= \frac{7}{9}$

11. $\frac{10}{11} - \frac{4}{11} = \frac{10-4}{11} = \frac{6}{11}$

12. $\frac{9}{13} - \frac{5}{13} = \frac{9-5}{13} = \frac{4}{13}$

13. $\frac{5}{11} + \frac{2}{11} = \frac{5+2}{11} = \frac{7}{11}$

14. $\frac{4}{7} + \frac{2}{7} = \frac{4+2}{7} = \frac{6}{7}$

15. $\frac{9}{15} - \frac{1}{15} = \frac{9-1}{15} = \frac{8}{15}$

16. $\frac{3}{15} - \frac{1}{15} = \frac{3-1}{15} = \frac{2}{15}$

Exercise Set 4.4

1. $-\frac{1}{2} + \frac{1}{2} = \frac{-1+1}{2} = \frac{0}{2} = 0$

3. $\frac{2}{9x} + \frac{4}{9x} = \frac{2+4}{9x} = \frac{6}{9x} = \frac{2 \cdot 3}{3 \cdot 3 \cdot x} = \frac{2}{3x}$

5. $-\frac{4}{13} + \frac{2}{13} + \frac{1}{13} = \frac{-4+2+1}{13} = \frac{-1}{13} = -\frac{1}{13}$

7. $\frac{7}{18} + \frac{3}{18} + \frac{2}{18} = \frac{7+3+2}{18} = \frac{12}{18} = \frac{2 \cdot 6}{3 \cdot 6} = \frac{2}{3}$

9. $\frac{1}{y} - \frac{4}{y} = \frac{1-4}{y} = \frac{-3}{y} = -\frac{3}{y}$

11. $\frac{7a}{4} - \frac{3}{4} = \frac{7a-3}{4}$

13. $\frac{1}{8} - \frac{7}{8} = \frac{1-7}{8} = \frac{-6}{8} = -\frac{3 \cdot 2}{4 \cdot 2} = -\frac{3}{4}$

13. $\frac{1}{8}-\frac{7}{8}=\frac{1-7}{8}=\frac{-6}{8}=-\frac{3\cdot 2}{4\cdot 2}=-\frac{3}{4}$

15. $\frac{20}{21}-\frac{10}{21}-\frac{17}{21}=\frac{20-10-17}{21}$
$=\frac{-7}{21}$
$=-\frac{7}{3\cdot 7}$
$=-\frac{1}{3}$

17. $\frac{9x}{15}+\frac{1x}{15}=\frac{9x+1x}{15}=\frac{10x}{15}=\frac{5\cdot 2x}{5\cdot 3}=\frac{2x}{3}$

19. $\frac{7x}{16}-\frac{15x}{16}=\frac{7x-15x}{16}$
$=\frac{-8x}{16}$
$=-\frac{8\cdot x}{2\cdot 8}$
$=-\frac{x}{2}$

21. $\frac{15}{16z}-\frac{3}{16z}=\frac{15-3}{16z}=\frac{12}{16z}=\frac{4\cdot 3}{4\cdot 4\cdot z}=\frac{3}{4z}$

23. $\frac{3}{10}-\frac{6}{10}=\frac{3-6}{10}=\frac{-3}{10}=-\frac{3}{10}$

25. $\frac{15}{17}+\frac{5}{17}+\frac{14}{17}=\frac{15+5+14}{17}$
$=\frac{34}{17}$
$=\frac{17\cdot 2}{17}$
$=\frac{2}{1}$
$=2$

27. $\frac{9}{12}-\frac{7}{12}-\frac{10}{12}=\frac{9-7-10}{12}$
$=\frac{-8}{12}$
$=-\frac{2\cdot 4}{3\cdot 4}$
$=-\frac{2}{3}$

29. $\frac{x}{4}+\frac{3x}{4}-\frac{2x}{4}+\frac{x}{4}=\frac{x+3x-2x+x}{4}=\frac{3x}{4}$

31. $x+y=\frac{3}{4}+\frac{2}{4}=\frac{5}{4}$

33. $x-y=-\frac{1}{5}-\left(-\frac{3}{5}\right)$
$=-\frac{1}{5}+\frac{3}{5}$
$=\frac{-1+3}{5}$
$=\frac{2}{5}$

35. $x-y+z=\frac{3}{12}-\frac{5}{12}+\left(-\frac{7}{12}\right)$
$=\frac{3-5-7}{12}$
$=\frac{-9}{12}$
$=-\frac{3\cdot 3}{3\cdot 4}$
$=-\frac{3}{4}$

37. $x+\frac{1}{3}=-\frac{1}{3}$
$x+\frac{1}{3}-\frac{1}{3}=-\frac{1}{3}-\frac{1}{3}$
$x=\frac{-1-1}{3}=\frac{-2}{3}=-\frac{2}{3}$

Check:
$x+\frac{1}{3}=-\frac{1}{3}$
$-\frac{2}{3}+\frac{1}{3}=-\frac{1}{3}$
$\frac{-2+1}{3}=-\frac{1}{3}$
$\frac{-1}{3}=-\frac{1}{3}$
$-\frac{1}{3}=-\frac{1}{3}$ True

39.
$$y-\frac{3}{13}=-\frac{2}{13}$$
$$y-\frac{3}{13}+\frac{3}{13}=-\frac{2}{13}+\frac{3}{13}$$
$$y=\frac{-2+3}{13}=\frac{1}{13}$$
Check:
$$y-\frac{3}{13}=-\frac{2}{13}$$
$$\frac{1}{13}-\frac{3}{13}=-\frac{2}{13}$$
$$\frac{1-3}{13}=-\frac{2}{13}$$
$$\frac{-2}{13}=-\frac{2}{13}$$
$$-\frac{2}{13}=-\frac{2}{13} \text{ True}$$

41.
$$3x-\frac{1}{5}-2x=\frac{1}{5}+\frac{2}{5}$$
$$(3x-2x)-\frac{1}{5}=\frac{1+2}{5}$$
$$x-\frac{1}{5}=\frac{3}{5}$$
$$x-\frac{1}{5}+\frac{1}{5}=\frac{3}{5}+\frac{1}{5}$$
$$x=\frac{4}{5}$$
Check:
$$3x-\frac{1}{5}-2x=\frac{1}{5}+\frac{2}{5}$$
$$3\cdot\frac{4}{5}-\frac{1}{5}-2\cdot\frac{4}{5}=\frac{1+2}{5}$$
$$\frac{12}{5}-\frac{1}{5}-\frac{8}{5}=\frac{3}{5}$$
$$\frac{12-1-8}{5}=\frac{3}{5}$$
$$\frac{11-8}{5}=\frac{3}{5}$$
$$\frac{3}{5}=\frac{3}{5} \text{ True}$$

43. The perimeter is the distance around. Add the lengths of the sides.
$$\frac{4}{20}+\frac{7}{20}+\frac{9}{20}=\frac{4+7+9}{20}=\frac{20}{20}=1$$
The perimeter is 1 inch.

45. The perimeter is the distance around. A rectangle has 2 sets of equal sides. Add the lengths of the sides.
$$\frac{5}{12}+\frac{7}{12}+\frac{5}{12}+\frac{7}{12}=\frac{5+7+5+7}{12}$$
$$=\frac{24}{12}$$
$$=\frac{2\cdot 12}{1\cdot 12}$$
$$=2$$
The perimeter is 2 meters.

47. Find the total workout time. Add the times in the morning and in the evening.
$$\frac{7}{8}+\frac{5}{8}=\frac{7+5}{8}=\frac{12}{8}=\frac{3\cdot 4}{2\cdot 4}=\frac{3}{2}$$
He worked out $\frac{3}{2}$ hours.

49. The fraction of employees enrolled in each plan in order from smallest to largest are
$\frac{7}{100}$, $\frac{14}{100}$, $\frac{29}{100}$, and $\frac{50}{100}$.
Thus, the health plans in order from the smallest fraction of employees to the largest fraction of employees are Traditional fee-for-service, Point-of-Service, Health Maintenance Organization, and Preferred Provider Organization.

51. $\frac{29}{100}+\frac{14}{100}+\frac{7}{100}=\frac{29+14+7}{100}=\frac{50}{100}=\frac{1}{2}$
$\frac{1}{2}$ of the employees are not covered by Preferred Provider Organization.

53. Subtract $\frac{18}{50}$ from $\frac{39}{50}$.
$$\frac{39}{50}-\frac{18}{50}=\frac{39-18}{50}=\frac{21}{50}$$
$\frac{21}{50}$ of the states had maximum speed limits that were less than 70 mph.

55. $3=3$
$4=2\cdot 2$
$\text{LCD}=3\cdot 2\cdot 2=12$

57. $9=3\cdot 3$
$15=3\cdot 5$
$\text{LCD}=3\cdot 3\cdot 5=45$

59. $12=2\cdot 2\cdot 3$
$18=2\cdot 3\cdot 3$
$\text{LCD}=2\cdot 2\cdot 3\cdot 3=36$

61. $24 = 2 \cdot 2 \cdot 2 \cdot 3$
$x = x$
$\text{LCD} = 2 \cdot 2 \cdot 2 \cdot 3 \cdot x = 24x$

63. $25 = 5 \cdot 5$
$15 = 3 \cdot 5$
$6 = 2 \cdot 3$
$\text{LCD} = 2 \cdot 3 \cdot 5 \cdot 5 = 150$

65. $18 = 2 \cdot 3 \cdot 3$
$21 = 3 \cdot 7$
$\text{LCD} = 2 \cdot 3 \cdot 3 \cdot 7 = 126$

67. $15 = 3 \cdot 5$
$25 = 5 \cdot 5$
$\text{LCD} = 3 \cdot 5 \cdot 5 = 75$

69. $8 = 2 \cdot 2 \cdot 2$
$24 = 2 \cdot 2 \cdot 2 \cdot 3$
$\text{LCD} = 2 \cdot 2 \cdot 2 \cdot 3 = 24$

71. $25 = 5 \cdot 5$
$10 = 2 \cdot 5$
$\text{LCD} = 5 \cdot 5 \cdot 2 = 50$

73. $a = a$
$12 = 2 \cdot 2 \cdot 3$
$\text{LCD} = 2 \cdot 2 \cdot 3 \cdot a = 12a$

75. $3 = 3$
$21 = 3 \cdot 7$
$56 = 2 \cdot 2 \cdot 2 \cdot 7$
$\text{LCD} = 2 \cdot 2 \cdot 2 \cdot 3 \cdot 7 = 168$

77. $11 = 11$
$33 = 3 \cdot 11$
$121 = 11 \cdot 11$
$\text{LCD} = 3 \cdot 11 \cdot 11 = 363$

79. $\frac{4}{5} \cdot \frac{3}{7} = \frac{4 \cdot 3}{5 \cdot 7} = \frac{12}{35}$

81. $-2 + 10 = 8$

83. $\frac{2}{5} \div \frac{1}{2} = \frac{2}{5} \cdot \frac{2}{1} = \frac{2 \cdot 2}{5 \cdot 1} = \frac{4}{5}$

85. $-12 - 16 = -12 + (-16) = -28$

87. $\frac{4}{11} + \frac{5}{11} - \frac{3}{11} + \frac{2}{11} = \frac{4+5-3+2}{11} = \frac{8}{11}$

89. Subtract the sum of $\frac{38}{50}$ and $\frac{7}{50}$ from the total of $\frac{50}{50}$.

$$\frac{50}{50} - \left(\frac{38}{50} + \frac{7}{50}\right) = \frac{50}{50} - \frac{45}{50} = \frac{50-45}{45} = \frac{5}{50} = \frac{1 \cdot 5}{10 \cdot 5} = \frac{1}{10}$$

$\frac{1}{10}$ of American men over age 65 are either single or divorced.

91. Answers may vary.

Section 4.5

Practice Problems

1. $\frac{4}{7} + \frac{3}{14}$:

Step 1. The LCD for the denominators 7 and 14 is 14.

Step 2. $\frac{4}{7} = \frac{4 \cdot 2}{7 \cdot 2} = \frac{8}{14}$; $\frac{3}{14}$ has a denominator of 14.

Step 3. $\frac{4}{7} + \frac{3}{14} = \frac{8}{14} + \frac{3}{14} = \frac{11}{14}$

Step 4. $\frac{11}{14}$ is in simplest form.

2. $\frac{3}{7} - \frac{9}{10}$:

Step 1. The LCD for denominators 7 and 10 is 70.

Step 2. $\frac{3}{7} = \frac{3 \cdot 10}{7 \cdot 10} = \frac{30}{70}$ and $\frac{9}{10} = \frac{9 \cdot 7}{10 \cdot 7} = \frac{63}{70}$

Step 3. $\frac{3}{7} - \frac{9}{10} = \frac{30}{70} - \frac{63}{70} = \frac{30-63}{70} = \frac{-33}{70}$ or $-\frac{33}{70}$

Step 4. $-\frac{33}{70}$ is in simplest form.

3. $-\frac{1}{5}+\frac{3}{20}$:
The LCD denominators 5 and 20 is 20.
$$-\frac{1}{5}+\frac{3}{20}=\frac{-1\cdot 4}{5\cdot 4}+\frac{3}{20}=\frac{-4}{20}+\frac{3}{20}=\frac{-1}{20}\text{ or }-\frac{1}{20}$$

4. $5+\frac{3y}{4}$:
Recall that $5=\frac{5}{1}$. The LCD for denominators 1 and 4 is 4.
$$\frac{5}{1}+\frac{3y}{4}=\frac{5\cdot 4}{1\cdot 4}+\frac{3y}{4}=\frac{20}{4}+\frac{3y}{4}=\frac{20+3y}{4}$$

5. $\frac{5}{8}-\frac{1}{3}-\frac{1}{12}$:
The LCD of 8, 3 and 12 is 24.
$$\frac{5}{8}-\frac{1}{3}-\frac{1}{12}=\frac{5\cdot 3}{8\cdot 3}-\frac{1\cdot 8}{3\cdot 8}-\frac{1\cdot 2}{12\cdot 2}=\frac{15}{24}-\frac{8}{24}-\frac{2}{24}=\frac{5}{24}$$

6. $\frac{3}{8}=\frac{3\cdot 5}{8\cdot 5}=\frac{15}{40}$ and $\frac{7}{20}=\frac{7\cdot 2}{20\cdot 2}=\frac{14}{40}$
Since $15>14$, $\frac{15}{40}>\frac{14}{40}$. Therefore, $\frac{3}{8}>\frac{7}{20}$.

7. $-\frac{17}{20}$ and $-\frac{4}{5}=-\frac{4\cdot 4}{5\cdot 4}=-\frac{16}{20}$
Since $-17<-16$, $-\frac{17}{20}<-\frac{16}{20}$.
Therefore, $-\frac{17}{20}<-\frac{4}{5}$.

8. $x+y=\frac{5}{11}+\frac{4}{9}$
The LCD of 11 and 9 is 99.
$$\frac{5}{11}+\frac{4}{9}=\frac{5\cdot 9}{11\cdot 9}+\frac{4\cdot 11}{9\cdot 11}=\frac{45}{99}+\frac{44}{99}=\frac{89}{99}$$

9.
$$y-\frac{2}{3}=\frac{5}{12}$$
$$y-\frac{2}{3}+\frac{2}{3}=\frac{5}{12}+\frac{2}{3}$$
$$y=\frac{5}{12}+\frac{2\cdot 4}{3\cdot 4}$$
$$y=\frac{5}{12}+\frac{8}{12}$$
$$y=\frac{13}{12}$$

10. The phrase "total amount" tells us to add. Add the three amounts: $\frac{3}{5}+\frac{2}{10}+\frac{2}{15}$.
The LCD for the denominators 5, 10, and 15 is 30.
$$\frac{3}{5}=\frac{3\cdot 6}{5\cdot 6}=\frac{18}{30},\ \frac{2}{10}=\frac{2\cdot 3}{10\cdot 3}=\frac{6}{30},$$
$$\frac{2}{15}=\frac{2\cdot 2}{15\cdot 2}=\frac{4}{30}$$
$$\frac{3}{5}+\frac{2}{10}+\frac{2}{15}=\frac{18}{30}+\frac{6}{30}+\frac{4}{30}=\frac{28}{30}$$
$$\frac{28}{30}=\frac{14\cdot 2}{15\cdot 2}=\frac{14}{15}$$
The homeowner needs $\frac{14}{15}$ of a cubic yard. Yes, she bought enough because 1 or $\frac{15}{15}$ is greater than $\frac{14}{15}$.

11. The phrase "find the difference" tells us to subtract. Subtract $\frac{2}{3}$ from $\frac{4}{5}$: $\frac{4}{5}-\frac{2}{3}$.
The LCD for the denominators 5 and 3 is 15.
$$\frac{4}{5}=\frac{4\cdot 3}{5\cdot 3}=\frac{12}{15},\ \frac{2\cdot 5}{3\cdot 5}=\frac{10}{15}$$
$$\frac{4}{5}-\frac{2}{3}=\frac{12}{15}-\frac{10}{15}=\frac{2}{15}$$
$\frac{2}{15}$ is in simplest form.
The difference in the lengths is $\frac{2}{15}$ of a foot.

Calculator Explorations

Use the calculator keystrokes discussed on page 292 of your textbook.

1. $\frac{1}{16}+\frac{2}{5}=\frac{37}{80}$

2. $\frac{3}{20}+\frac{2}{25}=\frac{23}{100}$

3. $\frac{4}{9}+\frac{7}{8}=\frac{95}{72}$

4. $\frac{9}{11}+\frac{5}{12}=\frac{163}{132}$

5. $\frac{10}{17}+\frac{12}{19}=\frac{394}{323}$

6. $\frac{14}{31}+\frac{15}{21}=\frac{253}{217}$

Mental Math

1. The LCD of 2 and 3 is $2 \cdot 3 = 6$.

2. The LCD of 2 and 4 is 4.

3. The LCD of 6 and 12 is 12.

4. The LCD of 5 and 10 is 10.

5. The LCD of 7 and 8 is $7 \cdot 2^3 = 56$.

6. The LCD of 24 and 3 is 24.

7. The LCD of 12 and 4 is 12.

8. The LCD of 3 and 11 is $3 \cdot 11 = 33$.

Exercise Set 4.5

1. The LCD of 3 and 6 is 6.
$\frac{2}{3}+\frac{1}{6}=\frac{2\cdot 2}{3\cdot 2}+\frac{1}{6}=\frac{4}{6}+\frac{1}{6}=\frac{5}{6}$

3. The LCD of 2 and 3 is 6.
$\frac{1}{2}-\frac{1}{3}=\frac{1\cdot 3}{2\cdot 3}-\frac{1\cdot 2}{3\cdot 2}=\frac{3}{6}-\frac{2}{6}=\frac{1}{6}$

5. The LCD of 11 and 33 is 33.
$$\begin{aligned}-\frac{2}{11}+\frac{2}{33}&=-\frac{2\cdot 3}{11\cdot 3}+\frac{2}{33}\\&=-\frac{6}{33}+\frac{2}{33}\\&=-\frac{4}{33}\end{aligned}$$

7. The LCD of 14 and 7 is 14.
$\frac{3x}{14}-\frac{3}{7}=\frac{3x}{14}-\frac{3\cdot 2}{7\cdot 2}=\frac{3x}{14}-\frac{6}{14}=\frac{3x-6}{14}$

9. The LCD of 35 and 7 is 35.
$$\begin{aligned}\frac{11}{35}+\frac{2}{7}&=\frac{11}{35}+\frac{2\cdot 5}{7\cdot 5}\\&=\frac{11}{35}+\frac{10}{35}\\&=\frac{21}{35}\\&=\frac{3\cdot 7}{5\cdot 7}\\&=\frac{3}{5}\end{aligned}$$

11. The LCD of 1 and 12 is 12.
$$\begin{aligned}\frac{2y}{1}-\frac{5}{12}&=\frac{2y\cdot 12}{1\cdot 12}-\frac{5}{12}\\&=\frac{24y}{12}-\frac{5}{12}\\&=\frac{24y-5}{12}\end{aligned}$$

13. The LCD of 12 and 9 is 36.
$\frac{5}{12}-\frac{1}{9}=\frac{5\cdot 3}{12\cdot 3}-\frac{1\cdot 4}{9\cdot 4}=\frac{15}{36}-\frac{4}{36}=\frac{11}{36}$

15. The LCD of 7 and 1 is 7.
$\frac{5}{7}+1=\frac{5}{7}+\frac{1}{1}=\frac{5}{7}+\frac{1\cdot 7}{1\cdot 7}=\frac{5}{7}+\frac{7}{7}=\frac{12}{7}$

17. The LCD of 11 and 9 is 99.
$$\begin{aligned}\frac{5a}{11}+\frac{4a}{9}&=\frac{5a\cdot 9}{11\cdot 9}+\frac{4a\cdot 11}{9\cdot 11}\\&=\frac{45a}{99}+\frac{44a}{99}\\&=\frac{89a}{99}\end{aligned}$$

19. The LCD of 3 and 6 is 6.
$\frac{2y}{3}-\frac{1}{6}=\frac{2y\cdot 2}{3\cdot 2}-\frac{1}{6}=\frac{4y}{6}-\frac{1}{6}=\frac{4y-1}{6}$

21. The LCD of 2 and x is $2x$.
$\frac{1}{2}+\frac{3}{x}=\frac{1\cdot x}{2\cdot x}+\frac{3\cdot 2}{x\cdot 2}=\frac{x}{2x}+\frac{6}{2x}=\frac{x+6}{2x}$

23. The LCD of 11 and 33 is 33.
$$\begin{aligned}-\frac{2}{11}-\frac{2}{33}&=-\frac{2\cdot 3}{11\cdot 3}-\frac{2}{33}\\&=-\frac{6}{33}-\frac{2}{33}\\&=-\frac{8}{33}\end{aligned}$$

25. The LCD of 14 and 7 is 14.
$$\frac{9}{14}-\frac{3}{7}=\frac{9}{14}-\frac{3\cdot 2}{7\cdot 2}=\frac{9}{14}-\frac{6}{14}=\frac{3}{14}$$

27. The LCD of 35 and 7 is 35.
$$\frac{11y}{35}-\frac{2}{7}=\frac{11y}{35}-\frac{2\cdot 5}{7\cdot 5}=\frac{11y}{35}-\frac{10}{35}=\frac{11y-10}{35}$$

29. The LCD of 9 and 12 is 36.
$$\frac{1}{9}-\frac{5}{12}=\frac{1\cdot 4}{9\cdot 4}-\frac{5\cdot 3}{12\cdot 3}=\frac{4}{36}-\frac{15}{36}=-\frac{11}{36}$$

31. The LCD of 15 and 12 is 60.
$$\frac{7}{15}-\frac{5}{12}=\frac{7\cdot 4}{15\cdot 4}-\frac{5\cdot 5}{12\cdot 5}=\frac{28}{60}-\frac{25}{60}=\frac{3}{60}=\frac{3}{3\cdot 20}=\frac{1}{20}$$

33. The LCD of 7 and 8 is 56.
$$\frac{5}{7}-\frac{1}{8}=\frac{5\cdot 8}{7\cdot 8}-\frac{1\cdot 7}{8\cdot 7}=\frac{40}{56}-\frac{7}{56}=\frac{33}{56}$$

35. The LCD of 8 and 16 is 16.
$$\frac{7}{8}+\frac{3}{16}=\frac{7\cdot 2}{8\cdot 2}+\frac{3}{16}=\frac{14}{16}+\frac{3}{16}=\frac{17}{16}$$

37. $\frac{5}{9}+\frac{3}{9}=\frac{8}{9}$

39. The LCD of 11 and 3 is 33.
$$\frac{5}{11}+\frac{y}{3}=\frac{5\cdot 3}{11\cdot 3}+\frac{y\cdot 11}{3\cdot 11}=\frac{15}{33}+\frac{11y}{33}=\frac{15+11y}{33}$$

41. The LCD of 6 and 7 is 42.
$$-\frac{5}{6}-\frac{3}{7}=-\frac{5\cdot 7}{6\cdot 7}-\frac{3\cdot 6}{7\cdot 6}=-\frac{35}{42}-\frac{18}{42}=-\frac{53}{42}$$

43. The LCD of 9 and 6 is 18.
$$\frac{7}{9}-\frac{1}{6}=\frac{7\cdot 2}{9\cdot 2}-\frac{1\cdot 3}{6\cdot 3}=\frac{14}{18}-\frac{3}{18}=\frac{11}{18}$$

45. The LCD of 3 and 13 is 39.
$$\frac{2a}{3}+\frac{6a}{13}=\frac{2a\cdot 13}{3\cdot 13}+\frac{6a\cdot 3}{13\cdot 3}=\frac{26a}{39}+\frac{18a}{39}=\frac{44a}{39}$$

47. The LCD of 30 and 12 is 60.
$$\frac{7}{30}-\frac{5}{12}=\frac{7\cdot 2}{30\cdot 2}-\frac{5\cdot 5}{12\cdot 5}=\frac{14}{60}-\frac{25}{60}=-\frac{11}{60}$$

49. The LCD of 9 and y is $9y$.
$$\frac{5}{9}+\frac{1}{y}=\frac{5\cdot y}{9\cdot y}+\frac{1\cdot 9}{y\cdot 9}=\frac{5y}{9y}+\frac{9}{9y}=\frac{5y+9}{9y}$$

51. The LCD of 5 and 9 is 45.
$$\frac{4}{5}+\frac{4}{9}=\frac{4\cdot 9}{5\cdot 9}+\frac{4\cdot 5}{9\cdot 5}=\frac{36}{45}+\frac{20}{45}=\frac{56}{45}$$

53. The LCD of $9x$ and 8 is $72x$.
$$\frac{5}{9x}+\frac{1}{8}=\frac{5\cdot 8}{9x\cdot 8}+\frac{1\cdot 9x}{8\cdot 9x}=\frac{40}{72x}+\frac{9x}{72x}=\frac{40+9x}{72x}$$

55. The LCD of 5, 3, and 10 is 30.
$$-\frac{2}{5}+\frac{1}{3}-\frac{3}{10}=-\frac{2\cdot 6}{5\cdot 6}+\frac{1\cdot 10}{3\cdot 10}-\frac{3\cdot 3}{10\cdot 3}=-\frac{12}{30}+\frac{10}{30}-\frac{9}{30}=-\frac{11}{30}$$

57. The LCD of 2, 4, and 16 is 16.

$$\begin{aligned}\frac{x}{2}+\frac{x}{4}+\frac{2x}{16} &= \frac{x\cdot 8}{2\cdot 8}+\frac{x\cdot 4}{4\cdot 4}+\frac{2x}{16}\\ &= \frac{8x}{16}+\frac{4x}{16}+\frac{2x}{16}\\ &= \frac{14x}{16}\\ &= \frac{2\cdot 7\cdot x}{2\cdot 4}\\ &= \frac{7x}{8}\end{aligned}$$

59. The LCD of 5, 4, and 2 is 20.

$$\begin{aligned}\frac{6}{5}-\frac{3}{4}+\frac{1}{2} &= \frac{6\cdot 4}{5\cdot 4}-\frac{3\cdot 5}{4\cdot 5}+\frac{1\cdot 10}{2\cdot 10}\\ &= \frac{24}{20}-\frac{15}{20}+\frac{10}{20}\\ &= \frac{19}{20}\end{aligned}$$

61. The LCD of 12, 24, and 6 is 24.

$$\begin{aligned}-\frac{9}{12}+\frac{17}{24}-\frac{1}{6} &= -\frac{9\cdot 2}{12\cdot 2}+\frac{17}{24}-\frac{1\cdot 4}{6\cdot 4}\\ &= -\frac{18}{24}+\frac{17}{24}-\frac{4}{24}\\ &= -\frac{5}{24}\end{aligned}$$

63. The LCD of 8, 7, and 14 is 56.

$$\begin{aligned}\frac{3x}{8}+\frac{2x}{7}-\frac{5}{14} &= \frac{3x\cdot 7}{8\cdot 7}+\frac{2x\cdot 8}{7\cdot 8}-\frac{5\cdot 4}{14\cdot 4}\\ &= \frac{21x}{56}+\frac{16x}{56}-\frac{20}{56}\\ &= \frac{37x-20}{56}\end{aligned}$$

65. $\frac{2\cdot 10}{7\cdot 10}=\frac{20}{70}<\frac{21}{70}=\frac{3\cdot 7}{10\cdot 7}$

67. $\frac{5}{6}>-\frac{13}{15}$

A positive number is always greater than a negative number.

69. $-\frac{3\cdot 7}{4\cdot 7}=-\frac{21}{28}>\frac{-22}{28}=-\frac{11\cdot 2}{14\cdot 2}$

71.
$$\begin{aligned}x+y &= \frac{1}{3}+\frac{3}{4}\\ &= \frac{1\cdot 4}{3\cdot 4}+\frac{3\cdot 3}{4\cdot 3}\\ &= \frac{4}{12}+\frac{9}{12}\\ &= \frac{13}{12}\end{aligned}$$

73. $xy=\frac{1}{3}\cdot\frac{3}{4}=\frac{1\cdot 3}{3\cdot 4}=\frac{1}{4}$

75.
$$\begin{aligned}2y+x &= 2\cdot\frac{3}{4}+\frac{1}{3}\\ &= \frac{2}{1}\cdot\frac{3}{4}+\frac{1}{3}\\ &= \frac{2\cdot 3}{1\cdot 2\cdot 2}+\frac{1}{3}\\ &= \frac{3}{2}+\frac{1}{3}\\ &= \frac{3\cdot 3}{2\cdot 3}+\frac{1\cdot 2}{3\cdot 2}\\ &= \frac{9}{6}+\frac{2}{6}\\ &= \frac{11}{6}\end{aligned}$$

77.
$$\begin{aligned}x-\frac{1}{12} &= \frac{5}{6}\\ x-\frac{1}{12}+\frac{1}{12} &= \frac{5}{6}+\frac{1}{12}\\ x &= \frac{5\cdot 2}{6\cdot 2}+\frac{1}{12}\\ x &= \frac{10}{12}+\frac{1}{12}\\ &= \frac{11}{12}\end{aligned}$$

Check:

$$\begin{aligned}x-\frac{1}{12} &= \frac{5}{6}\\ \frac{11}{12}-\frac{1}{12} &= \frac{5}{6}\\ \frac{10}{12} &= \frac{5}{6}\\ \frac{5\cdot 2}{6\cdot 2} &= \frac{5}{6}\\ \frac{5}{6} &= \frac{5}{6}\ \text{True}\end{aligned}$$

79.
$$\frac{2}{5}+y=-\frac{3}{10}$$
$$\frac{2}{5}+y-\frac{2}{5}=-\frac{3}{10}-\frac{2}{5}$$
$$y=-\frac{3}{10}-\frac{2\cdot 2}{5\cdot 2}$$
$$y=-\frac{3}{10}-\frac{4}{10}$$
$$=-\frac{7}{10}$$

Check:
$$\frac{2}{5}+y=-\frac{3}{10}$$
$$\frac{2}{5}+\left(-\frac{7}{10}\right)=-\frac{3}{10}$$
$$\frac{2\cdot 2}{5\cdot 2}-\frac{7}{10}=-\frac{3}{10}$$
$$\frac{4}{10}-\frac{7}{10}=-\frac{3}{10}$$
$$-\frac{3}{10}=-\frac{3}{10}\text{ True}$$

81.
$$7z+\frac{1}{16}-6z=\frac{3}{4}$$
$$(7z-6z)+\frac{1}{16}=\frac{3}{4}$$
$$z+\frac{1}{16}=\frac{3}{4}$$
$$z+\frac{1}{16}-\frac{1}{16}=\frac{3}{4}-\frac{1}{16}$$
$$z=\frac{3\cdot 4}{4\cdot 4}-\frac{1}{16}$$
$$z=\frac{12}{16}-\frac{1}{16}$$
$$=\frac{11}{16}$$

Check:
$$7z+\frac{1}{16}-6z=\frac{3}{4}$$
$$7\cdot\frac{11}{16}+\frac{1}{16}-6\cdot\frac{11}{16}=\frac{3}{4}$$
$$\frac{77}{16}+\frac{1}{16}-\frac{66}{16}=\frac{3}{4}$$
$$\frac{12}{16}=\frac{3}{4}$$
$$\frac{3\cdot 4}{4\cdot 4}=\frac{3}{4}$$
$$\frac{3}{4}=\frac{3}{4}\text{ True}$$

83.
$$-\frac{2}{9}=x-\frac{5}{6}$$
$$-\frac{2}{9}+\frac{5}{6}=x-\frac{5}{6}+\frac{5}{6}$$
$$-\frac{2\cdot 2}{9\cdot 2}+\frac{5\cdot 3}{6\cdot 3}=x$$
$$-\frac{4}{18}+\frac{15}{18}=x$$
$$\frac{11}{18}=x$$

Check:
$$-\frac{2}{9}=x-\frac{5}{6}$$
$$-\frac{2}{9}=\frac{11}{18}-\frac{5}{6}$$
$$-\frac{2}{9}=\frac{11}{18}-\frac{5\cdot 3}{6\cdot 3}$$
$$-\frac{2}{9}=\frac{11}{18}-\frac{15}{18}$$
$$-\frac{2}{9}=-\frac{4}{18}$$
$$-\frac{2}{9}=-\frac{2\cdot 2}{2\cdot 9}$$
$$-\frac{2}{9}=-\frac{2}{9}\text{ True}$$

85. Add the lengths of the 4 sides. A parallelogram has 2 sets of equal sides.
$$\frac{1}{3}+\frac{4}{5}+\frac{1}{3}+\frac{4}{5}=\frac{1\cdot 5}{3\cdot 5}+\frac{4\cdot 3}{5\cdot 3}+\frac{1\cdot 5}{3\cdot 5}+\frac{4\cdot 3}{5\cdot 3}$$
$$=\frac{5}{15}+\frac{12}{15}+\frac{5}{15}+\frac{12}{15}$$
$$=\frac{34}{15}$$
The perimeter is $\frac{34}{15}$ centimeters.

87. Add the lengths of the 4 sides.
$$\frac{1}{4}+\frac{1}{5}+\frac{1}{2}+\frac{3}{4}=\frac{1\cdot 5}{4\cdot 5}+\frac{1\cdot 4}{5\cdot 4}+\frac{1\cdot 10}{2\cdot 10}+\frac{3\cdot 5}{4\cdot 5}$$
$$=\frac{5}{20}+\frac{4}{20}+\frac{10}{20}+\frac{15}{20}$$
$$=\frac{34}{20}$$
$$=\frac{2\cdot 17}{2\cdot 10}$$
$$=\frac{17}{10}$$
The perimeter is $\frac{17}{10}$ meters.

89. Subtract $\frac{5}{264}$ from $\frac{1}{4}$.

$\frac{1}{4}-\frac{5}{264}=\frac{1\cdot 66}{4\cdot 66}-\frac{5}{264}=\frac{66-5}{264}=\frac{61}{264}$

A killer bee will chase a person $\frac{61}{264}$ mile farther.

91. $\frac{1}{2}+\frac{5}{8}+\frac{1}{4}=\frac{1\cdot 4}{2\cdot 4}+\frac{5}{8}+\frac{1\cdot 2}{4\cdot 2}$

$=\frac{4}{8}+\frac{5}{8}+\frac{2}{8}$

$=\frac{11}{8}$

The total length is $\frac{11}{8}$ in.

93. Subtract $\frac{4}{25}$ from $\frac{13}{20}$.

$\frac{13}{20}-\frac{4}{25}=\frac{13\cdot 5}{20\cdot 5}-\frac{4\cdot 4}{25\cdot 4}$

$=\frac{65}{100}-\frac{16}{100}$

$=\frac{49}{100}$

$\frac{49}{100}$ of students name math or science as their favorite subject.

95. Add the fractions for 1 or 2 times per week and 3 times per week.

$\frac{23}{50}+\frac{31}{100}=\frac{23\cdot 2}{50\cdot 2}+\frac{31}{100}=\frac{46}{100}+\frac{81}{100}=\frac{77}{100}$

$\frac{77}{100}$ of Americans eat pasta 1, 2, or 3 times per week.

97. Less than 50 miles per week includes 10 to 49 miles and less than 10 miles. Add these amounts.

$\frac{23}{100}+\frac{3}{50}=\frac{23}{100}+\frac{3\cdot 2}{50\cdot 2}=\frac{23}{100}+\frac{6}{100}=\frac{29}{100}$

$\frac{29}{100}$ of adults drive less than 50 miles in an average week.

99. $\left(\frac{5}{6}\right)^2=\frac{5}{6}\cdot\frac{5}{6}=\frac{5\cdot 5}{6\cdot 6}=\frac{25}{36}$

101. $\left(-\frac{5}{6}\right)^2=-\frac{5}{6}\cdot -\frac{5}{6}=\frac{5\cdot 5}{6\cdot 6}=\frac{25}{36}$

103. 57,236 rounded to the nearest hundred is 57,200.

105. 327 rounded to the nearest ten is 330.

107. $\frac{30}{55}+\frac{1000}{1760}=\frac{30\cdot 32}{55\cdot 32}+\frac{1000}{1760}$

$=\frac{960}{1760}+\frac{1000}{1760}$

$=\frac{1960}{1760}$

$=\frac{49\cdot 40}{44\cdot 40}$

$=\frac{49}{44}$

109. Answers may vary.

111.

$x=\frac{5}{117}=\frac{71}{27}$

$x-\frac{5}{117}+\frac{5}{117}=\frac{71}{27}+\frac{5}{117}$

$x=\frac{71\cdot 13}{27\cdot 13}+\frac{5\cdot 3}{117\cdot 3}$

$x=\frac{923}{351}+\frac{15}{351}$

$x=\frac{938}{351}$

113. $\frac{94}{579}+\frac{23}{193}=\frac{94}{579}+\frac{23\cdot 3}{193\cdot 3}$

$=\frac{94}{579}+\frac{69}{579}=\frac{163}{579}$

$\frac{163}{579}$ of the worlds land area is accounted for by North and South America.

115. $\frac{163}{579}\cdot 57{,}900{,}000=\frac{163\cdot 579\cdot 100{,}000}{579}$

$=16{,}300{,}000$

The combined land area of North and South America is 16,300,000 square miles.

117. Subtract $\frac{18}{193}$ from 1, which represents all of the land area added together.

$1-\frac{18}{193}=\frac{1\cdot 193}{1\cdot 193}-\frac{18}{193}=\frac{193}{193}-\frac{18}{193}=\frac{175}{193}$

$\frac{175}{193}$ of the world's land area is inhabited.

119. military parks $= \frac{3 \cdot 3}{128 \cdot 3} = \frac{9}{384}$

national preserves $= \frac{1 \cdot 16}{24 \cdot 16} = \frac{16}{384}$

Since $\frac{9}{384} < \frac{16}{384}$, the national preserves is the larger category.

121. $1-2$ videos $= \frac{127 \cdot 2}{500 \cdot 2} = \frac{254}{1000}$

$3-4$ videos $= \frac{31 \cdot 5}{200 \cdot 5} = \frac{155}{1000}$

Since $\frac{254}{1000} > \frac{155}{1000}$, the 1 - 2 video rental category is larger.

Integrated Review

1. The figure has 4 equal parts. One part is shaded. The fraction shaded is $\frac{1}{4}$.

2. The figure has 6 equal parts. Three parts are shaded. The fraction shaded is $\frac{3}{6}$ or $\frac{1}{2}$.

3. Each figure has 4 equal parts. Seven parts are shaded. The fraction shaded is $\frac{7}{4}$.

4. Number of people getting less than 8 hours of sleep → 73
Total number of people surveyed → 85
$\frac{73}{85}$

5. $6 = 2 \cdot 3$

6. $70 = 2 \cdot 35 = 2 \cdot 5 \cdot 7$

7. $$\begin{aligned} 252 &= 2 \cdot 126 \\ &= 2 \cdot 2 \cdot 63 \\ &= 2 \cdot 2 \cdot 7 \cdot 9 \\ &= 2 \cdot 2 \cdot 7 \cdot 3 \cdot 3 \\ &= 2^2 \cdot 3^2 \cdot 7 \end{aligned}$$

8. $\frac{2}{14} = \frac{2}{2 \cdot 7} = \frac{1}{7}$

9. $\frac{20}{24} = \frac{4 \cdot 5}{4 \cdot 6} = \frac{5}{6}$

10. $\frac{18}{38} = \frac{2 \cdot 9}{2 \cdot 19} = \frac{9}{19}$

11. $\frac{42}{110} = \frac{2 \cdot 21}{2 \cdot 55} = \frac{21}{55}$

12. $\frac{32}{64}=\frac{32}{2\cdot 32}=\frac{1}{2}$

13. $\frac{72}{80}=\frac{8\cdot 9}{8\cdot 10}=\frac{9}{10}$

14. Number of states that are not adjacent to any other state $\rightarrow$ 2
Number of states $\rightarrow$ 50 ($\frac{2}{50}$)

$\frac{2}{50}=\frac{2}{2\cdot 25}=\frac{1}{25}$

15. $\frac{1}{5}+\frac{3}{5}=\frac{1+3}{5}=\frac{4}{5}$

16. $\frac{1}{5}-\frac{3}{5}=\frac{1-3}{5}=\frac{-2}{5}=-\frac{2}{5}$

17. $\frac{1}{5}\cdot\frac{3}{5}=\frac{1\cdot 3}{5\cdot 5}=\frac{3}{25}$

18. $\frac{1}{5}\div\frac{3}{5}=\frac{1}{5}\cdot\frac{5}{3}=\frac{1\cdot 5}{5\cdot 3}=\frac{1}{3}$

19. $\frac{2}{3}\div\frac{5}{6}=\frac{2}{3}\cdot\frac{6}{5}=\frac{2\cdot 6}{3\cdot 5}=\frac{2\cdot 2\cdot 3}{3\cdot 5}=\frac{4}{5}$

20. $\frac{2}{3}\cdot\frac{5}{6}=\frac{2\cdot 5}{3\cdot 6}=\frac{2\cdot 5}{3\cdot 2\cdot 3}=\frac{5}{9}$

21. $\frac{2}{3}-\frac{5}{6}=\frac{2\cdot 2}{3\cdot 2}-\frac{5}{6}=\frac{4}{6}-\frac{5}{6}=\frac{4-5}{6}=\frac{-1}{6}=-\frac{1}{6}$

22.
$$\begin{aligned}\frac{2}{3}+\frac{5}{6}&=\frac{2\cdot 2}{3\cdot 2}+\frac{5}{6}\\&=\frac{4}{6}+\frac{5}{6}\\&=\frac{4+5}{6}\\&=\frac{9}{6}\\&=\frac{3\cdot 3}{3\cdot 2}\\&=\frac{3}{2}\end{aligned}$$

23. $-\frac{1}{7}\cdot-\frac{7}{18}=\frac{1\cdot 7}{7\cdot 18}=\frac{1}{18}$

24. $-\frac{4}{9}\cdot-\frac{3}{7}=\frac{4\cdot 3}{9\cdot 7}=\frac{4\cdot 3}{3\cdot 3\cdot 7}=\frac{4}{21}$

25. $-\frac{7}{8}\div 6=-\frac{7}{8}\div\frac{6}{1}=-\frac{7}{8}\cdot\frac{1}{6}=-\frac{7\cdot 1}{8\cdot 6}=-\frac{7}{48}$

26. $-\frac{9}{10}\div 5=-\frac{9}{10}\div\frac{5}{1}=-\frac{9}{10}\cdot\frac{1}{5}=-\frac{9\cdot 1}{10\cdot 5}=-\frac{9}{50}$

27. $\frac{7}{8}+\frac{1}{20}=\frac{7\cdot 5}{8\cdot 5}+\frac{1\cdot 2}{20\cdot 2}=\frac{35}{40}+\frac{2}{40}=\frac{37}{40}$

28. $\frac{5}{12}-\frac{1}{9}=\frac{5\cdot 3}{12\cdot 3}-\frac{1\cdot 4}{9\cdot 4}=\frac{15}{36}-\frac{4}{36}=\frac{11}{36}$

29. $\frac{9}{11}-\frac{2}{3}=\frac{9\cdot 3}{11\cdot 3}-\frac{2\cdot 11}{3\cdot 11}=\frac{27}{33}-\frac{22}{33}=\frac{5}{33}$

30. $\frac{2}{9}+\frac{1}{18}=\frac{2\cdot 2}{9\cdot 2}+\frac{1}{18}=\frac{4}{18}+\frac{1}{18}=\frac{5}{18}$

31.
$$\begin{aligned}\frac{2}{9}+\frac{1}{18}+\frac{1}{3}&=\frac{2\cdot 2}{9\cdot 2}+\frac{1}{18}+\frac{1\cdot 6}{3\cdot 6}\\&=\frac{4}{18}+\frac{1}{18}+\frac{6}{18}\\&=\frac{11}{18}\end{aligned}$$

32.
$$\begin{aligned}\frac{3}{10}+\frac{1}{5}+\frac{6}{25}&=\frac{3\cdot 5}{10\cdot 5}+\frac{1\cdot 10}{5\cdot 10}+\frac{6\cdot 2}{25\cdot 2}\\&=\frac{15}{50}+\frac{10}{50}+\frac{12}{50}\\&=\frac{37}{50}\end{aligned}$$

34. $\frac{7}{8}-\left(\frac{1}{16}+\frac{1}{16}\right)=\frac{7}{8}-\frac{2}{16}$
$=\frac{7}{8}-\frac{1}{8}$
$=\frac{6}{8}$
$=\frac{3}{4}$

The inner diameter is $\frac{3}{4}$ ft.

Section 4.6

Practice Problems

1. $\frac{\frac{7y}{10}}{\frac{1}{5}}=\frac{7y}{10}\div\frac{1}{5}=\frac{7y}{10}\cdot\frac{5}{1}=\frac{7\cdot y\cdot 5}{2\cdot 5}=\frac{7y}{2}$

2. $\frac{\frac{1}{2}+\frac{1}{6}}{\frac{3}{4}-\frac{2}{3}}=\frac{\frac{1\cdot 3}{2\cdot 3}+\frac{1}{6}}{\frac{3\cdot 3}{4\cdot 3}-\frac{2\cdot 4}{3\cdot 4}}$
$=\frac{\frac{3}{6}+\frac{1}{6}}{\frac{9}{12}+\frac{8}{12}}$
$=\frac{\frac{4}{6}}{\frac{1}{12}}$
$=\frac{4}{6}\div\frac{1}{12}$
$=\frac{4}{6}\cdot\frac{12}{1}$
$=\frac{4\cdot 6\cdot 2}{6\cdot 1}$
$=\frac{8}{1}$ or 8

3. $\frac{\frac{1}{2}+\frac{1}{6}}{\frac{3}{4}-\frac{2}{3}}=\frac{12\left(\frac{1}{2}+\frac{1}{6}\right)}{12\left(\frac{3}{4}-\frac{2}{3}\right)}$
$=\frac{\left(12\cdot\frac{1}{2}\right)+\left(12\cdot\frac{1}{6}\right)}{\left(12\cdot\frac{3}{4}\right)-\left(12\cdot\frac{2}{3}\right)}$
$=\frac{6+2}{9-8}$
$=\frac{8}{1}$ or 8

4. $\frac{\frac{3}{4}}{\frac{x}{5}-1}=\frac{20\left(\frac{3}{4}\right)}{20\left(\frac{x}{5}-1\right)}$
$=\frac{20\cdot\frac{3}{4}}{\left(20\cdot\frac{x}{5}\right)-(20\cdot 1)}$
$=\frac{15}{4x-20}$

5. $\left(2-\frac{2}{3}\right)^3$:

First evaluate $2-\frac{2}{3}$.

$2-\frac{2}{3}=\frac{2}{1}-\frac{2}{3}=\frac{2\cdot 3}{1\cdot 3}-\frac{2}{3}=\frac{6}{3}-\frac{2}{3}=\frac{4}{3}$

Next, evaluate $\left(\frac{4}{3}\right)^3$.

$\left(\frac{4}{3}\right)^3=\frac{4}{3}\cdot\frac{4}{3}\cdot\frac{4}{3}=\frac{4\cdot 4\cdot 4}{3\cdot 3\cdot 3}=\frac{64}{27}$.

6. $\left(-\frac{1}{2}+\frac{1}{5}\right)\left(\frac{7}{8}+\frac{1}{8}\right)=\left(\frac{-1\cdot 5}{2\cdot 5}+\frac{1\cdot 2}{5\cdot 2}\right)\left(\frac{8}{8}\right)$
$=\left(\frac{-5}{10}+\frac{2}{10}\right)(1)$
$=\left(-\frac{3}{10}\right)(1)$
$=-\frac{3}{10}$

7. $-\frac{3}{5}-xy=-\frac{3}{5}-\left(\frac{3}{10}\cdot\frac{2}{3}\right)$
$=-\frac{3}{5}-\left(\frac{3\cdot 2}{2\cdot 5\cdot 3}\right)$
$=-\frac{3}{5}-\frac{1}{5}$
$=\frac{-3-1}{5}$
$=\frac{-4}{5}$
$=-\frac{4}{5}$

Exercise Set 4.6

1. $\frac{\frac{1}{8}}{\frac{3}{4}} = \frac{1}{8} \div \frac{3}{4} = \frac{1}{8} \cdot \frac{4}{3} = \frac{1 \cdot 4}{2 \cdot 4 \cdot 3} = \frac{1}{6}$

3. $\frac{\frac{9}{10}}{\frac{21}{10}} = \frac{9}{10} \div \frac{21}{10} = \frac{9}{10} \cdot \frac{10}{21} = \frac{3 \cdot 3 \cdot 10}{10 \cdot 3 \cdot 7} = \frac{3}{7}$

5. $\frac{\frac{2x}{27}}{\frac{4}{9}} = \frac{2x}{27} \div \frac{4}{9} = \frac{2x}{27} \cdot \frac{9}{4} = \frac{2 \cdot x \cdot 3 \cdot 3}{3 \cdot 3 \cdot 3 \cdot 2 \cdot 2} = \frac{x}{6}$

7. $\frac{\frac{3}{4} + \frac{2}{5}}{\frac{1}{2} + \frac{3}{5}} = \frac{20\left(\frac{3}{4} + \frac{2}{5}\right)}{20\left(\frac{1}{2} + \frac{3}{5}\right)} = \frac{15 + 8}{10 + 12} = \frac{23}{22}$

9.
$$\begin{aligned} \frac{\frac{3x}{4}}{5 - \frac{1}{8}} &= \frac{8 \cdot \left(\frac{3x}{4}\right)}{8 \cdot \left(\frac{5}{1} - \frac{1}{8}\right)} \\ &= \frac{6x}{8 \cdot \left(\frac{5}{1}\right) - 8\left(\frac{1}{8}\right)} \\ &= \frac{6x}{40 - 1} \\ &= \frac{6x}{39} \\ &= \frac{3 \cdot 2 \cdot x}{3 \cdot 13} \\ &= \frac{2x}{13} \end{aligned}$$

11.
$$\begin{aligned} \frac{1}{5} + \frac{1}{3} \cdot \frac{1}{4} &= \frac{1}{5} + \frac{1}{12} \\ &= \frac{1 \cdot 12}{5 \cdot 12} + \frac{1 \cdot 5}{12 \cdot 5} \\ &= \frac{12}{60} + \frac{5}{60} \\ &= \frac{17}{60} \end{aligned}$$

13.
$$\begin{aligned} \frac{5}{6} \div \frac{1}{3} \cdot \frac{1}{4} &= \frac{5}{6} \cdot \frac{3}{1} \cdot \frac{1}{4} \\ &= \frac{5 \cdot 3}{2 \cdot 3} \cdot \frac{1}{4} \\ &= \frac{5}{2} \cdot \frac{1}{4} = \frac{5}{8} \end{aligned}$$

15.
$$\begin{aligned} 2^2 - \left(\frac{1}{3}\right)^2 &= 4 - \frac{1}{9} \\ &= \frac{4 \cdot 9}{1 \cdot 9} - \frac{1}{9} \\ &= \frac{36}{9} - \frac{1}{9} \\ &= \frac{35}{9} \end{aligned}$$

17.
$$\begin{aligned} \left(\frac{2}{9} + \frac{4}{9}\right)\left(\frac{1}{3} - \frac{9}{10}\right) &= \left(\frac{6}{9}\right)\left(\frac{1 \cdot 10}{3 \cdot 10} - \frac{9 \cdot 3}{10 \cdot 3}\right) \\ &= \left(\frac{6}{9}\right)\left(\frac{10}{30} - \frac{27}{30}\right) \\ &= \frac{6}{9} \cdot -\frac{17}{30} \\ &= -\frac{6 \cdot 17}{9 \cdot 5 \cdot 6} \\ &= -\frac{17}{45} \end{aligned}$$

19.
$$\begin{aligned} \left(\frac{7}{8} - \frac{1}{2}\right) \div \frac{3}{11} &= \left(\frac{7}{8} - \frac{1 \cdot 4}{2 \cdot 4}\right) \div \frac{3}{11} \\ &= \left(\frac{7}{8} - \frac{4}{8}\right) \cdot \frac{11}{3} \\ &= \frac{3}{8} \cdot \frac{11}{3} \\ &= \frac{3 \cdot 11}{8 \cdot 3} \\ &= \frac{11}{8} \end{aligned}$$

21.
$$\begin{aligned} 2 \cdot \left(\frac{1}{4} + \frac{1}{5}\right) + 2 &= 2 \cdot \left(\frac{1 \cdot 5}{4 \cdot 5} + \frac{1 \cdot 4}{5 \cdot 4}\right) + 2 \\ &= 2 \cdot \left(\frac{5}{20} + \frac{4}{20}\right) + 2 \\ &= 2\left(\frac{9}{20}\right) + 2 \\ &= \frac{2 \cdot 9}{2 \cdot 10} + 2 \\ &= \frac{9}{10} + \frac{2 \cdot 10}{1 \cdot 10} \\ &= \frac{9}{10} + \frac{20}{10} \\ &= \frac{29}{10} \end{aligned}$$

23. $$\left(\frac{3}{4}\right)^2 \div \left(\frac{3}{4}-\frac{1}{12}\right) = \left(\frac{3}{4}\right)^2 \div \left(\frac{3\cdot 3}{4\cdot 3}-\frac{1}{12}\right)$$
$$= \left(\frac{3}{4}\right)^2 \div \left(\frac{9}{12}-\frac{1}{12}\right)$$
$$= \left(\frac{3}{4}\right)^2 \div \frac{8}{12}$$
$$= \frac{9}{16}\cdot\frac{12}{8}$$
$$= \frac{9\cdot 3\cdot 4}{4\cdot 4\cdot 8}$$
$$= \frac{27}{32}$$

25. $$\left(\frac{2}{3}-\frac{5}{9}\right)^2 = \left(\frac{2\cdot 3}{3\cdot 3}-\frac{5}{9}\right)^2$$
$$= \left(\frac{6}{9}-\frac{5}{9}\right)^2$$
$$= \left(\frac{1}{9}\right)^2$$
$$= \frac{1}{81}$$

27. $$\left(\frac{3}{4}+\frac{1}{8}\right)^2 - \left(\frac{1}{2}+\frac{1}{8}\right)$$
$$= \left(\frac{3\cdot 2}{4\cdot 2}+\frac{1}{8}\right)^2 - \left(\frac{1\cdot 4}{2\cdot 4}+\frac{1}{8}\right)$$
$$= \left(\frac{6}{8}+\frac{1}{8}\right)^2 - \left(\frac{4}{8}+\frac{1}{8}\right)$$
$$= \left(\frac{7}{8}\right)^2 - \frac{5}{8}$$
$$= \frac{49}{64} - \frac{5\cdot 8}{8\cdot 8}$$
$$= \frac{49}{64} - \frac{40}{64}$$
$$= \frac{9}{64}$$

29. $$5y - z = 5\left(\frac{2}{5}\right) - \left(\frac{5}{6}\right)$$
$$= 2 - \frac{5}{6}$$
$$= \frac{2\cdot 6}{6} - \frac{5}{6}$$
$$= \frac{12}{6} - \frac{5}{6}$$
$$= \frac{7}{6}$$

31. $$\frac{x}{z} = \frac{-\frac{1}{3}}{\frac{5}{6}}$$
$$= -\frac{1}{3}\div\frac{5}{6}$$
$$= -\frac{1}{3}\cdot\frac{6}{5}$$
$$= -\frac{1\cdot 2\cdot 3}{3\cdot 5}$$
$$= -\frac{2}{5}$$

33. $$x^2 - yz = \left(-\frac{1}{3}\right)^2 - \left(\frac{2}{5}\right)\left(\frac{5}{6}\right)$$
$$= \frac{1}{9} - \left(\frac{2}{5}\right)\left(\frac{5}{6}\right)$$
$$= \frac{1}{9} - \frac{2\cdot 5}{5\cdot 2\cdot 3}$$
$$= \frac{1}{9} - \frac{1}{3}$$
$$= \frac{1}{9} - \frac{3}{9}$$
$$= -\frac{2}{9}$$

35. $$\frac{\frac{5}{24}}{\frac{1}{12}} = \frac{5}{24}\div\frac{1}{12} = \frac{5}{24}\cdot\frac{12}{1} = \frac{5\cdot 12}{2\cdot 12} = \frac{5}{2}$$

37. $$\left(\frac{3}{2}\right)^3 + \left(\frac{1}{2}\right)^3 = \frac{27}{8} + \frac{1}{8} = \frac{28}{8} = \frac{7\cdot 4}{2\cdot 4} = \frac{7}{2}$$

39. $$\left(-\frac{1}{3}\right)^2 + \frac{1}{3} = \frac{1}{9} + \frac{1}{3} = \frac{1}{9} + \frac{3}{9} = \frac{4}{9}$$

41. $$\frac{2+\frac{1}{6}}{1-\frac{4}{3}} = \frac{6\left(2+\frac{1}{6}\right)}{6\left(1-\frac{4}{3}\right)} = \frac{12+1}{6-8} = \frac{13}{-2} = -\frac{13}{2}$$

43. $$\left(1-\frac{2}{5}\right)^2 = \left(\frac{5}{5}-\frac{2}{5}\right)^2 = \left(\frac{3}{5}\right)^2 = \frac{9}{25}$$

45. $\left(\frac{3}{4}-1\right)\left(\frac{1}{8}+\frac{1}{2}\right)=\left(\frac{3}{4}-\frac{4}{4}\right)\left(\frac{1}{8}+\frac{4}{8}\right)$
$=\left(-\frac{1}{4}\right)\left(\frac{5}{8}\right)$
$=-\frac{1\cdot 5}{4\cdot 8}$
$=-\frac{5}{32}$

47. $\left(-\frac{2}{9}-\frac{7}{9}\right)^4=\left(-\frac{9}{9}\right)^4=(-1)^4=1$

49. $\frac{\left(\frac{1}{2}-\frac{3}{8}\right)}{\left(\frac{3}{4}+\frac{1}{2}\right)}=\frac{8\left(\frac{1}{2}-\frac{3}{8}\right)}{8\left(\frac{3}{4}+\frac{1}{2}\right)}$
$=\frac{8\cdot\frac{1}{2}-8\cdot\frac{3}{8}}{8\cdot\frac{3}{4}+8\cdot\frac{1}{2}}$
$=\frac{4-3}{6+4}$
$=\frac{1}{10}$

51. $\left(\frac{3}{4}\div\frac{6}{5}\right)-\left(\frac{3}{4}\cdot\frac{6}{5}\right)=\left(\frac{3}{4}\cdot\frac{5}{6}\right)-\left(\frac{3}{2\cdot 2}\cdot\frac{2\cdot 3}{5}\right)$
$=\frac{3\cdot 5}{4\cdot 3\cdot 2}-\frac{3\cdot 2\cdot 3}{2\cdot 2\cdot 5}$
$=\frac{5}{8}-\frac{9}{10}$
$=\frac{5\cdot 5}{8\cdot 5}-\frac{9\cdot 4}{10\cdot 4}$
$=\frac{25}{40}-\frac{36}{40}$
$=-\frac{11}{40}$

53. $\frac{\frac{x}{3}+2}{5+\frac{1}{3}}=\frac{3\left(\frac{x}{3}+2\right)}{3\left(5+\frac{1}{3}\right)}$
$=\frac{3\cdot\frac{x}{3}+3\cdot 2}{3\cdot 5+3\cdot\frac{1}{3}}$
$=\frac{x+6}{15+1}$
$=\frac{x+6}{16}$

55. $2^3=2\cdot 2\cdot 2=8$

57. $5^2=5\cdot 5=25$

59. $\frac{1}{3}(3x)=\frac{1}{3}\cdot\frac{3x}{1}=\frac{1\cdot 3\cdot x}{3\cdot 1}=x$

61. $\frac{2}{3}\left(\frac{3}{2}a\right)=\frac{2}{3}\cdot\frac{3}{2}\cdot\frac{a}{1}=\frac{2\cdot 3\cdot a}{3\cdot 2\cdot 1}=\frac{a}{1}=a$

63. No; answers may vary.

65. $\frac{2+x}{y}=\frac{2+\frac{3}{4}}{-\frac{4}{7}}$
$=\frac{28\left(2+\frac{3}{4}\right)}{28\left(-\frac{4}{7}\right)}$
$=\frac{28\cdot 2+28\cdot\frac{3}{4}}{-16}$
$=\frac{56+21}{-16}$
$=-\frac{77}{16}$

67. $x^2+7y=\left(\frac{3}{4}\right)^2+7\left(-\frac{4}{7}\right)$
$=\frac{9}{16}+\frac{7}{1}\cdot-\frac{4}{7}$
$=\frac{9}{16}+\left(-\frac{7\cdot 4}{1\cdot 7}\right)$
$=\frac{9}{16}-\frac{4}{1}$
$=\frac{9}{16}-\frac{4\cdot 16}{1\cdot 16}$
$=\frac{9}{16}-\frac{64}{16}$
$=-\frac{55}{16}$

69. $\frac{\frac{1}{2}+\frac{3}{4}}{2}=\frac{4\left(\frac{1}{2}+\frac{3}{4}\right)}{4\cdot 2}=\frac{4\cdot\frac{1}{2}+4\cdot\frac{3}{4}}{8}=\frac{2+3}{8}=\frac{5}{8}$

71. $\frac{\frac{1}{4}+\frac{2}{14}}{2}=\frac{28\left(\frac{1}{4}+\frac{2}{14}\right)}{28\cdot 2}$
$=\frac{28\cdot\left(\frac{1}{4}\right)+28\cdot\left(\frac{2}{14}\right)}{56}$
$=\frac{7+4}{56}$
$=\frac{11}{56}$

73. The average is halfway between a and b.

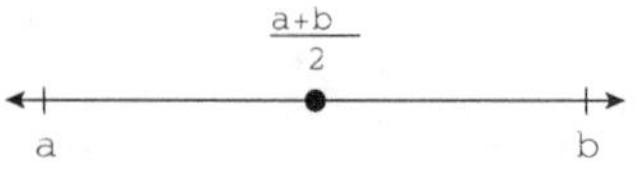

75. False, the average of two numbers is between the two numbers.

77. False, consider $-\frac{2}{3}+\frac{1}{3}=-\frac{1}{3}$.

79. True, consider $\frac{9}{4}-\frac{5}{4}=\frac{4}{4}=1$.

81. no; answer may vary.

Section 4.7

Practice Problems

1.
$$\begin{aligned}\frac{1}{5}y&=2\\5\cdot\frac{1}{2}y&=5\cdot 2\\1\cdot y&=10 \text{ or } y=10\end{aligned}$$

2.
$$\begin{aligned}\frac{5}{7}b&=25\\\frac{7}{5}\cdot\frac{5}{7}b&=\frac{7}{5}\cdot 25\\1b&=\frac{7\cdot 25}{5}\\b&=35\end{aligned}$$

3.
$$\begin{aligned}-\frac{7}{10}x&=\frac{2}{5}\\-\frac{10}{7}\cdot-\frac{7}{10}x&=-\frac{10}{7}\cdot\frac{2}{5}\\1x&=-\frac{10\cdot 2}{7\cdot 5}\\x&=-\frac{4}{7}\end{aligned}$$

4.
$$\begin{aligned}5x&=-\frac{3}{4}\\\frac{1}{5}\cdot 5x&=\frac{1}{5}\cdot-\frac{3}{4}\\1x&=-\frac{1\cdot 3}{5\cdot 4}\\x&=-\frac{3}{20}\end{aligned}$$

5.
$$\begin{aligned}\frac{y}{8}+\frac{3}{4}&=2\\8\left(\frac{y}{8}+\frac{3}{4}\right)&=8(2)\\8\left(\frac{y}{8}\right)+8\left(\frac{3}{4}\right)&=8(2)\\y+6&=16\\y+6+(-6)&=16+(-6)\\y&=10\end{aligned}$$

6.
$$\begin{aligned}\frac{x}{5}-x&=\frac{1}{5}\\5\left(\frac{x}{5}-x\right)&=5\cdot\frac{1}{5}\\5\left(\frac{x}{5}\right)-5(x)&=5\cdot\frac{1}{5}\\x-5x&=1\\-4x&=1\\\frac{-4x}{-4}&=\frac{1}{-4}\\x&=-\frac{1}{4}\end{aligned}$$

7.
$$\begin{aligned}\frac{y}{2}&=\frac{y}{5}+\frac{3}{2}\\10\left(\frac{y}{2}\right)&=10\left(\frac{y}{5}+\frac{3}{2}\right)\\10\left(\frac{y}{2}\right)&=10\left(\frac{y}{5}\right)+10\left(\frac{3}{2}\right)\\5y&=2y+15\\5y-2y&=2y+15-2y\\3y&=15\\\frac{3y}{3}&=\frac{15}{3}\\y&=5\end{aligned}$$

8. $\frac{9}{10}-\frac{y}{3}=\frac{9\cdot 3}{10\cdot 3}-\frac{y\cdot 10}{3\cdot 10}=\frac{27}{30}-\frac{10y}{30}=\frac{27-10y}{30}$

Exercise Set 4.7

1.
$$\begin{aligned}7x&=2\\\frac{7x}{7}&=\frac{2}{7}\\x&=\frac{2}{7}\end{aligned}$$

3.
$$\begin{aligned}\frac{1}{4}x&=3\\4\frac{1}{4}x&=4\cdot 3\\x&=12\end{aligned}$$

5.
$$\begin{aligned}\frac{2}{9}y&=-6\\\frac{9}{2}\cdot\frac{2}{9}y&=\frac{9}{2}\cdot-6\\y&=-27\end{aligned}$$

7.
$$-\frac{4}{9}z = -\frac{3}{2}$$
$$-\frac{9}{4}\cdot -\frac{4}{9}z = -\frac{9}{4}\cdot -\frac{3}{2}$$
$$z = \frac{27}{8}$$

9.
$$7a = \frac{1}{3}$$
$$\frac{1}{7}\cdot 7a = \frac{1}{7}\cdot\frac{1}{3}$$
$$a = \frac{1}{21}$$

11.
$$-3x = -\frac{6}{11}$$
$$-\frac{1}{3}\cdot -3x = -\frac{1}{3}\cdot -\frac{6}{11}$$
$$x = \frac{1\cdot 6}{3\cdot 11}$$
$$x = \frac{2\cdot 3}{3\cdot 11}$$
$$x = \frac{2}{11}$$

13. Multiply both sides of the equation by 3.
$$\frac{x}{3} + 2 = \frac{7}{3}$$
$$3\left(\frac{x}{3} + 2\right) = 3\cdot\frac{7}{3}$$
$$x + 6 = 7$$
$$x + 6 - 6 = 7 - 6$$
$$x = 1$$

15. Multiply both sides of the equation by the LCD of 5 and 10, 10.
$$\frac{x}{5} - \frac{5}{10} = 1$$
$$10\left(\frac{x}{5} - \frac{5}{10}\right) = 10\cdot 1$$
$$2x - 5 = 10$$
$$2x - 5 + 5 = 10 + 5$$
$$2x = 15$$
$$\frac{2x}{2} = \frac{15}{2}$$
$$x = \frac{15}{2}$$

17. Multiply both sides of the equation by the LCD of 2, 5, and 10:10.
$$\frac{1}{2} - \frac{3}{5} = \frac{x}{10}$$
$$10\left(\frac{1}{2} - \frac{3}{5}\right) = 10\left(\frac{x}{10}\right)$$
$$5 - 6 = x$$
$$-1 = x$$

19. Multiply both sides of the equation by the LCD of 3 and 5, 15.
$$\frac{x}{3} = \frac{x}{5} - 2$$
$$15\left(\frac{x}{3}\right) = 15\left(\frac{x}{5} - 2\right)$$
$$5x = 3x - 30$$
$$5x - 3x = 3x - 30 - 3x$$
$$2x = -30$$
$$\frac{2x}{2} = -\frac{30}{2}$$
$$x = -15$$

21.
$$\frac{x}{7} - \frac{4}{3} = \frac{x\cdot 3}{7\cdot 3} - \frac{4\cdot 7}{3\cdot 7} = \frac{3x}{21} - \frac{28}{21}$$
$$= \frac{3x - 28}{21}$$

23.
$$\frac{y}{2} + 5 = \frac{y}{2} + \frac{5\cdot 2}{1\cdot 2} = \frac{y}{2} + \frac{10}{2} = \frac{y + 10}{2}$$

25.
$$\frac{3x}{10} + \frac{x}{6} = \frac{3x\cdot 3}{10\cdot 3} + \frac{x\cdot 5}{6\cdot 5}$$
$$= \frac{9x}{30} + \frac{5x}{30}$$
$$= \frac{14x}{30}$$
$$= \frac{2\cdot 7x}{2\cdot 15x}$$
$$= \frac{7x}{15}$$

27.
$$\frac{3}{8}x = \frac{1}{2}$$
$$\frac{8}{3}\cdot\frac{3}{8}x = \frac{8}{3}\cdot\frac{1}{2}$$
$$x = \frac{2\cdot 4}{3\cdot 2}$$
$$x = \frac{4}{3}$$

29.
$$\frac{2}{3}-\frac{x}{5}=\frac{4}{15}$$
$$15\left(\frac{2}{3}-\frac{x}{5}\right)=15\left(\frac{4}{15}\right)$$
$$10-3x=4$$
$$10-10-3x=4-10$$
$$-3x=-6$$
$$\frac{-3x}{-3}=\frac{-6}{-3}$$
$$x=2$$

31.
$$\frac{9}{14}z=\frac{27}{20}$$
$$\left(\frac{14}{9}\right)\left(\frac{9}{14}\right)z=\left(\frac{14}{9}\right)\left(\frac{27}{20}\right)$$
$$z=\frac{2\cdot7\cdot9\cdot3}{9\cdot2\cdot10}$$
$$=\frac{7\cdot3}{10}$$
$$=\frac{21}{10}$$

33.
$$-3m-5m=\frac{4}{7}$$
$$-8m=\frac{4}{7}$$
$$\left(-\frac{1}{8}\right)(-8m)=\left(-\frac{1}{8}\right)\left(\frac{4}{7}\right)$$
$$m=-\frac{1\cdot4}{2\cdot4\cdot7}$$
$$m=-\frac{1}{14}$$

35.
$$\frac{x}{4}+1=\frac{1}{4}$$
$$4\left(\frac{x}{4}+1\right)=4\cdot\frac{1}{4}$$
$$x+4=1$$
$$x+4-4=1-4$$
$$x=-3$$

37.
$$\frac{1}{5}y=10$$
$$5\left(\frac{1}{5}y\right)=5\cdot10$$
$$y=50$$

39. $\frac{5}{9}-\frac{2}{3}=\frac{5}{9}-\frac{2\cdot3}{3\cdot3}=\frac{5}{9}-\frac{6}{9}=-\frac{1}{9}$

41.
$$-\frac{3}{4}x=\frac{9}{2}$$
$$-\frac{4}{3}\cdot-\frac{3}{4}x=-\frac{4}{3}\cdot\frac{9}{2}$$
$$x=-\frac{2\cdot2\cdot3\cdot3}{3\cdot2}$$
$$x=-6$$

43.
$$\frac{x}{2}-x=-2$$
$$2\left(\frac{x}{2}-x\right)=2(-2)$$
$$x-2x=-4$$
$$-x=-4$$
$$\frac{-x}{-1}=\frac{-4}{-1}$$
$$x=4$$

45.
$$-\frac{5}{8}y=\frac{3}{16}-\frac{9}{16}$$
$$-\frac{5}{8}y=-\frac{6}{16}$$
$$-\frac{5}{8}y=-\frac{2\cdot3}{2\cdot8}$$
$$-\frac{5}{8}y=-\frac{3}{8}$$
$$\left(-\frac{8}{5}\right)\left(-\frac{5}{8}y\right)=\left(-\frac{8}{5}\right)\left(-\frac{3}{8}\right)$$
$$y=\frac{8\cdot3}{5\cdot8}$$
$$y=\frac{3}{5}$$

47.
$$17x-25x=\frac{1}{3}$$
$$-8x=\frac{1}{3}$$
$$\left(-\frac{1}{8}\right)(-8x)=\left(-\frac{1}{8}\right)\left(\frac{1}{3}\right)$$
$$x=-\frac{1}{24}$$

49.
$$\frac{7}{6}x=\frac{1}{4}-\frac{2}{3}$$
$$12\left(\frac{7}{6}x\right)=12\left(\frac{1}{4}-\frac{2}{3}\right)$$
$$14x=3-8$$
$$14x=-5$$
$$\frac{14x}{14}=\frac{-5}{14}$$
$$x=-\frac{5}{14}$$

51.
$$\frac{b}{4}=\frac{b}{12}+\frac{2}{3}$$
$$12\left(\frac{b}{4}\right)=12\left(\frac{b}{12}+\frac{2}{3}\right)$$
$$3b=b+8$$
$$3b-b=b+8-b$$
$$2b=8$$
$$\frac{2b}{2}=\frac{8}{2}$$
$$b=4$$

53.
$$\frac{x}{3}+2=\frac{x}{2}+8$$
$$6\left(\frac{x}{3}+2\right)=6\left(\frac{x}{2}+8\right)$$
$$2x+12=3x+48$$
$$2x+12-2x=3x+48-2x$$
$$12=x+48$$
$$12-48=x+48-48$$
$$-36=x$$

55.
$$3+\frac{1}{2}=\frac{3}{1}+\frac{1}{2}$$
$$=\frac{3\cdot 2}{1\cdot 2}+\frac{1}{2}$$
$$=\frac{6}{2}+\frac{1}{2}$$
$$=\frac{6+1}{2}$$
$$=\frac{7}{2}$$

57.
$$5+\frac{9}{10}=\frac{5}{1}+\frac{9}{10}$$
$$=\frac{5\cdot 10}{1\cdot 10}+\frac{9}{10}$$
$$=\frac{50}{10}+\frac{9}{10}$$
$$=\frac{50+9}{10}$$
$$=\frac{59}{10}$$

59.
$$9-\frac{5}{6}=\frac{9}{1}-\frac{5}{6}$$
$$=\frac{9\cdot 6}{1\cdot 6}-\frac{5}{6}$$
$$=\frac{54}{6}-\frac{5}{6}$$
$$=\frac{54-5}{6}$$
$$=\frac{49}{6}$$

61. Answers will vary.

63.
$$\frac{19}{53}=\frac{353x}{1431}+\frac{23}{27}$$
$$1431\left(\frac{19}{53}\right)=1431\left(\frac{353x}{1431}+\frac{23}{27}\right)$$
$$513=353x+1219$$
$$513-1219=353x+1219-1219$$
$$-706=353x$$
$$\frac{-706}{353}=\frac{353x}{353}$$
$$-2=x$$

Section 4.8

Practice Problems

1. Each part is $\frac{1}{3}$, and there are 8 parts shaded, or 2 wholes and 2 more parts: $\frac{8}{3}$ or $2\frac{2}{3}$.

2. Each part is $\frac{1}{4}$, and there are 5 parts shaded, or 1 whole and 1 more part: $\frac{5}{4}$ or $1\frac{1}{4}$.

3. **a.** $2\frac{5}{7}=\frac{7\cdot 2+5}{7}=\frac{19}{7}$

   b. $5\frac{1}{3}=\frac{3\cdot 5+1}{3}=\frac{16}{3}$

   c. $9\frac{3}{10}=\frac{10\cdot 9+3}{10}=\frac{93}{10}$

   d. $1\frac{1}{5}=\frac{5\cdot 1+1}{5}=\frac{6}{5}$

4. a. $\begin{array}{r} 1 \\ 5\overline{)\ 8} \\ \underline{-5} \\ 3 \end{array}$

$\frac{8}{5}=1\frac{3}{5}$

b. $\begin{array}{r} 2 \\ 6\overline{)\ 17} \\ \underline{-12} \\ 5 \end{array}$

$\frac{17}{6}=2\frac{5}{6}$

c. $\begin{array}{r} 12 \\ 4\overline{)\ 48} \\ \underline{-4} \\ 08 \\ \underline{-8} \\ 0 \end{array}$

$\frac{48}{4}=12$

d. $\begin{array}{r} 8 \\ 4\overline{)\ 35} \\ \underline{-32} \\ 3 \end{array}$

$\frac{35}{4}=8\frac{3}{4}$

e. $\begin{array}{r} 7 \\ 7\overline{)\ 51} \\ \underline{-49} \\ 2 \end{array}$

$\frac{51}{7}=7\frac{2}{7}$

f. $\begin{array}{r} 1 \\ 20\overline{)\ 21} \\ \underline{-20} \\ 1 \end{array}$

$\frac{21}{20}=1\frac{1}{20}$

5. $$\begin{aligned} 2\frac{1}{2}\cdot\frac{8}{15} &= \frac{5}{2}\cdot\frac{8}{15} \\ &= \frac{5\cdot 8}{2\cdot 15} \\ &= \frac{5\cdot 2\cdot 4}{2\cdot 5\cdot 3} \\ &= \frac{4}{3} \text{ or } 1\frac{1}{3} \end{aligned}$$

6. $$\begin{aligned} 3\frac{1}{5}\cdot 2\frac{3}{4} &= \frac{16}{5}\cdot\frac{11}{4} \\ &= \frac{16\cdot 11}{5\cdot 4} \\ &= \frac{4\cdot 4\cdot 11}{5\cdot 4} \\ &= \frac{4\cdot 11}{5} \\ &= \frac{44}{5} \text{ or } 8\frac{4}{5} \end{aligned}$$

7. $$\begin{aligned} \frac{2}{3}\cdot 18 &= \frac{2}{3}\cdot\frac{18}{1} \\ &= \frac{2\cdot 18}{3\cdot 1} \\ &= \frac{2\cdot 3\cdot 6}{3\cdot 1} \\ &= \frac{2\cdot 6}{1\cdot 1} \\ &= \frac{12}{1} \text{ or } 12 \end{aligned}$$

8. $\frac{4}{9}\div 5=\frac{4}{9}\div\frac{5}{1}=\frac{4}{9}\cdot\frac{1}{5}=\frac{4\cdot 1}{9\cdot 5}=\frac{4}{45}$

9. $$\begin{aligned} \frac{8}{15}\div 3\frac{4}{5} &= \frac{8}{15}\div\frac{19}{5} \\ &= \frac{8}{15}\cdot\frac{5}{19} \\ &= \frac{8\cdot 5}{15\cdot 19} \\ &= \frac{8\cdot 5}{5\cdot 3\cdot 19} \\ &= \frac{8}{3\cdot 19} \\ &= \frac{8}{57} \end{aligned}$$

10. $3\frac{2}{5} \div 2\frac{2}{15} = \frac{17}{5} \div \frac{32}{15}$
$= \frac{17}{5} \cdot \frac{15}{32}$
$= \frac{17 \cdot 15}{5 \cdot 32}$
$= \frac{17 \cdot 5 \cdot 3}{5 \cdot 32}$
$= \frac{17 \cdot 3}{32}$
$= \frac{51}{32}$ or $1\frac{19}{32}$

11.
$$\begin{array}{rcr} 4\frac{2}{5} & = & 4\frac{4}{10} \\ +\ 5\frac{3}{10} & = & +\ 5\frac{3}{10} \\ \hline & & 9\frac{7}{10} \end{array}$$

12.
$$\begin{array}{rcl} 2\frac{5}{14} & = & 2\frac{5}{14} \\ +\ 5\frac{6}{7} & = & +\ 5\frac{12}{14} \\ \hline & & 7\frac{17}{14} = 7 + 1\frac{3}{14} = 8\frac{3}{14} \end{array}$$

13.
$$\begin{array}{rcr} 10 & = & 10 \\ 2\frac{1}{7} & = & 2\frac{5}{35} \\ +\ 3\frac{1}{5} & = & +\ 3\frac{7}{35} \\ \hline & & 15\frac{12}{35} \end{array}$$

14.
$$\begin{array}{rcr} 29\frac{7}{8} & = & 29\frac{14}{16} \\ -\ 13\frac{3}{16} & = & -\ 13\frac{3}{16} \\ \hline & & 16\frac{11}{16} \end{array}$$

15.
$$\begin{array}{rcrcl} 9\frac{7}{15} & = & 9\frac{7}{15} & = & 8\frac{22}{15} \\ -\ 5\frac{4}{5} & = & -\ 5\frac{12}{15} & = & -\ 5\frac{12}{15} \\ \hline & & & & 3\frac{10}{15} = 3\frac{2}{3} \end{array}$$

16.
$$\begin{array}{rcr} 25 & = & 24\frac{9}{9} \\ -10\frac{2}{9} & = & -10\frac{2}{9} \\ \hline & & 14\frac{7}{9} \end{array}$$

17. The phrase "how much larger" tells us to subtract. Subtract $19\frac{5}{12}$ feet from $23\frac{1}{4}$ feet.

$$\begin{array}{rcrcl} 23\frac{1}{4} & = & 23\frac{3}{12} & = & 22\frac{15}{12} \\ -19\frac{5}{12} & = & -19\frac{5}{12} & = & -19\frac{5}{12} \\ \hline & & & & 3\frac{10}{12} = 3\frac{5}{6} \end{array}$$

The girth of the largest known American Beech tree is $3\frac{5}{6}$ feet larger than the girth of the largest known Sugar Maple tree.

18. $30 \div 2\frac{1}{7} = \frac{30}{1} \div \frac{15}{7}$
$= \frac{30}{1} \cdot \frac{7}{15}$
$= \frac{30 \cdot 7}{1 \cdot 15}$
$= \frac{15 \cdot 2 \cdot 7}{1 \cdot 15}$
$= \frac{2 \cdot 7}{1}$
$= \frac{14}{1}$
$= 14$

14 dresses can be made.

19. $-7\frac{3}{7} = -\frac{7 \cdot 7 + 3}{3} = -\frac{52}{7}$

20. $-4\frac{10}{11} = -\frac{11 \cdot 4 + 10}{11} = -\frac{54}{11}$

21. $-\frac{29}{8} = -3\frac{5}{8}$

$$\begin{array}{r} 3 \\ 8\overline{)\ 29} \\ -24 \\ \hline 5 \end{array}$$

22. $-\frac{31}{5} = -6\frac{1}{5}$

$$\begin{array}{r} 6 \\ 5\overline{)\ 31} \\ -30 \\ \hline 1 \end{array}$$

23. $3\frac{3}{4} \cdot \left(-2\frac{3}{5}\right) = \frac{15}{4} \cdot \left(-\frac{13}{5}\right)$
$= -\frac{3 \cdot 5 \cdot 13}{4 \cdot 5}$
$= -\frac{39}{4}$ or $-9\frac{3}{4}$

24. $-1\frac{2}{7} \div 4\frac{1}{4} = -\frac{9}{7} \div \frac{17}{4}$
$= -\frac{9}{7} \cdot \frac{4}{17}$
$= -\frac{36}{119}$

25. $7\frac{2}{3} + \left(-11\frac{3}{4}\right)$

Subtract the absolute values.

$$\begin{array}{rcr} 11\frac{3 \cdot 3}{4 \cdot 3} & = & 11\frac{9}{12} \\ -7\frac{2 \cdot 4}{3 \cdot 4} & = & -7\frac{8}{12} \\ \hline & & 4\frac{1}{12} \end{array}$$

Since $-11\frac{3}{4}$ has the larger absolute value, the answer is $-4\frac{1}{12}$.

26. $-9\frac{2}{7} - 15\frac{11}{14}$

Add the absolute values.

$$\begin{array}{rcr} 9\frac{2 \cdot 2}{7 \cdot 2} & = & 9\frac{4}{14} \\ +15\frac{11}{14} & = & +15\frac{11}{14} \\ \hline & & 24\frac{15}{14} \end{array}$$

Since $\frac{15}{14} = 1\frac{1}{14}$, $24 + 1\frac{1}{14} = 25\frac{1}{14}$.

Keep the common sign: $-25\frac{1}{14}$

Calculator Explorations

Press the keys as instructed on p.328 of your textbook.

1. $25\frac{5}{11} = \frac{280}{11}$

2. $67\frac{14}{15} = \frac{1019}{15}$

3. $107\frac{31}{35} = \frac{3776}{35}$

4. $186\frac{17}{21} = \frac{3923}{21}$

5. $\frac{365}{14} = 26\frac{1}{14}$

6. $\frac{290}{13} = 22\frac{4}{13}$

7. $\frac{2769}{30} = 92\frac{3}{10}$

8. $\frac{3941}{17} = 231\frac{14}{17}$

Exercise Set 4.8

1. Each part is $\frac{1}{4}$, and there are 11 parts shaded, or 2 wholes and 3 more parts.

   a. $\frac{11}{4}$

   b. $2\frac{3}{4}$

3. Each part is $\frac{1}{3}$, and there are 11 parts shaded, or 3 wholes and 2 more parts.

   a. $\frac{11}{3}$

   b. $3\frac{2}{3}$

5. Each part is $\frac{1}{2}$, and there are 3 parts shaded or 1 whole part and 1 more part.

a. $\frac{3}{2}$

b. $1\frac{1}{2}$

7. Each part is $\frac{1}{3}$, and there are 4 parts shaded, or 1 whole and 1 more part.

a. $\frac{4}{3}$

b. $1\frac{1}{3}$

9. $2\frac{1}{3} = \frac{2 \cdot 3 + 1}{3} = \frac{7}{3}$

11. $3\frac{3}{8} = \frac{3 \cdot 8 + 3}{8} = \frac{27}{8}$

13. $11\frac{6}{7} = \frac{11 \cdot 7 + 6}{7} = \frac{83}{7}$

15.
$$\begin{array}{r} 1 \\ 7\overline{)13} \\ \underline{-7} \\ 6 \end{array}$$
$$\frac{13}{7} = 1\frac{6}{7}$$

17.
$$\begin{array}{r} 3 \\ 15\overline{)\ 47} \\ \underline{-45} \\ 2 \end{array}$$
$$\frac{47}{15} = 3\frac{2}{15}$$

19.
$$\begin{array}{r} 4 \\ 8\overline{)\ 37} \\ \underline{-32} \\ 5 \end{array}$$
$$\frac{37}{8} = 4\frac{5}{8}$$

21. $2\frac{2}{3} \cdot \frac{1}{7} = \frac{8}{3} \cdot \frac{1}{7} = \frac{8 \cdot 1}{3 \cdot 7} = \frac{8}{21}$

23.
$$\begin{aligned} 8 \div 1\frac{5}{7} &= 8 \div \frac{12}{7} \\ &= \frac{8}{1} \cdot \frac{7}{12} \\ &= \frac{2 \cdot 4 \cdot 7}{4 \cdot 3} \\ &= \frac{14}{3} \\ &= 4\frac{2}{3} \end{aligned}$$

25. $3\frac{2}{3} \cdot 1\frac{1}{2} = \frac{11}{3} \cdot \frac{3}{2} = \frac{11 \cdot 3}{3 \cdot 2} = \frac{11}{2} = 5\frac{1}{2}$

27. $2\frac{2}{3} \div \frac{1}{7} = \frac{8}{3} \div \frac{!}{7} = \frac{8}{3} \cdot \frac{7}{1} = \frac{8 \cdot 7}{3 \cdot 1} = \frac{56}{3} = 18\frac{2}{3}$

29. $4\frac{7}{10} + 2\frac{1}{10} = 6\frac{8}{10} = 6\frac{4}{5}$

31.
$$\begin{array}{rcr} 15\frac{4}{7} & = & 15\frac{8}{14} \\ \underline{+\ 9\frac{11}{14}} & = & \underline{9\frac{11}{14}} \\ & & 24\frac{19}{14} = 25\frac{5}{14} \end{array}$$

33.
$$\begin{array}{r} 3\frac{5}{8} = 3\frac{15}{24} \\ 2\frac{1}{6} = 2\frac{4}{24} \\ \underline{+\ 7\frac{3}{4} = 7\frac{18}{24}} \\ 12\frac{37}{24} = 13\frac{13}{24} \end{array}$$

35.
$$\begin{array}{r} 4\frac{7}{10} \\ \underline{-\ 2\frac{1}{10}} \\ 2\frac{6}{10} = 2\frac{3}{5} \end{array}$$

37.
$$\begin{array}{rcr} 10\frac{13}{14} & = & 10\frac{13}{14} \\ \underline{-\ 3\frac{4}{7}} & = & \underline{-\ 3\frac{8}{14}} \\ & & 7\frac{5}{14} \end{array}$$

39.
$$\begin{array}{rcrcr} 9\frac{1}{5} & = & 9\frac{5}{25} & = & 8\frac{30}{25} \\ -\ 8\frac{6}{25} & = & -\ 8\frac{6}{25} & = & -\ 8\frac{6}{25} \\ \hline & & & & \frac{24}{25} \end{array}$$

41.
$$\begin{array}{r} 2\frac{3}{4} \\ +\ 1\frac{1}{4} \\ \hline 3\frac{4}{4} = 3+1 = 4 \end{array}$$

43.
$$\begin{array}{rcrcr} 15\frac{4}{7} & = & 15\frac{8}{14} & = & 14\frac{22}{14} \\ -\ 9\frac{11}{14} & = & -\ 9\frac{11}{14} & = & -\ 9\frac{11}{14} \\ \hline & & & & 5\frac{11}{14} \end{array}$$

45. $3\frac{1}{9}\cdot 2 = \frac{28}{9}\cdot\frac{2}{1} = \frac{56}{9} = 6\frac{2}{9}$

47. $1\frac{2}{3} \div 2\frac{1}{5} = \frac{5}{3} \div \frac{11}{5} = \frac{5}{3}\cdot\frac{5}{11} = \frac{25}{33}$

49. $22\frac{4}{9} + 13\frac{5}{18} = 22\frac{8}{18} + 13\frac{5}{18} = 35\frac{13}{18}$

51.
$$\begin{array}{rcr} 5\frac{2}{3} & = & 5\frac{4}{6} \\ -\ 3\frac{1}{6} & = & -\ 3\frac{1}{6} \\ \hline & & 2\frac{3}{6} = 2\frac{1}{2} \end{array}$$

53.
$$\begin{array}{rcr} 15\frac{1}{5} & = & 15\frac{6}{30} \\ 20\frac{3}{10} & = & 20\frac{9}{30} \\ +\ 37\frac{2}{15} & = & +\ 37\frac{4}{30} \\ \hline & & 72\frac{19}{30} \end{array}$$

55.
$$\begin{array}{rcrcr} 6\frac{4}{7} & = & 6\frac{8}{14} & = & 6\frac{22}{14} \\ -\ 5\frac{11}{14} & = & -\ 5\frac{11}{14} & = & -\ 5\frac{11}{14} \\ \hline & & & & \frac{11}{14} \end{array}$$

57. $4\frac{2}{7}\cdot 1\frac{3}{10} = \frac{30}{7}\cdot\frac{13}{10} = \frac{3\cdot 10\cdot 13}{7\cdot 10} = \frac{39}{7} = 5\frac{4}{7}$

59.
$$\begin{array}{rcr} 6\frac{2}{11} & = & 6\frac{6}{33} \\ 3 & = & 3 \\ +\ 4\frac{10}{33} & = & 4\frac{10}{33} \\ \hline & & 13\frac{16}{33} \end{array}$$

61. The phrase "total duration" tells us to add. Find the sum of the three durations.
$$\begin{array}{rcr} 4\frac{14}{15} & = & 4\frac{56}{60} \\ 4\frac{7}{60} & = & 4\frac{7}{60} \\ +\ 1\frac{2}{3} & = & +\ 1\frac{40}{60} \\ \hline & & 9\frac{103}{60} = 10\frac{43}{60} \end{array}$$

The total duration is $10\frac{43}{60}$ minutes.

63. The phrase "how much longer" tells us to subtract. Subtract $4\frac{7}{60}$ minutes from $4\frac{14}{15}$ minutes.
$$\begin{array}{rcr} 4\frac{14}{15} & = & 4\frac{56}{60} \\ -\ 4\frac{7}{60} & = & -\ 4\frac{7}{60} \\ \hline & & \frac{49}{60} \end{array}$$

The June 21, 2001 eclipse will be $\frac{49}{60}$ minutes longer than the March 29, 2006 eclipse.

65.
$$\begin{aligned} 6\cdot 3\frac{1}{4} &= \frac{6}{1}\cdot\frac{13}{4} \\ &= \frac{2\cdot 3\cdot 13}{1\cdot 2\cdot 2} \\ &= \frac{39}{2} \\ &= 19\frac{1}{2} \end{aligned}$$

The sidewalk is $19\frac{1}{2}$ inches wide.

67. $423 \div 28\frac{1}{5} = \frac{423}{1} \div \frac{141}{5}$
$= \frac{3 \cdot 141}{1} \cdot \frac{5}{141}$
$= 15$

He purchased 15 shares.

69. Subtract $1\frac{1}{2}$ inches from $1\frac{9}{16}$ inches.

$$\begin{array}{rcr} 1\frac{9}{16} & = & 1\frac{9}{16} \\ -\;1\frac{1}{2} & = & -\;1\frac{8}{16} \\ \hline & & \frac{1}{16} \end{array}$$

The entrance holes for Mountain Bluebirds should be $\frac{1}{16}$ inch wider than the entrance for Eastern Bluebirds.

71. The phrase "cuts off" tells us to subtract. First subtract $2\frac{1}{2}$ feet from $15\frac{2}{3}$ feet. Then subtract $3\frac{1}{4}$ feet from that result.

$$\begin{array}{rcr} 15\frac{2}{3} & = & 15\frac{4}{6} \\ -2\frac{1}{2} & = & -2\frac{3}{6} \\ \hline & & 13\frac{1}{6} \end{array}$$

$$\begin{array}{rcrcr} 13\frac{1}{6} & = & 13\frac{2}{12} & = & 12\frac{14}{12} \\ -3\frac{1}{4} & = & -3\frac{3}{12} & = & -3\frac{3}{12} \\ \hline & & & & 9\frac{11}{12} \end{array}$$

No, the pipe will be $\frac{1}{12}$ of a foot short.

73. $58\frac{3}{4} \div 7\frac{1}{2} = \frac{235}{4} \div \frac{15}{2}$
$= \frac{235}{4} \cdot \frac{2}{15}$
$= \frac{5 \cdot 47 \cdot 2}{2 \cdot 2 \cdot 3 \cdot 5}$
$= \frac{47}{6}$ or $7\frac{5}{6}$

$7\frac{5}{6}$ gallons were used each hour.

75.

$$\begin{array}{rcr} 65\frac{9}{10} & = & 65\frac{9}{10} \\ -56\frac{1}{2} & = & -56\frac{5}{10} \\ \hline & & 9\frac{4}{10} = 9\frac{2}{5} \end{array}$$

Spain's standard guage is $9\frac{2}{5}$ wider than the U.S. standard guage.

77. The phrase "how much more" tells us to subtract. Subtract $3\frac{3}{5}$ inches from $11\frac{1}{4}$ inches.

$$\begin{array}{rcrcr} 11\frac{1}{4} & = & 11\frac{5}{20} & = & 10\frac{25}{20} \\ -3\frac{3}{5} & = & -3\frac{12}{20} & = & -3\frac{12}{20} \\ \hline & & & & 7\frac{13}{20} \end{array}$$

Tucson gets $7\frac{13}{20}$ inches more, on average, than Yuma.

79. $2 \cdot 1\frac{3}{4} = \frac{2}{1} \cdot \frac{7}{4}$
$= \frac{2 \cdot 7}{1 \cdot 4}$
$= \frac{2 \cdot 7}{1 \cdot 2 \cdot 2}$
$= \frac{7}{1 \cdot 2}$
$= \frac{7}{2}$ or $3\frac{1}{2}$

The area is $\frac{7}{2}$ or $3\frac{1}{2}$ square yards.

81. $A = lw$
$A = \frac{3}{4} \cdot 1\frac{1}{4} = \frac{3}{4} \cdot \frac{5}{4} = \frac{5}{16}$

The area of the computer chip is $\frac{15}{16}$ sq. in.

83. Find the distance around. Add the lengths of the three sides.

$$\begin{array}{r} 2\frac{1}{3} \\ 2\frac{1}{3} \\ +\ 2\frac{1}{3} \\ \hline 6\frac{3}{3} = 7 \end{array}$$

The perimeter is 7 miles.

85. Find the distance around. Add the lengths of the four sides.

$$\begin{array}{rl} 3 & = 3 \\ 5\frac{1}{3} & = 5\frac{8}{24} \\ 5 & = 5 \\ +\ 7\frac{7}{8} & = 7\frac{21}{24} \\ \hline & 20\frac{29}{24} = 21\frac{5}{24} \end{array}$$

The perimeter is $21\frac{5}{24}$ meters.

87. $\frac{1}{20} \cdot 30 = \frac{1 \cdot 3 \cdot 10}{2 \cdot 10} = \frac{3}{2}$ or $1\frac{1}{2}$

The life expectancy of circulating paper money is $1\frac{1}{2}$ years.

89. The phrase "overall height' tells us to add. Add the two heights.

$$\begin{array}{rl} 152\frac{1}{6} & = 152\frac{1}{6} \\ +\ 154\frac{1}{2} & = 154\frac{3}{6} \\ \hline & 306\frac{4}{6} = 306\frac{2}{3} \end{array}$$

The overall height is $306\frac{2}{3}$ feet.

91.

$$\begin{aligned} 15\frac{1}{5} \div 24 &= \frac{76}{5} \div \frac{24}{1} \\ &= \frac{76}{5} \cdot \frac{1}{24} \\ &= \frac{76 \cdot 1}{5 \cdot 24} \\ &= \frac{4 \cdot 19 \cdot 1}{5 \cdot 4 \cdot 6} \\ &= \frac{19 \cdot 1}{5 \cdot 6} \\ &= \frac{19}{30} \end{aligned}$$

On average $\frac{19}{30}$ inch fell each hour.

93.

$$\begin{aligned} -4\frac{2}{5} \cdot 2\frac{3}{10} &= -\frac{22}{5} \cdot \frac{23}{10} \\ &= -\frac{2 \cdot 11 \cdot 23}{5 \cdot 2 \cdot 5} \\ &= -\frac{253}{25} \\ &= -10\frac{3}{25} \end{aligned}$$

95.

$$\begin{array}{rcr} -\ 5\frac{1}{8} & = & -5\frac{1}{8} \\ -19\frac{3}{4} & = & -19\frac{6}{8} \\ \hline & & -24\frac{7}{8} \end{array}$$

97.

$$\begin{array}{rcrcr} -31\frac{2}{15} & = & -31\frac{8}{60} & = & -30\frac{68}{60} \\ +17\frac{3}{20} & = & +17\frac{9}{60} & = & +17\frac{9}{60} \\ \hline & & & & -13\frac{59}{60} \end{array}$$

99.

$$\begin{aligned} 1\frac{3}{4} \div \left(-3\frac{1}{2}\right) &= \frac{7}{4} \div \left(-\frac{7}{2}\right) \\ &= \frac{7}{4} \cdot \left(-\frac{2}{7}\right) \\ &= -\frac{7 \cdot 2}{2 \cdot 2 \cdot 7} \\ &= -\frac{1}{2} \end{aligned}$$

101.
$$\begin{aligned} -13\tfrac{5}{6} &= -13\tfrac{20}{24} = -12\tfrac{44}{24} \\ +11\tfrac{7}{8} &= +11\tfrac{21}{24} = +11\tfrac{21}{24} \\ \hline & \qquad\qquad\quad -1\tfrac{23}{24} \end{aligned}$$

103.
$$\begin{aligned} -7\frac{3}{10} \div (-100) &= -\frac{73}{10} \div \left(-\frac{100}{1}\right) \\ &= -\frac{73}{10} \cdot \left(-\frac{1}{100}\right) \\ &= \frac{73}{1000} \end{aligned}$$

105.
$$\begin{aligned} -3\frac{1}{6} \cdot \left(-2\frac{3}{4}\right) &= -\frac{19}{6} \cdot \left(-\frac{11}{4}\right) \\ &= \frac{209}{24} \\ &= 8\frac{17}{24} \end{aligned}$$

107.
$$\begin{aligned} -21\tfrac{5}{12} &= -21\tfrac{5}{12} \\ -10\tfrac{3}{4} &= -10\tfrac{9}{12} \\ \hline & -31\tfrac{14}{12} = -32\tfrac{2}{12} = -32\tfrac{1}{6} \end{aligned}$$

109.
$$\begin{aligned} 2x - 5 + 7x - 8 &= 2x + 7x - 5 - 8 \\ &= 9x - 13 \end{aligned}$$

111.
$$\begin{aligned} 3(y-2) - 6y &= 3y - 6 - 6y \\ &= 3y - 6y - 6 \\ &= -3y - 6 \end{aligned}$$

113. $2^3 + 3^2 = 2 \cdot 2 \cdot 2 + 3 \cdot 3 = 8 + 9 = 17$

115. $\dfrac{7-3}{2^2} = \dfrac{4}{4} = 1$

117. Weight of Supreme box:

$$\begin{aligned} 2\tfrac{1}{4}\text{ lb} &= 2\tfrac{1}{4}\text{ lb} \\ +3\tfrac{1}{2}\text{ lb} &= +3\tfrac{2}{4}\text{ lb} \\ \hline & \;\; 5\tfrac{3}{4}\text{ lb} = 5\tfrac{6}{8}\text{ lb} \end{aligned}$$

Weight of Deluxe box:

$$\begin{aligned} 1\tfrac{3}{8}\text{ lb} &= 1\tfrac{3}{8}\text{ lb} \\ +4\tfrac{1}{4}\text{ lb} &= +4\tfrac{2}{8}\text{ lb} \\ \hline & \;\; 5\tfrac{5}{8}\text{ lb} \end{aligned}$$

The Supreme box is heavier.

$$\begin{aligned} & 5\tfrac{6}{8}\text{ lb} \\ & -5\tfrac{5}{8}\text{ lb} \\ \hline & \tfrac{1}{8}\text{ lb} \end{aligned}$$

It is $\frac{1}{8}$ pound heavier.

119. Answers may vary.

121. Answers may vary.

Chapter 4 Review

1. $\dfrac{3}{4}$ ← Three parts shaded / ← Four equal parts

So the answer expressed as a fraction is $\frac{3}{4}$.

2. $\dfrac{2}{5}$ ← Two parts shaded / ← Five equal parts

So the answer expressed as a fraction is $\frac{2}{5}$.

3. To graph $\frac{7}{9}$ on a number line, divide the distance from 0 to 1 into 9 equal parts. Then start at 0 and count over 7 parts.

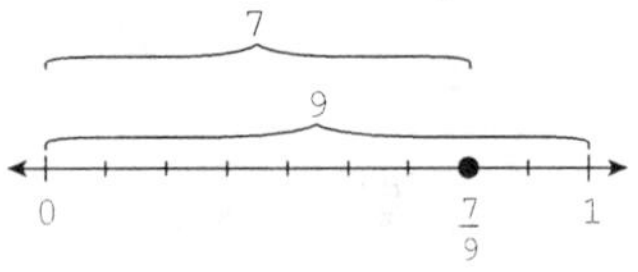

4. To graph $\frac{4}{7}$ on a number line, divide the distance from 0 to 1 into 7 equal parts. Then start at 0 and count over 4 parts.

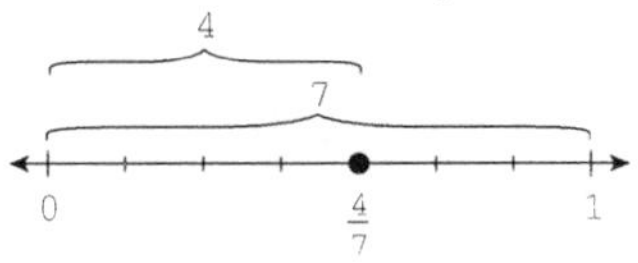

5. To graph $\frac{5}{4}$ on a number line, divide the distances from 0 to 1 and 1 to 2 into 4 equal parts. Then start at 0 and count over 5 parts.

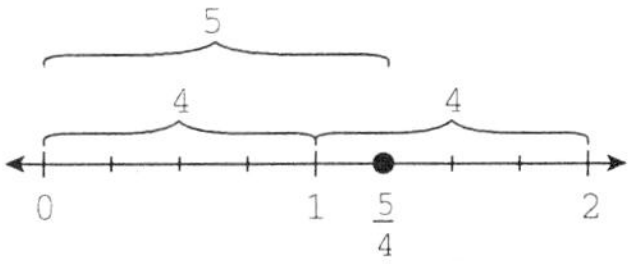

6. To graph $\frac{7}{5}$ on a number line, divide the distances from 0 to 1 and from 1 to 2 into 5 equal parts. Then start at 0 and count over 7 parts.

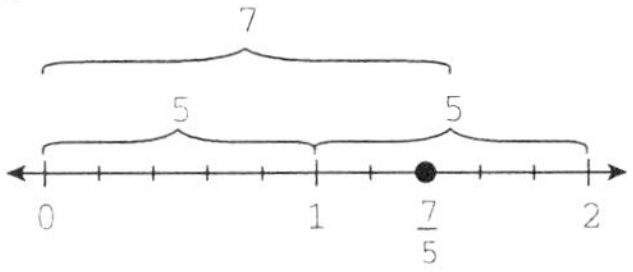

7. $\frac{\text{Number closed}}{\text{Total number}} = \frac{35}{242}$

$\frac{35}{242}$ of job specialties are closed to women.

8. $\frac{43}{50}$ of the U.S. Armed Forces are men.

9. $\frac{2}{3} = \frac{2 \cdot 10}{3 \cdot 10} = \frac{20}{30}$

10. $\frac{5}{8} = \frac{5 \cdot 7}{8 \cdot 7} = \frac{35}{56}$

11. $\frac{7a}{6} = \frac{7a \cdot 7}{6 \cdot 7} = \frac{49a}{42}$

12. $\frac{9b}{4} = \frac{9b \cdot 5}{4 \cdot 5} = \frac{45b}{20}$

13. $\frac{4}{5x} = \frac{4 \cdot 10}{5x \cdot 10} = \frac{40}{50x}$

14. $\frac{5}{9y} = \frac{5 \cdot 2}{9y \cdot 2} = \frac{10}{18y}$

15. $\frac{12}{28} = \frac{2 \cdot 2 \cdot 3}{2 \cdot 2 \cdot 7} = \frac{3}{7}$

16. $\frac{15}{27} = \frac{3 \cdot 5}{3 \cdot 9} = \frac{5}{9}$

17. $\frac{25x}{75x^2} = \frac{5 \cdot 5 \cdot x}{3 \cdot 5 \cdot 5 \cdot x \cdot x} = \frac{1}{3x}$

18. $\frac{36y^3}{72y} = \frac{36y \cdot y^2}{2 \cdot 36y} = \frac{y^2}{2}$

19. $\frac{29ab}{32abc} = \frac{29 \cdot a \cdot b}{32 \cdot a \cdot b \cdot c} = \frac{29}{32c}$

20. $\frac{18xyz}{23xy} = \frac{18z}{23}$

21. $\frac{45x^2y}{27xy^3} = \frac{3 \cdot 3 \cdot 5 \cdot x \cdot x \cdot y}{3 \cdot 3 \cdot 3 \cdot x \cdot y \cdot y^2} = \frac{5x}{3y^2}$

22. $\frac{42ab^2c}{30abc^3} = \frac{2 \cdot 3 \cdot 7a \cdot b \cdot b \cdot c}{2 \cdot 3 \cdot 5a \cdot b \cdot c \cdot c^2} = \frac{7b}{5c^2}$

23. $\frac{\text{inches in the part}}{\text{inches in a foot}} = \frac{8}{12} = \frac{4 \cdot 2}{4 \cdot 3} = \frac{2}{3}$

8 inches is $\frac{2}{3}$ of a foot.

24. $1 - \frac{6}{15} = \frac{15 - 6}{15} = \frac{9}{15} = \frac{3 \cdot 3}{3 \cdot 5} = \frac{3}{5}$

$\frac{3}{5}$ of the cars are not white.

25. $\frac{3}{5} \cdot \frac{1}{2} = \frac{3 \cdot 1}{5 \cdot 2} = \frac{3}{10}$

26. $-\frac{6}{7} \cdot \frac{5}{12} = -\frac{6 \cdot 5}{7 \cdot 2 \cdot 6} = -\frac{5}{14}$

27. $\frac{7}{8x} \cdot -\frac{2}{3} = -\frac{7 \cdot 2}{4 \cdot 2 \cdot x \cdot 3} = -\frac{7}{12x}$

28. $\frac{6}{15} \cdot \frac{5y}{8} = \frac{2 \cdot 3 \cdot 5y}{3 \cdot 5 \cdot 2 \cdot 4} = \frac{y}{4}$

29. $-\frac{24x}{5} \cdot -\frac{15}{8x^3} = \frac{3 \cdot 8 \cdot x \cdot 3 \cdot 5}{5 \cdot 8 \cdot x \cdot x \cdot x} = \frac{9}{x^2}$

30. $\frac{27y^3}{21} \cdot \frac{7}{18y^2} = \frac{3 \cdot 9 \cdot y \cdot y^2 \cdot 7}{3 \cdot 7 \cdot 2 \cdot 9 \cdot y^2} = \frac{y}{2}$

31. $\left(-\frac{1}{3}\right)^3 = -\frac{1}{3} \cdot -\frac{1}{3} \cdot -\frac{1}{3} = -\frac{1 \cdot 1 \cdot 1}{3 \cdot 3 \cdot 3} = -\frac{1}{27}$

32. $\left(-\frac{5}{12}\right)^2 = -\frac{5}{12} \cdot -\frac{5}{12} = \frac{5 \cdot 5}{12 \cdot 12} = \frac{25}{144}$

33. $\frac{x^3}{y} \cdot \frac{y^3}{x} = \frac{x \cdot x^2 \cdot y \cdot y^2}{y \cdot x} = x^2y^2$

34. $\frac{ac}{b} \cdot \frac{b^2}{a^3c} = \frac{a \cdot c \cdot b \cdot b}{b \cdot a \cdot a^2 \cdot c} = \frac{b}{a^2}$

35. $xy = \frac{2}{3} \cdot \frac{1}{5} = \frac{2 \cdot 1}{3 \cdot 5} = \frac{2}{15}$

36. $ab = -7 \cdot \frac{9}{10} = -\frac{7}{1} \cdot \frac{9}{10} = -\frac{7 \cdot 9}{1 \cdot 10} = -\frac{63}{10}$

37. $-\frac{3}{4} \div \frac{3}{8} = -\frac{3}{4} \cdot \frac{8}{3} = -\frac{3 \cdot 2 \cdot 4}{4 \cdot 3} = -2$

38. $\frac{21a}{4} \div \frac{7a}{5} = \frac{21a}{4} \cdot \frac{5}{7a} = \frac{3 \cdot 7 \cdot a \cdot 5}{4 \cdot 7 \cdot a} = \frac{15}{4}$

39.
$$\begin{aligned} \frac{18x}{5} \div \frac{2}{5x} &= \frac{18x}{5} \cdot \frac{5x}{2} \\ &= \frac{2 \cdot 9 \cdot x \cdot 5 \cdot x}{5 \cdot 2} \\ &= 9x^2 \end{aligned}$$

40. $-\frac{9}{2} \div -\frac{1}{3} = \frac{9}{2} \cdot \frac{3}{1} = \frac{9 \cdot 3}{2 \cdot 1} = \frac{27}{2}$

41. $-\frac{5}{3} \div 2y = -\frac{5}{3} \cdot \frac{1}{2y} = -\frac{5 \cdot 1}{3 \cdot 2y} = -\frac{5}{6y}$

42. $\frac{5x^2}{y} \div \frac{10x^3}{y^3} = \frac{5x^2}{y} \cdot \frac{y^3}{10x^3} = \frac{5x^2y \cdot y^2}{y \cdot 2 \cdot 5 \cdot x \cdot x^2} = \frac{y^2}{2x}$

43. $x \div y = \frac{9}{7} \div \frac{3}{4} = \frac{9}{7} \cdot \frac{4}{3} = \frac{3 \cdot 3 \cdot 4}{7 \cdot 3} = \frac{12}{7}$

44. $a \div b = -5 \div \frac{2}{3} = -\frac{5}{1} \cdot \frac{3}{2} = -\frac{5 \cdot 3}{1 \cdot 2} = -\frac{15}{2}$

45. $A = \frac{11}{6} \cdot \frac{7}{8} = \frac{77}{48}$ or $1\frac{29}{48}$ sq. ft.

46. $A = \left(\frac{2}{3}\right)^2 = \frac{2}{3} \cdot \frac{2}{3} = \frac{4}{9}$ sq. m

47. $\frac{7}{11} + \frac{3}{11} = \frac{7+3}{11} = \frac{10}{11}$

48. $\frac{4}{9} + \frac{2}{9} = \frac{6}{9} = \frac{2}{3}$

49. $\frac{1}{12} - \frac{5}{12} = \frac{1-5}{12} = \frac{-4}{12} = -\frac{4}{4 \cdot 3} = -\frac{1}{3}$

50. $\frac{3}{y} - \frac{1}{y} = \frac{2}{y}$

51.
$$\begin{aligned} \frac{11x}{15} + \frac{x}{15} &= \frac{11x + x}{15} \\ &= \frac{12x}{15} \\ &= \frac{3 \cdot 4 \cdot x}{3 \cdot 5} \\ &= \frac{4x}{5} \end{aligned}$$

52. $\frac{4y}{21} - \frac{3}{21} = \frac{4y - 3}{21}$

53. $\frac{4}{15} + \frac{3}{15} - \frac{2}{15} = \frac{4+3-2}{15} = \frac{5}{15} = \frac{5}{3 \cdot 5} = \frac{1}{3}$

54. $\frac{4}{15} - \frac{3}{15} - \frac{2}{15} = \frac{4-3-2}{15} = \frac{-1}{15} = -\frac{1}{15}$

55. $3 = 3$
$x = x$
LCD $= 3x$

56. $4 = 2 \cdot 2$
$8 = 2 \cdot 2 \cdot 2$
$12 = 2 \cdot 2 \cdot 3$
LCD $= 2 \cdot 2 \cdot 2 \cdot 3 = 24$

57.
$$\begin{aligned} z + \frac{1}{5} &= 1 \\ \frac{4}{5} + \frac{1}{5} &= 1 \\ \frac{5}{5} &= 1 \\ 1 &= 1 \end{aligned}$$
Yes, it is a solution.

58.
$$\begin{aligned} x - \frac{2}{4} &= \frac{1}{4} \\ \frac{3}{4} - \frac{2}{4} &= \frac{1}{4} \\ \frac{1}{4} &= \frac{1}{4} \end{aligned}$$
Yes, it is a solution.

59. $\frac{3}{8}+\frac{1}{8}=\frac{4}{8}=\frac{4\cdot 1}{4\cdot 2}=\frac{1}{2}$

She studied $\frac{1}{2}$ hour.

60. $\frac{5}{8}+\frac{1}{8}-\frac{3}{8}=\frac{3}{8}$

$\frac{3}{8}$ gallon is left.

61. $\frac{3}{8}+\frac{2}{8}+\frac{1}{8}=\frac{6}{8}=\frac{2\cdot 3}{2\cdot 4}=\frac{3}{4}$

He did $\frac{3}{4}$ of his homework.

62. Recall that perimeter means distance around. Find the sum of the lengths of the four sides.

$$\begin{aligned}\frac{3}{16}+\frac{9}{16}+\frac{3}{16}+\frac{9}{16}&=\frac{3+9+3+9}{16}\\&=\frac{24}{16}\\&=\frac{3\cdot 8}{2\cdot 8}\\&=\frac{3}{2}\text{ or }1\frac{1}{2}\end{aligned}$$

The perimeter is $\frac{3}{2}$ or $1\frac{1}{2}$ miles.

63. $\frac{7}{18}+\frac{2}{9}=\frac{7}{18}+\frac{4}{18}=\frac{11}{18}$

64. $\frac{4}{13}-\frac{1}{26}=\frac{4\cdot 2}{13\cdot 2}-\frac{1}{26}=\frac{8}{26}-\frac{1}{26}=\frac{7}{26}$

65. $-\frac{1}{3}+\frac{1}{4}=-\frac{4}{12}+\frac{3}{12}=-\frac{1}{12}$

66. $-\frac{2}{3}+\frac{1}{4}=\frac{-2\cdot 4}{3\cdot 4}+\frac{1\cdot 3}{4\cdot 3}=\frac{-8}{12}+\frac{3}{12}=\frac{-5}{12}=-\frac{5}{12}$

67. $\frac{5x}{11}+\frac{2}{55}=\frac{25x}{55}+\frac{2}{55}=\frac{25x+2}{55}$

68. $\frac{4}{15}+\frac{b}{5}=\frac{4}{15}+\frac{b\cdot 3}{5\cdot 3}=\frac{4+3b}{15}$

69. $\frac{5y}{12}-\frac{2y}{9}=\frac{5y\cdot 3}{12\cdot 3}-\frac{2y\cdot 4}{9\cdot 4}=\frac{15y}{36}-\frac{8y}{36}=\frac{7y}{36}$

70. $\frac{7x}{18}+\frac{2x}{9}=\frac{7x}{18}+\frac{2x\cdot 2}{9\cdot 2}=\frac{7x+4x}{18}=\frac{11x}{18}$

71. $\frac{4}{9}+\frac{5}{y}=\frac{4y}{9y}+\frac{45}{9y}=\frac{4y+45}{9y}$

72. $-\frac{9}{14}-\frac{3}{7}=-\frac{9}{14}-\frac{3\cdot 2}{7\cdot 2}=-\frac{9}{14}-\frac{6}{14}=-\frac{15}{14}$

73. $\frac{4}{25}+\frac{23}{75}+\frac{7}{50}=\frac{24}{150}+\frac{46}{150}+\frac{21}{150}=\frac{91}{150}$

74.
$$\begin{aligned}\frac{2}{3}-\frac{2}{9}-\frac{1}{6}&=\frac{2\cdot 6}{3\cdot 6}-\frac{2\cdot 2}{9\cdot 2}-\frac{1\cdot 3}{6\cdot 3}\\&=\frac{12}{18}-\frac{4}{18}-\frac{3}{18}\\&=\frac{5}{18}\end{aligned}$$

75.
$$\begin{aligned}a-\frac{2}{3}&=\frac{1}{6}\\a-\frac{2}{3}+\frac{2}{3}&=\frac{1}{6}+\frac{2}{3}\\a&=\frac{1}{6}+\frac{4}{6}\\a&=\frac{5}{6}\end{aligned}$$

76.
$$\begin{aligned}9x+\frac{1}{5}-8x&=-\frac{7}{10}\\(9x-8x)+\frac{1}{5}&=-\frac{7}{10}\\x+\frac{1}{5}-\frac{1}{5}&=-\frac{7}{10}-\frac{1}{5}\\x&=-\frac{7}{10}-\frac{1\cdot 2}{5\cdot 2}\\x&=\frac{-7-2}{10}\\&=-\frac{9}{10}\end{aligned}$$

77. Find the sum of the lengths of the four sides.

$$\begin{aligned}\frac{2}{9}+\frac{5}{6}+\frac{2}{9}+\frac{5}{6}&=\frac{4}{9}+\frac{10}{6}\\&=\frac{4\cdot 2}{9\cdot 2}+\frac{10\cdot 3}{6\cdot 3}\\&=\frac{8}{18}+\frac{30}{18}\\&=\frac{38}{18}\\&=\frac{19}{9}\end{aligned}$$

The perimeter is $\frac{19}{9}$ meters.

78. Find the sum of the three sides.

$$\frac{1}{5}+\frac{3}{5}+\frac{7}{10}=\frac{2\cdot 1}{2\cdot 5}+\frac{2\cdot 3}{2\cdot 5}+\frac{7}{10}$$
$$=\frac{2+6+7}{10}$$
$$=\frac{15}{10}$$
$$=\frac{3\cdot 5}{2\cdot 5}$$
$$=\frac{3}{2}$$

The perimeter is $\frac{3}{2}$ feet.

79.
$$x+\frac{1}{3}=\frac{35}{11}$$
$$\frac{8}{11}+\frac{1}{3}=\frac{35}{11}$$
$$\frac{24}{33}+\frac{11}{33}=\frac{105}{33}$$
$$\frac{35}{33}\neq\frac{105}{33}$$

No, it is not a solution.

80.
$$\frac{1}{9}y-\frac{1}{4}=\frac{1}{4}$$
$$\frac{1}{9}\left(\frac{9}{2}\right)-\frac{1}{4}=\frac{1}{4}$$
$$\frac{1}{2}-\frac{1}{4}=\frac{1}{4}$$
$$\frac{2}{4}-\frac{1}{4}=\frac{1}{4}$$
$$\frac{1}{4}=\frac{1}{4}$$

Yes, it is a solution.

81. $\frac{9}{25}+\frac{3}{50}=\frac{9\cdot 2}{25\cdot 2}+\frac{3}{50}=\frac{18+3}{50}=\frac{21}{50}$

$\frac{21}{50}$ have type A blood.

82. $\frac{2}{3}-\frac{5}{12}=\frac{8}{12}-\frac{5}{12}=\frac{3}{12}=\frac{1}{4}$

The difference is $\frac{1}{4}$ yard.

83. $\frac{\frac{2x}{5}}{\frac{7}{10}}=\frac{2x}{5}\div\frac{7}{10}=\frac{2x}{5}\cdot\frac{10}{7}=\frac{4x}{7}$

84. $\frac{\frac{3y}{7}}{\frac{11}{7}}=\frac{7\cdot\frac{3y}{7}}{7\cdot\frac{11}{7}}=\frac{3y}{11}$

85. The LCD of 4 and 8 is 8.

$$\frac{2+\frac{3}{4}}{1-\frac{1}{8}}=\frac{8\left(2+\frac{3}{4}\right)}{8\left(1-\frac{1}{8}\right)}$$
$$=\frac{8\cdot 2+8\cdot\frac{3}{4}}{8\cdot 1-8\cdot\frac{1}{8}}$$
$$=\frac{16+6}{8-1}$$
$$=\frac{22}{7}$$

86. The LCD of 3 and 6 is 6.

$$\frac{\frac{5}{6}+2}{\frac{11}{3}-1}=\frac{6\left(\frac{5}{6}+2\right)}{6\left(\frac{11}{3}-1\right)}=\frac{6\cdot\frac{5}{6}+6\cdot 2}{6\cdot\frac{11}{3}-6\cdot 1}=\frac{5+12}{22-6}=\frac{17}{16}$$

87. The LCD of 5, 2, 4, and 10 is 20.

$$\frac{\frac{2}{5}-\frac{1}{2}}{\frac{3}{4}-\frac{7}{10}}=\frac{20\left(\frac{2}{5}-\frac{1}{2}\right)}{20\left(\frac{3}{4}-\frac{7}{10}\right)}$$
$$=\frac{20\cdot\frac{2}{5}-20\cdot\frac{1}{2}}{20\cdot\frac{3}{4}-20\cdot\frac{7}{10}}$$
$$=\frac{8-10}{15-14}$$
$$=\frac{-2}{1}$$
$$=-2$$

88. The LCD of 6, 4, and $12y$ is $12y$.

$$\frac{\frac{5}{6}-\frac{1}{4}}{\frac{-1}{12y}}=\frac{12y\left(\frac{5}{6}-\frac{1}{4}\right)}{12y\left(\frac{-1}{12y}\right)}$$
$$=\frac{12y\left(\frac{5}{6}\right)-12y\left(\frac{1}{4}\right)}{12y\left(\frac{-1}{12y}\right)}$$
$$=\frac{10y-3y}{-1}$$
$$=\frac{7y}{-1}$$
$$=-7y$$

89. $2x+y=2\cdot\frac{1}{2}+\left(-\frac{2}{3}\right)=1-\frac{2}{3}=\frac{3}{3}-\frac{2}{3}=\frac{1}{3}$

90. $\frac{x}{y+z}=\frac{\frac{1}{2}}{-\frac{2}{3}+\frac{4}{5}}$
$=\frac{30\left(\frac{1}{2}\right)}{30\left(-\frac{2}{3}+\frac{4}{5}\right)}$
$=\frac{15}{30\left(-\frac{2}{3}\right)+30\left(\frac{4}{5}\right)}$
$=\frac{15}{-20+24}$
$=\frac{15}{4}$

91. $\frac{x+y}{z}=\frac{\frac{1}{2}+\left(-\frac{2}{3}\right)}{\frac{4}{5}}$
$\frac{\frac{1}{2}-\frac{2}{3}}{\frac{4}{5}}=\frac{30\left(\frac{1}{2}-\frac{2}{3}\right)}{30\left(\frac{4}{5}\right)}$
$=\frac{30\cdot\frac{1}{2}-30\cdot\frac{2}{3}}{24}$
$=\frac{15-20}{24}$
$=-\frac{5}{24}$

92. $x+y+z=\frac{1}{2}+\left(-\frac{2}{3}\right)+\frac{4}{5}$
$=\frac{15}{30}+\frac{-20}{30}+\frac{24}{30}$
$=\frac{19}{30}$

93. $y^2=\left(-\frac{2}{3}\right)^2=-\frac{2}{3}\cdot-\frac{2}{3}=\frac{2\cdot 2}{3\cdot 3}=\frac{4}{9}$

94. $x-z=\frac{1}{2}-\frac{4}{5}=\frac{5}{10}-\frac{8}{10}=-\frac{3}{10}$

95. $-\frac{3}{5}x=6$
$-\frac{5}{3}\cdot-\frac{3}{5}x=-\frac{5}{3}\cdot 6$
$x=-10$

96. $\frac{2}{9}y=-\frac{4}{3}$
$\frac{9}{2}\cdot\frac{2}{9}y=\frac{9}{2}\cdot\left(-\frac{4}{3}\right)$
$y=-\frac{9\cdot 4}{2\cdot 3}$
$=-\frac{3\cdot 3\cdot 2\cdot 2}{2\cdot 3}$
$=-\frac{3\cdot 2}{1}$
$=-6$

97. $\frac{x}{7}-3=-\frac{6}{7}$
$7\left(\frac{x}{7}-3\right)=7\cdot-\frac{6}{7}$
$7\cdot\frac{x}{7}-7\cdot 3=-6$
$x-21=-6$
$x-21+21=-6+21$
$x=15$

98. $\frac{y}{5}+2=\frac{11}{5}$
$5\left(\frac{y}{5}+2\right)=5\cdot\frac{11}{5}$
$5\cdot\frac{y}{5}+5\cdot 2=11$
$y+10=11$
$y+10-10=11-10$
$y=1$

99. $\frac{1}{6}+\frac{x}{4}=\frac{17}{12}$
$12\left(\frac{1}{6}+\frac{x}{4}\right)=12\cdot\frac{17}{12}$
$12\cdot\frac{1}{6}+12\cdot\frac{x}{4}=17$
$2+3x=17$
$2+3x-2=17-2$
$3x=5$
$\frac{3x}{3}=\frac{15}{3}$
$x=5$

100.
$$\frac{x}{5}-\frac{5}{4}=\frac{x}{2}-\frac{1}{20}$$
$$20\left(\frac{x}{5}-\frac{5}{4}\right)=20\left(\frac{x}{2}-\frac{1}{20}\right)$$
$$20\cdot\frac{x}{5}-20\cdot\frac{5}{4}=20\cdot\frac{x}{2}-20\cdot\frac{1}{20}$$
$$4x-25=10x-1$$
$$4x-25+25=10x-1+25$$
$$4x=10x+24$$
$$4x-10x=10x+24-10x$$
$$-6x=24$$
$$\frac{-6x}{-6}=\frac{24}{-6}$$
$$x=-4$$

101.
$$\begin{array}{r} 3 \\ 4\overline{)\ 15} \\ \underline{-12} \\ 3 \end{array}$$
$$\frac{15}{4}=3\frac{3}{4}$$

102. $\frac{39}{13}=\frac{3\cdot 13}{13}=3$

103. $\frac{7}{7}=1$

104.
$$\begin{array}{r} 31 \\ 4\overline{)\ 125} \\ \underline{-12} \\ 5 \\ \underline{-4} \\ 1 \end{array}$$
$$\frac{125}{4}=31\frac{1}{4}$$

105. $2\frac{1}{5}=\frac{2\cdot 5+1}{5}=\frac{11}{5}$

106. $5=\frac{5}{1}$

107. $3\frac{8}{9}=\frac{3\cdot 9+8}{9}=\frac{35}{9}$

108. $3=\frac{3}{1}$

109.
$$\begin{array}{rcr} 31\frac{2}{7} & = & 31\frac{6}{21} \\ \underline{+\ 14\frac{10}{21}} & = & \underline{14\frac{10}{21}} \\ & & 45\frac{16}{21} \end{array}$$

110.
$$\begin{array}{r} 24\frac{4}{5} \\ \underline{+\ 35\frac{1}{5}} \\ 59\frac{5}{5}=59+1=60 \end{array}$$

111.
$$\begin{array}{rcrcr} 69\frac{5}{22} & = & 69\frac{5}{22} & = & 68\frac{27}{22} \\ \underline{-\ 36\frac{7}{11}} & = & \underline{-\ 36\frac{14}{22}} & = & \underline{-\ 36\frac{14}{22}} \\ & & & & 32\frac{13}{22} \end{array}$$

112.
$$\begin{array}{rcrcr} 36\frac{3}{20} & = & 36\frac{9}{60} & = & 35\frac{69}{60} \\ \underline{-\ 32\frac{5}{6}} & = & \underline{-\ 32\frac{50}{60}} & = & \underline{-\ 32\frac{50}{60}} \\ & & & & 3\frac{19}{60} \end{array}$$

113.
$$\begin{array}{rcl} 29\frac{2}{9} & = & 29\frac{4}{18} \\ 27\frac{7}{18} & = & 27\frac{7}{18} \\ \underline{+\ 54\frac{2}{3}} & = & \underline{54\frac{12}{18}} \end{array}$$
$$110\frac{23}{18}=110+1\frac{5}{8}=111\frac{5}{18}$$

114.
$$\begin{array}{rcl} 7\frac{3}{8} & = & 7\frac{9}{24} \\ 9\frac{5}{6} & = & 9\frac{20}{24} \\ \underline{+\ 3\frac{1}{12}} & = & \underline{3\frac{2}{24}} \end{array}$$
$$19\frac{31}{24}=19+1\frac{7}{24}=20\frac{7}{24}$$

115. $1\frac{5}{8}\cdot\frac{2}{3}=\frac{13}{8}\cdot\frac{2}{3}=\frac{13\cdot 2}{4\cdot 2\cdot 3}=\frac{13}{12}=1\frac{1}{12}$

116. $3\frac{6}{11}\cdot\frac{5}{13}=\frac{39}{11}\cdot\frac{5}{13}=\frac{3\cdot 13\cdot 5}{11\cdot 13}=\frac{15}{11}=1\frac{4}{11}$

117. $4\frac{1}{6}\cdot 2\frac{2}{5}=\frac{25}{6}\cdot\frac{12}{5}=\frac{5\cdot 5\cdot 6\cdot 2}{6\cdot 5}=\frac{10}{1}=10$

118. $5\frac{2}{3}\cdot 2\frac{1}{4}=\frac{17}{3}\cdot\frac{9}{4}=\frac{17\cdot 3\cdot 3}{3\cdot 4}=\frac{51}{4}=12\frac{3}{4}$

119. $6\frac{3}{4}\div 1\frac{2}{7}=\frac{27}{4}\div\frac{9}{7}=\frac{27}{4}\cdot\frac{7}{9}=\frac{3\cdot 9\cdot 7}{4\cdot 9}=\frac{21}{4}=5\frac{1}{4}$

120.
$$\begin{aligned}5\frac{1}{2}\div 2\frac{1}{11}&=\frac{11}{2}\div\frac{23}{11}\\&=\frac{11}{2}\cdot\frac{11}{23}\\&=\frac{11\cdot 11}{2\cdot 23}\\&=\frac{121}{46}\\&=2\frac{29}{46}\end{aligned}$$

121. $\frac{7}{2}\div 1\frac{1}{2}=\frac{7}{2}\div\frac{3}{2}=\frac{7}{2}\cdot\frac{2}{3}=\frac{7\cdot 2}{2\cdot 3}=\frac{7}{3}$ or $2\frac{1}{3}$

122. $1\frac{3}{5}\div\frac{1}{4}=\frac{8}{5}\cdot\frac{4}{1}=\frac{8\cdot 4}{5\cdot 1}=\frac{32}{5}=6\frac{2}{5}$

123.
$$\begin{aligned}3\frac{3}{4}&=3\frac{15}{20}\\+\ 2\frac{3}{5}&=2\frac{12}{20}\\ &\quad 5\frac{27}{20}=5+1\frac{7}{20}=6\frac{7}{20}\end{aligned}$$

Their combined weight is $6\frac{7}{20}$ pounds.

124.
$$\begin{aligned}50&=49\frac{2}{2}\\-\ 5\frac{1}{2}&=-\ 5\frac{1}{2}\\ &\quad 44\frac{1}{2}\end{aligned}$$

The amount remaining on the reel is $44\frac{1}{2}$ yards.

125.
$$\begin{aligned}62\frac{3}{10}&=62\frac{3}{10}=61\frac{13}{10}\\-\ 54\frac{1}{2}&=-\ 54\frac{5}{10}=-\ 54\frac{5}{10}\\ &\quad 7\frac{8}{10}=7\frac{4}{5}\end{aligned}$$

The annual snowfall was $7\frac{4}{5}$ inches below normal.

126.
$$\begin{aligned}2\frac{1}{4}\cdot 3\frac{1}{3}&=\frac{9}{4}\cdot\frac{10}{3}\\&=\frac{9\cdot 10}{4\cdot 3}\\&=\frac{90}{12}\\&=\frac{2\cdot 3\cdot 3\cdot 5}{2\cdot 2\cdot 3}\\&=\frac{15}{2}\\&=7\frac{1}{2}\end{aligned}$$

The area is $7\frac{1}{2}$ square feet.

127. Find the sum of 4 sides.
$$\begin{aligned}1\frac{1}{4}+1\frac{1}{4}+1\frac{1}{4}+1\frac{1}{4}&=\frac{5}{4}+\frac{5}{4}+\frac{5}{4}+\frac{5}{4}\\&=\frac{20}{4}\\&=5\end{aligned}$$

The perimeter is 5 feet.

128.
$$\begin{aligned}\frac{7}{10}\cdot 2\frac{1}{8}&=\frac{7}{10}\cdot\frac{17}{8}\\&=\frac{7\cdot 17}{10\cdot 8}\\&=\frac{119}{80}\text{ or }1\frac{39}{80}\end{aligned}$$

The area is $\frac{119}{80}$ or $1\frac{39}{80}$ square inches.

129. Find the sum of the eight sides of his flower beds.
$$\begin{aligned}&\frac{2}{3}+\frac{2}{3}+\frac{2}{3}+\frac{2}{3}+\frac{7}{8}+\frac{1}{3}+\frac{7}{8}+\frac{1}{3}\\&=\frac{2+2+2+2+1+1}{3}+\frac{7+7}{8}\\&=\frac{10}{3}+\frac{14}{8}\\&=\frac{10\cdot 8}{3\cdot 8}+\frac{14\cdot 3}{8\cdot 3}\\&=\frac{80}{24}+\frac{42}{24}\\&=\frac{122}{24}\\&=\frac{2\cdot 61}{2\cdot 12}\\&=\frac{61}{12}\text{ or }5\frac{1}{12}\end{aligned}$$

The total perimeter of his flower beds is $5\frac{1}{12}$ meters.

130. $58 \cdot 3\frac{1}{2} = \frac{58}{1} \cdot \frac{7}{2} = 203$ calories

131. $3\frac{1}{3} \cdot 4 = \frac{10}{3} \cdot \frac{4}{1} = \frac{40}{3}$ grams or $13\frac{1}{3}$ grams

132. $5\frac{1}{4} \div 5 = \frac{21}{4} \cdot \frac{1}{5} = \frac{21 \cdot 1}{4 \cdot 5} = \frac{21}{20}$ or $1\frac{1}{20}$

He walks $\frac{21}{20}$ or $1\frac{1}{20}$ mile each day.

133.
$$\begin{array}{rcr} 12\frac{1}{7} & = & 12\frac{2}{14} \\ +\ 15\frac{4}{14} & = & +15\frac{3}{14} \\ \hline & & 27\frac{5}{14} \end{array}$$

Answer: $27\frac{5}{14}$

134.
$$\begin{aligned} -3\frac{1}{5} \div \left(-2\frac{7}{10}\right) &= -\frac{16}{5} \div \left(-\frac{27}{10}\right) \\ &= -\frac{16}{5} \cdot \left(-\frac{10}{27}\right) \\ &= \frac{16 \cdot 2 \cdot 5}{5 \cdot 27} \\ &= \frac{32}{27} \text{ or } 1\frac{5}{27} \end{aligned}$$

135.
$$\begin{aligned} -2\frac{1}{4} \cdot 1\frac{3}{4} &= -\frac{9}{4} \cdot \frac{7}{4} \\ &= -\frac{63}{16} \text{ or } -3\frac{15}{16} \end{aligned}$$

136.
$$\begin{array}{rcrcr} 24\frac{7}{10} & = & 24\frac{28}{40} & = & 23\frac{68}{40} \\ -\ 23\frac{7}{8} & = & -\ 23\frac{35}{40} & = & 23\frac{35}{40} \\ \hline & & & & \frac{33}{40} \end{array}$$

Answer: $-\frac{33}{40}$

Chapter 4 Test

1. $7\frac{2}{3} = \frac{3 \cdot 7 + 2}{3} = \frac{23}{3}$

2. $3\frac{6}{11} = \frac{11 \cdot 3 + 6}{11} = \frac{39}{11}$

3.
$$\begin{array}{r} 4 \\ 5\overline{)\ 23} \\ \underline{-20} \\ 3 \end{array}$$

$\frac{23}{5} = 4\frac{3}{5}$

4.
$$\begin{array}{r} 18 \\ 4\overline{)\ 75} \\ \underline{-4} \\ 35 \\ \underline{-32} \\ 3 \end{array}$$

$\frac{75}{4} = 18\frac{3}{4}$

5. $\frac{54}{210} = \frac{9 \cdot 6}{35 \cdot 6} = \frac{9}{35}$

6. $-\frac{42}{70} = -\frac{3 \cdot 14}{5 \cdot 14} = -\frac{3}{5}$

7. $\frac{4}{4} \div \frac{3}{4} = \frac{4}{4} \cdot \frac{4}{3} = \frac{4}{3}$

8. $-\frac{4}{3} \cdot \frac{4}{4} = -\frac{4}{3}$

9. $\frac{7x}{9} + \frac{x}{9} = \frac{7x + x}{9} = \frac{8x}{9}$

10.
$$\begin{aligned} \frac{1}{7} - \frac{3}{x} &= \frac{1 \cdot x}{7 \cdot x} - \frac{3 \cdot 7}{x \cdot 7} \\ &= \frac{x}{7x} - \frac{21}{7x} \\ &= \frac{x - 21}{7x} \end{aligned}$$

11. $\frac{xy^3}{z} \cdot \frac{z}{xy} = \frac{x \cdot y \cdot y^2 \cdot z}{z \cdot x \cdot y} = \frac{y^2}{1} = y^2$

12. $-\frac{2}{3} \cdot -\frac{8}{15} = \frac{2 \cdot 8}{3 \cdot 15} = \frac{16}{45}$

13. $\frac{9a}{10} + \frac{2}{5} = \frac{9a}{10} + \frac{2 \cdot 2}{5 \cdot 2} = \frac{9a + 4}{10}$

14. $-\frac{8}{15y} - \frac{2}{15y} = \frac{-8 - 2}{15y} = \frac{-10}{15y} = -\frac{2}{3y}$

15. $8y^3 \div \frac{y}{3} = \frac{8y^3}{1} \div \frac{y}{3}$
$= \frac{8y^3}{1} \cdot \frac{3}{y}$
$= \frac{8 \cdot 3 \cdot y \cdot y^2}{y}$
$= \frac{24y^2}{1}$
$= 24y^2$

16. $5\frac{1}{4} \div \frac{7}{12} = \frac{21}{4} \cdot \frac{12}{7} = \frac{3 \cdot 7 \cdot 3 \cdot 4}{4 \cdot 7} = 9$

17. $3\frac{7}{8} = 3\frac{7 \cdot 5}{8 \cdot 5} = 3\frac{35}{40}$
$7\frac{2}{5} = 7\frac{2 \cdot 8}{5 \cdot 8} = 7\frac{16}{40}$
$2\frac{3}{4} = 2\frac{3 \cdot 10}{4 \cdot 10} = 2\frac{30}{40}$
$12\frac{81}{40} = 12 + 2\frac{1}{40} = 14\frac{1}{40}$

18. $\frac{3a}{8} \cdot \frac{16}{6a^3} = \frac{3a \cdot 2 \cdot 8}{8 \cdot 3 \cdot 2a \cdot a^2} = \frac{2 \cdot 3 \cdot 8 \cdot a}{2 \cdot 3 \cdot 8 \cdot a \cdot a^2} = \frac{1}{a^2}$

19. $-\frac{16}{3} \div -\frac{3}{12} = \frac{16}{3} \cdot \frac{12}{3} = \frac{16 \cdot 3 \cdot 4}{3 \cdot 3} = \frac{64}{3}$

20. $3\frac{1}{3} \cdot 6\frac{3}{4} = \frac{10}{3} \cdot \frac{27}{4} = \frac{5 \cdot 9}{2} = \frac{45}{2}$ or $22\frac{1}{2}$

21. $12 \div 3\frac{1}{3} = 12 \div \frac{10}{3}$
$= 12 \cdot \frac{3}{10}$
$= \frac{2 \cdot 6 \cdot 3}{2 \cdot 5}$
$= \frac{18}{5}$
$= 3\frac{3}{5}$

22. $\left(\frac{14}{5} \cdot \frac{25}{21}\right) \div 10 = \frac{14}{5} \cdot \frac{25}{21} \cdot \frac{1}{10} = \frac{2 \cdot 7 \cdot 5 \cdot 5}{5 \cdot 3 \cdot 7 \cdot 2 \cdot 5} = \frac{1}{3}$

23. $\frac{11}{12} - \frac{3}{8} + \frac{5}{24} = \frac{11 \cdot 2}{12 \cdot 2} - \frac{3 \cdot 3}{8 \cdot 3} + \frac{5}{24}$
$= \frac{22}{24} - \frac{9}{24} + \frac{5}{24}$
$= \frac{22 - 9 + 5}{24}$
$= \frac{18}{24}$
$= \frac{3 \cdot 6}{4 \cdot 6}$
$= \frac{3}{4}$

24. $\frac{\frac{5x}{7}}{\frac{20x^2}{21}} = \frac{21 \cdot \frac{5x}{7}}{21 \cdot \frac{20x^2}{21}} = \frac{15x}{20x^2} = \frac{3 \cdot 5x}{4 \cdot 5 \cdot x \cdot x} = \frac{3}{4x}$

25. $\frac{5 + \frac{3}{7}}{2 - \frac{1}{2}} = \frac{14\left(5 + \frac{3}{7}\right)}{14\left(2 - \frac{1}{2}\right)} = \frac{14 \cdot 5 + 14 \cdot \frac{3}{7}}{14 \cdot 2 - 14 \cdot \frac{1}{2}} = \frac{70 + 6}{28 - 7} = \frac{76}{21}$

26. $-\frac{3}{8}x = \frac{3}{4}$
$-\frac{8}{3} \cdot -\frac{3}{8}x = -\frac{8}{3} \cdot \frac{3}{4}$
$x = -\frac{8 \cdot 3}{3 \cdot 4}$
$x = -2$

27. $\frac{x}{5} + x = -\frac{24}{5}$
$5 \cdot \left(\frac{x}{5} + x\right) = 5 \cdot -\frac{24}{5}$
$5 \cdot \frac{x}{5} + 5x = -24$
$x + 5x = -24$
$6x = -24$
$\frac{6x}{6} = -\frac{24}{6}$
$x = -4$

28.
$$\begin{aligned}
\frac{2}{3}+\frac{x}{4}&=\frac{5}{12}+\frac{x}{2}\\
12\left(\frac{2}{3}+\frac{x}{4}\right)&=12\left(\frac{5}{12}+\frac{x}{2}\right)\\
12\left(\frac{2}{3}\right)+12\left(\frac{x}{4}\right)&=12\left(\frac{5}{12}\right)+12\left(\frac{x}{2}\right)\\
8+3x&=5+6x\\
8+3x-6x&=5+6x-6x\\
8-3x&=5\\
8-3x-8&=5-8\\
-3x&=-3\\
\frac{-3x}{-3}&=\frac{-3}{-3}\\
x&=1
\end{aligned}$$

29. $-5x=-5\left(-\frac{1}{2}\right)=\frac{5}{2}$

30. $x\div y=\frac{1}{2}\div 3\frac{7}{8}=\frac{1}{2}\div\frac{31}{8}=\frac{1}{2}\cdot\frac{8}{31}=\frac{1\cdot 2\cdot 4}{2\cdot 31}=\frac{4}{31}$

31. $\frac{280\text{ calories}}{560\text{ calories}}=\frac{28\cdot 10}{28\cdot 2\cdot 10}=\frac{1}{2}$

$\frac{1}{2}$ of the calories are from fat.

32. The phrase "How long is the remaining" tells us to subtract. Subtract $2\frac{3}{4}$ feet from $6\frac{1}{2}$ feet.

$$\begin{array}{rcrcr}
6\frac{1}{2} & = & 6\frac{2}{4} & = & 5\frac{6}{4}\\
-\ 2\frac{3}{4} & = & -\ 2\frac{3}{4} & = & -\ 2\frac{3}{4}\\
\hline
 & & & & 3\frac{3}{4}
\end{array}$$

The remaining piece is $3\frac{3}{4}$ feet.

33. Find the sum of the fractions representing Back Woods and Westward.
$$\begin{aligned}
\frac{3}{16}+\frac{1}{8}&=\frac{3}{16}+\frac{1\cdot 2}{8\cdot 2}\\
&=\frac{3}{16}+\frac{2}{16}\\
&=\frac{5}{16}
\end{aligned}$$
$\frac{5}{16}$ of backpack sales go to Back Woods and Westward.

34. Multiply the fraction representing Wilderness, Inc. $\left(\frac{1}{4}\right)$ by 500,000.
$$\begin{aligned}
\frac{1}{4}\cdot 500{,}000&=\frac{1}{4}\cdot\frac{500{,}000}{1}\\
&=\frac{1\cdot 500{,}000}{4\cdot 1}\\
&=\frac{1\cdot 4\cdot 125{,}000}{4\cdot 1}\\
&=\frac{1\cdot 125{,}000}{1}\\
&=\frac{125{,}000}{1}\\
&=125{,}000
\end{aligned}$$
Wilderness, Inc. sells 125,000 backpacks each year.

35.
$$\begin{aligned}
\text{Area} &= \text{length}\cdot\text{width}\\
&=(100+10+10)\cdot\left(53\frac{1}{3}+10+10\right)\\
&=120\cdot 73\frac{1}{3}\\
&=\frac{120}{1}\cdot\frac{220}{3}\\
&=\frac{120\cdot 220}{1\cdot 3}\\
&=\frac{40\cdot 220}{1}\\
&=\frac{8800}{1}\\
&=8800
\end{aligned}$$

8800 square yards of turf are needed.

36. $1\frac{8}{9}\cdot\frac{2}{3}=\frac{17}{9}\cdot\frac{2}{3}=\frac{17\cdot 2}{9\cdot 3}=\frac{34}{27}$ or $1\frac{7}{27}$

The area of the figure is $\frac{34}{27}$ or $1\frac{7}{27}$ square miles.

37.
$$\begin{aligned}
258\div 10\frac{3}{4}&=\frac{258}{1}\div\frac{43}{4}\\
&=\frac{258}{1}\cdot\frac{4}{43}\\
&=\frac{258\cdot 4}{1\cdot 43}\\
&=\frac{43\cdot 6\cdot 4}{1\cdot 43}\\
&=\frac{24}{1}\\
&=24
\end{aligned}$$

We can expect the car to travel 24 miles.

38. $120 \cdot \frac{3}{4} = \frac{120}{1} \cdot \frac{3}{4}$
$= \frac{120 \cdot 3}{1 \cdot 4}$
$= \frac{4 \cdot 30 \cdot 3}{4}$
$= \frac{30 \cdot 3}{1}$
$= 90$
The stock sold for \$90 after the spill.

Chapter 4 Cumulative Review

1. 126 in words is one hundred twenty-six.

2. 115 in words is one hundred fifteen.

3. 3005 in words is three thousand, five.

4. 6573 in words is six thousand, five hundred seventy-three.

5.
$$\begin{array}{r} 23 \\ +136 \\ \hline 159 \end{array}$$

6.
$$\begin{array}{r} 587 \\ +44 \\ \hline 631 \end{array}$$

7.
$$\begin{array}{r} 43 \\ -29 \\ \hline 14 \end{array}$$
Check: $\begin{array}{r} 14 \\ +29 \\ \hline 43 \end{array}$

8.
$$\begin{array}{r} 995 \\ -62 \\ \hline 933 \end{array}$$
Check: $\begin{array}{r} 933 \\ +62 \\ \hline 995 \end{array}$

9. Since there is a 3 in the hundreds place, 278,362 rounded to the nearest thousand is 278,000.

10. Since there is a 6 in the ones place, 1436 rounded to the nearest ten is 1440.

11. $1510 \times 42 = 63,420$
42 disks can hold 63,420 thousand bytes

12. $435 \times 3 = 1305$
He travels a total of 1305.

13.
$$\begin{array}{r} 7089 \text{ R } 5 \\ 8\overline{)56717} \\ -56 \\ \hline 07 \\ -0 \\ \hline 71 \\ -64 \\ \hline 77 \\ -72 \\ \hline 5 \end{array}$$
Check: $7089 \times 8 + 5 = 56,712 + 5 = 56717$

14.
$$\begin{array}{r} 379 \text{ R } 10 \\ 12\overline{)4558} \\ -36 \\ \hline 95 \\ -84 \\ \hline 118 \\ -108 \\ \hline 10 \end{array}$$
Check: $379 \times f12 + 10 - 4548 + 10 = 4558$

15. $4 \cdot 4 \cdot 4 = 4^3$

16. $7 \cdot 7 = 7^2$

17. $6 \cdot 6 \cdot 6 \cdot 8 \cdot 8 \cdot 8 \cdot 8 \cdot 8 = 6^3 \cdot 8^5$

18. $9 \cdot 9 \cdot 9 \cdot 9 \cdot 5 \cdot 5 = 9^4 \cdot 5^2$

19. $2(x - y) = 2(8 - 4)$
$= 2(4)$
$= 8$

20. $8a + 3(b - 5) = 8 \cdot 5 + 3(9 - 5)$
$= 8 \cdot 5 + 3(4)$
$= 40 + 12$
$= 52$

21. 150 ft. below the surface is represented by −150.

22. 21° F below zero is represented by −21.

23.
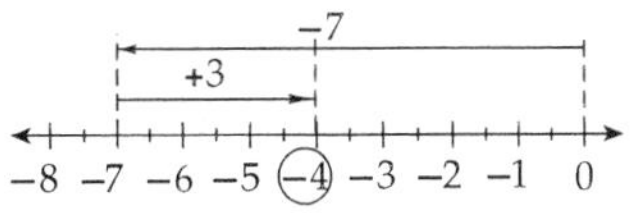

24. 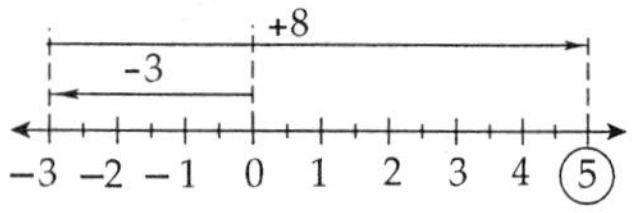

25. $7-8-(-5)-1=7-8+5-1=3$

26. $6+(-8)--(-9)+3=6+(-8)+9+3=10$

27. $(-5)^2=(-5)(-5)=25$

28. $-2^4=-(2)(2)(2)(2)=-16$

29. $\frac{12-16}{-1+3}=\frac{-4}{2}=-2$

30. $$\begin{aligned}\left(20-5^2\right)^2 &= (20-25)^2\\ &= (-5)^2\\ &= 25\end{aligned}$$

31. $5(3y)=(5\cdot 3)y=15y$

32. $12(3c)=(12\cdot 3)c=36c$

33. $-2(4x)=(-2\cdot 4)x=-8x$

34. $-7(14a)=(-7\cdot 14)a=-98a$

35. $$\begin{aligned}-8 &= x+1\\ -8-1 &= x+1-1\\ -9 &= x\end{aligned}$$

36. $$\begin{aligned}x-3 &= 5\\ x-3+3 &= 5+3\\ x &= 8\end{aligned}$$

37. $$\begin{aligned}8x-9x &= 12-17\\ -x &= -5\\ \frac{-1x}{-1} &= \frac{-5}{-1}\\ x &= 5\end{aligned}$$

38. $$\begin{aligned}2x+5x &= 0-7\\ 7x &= -7\\ \frac{7x}{7} &= \frac{-7}{7}\\ x &= -1\end{aligned}$$

39. **a.** The product 7 and 6 is 42 translates to: $7\cdot 6=42$.

b. Twice the sum of 3 and 5 is equal to 16 translates to: 2(3+5)=16.

c. The quotient of –45 and 5 yields –9 translates to $\frac{-45}{5}=-9$.

40. **a.** The sum of 4 and 3 is 7 translates to: 4+3=7.

b. Four times the difference of 5 and 2 equals 12 translates to: 4(5–2)=12.

c. The product –4 and –6 yields 24 translates to (–4)(–6)=24.

41. $$\begin{aligned}3+2x &= x-6\\ 3+2x-x &= x-6-x\\ 3+x &= -6\\ 3+x-3 &= -6-3\\ x &= -9\end{aligned}$$

42. $$\begin{aligned}4+3x &= x-6\\ 4+3x-x &= x-6-x\\ 4+2x &= -6\\ 4+2x-4 &= -6-4\\ 2x &= -10\\ \frac{2x}{2} &= \frac{-10}{2}\\ x &= -5\end{aligned}$$

43. $\frac{9x}{11}=\frac{9x\cdot 4}{11\cdot 4}=\frac{36x}{44}$

44. $\frac{2a}{3}=\frac{2a\cdot 5}{3\cdot 5}=\frac{10a}{15}$

45. $$\begin{aligned}45 &= 5\cdot 9\\ &= 5\cdot 3\cdot 3\\ &= 3\cdot 3\cdot 5 \text{ or } 3^2\cdot 5\end{aligned}$$

46. $$\begin{aligned}92 &= 2\cdot 46\\ &= 2\cdot 2\cdot 23 \text{ or } 2^2\cdot 23\end{aligned}$$

47. $\frac{2}{3}\cdot\frac{5}{11}=\frac{10}{33}$

48. $\frac{1}{7}\cdot\frac{2}{5}=\frac{2}{35}$

49. $\frac{1}{4}\cdot\frac{1}{2}=\frac{1}{8}$

50. $\frac{3}{5}\cdot\frac{1}{5}=\frac{3}{25}$

Chapter 5

Pretest

1. $0.27 = \frac{27}{100}$

2. Since $0 < 1$, $0.205 < 0.213$.

3. 54.651 rounded to the nearest tenth is 54.7. We round up because the digit in the hundredths place is greater than or equal to 5.

4. $$\begin{array}{r} {}^{2\,1} \\ 38.410 \\ 14.032 \\ +\ 7.600 \\ \hline 60.042 \end{array}$$

5. $$\begin{array}{rl} 3.4 & \text{1 decimal} \\ \times\ 2.1 & \text{1 decimal} \\ \hline 34 & \\ 680 & \\ \hline 7.14 & \text{2 decimal places} \end{array}$$

6. $(2.016)(100) = 201.6$

7. $0.4\overline{)16.24}$

   Move decimal points 1 place.

   $$\begin{array}{r} 40.6 \\ 4.\overline{)\ 162.4} \\ -16 \\ \hline 02 \\ -0 \\ \hline 24 \\ -24 \\ \hline 0 \end{array}$$

   $16.24 \div 0.4 = 40.6$

8. $\frac{891}{10{,}000} = 0.0891$

9. $x - y = 12.3 - 0.61 = 11.69$

   $$\begin{array}{r} 12.30 \\ -\ \ 0.61 \\ \hline 11.69 \end{array}$$

10. $-9.8 - 6.2x - 7.9 + 1.4x$
    $= -9.8 - 7.9 - 6.2x + 1.4x$
    $= -17.7 - 4.8x$

11. $xy = (4.2)(0.03) = 0.126$

    $$\begin{array}{rl} 4.2 & \text{1 decimal place} \\ \times\ 0.03 & \text{2 decimal places} \\ \hline 0.126 & \text{3 decimal places} \end{array}$$

12. $$\begin{aligned} \text{Circumference} &= 2\pi r \\ &= 2\pi \cdot 6 \\ &= 12\pi \\ &\approx 12(3.14) \\ &= 37.68 \end{aligned}$$

    The circumference is 12π inches which is approximately 37.68 inches.

13. $\frac{\$576}{20} = \$28.80$

    $$\begin{array}{r} 28.8 \\ 20\overline{)\ 576.0} \\ -40 \\ \hline 176 \\ -160 \\ \hline 160 \\ -160 \\ \hline 0 \end{array}$$

14. $0.2(6.9 - 3.01) = 0.2(3.89) = 0.778$

15. $\frac{3}{8} = 0.375$

    $$\begin{array}{r} 0.375 \\ 8\overline{)\ 3.000} \\ -2\,4 \\ \hline 60 \\ -56 \\ \hline 40 \\ -40 \\ \hline 0 \end{array}$$

16. $\frac{9}{11} \approx 0.81818 < 0.8182$

    $\frac{9}{11} < 0.8182$

17.
$$\begin{aligned} 4(x+0.22) &= 2x-3.4 \\ 4x+0.88 &= 2x-3.4 \\ 4x+0.88-0.88 &= 2x-3.4-0.88 \\ 4x &= 2x-4.28 \\ 4x-2x &= 2x-4.28-2x \\ 2x &= -4.28 \\ \frac{2x}{2} &= -\frac{4.28}{2} \\ x &= -2.14 \end{aligned}$$

18. $\sqrt{\frac{36}{49}} = \frac{6}{7}$ since $\frac{6}{7} \cdot \frac{6}{7} = \frac{36}{49}$.

19. $\sqrt{46} \approx 6.78$

20.
$$\begin{aligned} a^2+b^2 &= c^2 \\ 9^2+12^2 &= c^2 \\ 81+144 &= c^2 \\ 225 &= c^2 \\ \sqrt{225} &= c \\ 15 &= c \end{aligned}$$
The length of the hypotenuse is 15 inches.

Section 5.1

Practice Problems

1. **a.** 0.08 is eight hundredths

   b. –500.025 is negative five hundred and twenty-five thousandths.

   c. 0.0329 is three hundred twenty-nine ten-thousandths.

2. Ninety-seven and twenty-eight hundredths

3. Seventy-two and one thousand eighty-five ten-thousandths.

4. *Two hundred seven and* ____ $^{40}/_{100}$

5. 300.96

6. 39.042

5. $0.037 = \frac{37}{1000}$

6. $14.97 = 14\frac{97}{100}$

9. $0.12 = \frac{12}{100} = \frac{3}{25}$

10. $57.8 = 57\frac{8}{10} = 57\frac{4}{5}$

11. $-209.986 = -209\frac{986}{1000} = -209\frac{493}{500}$

12. The tens, ones, and tenths places are all the same. The hundredths places are different. Since $0 < 8$, then $13.208 < 13.28$.

13. In the tenths place, 1 is greater than 0 so $0.12 > 0.086$.

14. The tenths and the hundredths places are the same. The thousandths places are different. Since $-9<0$, $-0.029 < -0.0209$.

15. To round 123.7817 to the nearest thousandth, observe that the digit in the ten-thousandths place is 7. Since this digit is at least 5, we need to add 1 to the digit in the thousandths place. The number 123.7817 rounded to the nearest thousandth is 123.782.

16. To round –0.072 to the nearest hundredth, observe that the digit in the thousandths place is 2. Since this is less than 5, we do not add 1 to the digit in the hundredths place. The number –0.072 rounded to the nearest hundredth is –0.07.

17. To round 1.2789 to the nearest hundredth, observe that the digit in the thousandths place is 8. Since this digit is at least 5, we need to add 1 to the digit in the hundredths place. The number 1.0789 rounded to the nearest hundredth is 1.28. The price is $1.28.

18. To round 24.43 to the nearest tenth, observe that the digit in the hundredths place is 3. Since this digit is less than 5, we do not add 1 to the digit in the tenths place. The number 24.43 rounded to the nearest tenth is 24.4. The bill is $24.40.

Mental Math

1. 70
$\uparrow$ tens

2. 700
$\uparrow$ hundreds

3. 0.7
$\uparrow$ tenths

4. 0.07
$\uparrow$ hundredths

Exercise Set 5.1

1. 6.52 is six and fifty-two hundredths.

3. 16.23 is sixteen and twenty-three hundredths.

5. –3.205 is negative three and two hundred five thousandths.

7. 167.009 is one hundred sixth-seven and nine thousanths.

9. *Three hundred twenty-one and* ___ 42/100

11. *Fifty-nine and* ___ 68/100

13. Six and five-tenths is 6.5.

15. Nine and eight-hundredths is 9.08.

17. Negative five and six hundred twenty-five thousandths is –5.625.

19. Sixty-four ten-thousandths is 0.0064.

21. Sixty-four and sixteen hundredths is 64.16.

23. Five and four tenths is 5.4.

25. $0.3 = \frac{3}{10}$

27. $0.27 = \frac{27}{100}$

29. $-5.47 = -5\frac{47}{100}$

31. $0.048 = \frac{48}{1000} = \frac{6}{125}$

33. $7.07 = 7\frac{7}{100}$

35. $15.802 = 15\frac{802}{1000} = 15\frac{401}{500}$

37. $0.3005 = \frac{3005}{10,000} = \frac{601}{2000}$

39. $487.32 = 487\frac{32}{100} = 487\frac{8}{25}$

41. 0.15 0.16
$\uparrow$ $\uparrow$
5 < 6 so
$0.15 < 0.16$

43. $-0.57 < -0.54$

45. 0.098 0.1
$\uparrow$ $\uparrow$
0 < 1 so
$0.098 < 0.1$

47. 0.54900 0.549_
$\uparrow$ $\uparrow$
0 = 0 so
$0.54900 = 0.549$

49. 167.908 167.980
$\uparrow$ $\uparrow$
0 < 8 so
$167.908 < 167.980$

51. 420,000 0.000042
$\uparrow$ $\uparrow$
4 > 0 so
$420,000 > 0.000042$

53. $-1.0621 < -1.07$

55. $-7.052 < -7.0052$

57. $-0.023 > -0.024$

59. To round 0.57 to the nearest tenth, observe that the digit in the hundredths place is 7. Since this digit is at least 5, we need to add 1 to the digit in the tenths place. The number 0.57 rounded to the nearest tenth is 0.6.

61. To round 0.234 to the nearest hundredth, observe that the digit in the thousandths place is 4. Since this digit is less than 5, we do not add 1 to the digit in the hundredths place. The number 0.234 rounded to the nearest hundredth is 0.23.

63. To round 0.5942 to the nearest thousandth, observe that the digit in the ten-thousandths place is 2. Since this digit is less than 5, we do not add 1 to the digit in the thousandths place. The number 0.5942 rounded to the nearest thousandth is 0.594.

65. To round 98,207.23 to the nearest ten, observe that the digit in the ones place is 7. Since this digit is at least 5, we need to add 1 to the digit in the tens place. The number 98,207.32 rounded to the nearest ten is 98,210.

67. To round 12,999 to the nearest tenth, observe that the digit in the hundredths place is 9. Since this digit is at least 5, we need to add 1 to the digit in the tenths place. The number 12.999 rounded to the nearest tenth is 13.0.

69. To round –17.667 to the nearest hundredth, observe that the digit in the thousandths place is 7. Since this digit is less than 5, we do not need to add 1 to the digit in the tenths place. The number –17.667 rounded to the nearest hundredth is –17.67.

71. To round –0.501 to the nearest tenth, observe that the digit in the hundredths place is 0. Since the digit is less than 5, we do not add 1 to the digit in the tenths place. The number –0.501 rounded to the nearest tenth is –0.5.

73. To round 0.067 to the nearest hundredth, observe that the digit in the thousandths place is 7. Since this digit is at least 5, we need to add 1 to the digit in the hundredths place. The number 0.067 rounded to the nearest hundredth is 0.07. The amount is $0.07.

75. To round 26.95 to the nearest one, observe that the digit in the tenths place is 9. Since this digit is at least 5, we need to add 1 to the digit in the ones place. The number 26.95 rounded to the nearest one is 27. The amount is $27.

77. To round 0.1992 to the nearest hundredth, observe that the digit in the thousandths place is 9. Since the digit is at least 5, we need to add 1 the digit in the hundredths place. The number 0.1992 rounded to the nearest hundredth is 0.2. The amount is $0.20.

79. 0.26559 rounds to 0.27
0.26499 rounds to 0.26
0.25786 rounds to 0.26
0.25186 rounds to 0.25
Therefore, 0.26499 and 0.25786 round to 0.26.

81. Since there is a 9 in the tenths place, 15.99 rounded to the nearest dollar is $16.

83. Since there is a 5 in the thousandths place, 2.34528 rounded to the nearest hundredth is 2.35.

85. To round 24.6229 to the nearest thousandth, observe that the digit in the ten-thousandths place is 9. Since this digit is at least 5, we need to add 1 to the digit in the thousandths place. The number 24.6229 rounded to the nearest thousandth is 24.623. The length is 24.623 hours.

87. To round 135.74 to the nearest one, observe that the digit in the tenths place is 7. Since this digit is at least 5, we need to add 1 to the digit in the ones place. The number 135.74 rounded to the nearest one is 136. The record is 136 mph

89. Since there is a 3 in the tenths place, 31.3833 rounded to the nearest whole point is 31.

91. Compare each place value.
0.10299, 0.1037, 0.1038, 0.9

93.
$$\begin{array}{r} 3452 \\ +2314 \\ \hline 5766 \end{array}$$

95.
$$\begin{array}{r} 94 \\ -23 \\ \hline 71 \end{array}$$

97.
$$\begin{array}{r} 482 \\ -239 \\ \hline 243 \end{array}$$

99. Compare each place value. 228.040 is the highest average score bowled by Parker Bohn.

101. Compare each place value and list from greatest to least.
226.130, 225.490, 225.370, 222.980, 222.830, 222.008, 219.702, 218.158, 215.432.

103. Answers may vary.

105. 0.0000203 in words is two hundred three ten-millionths.

Section 5.2

Practice Problems

1. a.
$$\begin{array}{r} 15.520 \\ +2.371 \\ \hline 17.891 \end{array}$$

b.
$$\begin{array}{r} 20.060 \\ +\ 17.612 \\ \hline 37.672 \end{array}$$

c.
$$\begin{array}{r} 0.125 \\ +\ 122.800 \\ \hline 122.925 \end{array}$$

2. a.
$$\begin{array}{r} \scriptstyle 1\ 1\ 1 \quad\ \ \\ 34.5670 \\ 129.4300 \\ +\ 2.8903 \\ \hline 166.8873 \end{array}$$

b.
$$\begin{array}{r} \scriptstyle 1 \qquad\quad \\ 11.210 \\ 46.013 \\ +\ 362.526 \\ \hline 419.749 \end{array}$$

3.
$$\begin{array}{r} 27.00000 \\ +\ 0.00043 \\ \hline 27.00043 \end{array}$$

4. Subtract the absolute values.
$$\begin{array}{r} 99.2 \\ -\ 8.1 \\ \hline 91.1 \end{array}$$
Thus, 8.1 + (−99.2) = −91.1.

5.
$$\begin{array}{r} 5.80 \\ -3.92 \\ \hline 1.88 \end{array}$$
Check:
$$\begin{array}{r} \scriptstyle 1\ 1 \quad \\ 1.88 \\ +\ 3.92 \\ \hline 5.80 \end{array}$$
5.80 or 5.8

6.
$$\begin{array}{r} 53.00 \\ -29.31 \\ \hline 23.69 \end{array}$$
Check:
$$\begin{array}{r} \scriptstyle 1\ 1\ 1 \quad \\ 23.69 \\ +29.31 \\ \hline 53.00 \end{array}$$
53.00 or 53

7.
$$\begin{array}{r} \scriptstyle 1\ 16 \quad \\ 26.99 \\ -\ 18.00 \\ \hline 8.99 \end{array}$$
Check:
$$\begin{array}{r} 8.99 \\ +\ 18.00 \\ \hline 26.99 \end{array}$$

8. To subtract 9.6, add the opposite of 9.6, or −9.6.
−3.4 − 9.6 = −3.4 + (−9.6)
To add two numbers with the same sign, add their absolute values.

$$\begin{array}{r} 3.4 \\ +\ 9.6 \\ \hline 13.0 \end{array}$$

The sign in the answer is the common sign.
Thus, (–3.4) + (–9.6) = –13.

9. $-1.05-(-7.23)=-1.05+7.23$

$$\begin{array}{r} 7.23 \\ -1.05 \\ \hline 6.18 \end{array}$$

10. $y-z=11.6-10.8$
$=0.8$

$$\begin{array}{r} 11.6 \\ -10.8 \\ \hline 0.8 \end{array}$$

11. $y-4.3=7.8$
$12.1-4.3 \stackrel{?}{=} 7.8$
$7.8=7.8$ True
Yes, 12.1 is a solution.

12. $-4.3y+7.8-20.1y+14.6$
$=(-4.3y)+(-20.1y)+7.8+14.6$
$=(-24.4y)+22.4$
$=-24.4y+22.4$

13. The phrase "total monthly cost" tells us to add.
Find the sum of the three expenses.

$$\begin{array}{r} {}^{111} \\ 52.70 \\ 536.50 \\ +\ 87.50 \\ \hline 676.70 \end{array}$$

The total monthly cost is \$676.70.

14. The phrase "how much taller" tells us to subtract.
Subtract 70.8 from 72.6.

$$\begin{array}{r} 72.6 \\ -70.8 \\ \hline 1.8 \end{array}$$

Check:

$$\begin{array}{r} 1.8 \\ +\ 70.8 \\ \hline 72.6 \end{array}$$

The difference in average height is 1.8 inches.

Calculator Explorations

1. Press the keys 315.782 [+] 12.96 [= or ENTER].
The display will read 328.742.

2. Press the keys 29.68 [+] 85.902 [= or ENTER].
The display will read 115.582.

3. Press the keys 6.249 [–] 1.0076 [= or ENTER].
The display will read 5.2414.

4. Press the keys 5.238 [–] 0.682 [= or ENTER].
The display will read 4.556.

5. Press the keys 12.555 [+] 224.987 [+] 5.2 [+] 622.65 [= or ENTER].
The display will read 865.392.

6. Press the keys 47.006 [+] 0.17 [+] 313.259 [+] 139.088 [= or ENTER].
The display will read 499.523.

Mental Math

1.
$$\begin{array}{r} 0.3 \\ +\ 0.2 \\ \hline 0.5 \end{array}$$

2.
$$\begin{array}{r} 0.4 \\ +0.5 \\ \hline 0.9 \end{array}$$

3.
$$\begin{array}{r} 1.00 \\ +0.26 \\ \hline 1.26 \end{array}$$

4.
$$\begin{array}{r} 3.00 \\ +0.19 \\ \hline 3.19 \end{array}$$

5.
$$\begin{array}{r} 7.6 \\ +\ 1.3 \\ \hline 8.9 \end{array}$$

6. $\begin{array}{r} 4.5 \\ +3.2 \\ \hline 7.7 \end{array}$

7. $\begin{array}{r} 0.9 \\ -0.3 \\ \hline 0.6 \end{array}$

8. $\begin{array}{r} 0.6 \\ -0.2 \\ \hline 0.4 \end{array}$

Exercise Set 5.2

1. $\begin{array}{r} 1.3 \\ +2.2 \\ \hline 3.5 \end{array}$

3. $5.7 = 5.70$

$\begin{array}{r} 5.70 \\ +\ 1.13 \\ \hline 6.83 \end{array}$

5. $\begin{array}{r} 24.6000 \\ 2.3900 \\ +0.0678 \\ \hline 27.0578 \end{array}$

7. $\begin{array}{r} 45.023 \\ 3.006 \\ +8.403 \\ \hline 56.432 \end{array}$

9. $-2.6 + (-5.97)$

Add the absolute values.

$\begin{array}{r} 2.60 \\ +\ 5.97 \\ \hline 8.57 \end{array}$

Attach the common sign.

-8.57

11. $15.78 + (-4.62)$

Subtract the absolute values.

$\begin{array}{r} 15.78 \\ -4.62 \\ \hline 11.16 \end{array}$

Attach the sign of the number with the larger absolute value.

11.16

13. $\begin{array}{r} 8.8 \\ -2.3 \\ \hline 6.5 \end{array}$

15. $\begin{array}{r} 18.0 \\ -2.7 \\ \hline 15.3 \end{array}$

17. $\begin{array}{r} 654.90 \\ -56.67 \\ \hline 598.23 \end{array}$

19. $\begin{array}{r} 23.0 \\ -6.7 \\ \hline 16.3 \end{array}$

21. $-1.12 - 5.2 = -1.12 + (-5.2)$

Add the absolute values.

$\begin{array}{r} 1.2 \\ +\ 5.20 \\ \hline 6.32 \end{array}$

Attach the common sign.

-6.32

23. $7.7 - 14.1 = 7.7 + (-14.1)$

Subtract the absolute values.

$\begin{array}{r} 14.1 \\ -\ 7.7 \\ \hline 6.4 \end{array}$

Attach the sign of the number with the larger absolute value.

-6.4

25. $-2.6 - (-5.7) = -2.6 + 5.7$

$\begin{array}{r} 5.7 \\ -2.6 \\ \hline 3.1 \end{array}$

27. $\begin{array}{r} 0.9 \\ +\ 2.2 \\ \hline 3.1 \end{array}$

29. $-5.9 - 4 = -5.9 + (-4)$

Add the absolute values.

$\begin{array}{r} 5.9 \\ +4.0 \\ \hline 9.9 \end{array}$

Attach the common sign.
–9.9

31. $\begin{array}{r} 45.67 \\ -20.00 \\ \hline 25.67 \end{array}$

33. –6.06 + 0.44
Subtract the absolute values.
$\begin{array}{r} 6.06 \\ -\ 0.44 \\ \hline 5.62 \end{array}$
Attach the sign of the number with the largest absolute value.
–5.62

35. $\begin{array}{r} 900.34 \\ -123.45 \\ \hline 776.89 \end{array}$

37. $\begin{array}{r} 3490.23 \\ +8493.09 \\ \hline 11,983.32 \end{array}$

39. $\begin{array}{r} 234.89 \\ +230.67 \\ \hline 465.56 \end{array}$

41. 50.2 – 600 = 50.2 + (–600)
Subtract the absolute values.
$\begin{array}{r} 600.0 \\ -50.2 \\ \hline 549.8 \end{array}$
Attach the sign of the number with the larger absolute value.
–549.8

43. $\begin{array}{r} 923.5 \\ -\ 61.9 \\ \hline 861.6 \end{array}$

45. $\begin{array}{r} 100.009 \\ 6.080 \\ +9.034 \\ \hline 115.123 \end{array}$

47. $\begin{array}{r} 1000.0 \\ -123.4 \\ \hline 876.6 \end{array}$

49. –0.003 + 0.091
Subtract the absolute values.
$\begin{array}{r} 0.091 \\ -\ 0.003 \\ \hline 0.088 \end{array}$
Attach the sign of the number with the larger absolute value.
0.088

51. $\begin{array}{r} 500.000 \\ -\ \ 34.098 \\ \hline 465.902 \end{array}$

53. $\begin{array}{r} -102.40 \\ -78.04 \\ \hline -180.44 \end{array}$

55. $-2.9-(-1.8)=-2.9+1.8$
$\begin{array}{r} -2.9 \\ +1.8 \\ \hline -1.1 \end{array}$

57. $x + z = 3.6 + 0.21 = 3.81$

59. $x - z = 3.6 - 0.21 = 3.39$

61. $y-x+z=5-3.6+0.217$
$=5.00-3.60$
$=1.40+0.21$
$=1.61$

63. $x+2.7=9.3$
$7+2.7=9.3$
$9.7=9.3$ False
No, it is not a solution.

65. $27.4-y=16$
$27.4-11.4=16$
$16=16$
Yes, it is a solution.

67. $2.3+x=5.3-x$
$2.3+1=5.3-1$
$3.3 \neq 4.3$ False
No, it is not a solution.

69. $30.7x + 17.6 - 23.8x - 10.7$
$= 30.7x + (-23.8x) + 17.6 + (-10.7)$
$= 6.9x + 6.9$

71. $-8.61 + 4.23y - 2.36 - 0.76y$
$= -8.61 + (-2.36) + 4.23y + (-0.76y)$
$= -10.97 + 3.47y$

73. The phrase "total monthly cost" tells us to add. Find the sum of the four expenses.

```
 21 1 1
 275.36
  83.00
  81.60
+ 14.75
-------
 454.71
```

The total monthly cost is $454.71.

75. The phrase "By how much did the price change" tells us to subtract. Subtract 0.979 from 1.039.

```
  1.039
- 0.979
-------
  0.060
```

Check:

```
   1 1
  0.060
+ 0.979
-------
  1.039
```

The price changed by $0.06.

77. Subtract the cost of the book from what she paid ($20 + $20 = $40).

```
  40.00
- 32.48
-------
   7.52
```

Check:

```
  11 1
   7.52
+ 32.48
-------
  40.00 or 40
```

Her change was $7.52.

79. "How much more" tells us to subtract 136.8 from 150.1.

```
  150.1
 -136.8
 ------
   13.3
```

The average American consumed 13.3 more pounds of sugar in 2000 than 1990.

81. "How much faster" tells us to subtract 35.2 from 321.0

```
 321.0
 -35.2
 -----
 285.8
```

The highest speed is 285.8 mph faster than the average wind speed.

83. To find Green's speed, we must add the old record and the increase.

```
   1 1 1 1
   633.468
 + 129.567
 ---------
   763.035
```

The new record by Green is 763.035 mph.

85. The phrase "total amount" tells us to add. Find the sum of the 3 concert's earnings.

```
  121.2
  103.5
 +109.7
 ------
  334.4
```

The total amount of money these three concert's have earned is $334.4 million.

87. To find the total amount of snow Blue Canyon receives we must add Marquette's snow fall to that of the stated increase.

```
    1
   129.2
 + 111.6
 -------
   240.8
```

Blue Canyon receives an average of 240.8 inches of snow annually.

89. Find the sum of the lengths of the three sides.

```
   12.40
   29.34
 + 25.70
 -------
   67.44
```

The architect needs 67.44 feet of border material.

91.

```
  160.875
 -148.466
 --------
   12.409
```

The average Daytona 500 winning speed was 12.409 mph slower in 1989 than in 1969.

93.

```
  2059.817
 -  15.467
 ---------
  2044.350
```

The last Mercury mission was 2044.35 minutes longer than the first Mercury mission.

95. Compare the five numbers, finding the largest. Switzerland has the largest number of 22 pounds. Switzerland has the greatest chocolate consumption per person.

97. Subtract 13.9 from 22.

$$\begin{array}{r} 22.0 \\ -\ 13.9 \\ \hline 8.1 \end{array}$$

Check:

$$\begin{array}{r} {}^{11} \\ 8.1 \\ +\ 13.9 \\ \hline 22.0 \end{array}$$ or 22

The difference in consumption is 8.1 pounds per person.

99.

Country	Pounds of Chocolate per person
Switzerland	22.0
Norway	16.0
Germany	15.8
United Kingdom	14.5
Belgium	13.9

101. $\left(\frac{1}{5}\right)^3 = \frac{1}{5}\cdot\frac{1}{5}\cdot\frac{1}{5} = \frac{1}{125}$

103. $\frac{25}{36}\cdot\frac{24}{40} = \frac{25}{36}\cdot\frac{3\cdot 8}{5\cdot 8}$
$= \frac{25\cdot 3}{36\cdot 5}$
$= \frac{5\cdot 5\cdot 3}{3\cdot 12\cdot 5}$
$= \frac{5\cdot 1}{12\cdot 1}$
$= \frac{5}{12}$

105.

$$\begin{array}{lr} \text{2 quarters} & =\ 0.50 \\ \text{3 dimes} & =\ 0.30 \\ \text{4 nickels} & =\ 0.20 \\ \text{2 pennies} & =+0.02 \\ \hline & \$1.02 \end{array}$$

107. 5 nickels, 2 dimes, and 1 nickel; 1 dime and 3 nickels; 1 quarter

109. Answers may vary.

111. $14.271 - 8.968x + 1.333 - 201.815x + 101.239x = -109.544x + 15.604$Section 5.3

113. $10.68 - (2.3 + 2.3) = 10.68 - 46$

$$\begin{array}{r} 10.68 \\ \underline{-4.60} \\ 6.08 \end{array}$$ inches

Section 5.3

Practice Problems

1.
$$\begin{array}{r} 45.9 \\ \times\ 0.42 \\ \hline 918 \\ 18360 \\ 000 \\ \hline 19.278 \end{array}$$

2.
$$\begin{array}{r} 0.112 \\ \times\ \ 0.6 \\ \hline 672 \\ 00 \\ \hline 0.0672 \end{array}$$

3.
$$\begin{array}{r} 0.0721 \\ \times\ \ 48 \\ \hline 5768 \\ 28840 \\ \hline 3.4608 \end{array}$$

4. The product of a positive number and a negative number is a negative number.
$(5.4)(-1.3) = -7.02$

5. To find 23.7×10, note that 10 has 1 zero. Therefore, we move the decimal point of 23.7 to the right 1 place. The product is 237.

6. To find 203.004×100, note that 100 has 2 zeros. Therefore, we move the decimal point of 203.004 to the right 2 places. The product is 20,300.4.

7. To find 1.15×1000, note that 1000 has 3 zeros. Therefore, we move the decimal point of 1.15 to the right 3 places. The product is 1150.

8. To find 7.62×0.1, note that 0.1 has 1 decimal place. Therefore, we move the decimal point of 7.62 to the left 1 place. The product is 0.762.

9. To find 1.9×0.01, note that 0.01 has 2 decimal places. Therefore, we move the decimal point of 1.9 to the left 2 places. The product is 0.019.

10. To find 7682×0.001, note that 0.001 has 3 decimal places. Therefore, we move the decimal point of 7682 to the left 3 places. The product is 7.682.

11. $2158 \text{ thousand} = 2158 \times 1000$
$= 2{,}158{,}000$
There are 2,158,000 farms in the U.S.

12. Recall that $7y$ means $7 \cdot y$.
$7y = (7)(-0.028)$ -0.028
$\times \quad 7$
$= -0.196 \leftarrow$ -0.196

13. $-4x = 22$
$-4(-5.5) = 22$
$22 = 22$ True
Since $22 = 22$ is a true statement, -5.5 is a solution.

14. $\text{Circumference} = 2 \cdot \pi \cdot \text{radius}$
$= 2 \cdot \pi \cdot 11$
$= 22\pi$
$= 22(3.14)$
$= 69.08$
The circumference is $22\pi \approx 69.08$ meters.

15. Multiply 60.5 by 5.6.
60.5
$\times$ 5.6
3630
3025
338.80 or 338.8
She needs 338.8 ounces of fertilizer.

Exercise Set 5.3

1. 0.2 1 decimal place
$\times$ 0.6 1 decimal place
0.12 2 decimal places

3. 1.2 1 decimal place
$\times$ 0.5 2 decimal places
0.60 2 decimal places
0.6 The trailing 0 can be dropped.

5. $(-2.3)(7.65)$
7.65 2 decimal places
$\times$ -2.3 1 decimal place
2295
15300
-17.595 3 decimal places

7. $(-6.89)(-5.7)$
6.89 2 decimal places
$\times$ 5.7 1 decimal place
4823
34450
39.273 3 decimal places

9. 6.5 3 10 = 65

11. 6.5 3 0.1 = 0.65

13. $(-7.093)(1000) = -7093$

15. $(-9.83)(-0.01) = (9.83)(0.01) = 0.0983$

17. 5.62 2 decimal places
$\times$ 7.7 1 decimal place
3934
39340
43.274 3 decimal places

19. 1.0047 4 decimal places
$\times$ 8.2 1 decimal place
20094
80376
8.23854 5 decimal places

21. $(147.9)(100) = 14{,}790$

23. $(937.62)(-0.01) = -9.3762$

25. 49.02 3 decimals
$\times$ 0.023 3 decimal places
14706
98080
1.12746 5 decimal places

27. -0.023 3 decimal places
$\times$ 6.28 2 decimal places
184
0460
13800
-0.14444 5 decimal places

29. $5.5 \text{ billion} = 5.5 \times 1{,}000{,}000{,}000$
$= 5{,}500{,}000{,}000$

31. $36.4 \text{ million} = 36.4 \times 1{,}000{,}000$
$= 36{,}400{,}000$

33. $1.6 \text{ million} = 1.6 \times 1{,}000{,}000$
$= 1{,}600{,}000$

35. Recall that xy means $x \cdot y$.

$$xy = (3)(-0.2) = -0.6$$

$$\begin{array}{r} 3.0 \\ \times\ -0.2 \\ \hline -0.60 \end{array}$$

37. $$\begin{aligned} xz - y &= 3(5.7) - (-0.2) \\ &= 17.1 + 0.2 \\ &= 17.3 \end{aligned}$$

39. $$\begin{aligned} SA &= 2LW + 2WH + 2HL \\ &= 2(10)(2.1) + 2(2.1)(0.6) + 2(0.6)(10) \\ &= 42 + 2.52 + 12 \\ &= 44.52 + 12 \\ &= 56.52 \end{aligned}$$

41. $0.6x = 4.92$ Show substitution exactly.

$0.6(14.2) = 4.92$

$8.52 = 4.92$ False

No, it is not a solution.

43. $-3x = -2.4$

$-3(0.08) = -2.4$

$-0.24 = -2.4$ False

No, it is not a solution.

45. $3.5y = -14$

$3.5(-4) = -14$

$-14.0 = -14$

$-14 = -14$ True

Yes, it is a solution.

47. Circumference = $2 \cdot \pi \cdot$ radius

$C = 2 \cdot \pi \cdot 4 = 8\pi$

$C \approx 8(3.14) = 25.12$

The circumference is 8π meters, which is approximately 25.12 meters.

49. Circumference = $\pi \cdot$ diameter

$C = \pi \cdot 10 = 10\pi$

$C \approx 10(3.14) = 31.4$

The circumference is 10π centimeters, which is approximately 31.4 centimeters.

51. Circumference = $2 \cdot \pi \cdot$ radius

$C = 2 \cdot \pi \cdot 9.1 = 18.2\pi$

$C \approx 57.148$

The circumference is 18.2π yards, which is approximately 57.148 yards.

53. Circumference = $\pi \cdot$ diameter

$C = \pi \cdot 250 = 250\pi$

$C \approx 250(3.14) = 785$

The circumference of the ferris wheel is 250π feet which is approximately 785 feet.

55. One revolution is equal to the circumference.

$C = \pi d$

$C = \pi(135)$

$C = 135\pi$ meters

$C \approx 135(3.14) = 423.9$ meters

One revolution is 135π meters which is approximately 423.9 meters.

57. **a.** $C = 2 \cdot \pi \cdot 10 = 20\pi \approx 20(3.14) = 62.8$ m

$$\begin{aligned} C &= 2 \cdot \pi \cdot 20 \\ &= 40\pi \\ &\approx 40(3.14) \\ &= 125.6 \text{ m} \end{aligned}$$

b. yes

59. Multiply the number of ounces by the number of grams of fat in 1 ounce to get the total amount of fat.

$$\begin{array}{r} 6.2 \\ \times\ 4 \\ \hline 24.8 \end{array}$$

There are 24.8 grams of fat in a 4-ounce serving of cream cheese.

61. To find 2.8×1000, note that 1000 has 3 zeros. Therefore, we move the decimal point of 2.8 to the right 3 places. The product is 2800. The farmer received $2800.

63. Multiply 39.37 by 1.65.

$$\begin{array}{r} 39.37 \\ \times\ 1.65 \\ \hline 19685 \\ 236220 \\ 393700 \\ \hline 64.9605 \end{array}$$

She is about 64.9605 inches tall.

65. Multiply the number of hours by the hourly wage.

$$\begin{array}{r} 13.88 \\ \times\ 40 \\ \hline 0 \\ 55520 \\ \hline 555.20 \end{array}$$

His pay was $555.20

67. $675 \times 118.07 = 79{,}697.25$ yen

69. $350 \times 1.4695 \approx 514$ Canadian dollars

71.
$$\begin{array}{r} 26 \\ 5\overline{)\ 130} \\ \underline{-10} \\ 30 \\ \underline{-30} \\ 0 \end{array}$$

73.
$$\begin{array}{r} 36 \\ 56\overline{)\ 2016} \\ \underline{-168} \\ 336 \\ \underline{-336} \\ 0 \end{array}$$

75.
$$\begin{array}{r} 8 \\ 365\overline{)\ 2920} \\ \underline{-2920} \\ 0 \end{array}$$

77.
$$\begin{aligned} -\frac{24}{7} \div \frac{8}{21} &= -\frac{24}{7} \cdot \frac{21}{8} \\ &= -\frac{24 \cdot 21}{7 \cdot 8} \\ &= -\frac{8 \cdot 3 \cdot 7 \cdot 3}{7 \cdot 8} \\ &= -\frac{3 \cdot 3}{1 \cdot 1} \\ &= -\frac{9}{1} \\ &= -9 \end{aligned}$$

79. (20.6)(1.86)(100,000) = 3,831,600 miles

81. Answers may vary.

83.
$$\begin{aligned} 4\pi r^2 &= 4(3.14)(7.68)^2 \\ &= 4(3.14)(58.9824) \\ &= 12.56(58.9824) \\ &\approx 740.82 \end{aligned}$$

Section 5.4

Practice Problems

1.
$$\begin{array}{r} 0.71 \\ 48\overline{)\ 34.08} \\ \underline{-336} \\ 48 \\ \underline{-48} \\ 0 \end{array}$$

2. $5.6\overline{)166.88}$ becomes
$$\begin{array}{r} 29.8 \\ 56\overline{)\ 1668.8} \\ \underline{-112} \\ 548 \\ \underline{-504} \\ 448 \\ \underline{-448} \\ 0 \end{array}$$

3. Recall that a negative number divided by a negative number gives a positive quotient.
$$\begin{array}{r} 0.027 \\ 104\overline{)\ 2.808} \\ \underline{-2\,08} \\ 728 \\ \underline{-728} \\ 0 \end{array}$$
Thus –2.808 (–104) = 0.027.

4. $0.57\overline{)23.4}$ becomes
$$\begin{array}{r} 41.052 \approx 41.05 \\ 57.\overline{)\ 2340.000} \\ \underline{-228} \\ 60 \\ \underline{-57} \\ 30 \\ \underline{-0} \\ 300 \\ \underline{-285} \\ 150 \\ \underline{-114} \\ 36 \end{array}$$

5. To find 28 × 1000, note that 1000 has 3 zeros. Therefore, we move the decimal point of 28 to the left 3 places. The quotient is 0.028.

6. To find 8.56×100, note that 100 has 2 zeros. Therefore, we move the decimal point of 8.56 to the left 2 places. The quotient is 0.0856.

7. $x \div y = 0.035 \div 0.02$

$0.02\overline{)0.035}$ becomes $\begin{array}{r} 1.75 \\ 2\overline{)3.50} \end{array}$

$= 1.75$

8. $\frac{x}{100} = 3.9$

$\frac{39}{100} = 3.9$

$0.39 = 3.9$ False

Since $0.39 = 3.9$ is a false statement, 39 is not a solution.

9.

$$\begin{array}{r} 11.84 \\ 1250\overline{)\ 14,800.00} \\ -1250 \\ \hline 2300 \\ -1250 \\ \hline 10500 \\ -10000 \\ \hline 5000 \\ -5000 \\ \hline 0 \end{array}$$

He needs 12 bags.

Exercise Set 5.4

1.

$$\begin{array}{r} 0.094 \\ 5\overline{)0.470} \\ -45 \\ \hline 20 \\ -20 \\ \hline 0 \end{array}$$

$0.47 \div 5 = 0.094$

3. $0.06\overline{)18.00}$

Move the decimal points 2 places.

$$\begin{array}{r} 300 \\ 6.\overline{)\ 1800.} \\ -18 \\ \hline 00 \\ -0 \\ \hline 00 \\ -0 \\ \hline 0 \end{array}$$

$-18 \div 0.06 = -300$

5. $0.82\overline{)4.756}$

Move the decimal points 2 places.

$$\begin{array}{r} 5.8 \\ 82.\overline{)\ 475.6} \\ -410 \\ \hline 656 \\ -656 \\ \hline 0 \end{array}$$

$4.756 \div 0.82 = 5.8$

7. $5.5\overline{)36.3}$

Move the decimal points 1 place.

$$\begin{array}{r} 6.6 \\ 55.\overline{)\ 363.0} \\ -330 \\ \hline 330 \\ -330 \\ \hline 0 \end{array}$$

The answer is negative.

$-36.3 \div 5.5 = -6.6$

9. $2.4\overline{)429.34}$

Move the decimal points one place.

$$\begin{array}{r} 178.\ldots \\ 24.\overline{)4293.4} \\ -24 \\ \hline 189 \\ -168 \\ \hline 213 \\ -192 \\ \hline 21 \end{array}$$

178 rounded to the nearest hundred is 200.

11. $0.023\overline{)0.549}$

Move the decimal points 3 places.

$$\begin{array}{r} 23.869 \\ 23.\overline{)\ 549.00} \\ -46 \\ \hline 89 \\ -69 \\ \hline 200 \\ -184 \\ \hline 160 \\ -138 \\ \hline 220 \\ -207 \\ \hline 13 \end{array}$$

23.869 rounded to the nearest hundredth is 23.87.

13. $0.4\overline{)45.23}$

Move the decimal points one place.

$$\begin{array}{r} 113.0 \\ 4.\overline{)\ 452.300} \\ \underline{-4} \\ 05 \\ \underline{-4} \\ 12 \\ \underline{-12} \\ 03 \\ \underline{-0} \\ 3 \end{array}$$

-113.0 rounded to the nearest ten is -110.

15. 54.982×100 Move decimal point 2 places to the left.

$= 0.54982$

17. $12.9(-1000)$ Move the decimal point 3 places to the left and attach the negative sign.

$= -0.0129$

19. 87×10 Move the decimal point 1 place to the left.

$= 8.7$

21.

$$\begin{array}{r} 0.413 \\ 3\overline{)\ 1.239} \\ \underline{-1\ 2} \\ 03 \\ \underline{-3} \\ 09 \\ \underline{-9} \\ 0 \end{array}$$

$1.239 \times 3 = 0.413$

23. $0.6\overline{)4.2}$

Move the decimal points 1 place.

$$\begin{array}{r} 7. \\ 6.\overline{)\ 42.} \\ \underline{-42} \\ 0 \end{array}$$

The answer is negative.

$-4.2 \times 0.6 = -7$

25. $0.27\overline{)1.296}$

Move the decimal points 2 places.

$$\begin{array}{r} 4.8 \\ 27.\overline{)\ 129.6} \\ \underline{-108} \\ 21\ 6 \\ \underline{-21\ 6} \\ 0 \end{array}$$

$1.296 \div 0.27 = 4.8$

27. $0.02\overline{)42.}$

Move the decimal points 2 places.

$$\begin{array}{r} 2100. \\ 2.\overline{)\ 4200.} \\ \underline{-4200} \\ 0 \end{array}$$

29. $-18 \times -0.6 = 180 \div -6 = 30$

31. $35 \div 0.005 = 35{,}000 \div 5 = 7000$

33. $1.6\overline{)1.104}$

Move the decimal points 1 place.

$$\begin{array}{r} 0.69 \\ 16.\overline{)\ 11.04} \\ \underline{-96} \\ 1\ 44 \\ \underline{-1\ 44} \\ 0 \end{array}$$

The answer is negative.

$-1.104 \div 1.6 = -0.69$

35. -2.4×-100 Move the decimal point 2 places to the left. The answer is positive.

$= 0.024$

37. $\dfrac{4.615}{0.071} = \dfrac{4615}{71} = 65$

39. $8.9\overline{)0.00263}$

Move the decimal points 1 place.

$$\begin{array}{r} 0.00029\ldots \\ 89.\overline{)0.02630} \end{array}$$

0.00029 rounded to the nearest ten-thousandth is 0.0003.

41. $0.0043\overline{)500}$

Move the decimal points 4 places.

$$\begin{array}{r} 116279.\\ 43.\overline{)\ 5000000.}\\ \underline{-43}\\ 70\\ \underline{-43}\\ 270\\ \underline{-258}\\ 120\\ \underline{-86}\\ 340\\ \underline{-301}\\ 390.\\ \underline{-387}.\\ 3 \end{array}$$

116,279 rounded to the nearest ten-thousand is 120,000.

43. $z \div y = 4.52\ 4\ 0.8$

$0.8\overline{)4.52}$

Move the decimal points one place.

$$\begin{array}{r} 5.65\\ 8.\overline{)\ 45.20}\\ \underline{-40}\\ 52\\ \underline{-48}\\ 40\\ \underline{-40}\\ 0 \end{array}$$

45. $x \div y = 5.65 \div -0.8 = -7.0625$

$0.8\overline{)5.65}$

Move the decimal point 1 place.

$$\begin{array}{r} 7.0625\\ 8.\overline{)\ 56.5000}\\ \underline{-56}\\ 0\ 5\\ \underline{-\ 0}\\ 50\\ \underline{-48}\\ 20\\ \underline{-16}\\ 40\\ \underline{-40}\\ 0 \end{array}$$

47. $x \div 5 = 5.65 \div 5 = 1.13$

$$\begin{array}{r} 1.13\\ 5\overline{)\ 5.65}\\ \underline{-5}\\ 06\\ \underline{-5}\\ 15\\ \underline{-15}\\ 0 \end{array}$$

49. $\dfrac{x}{4} = 3.04$

$\dfrac{12.16}{4} = 3.04$

$3.04 = 3.04$ True

Yes, it is a solution.

51. $\dfrac{x}{4.3} = 2$

$\dfrac{0.86}{4.3} = 2$

$0.2 = 2$ False

Not, it is not a solution.

53. $\dfrac{z}{10} = 0.8$

$\dfrac{8}{10} = 0.8$

$08. = 0.8$ True

Yes, it is a solution.

55. Divide the total amount by the amount per month to get the number of months.

$73.86\overline{)1772.64}$

Move the decimal points 2 places.

$$\begin{array}{r} 24\\ 7386.\overline{)\ 177{,}264.}\\ \underline{-147\ 72}\\ 29\ 544.\\ \underline{-\ 29\ 544.}\\ 0 \end{array}$$

It will be paid off in 24 months.

57. There are 52 weeks per year and 40 hours per week. Therefore, there are $52 \times 40 = 2080$ hours per year.

$$\begin{array}{r} 2734.508 \\ 2080\overline{)\,5{,}687{,}777.000} \\ \underline{-4160} \\ 15277 \\ \underline{-14560} \\ 7177 \\ \underline{-6240} \\ 9377 \\ \underline{-8320} \\ 10570 \\ \underline{-10400} \\ 1700 \\ \underline{-\ \ 0} \\ 17000 \\ \underline{-16640} \\ 360 \end{array}$$

His hourly wage would be $2734.51.

59. $202.14 \approx 202.1$

$$\begin{array}{r} 39.\overline{)\,7883.50} \\ \underline{-78} \\ 08 \\ \underline{-0} \\ 83 \\ \underline{-78} \\ 55 \\ \underline{-39} \\ 160 \\ \underline{-156} \\ 4 \end{array}$$

She needs to buy 202.1 pounds.

61. $39.37\overline{)200}$

Move the decimal points 2 places.

$5.08 \approx 5.1$

$$\begin{array}{r} 3937.\overline{)\,20{,}000.00} \\ \underline{-19\,685} \\ 3150 \\ \underline{-0} \\ 31500 \\ \underline{-31496} \\ 4 \end{array}$$

There are 5.1 meters in 200 inches.

63. $11.40 \approx 11.41$ boxes

$$\begin{array}{r} 64\overline{)\,730.00} \\ \underline{-66} \\ 90 \\ \underline{-64} \\ 260 \\ \underline{-256} \\ 40 \\ \underline{-0} \\ 40 \end{array}$$

65.

$$\begin{array}{r} 132.5 \\ 24\overline{)\,3180.0} \\ \underline{-24} \\ 78 \\ \underline{-72} \\ 60 \\ \underline{-48} \\ 120 \\ \underline{-120} \\ 0 \end{array}$$

Their average speed was 132.5 mph.

67. $6 \times 4 = 24$ teaspoons

69. $24 \div 4 = 6$ doses per day
$48 \div 6 = 8$ days

71. To round 345.219 to the nearest hundredth, observe that the digit in the thousandths place is 9. Since this digit is at least 5, we need to add 1 to the digit in the hundredths place. The number 345.219 rounded to the nearest hundredth is 345.22.

73. To round −1000.994 to the nearest tenth, observe that the digit in the hundredths place is 9. Since this digit is at least 5, we need to add 1 to the digit in the tenths place. The number −1000.994 rounded to the nearest tenth is −1001.0.

75. $2 + 3 \cdot 6 = 2 + 18 = 20$

77. $20 - 10 \div (-5) = 20 + 2 = 22$

79. $(86+78+91+85) \div 4 = 340 \div 4$

$$\begin{array}{r} 85 \\ 4\overline{)\ 340} \\ \underline{-32} \\ 20 \\ \underline{-20} \\ 0 \end{array}$$

The average is 85.

81. $(9.6+8.5+4.1+4.1+9.8) \div 5$
$= 36.1 \div 5$

$$\begin{array}{r} 8.6 \\ 5\overline{)\ 36.10} \\ \underline{-35} \\ 11 \\ \underline{-10} \\ 10 \\ \underline{-10} \\ 0 \end{array}$$

83.

$$A = lw$$
$$38.7 = l(4.5)$$
$$\frac{38.7}{4.5} = l$$
$$8.6 = l$$

The length is 8.6 feet.

85. Answers may vary.

87. 75 mph ÷ 1.15

$1.15\overline{)75}$

Move the decimal points 2 places.

$$\begin{array}{r} 65.21 \approx 65.2 \\ 115.\overline{)\ 7500.00} \\ \underline{-690} \\ 600 \\ \underline{-575} \\ 250 \\ \underline{-230} \\ 200 \\ \underline{-115} \\ 85 \end{array}$$

95 mph ÷ 1.15

$1.15\overline{)95}$

Move the decimal points 2 places.

$$\begin{array}{r} 82.60 \approx 82.6 \\ 115.\overline{)\ 9500.00} \\ \underline{-920} \\ 300 \\ \underline{-230} \\ 70\ 0 \\ \underline{-69\ 0} \\ 1\ 00 \\ \underline{-\ 0} \\ 1\ 00 \end{array}$$

The wind speed range for a Category 1 hurricane is from 65.2 knots to 82.6 knots.

Integrated Review

1.
$$\begin{array}{r} 1.60 \\ \underline{+0.97} \\ 2.57 \end{array}$$

2.
$$\begin{array}{r} 3.20 \\ \underline{+0.85} \\ 4.05 \end{array}$$

3.
$$\begin{array}{r} 9.8 \\ \underline{-0.9} \\ 8.9 \end{array}$$

4.
$$\begin{array}{r} 10.2 \\ \underline{-6.7} \\ 3.5 \end{array}$$

5.
$$\begin{array}{r} 0.8 \\ \underline{\times\ 0.2} \\ 0.16 \end{array}$$

6.
$$\begin{array}{r} 0.6 \\ \underline{\times 0.4} \\ 0.24 \end{array}$$

7.
$$\begin{array}{r} 0.27 \\ 8\overline{)\ 2.16} \\ \underline{-1\ 6} \\ 56 \\ \underline{-56} \\ 0 \end{array}$$

8.
$$\begin{array}{r} 0.52 \\ 6\overline{)\ 3.12} \\ \underline{-30} \\ 12 \\ \underline{-12} \\ 0 \end{array}$$

9.
$$\begin{array}{r} 9.6 \\ \underline{\times 0.5} \\ 4.80 \end{array}$$
or $(9.6)(-0.5) = -4.8$

10.
$$\begin{array}{r} 8.7 \\ \underline{\times\ 0.7} \\ 6.09 \end{array}$$
$(-8.7)(-0.7) = 6.09$

11.
$$\begin{array}{r} 123.60 \\ \underline{-\ 48.04} \\ 75.56 \end{array}$$

12.
$$\begin{array}{r} 325.20 \\ \underline{-\ 36.08} \\ 289.12 \end{array}$$

13. $-25 + 0.026 = -24.974$

14.
$$\begin{array}{r} 44.000 \\ \underline{-0.125} \\ 43.875 \end{array}$$
$0.125 + (-44) = -43.875$

15. $3.4\overline{)29.24}$ becomes
$$\begin{array}{r} 8.6 \\ 34\overline{)\ 292.4} \\ \underline{-272} \\ 204 \\ \underline{-204} \\ 0 \end{array}$$
-8.6
The answer is negative.

16. $1.9\overline{)10.26}$ becomes
$$\begin{array}{r} 5.4 \\ 19\overline{)102.6} \\ \underline{95} \\ 76 \\ \underline{76} \\ 0 \end{array}$$
$-10.26 \div (-1.9) = 5.4$

17. $-2.8 \times 100 = -280$

18. $1.6 \times 1000 = 1600$

19.
$$\begin{array}{r} 96210 \\ 7.028 \\ \underline{+121.700} \\ 224.938 \end{array}$$

20.
$$\begin{array}{r} 0.268 \\ 1.940 \\ \underline{+142.881} \\ 145.079 \end{array}$$

21.
$$\begin{array}{r} 0.56 \\ 46\overline{)\ 25.76} \\ \underline{-230} \\ 276 \\ \underline{-276} \\ 0 \end{array}$$

22.
$$\begin{array}{r} -0.63 \\ 43\overline{)\ 27.09} \\ \underline{-258} \\ 129 \\ \underline{-129} \\ 0 \end{array}$$

23.
$$\begin{array}{r} 12.004 \\ \underline{\times\ 2.3} \\ 36012 \\ \underline{240080} \\ 26.6092 \end{array}$$

24.
$$\begin{array}{r} 28.006 \\ \underline{\times\ 5.2} \\ 56012 \\ \underline{1400300} \\ 145.6312 \end{array}$$

25.
$$\begin{array}{r} 10.0 \\ \underline{-\ 4.6} \\ 5.4 \end{array}$$

26.
$$\begin{array}{r} 18.00 \\ \underline{-\ 0.26} \\ 17.74 \end{array}$$
$0.26 - 18 = -17.74$

27.
$$\begin{array}{r} 268.19 \\ \underline{+\ 146.25} \\ 414.44 \end{array}$$
$-268.19 - 414.44 = -414.44$

28. $\begin{array}{r} 860.18 \\ +\ 434.85 \\ \hline 1295.03 \end{array}$

$-860.18 - 434.85 = -1295.03$

29. $0.087\overline{)2.958}$ becomes

$\begin{array}{r} 34 \\ 87.\overline{)\ 2958} \\ -261 \\ \hline 348 \\ -348 \\ \hline 0 \end{array}$

−34

The answer is negative.

30. $0.061\overline{)1.708}$ becomes

$\begin{array}{r} 28 \\ 61.\overline{)\ 1708} \\ -122 \\ \hline 488 \\ -488 \\ \hline 0 \end{array}$

−28

The answer is negative.

31. $\begin{array}{r} 160.00 \\ -43.19 \\ \hline 116.81 \end{array}$

32. $\begin{array}{r} 120.00 \\ -\ 101.21 \\ \hline 18.79 \end{array}$

33. $\begin{array}{r} 15.62 \\ \times 10 \\ \hline 156.20 \end{array}$

Answer: 156.2

34. $\begin{array}{r} 1.562 \\ 10\overline{)\ 15.620} \\ -10 \\ \hline 56 \\ -50 \\ \hline 62 \\ -60 \\ \hline 20 \\ -20 \\ \hline 0 \end{array}$

35. $\begin{array}{r} 15.62 \\ +10.00 \\ \hline 25.62 \end{array}$

36. $\begin{array}{r} 15.62 \\ -10.00 \\ \hline 5.62 \end{array}$

37. The tenths place in 0.38 is less than the tenths place in 0.5. Thus, the cookie can be labeled "Fat Free."

38. $\begin{array}{r} 32.09 \approx 32.1 \\ 75.\overline{)\ 2407.00} \\ -225 \\ \hline 157 \\ -150 \\ \hline 70 \\ -0 \\ \hline 700 \\ -675 \\ \hline 25 \end{array}$

His average number of points per game is 32.1.

Section 5.5

Practice Problems

1. $\begin{array}{r} 65.34 \\ -14.68 \\ \hline 50.66 \end{array}$ Estimate $\begin{array}{r} 65 \\ -15 \\ \hline 50 \end{array}$

The estimated difference is \$50, so \$50.66 is reasonable.

2. $\begin{array}{r} 30.26 \\ \times 2.98 \\ \hline 24208 \\ 272340 \\ 605200 \\ \hline 90.1748 \end{array}$ Estimate $\begin{array}{r} 30 \\ \times 3 \\ \hline 90 \end{array}$

The answer 90.1748 is reasonable.

3. $91.5\overline{)713.7}$ Estimate $\begin{array}{r} 8 \\ 90\overline{)720} \end{array}$

becomes

$\begin{array}{r} 7.8 \\ 915.\overline{)\ 7137.0} \\ -6405 \\ \hline 732\ 0 \\ -732\ 0 \\ \hline 0 \end{array}$

The estimate is 8, so 7.8 is reasonable.

4. $\begin{array}{r} 79.2 \\ -53.7 \\ \hline \end{array}$ Estimate $\begin{array}{r} 79 \\ -\ 54 \\ \hline 25 \end{array}$

The estimate is 25 miles.

5. Round each number to the nearest ten. Since $50 \div 10 = 5$, the calculator display 19.612 is not reasonable.

6. $-8.6(3.2-1.8) = -8.6(1.4)$
$= -12.04$

7. $(0.7)^2 = (0.7)(0.7)$
$= 0.49$

8. $\dfrac{8.78-2.8}{20} = \dfrac{5.98}{20} = 0.299$

9. $1.7y - 2 = 1.7(2.3) - 2$
$= 3.91 - 2$
$= 1.91$

10. $3x + 7.5 = 1.2$
$3(-2.1) + 7.50\ 1.2$
$-6.3 + 7.50\ 1.2$
$1.2 = 1.2$ True
Since 1.2 = 1.2 is a true statement, –2.1 is a solution.

Exercise Set 5.5

1. $4.9 - 2.1 = 2.8$
$5 - 2 = 3$
3 is close to 2.8, so the answer is reasonable.

3.
$$\begin{array}{r} 6 \\ \times\ 483.11 \\ \hline 2898.66 \end{array} \qquad \text{Estimate:} \quad \begin{array}{r} 6 \\ \times\ 500 \\ \hline 3000 \end{array}$$
3000 is close to 2898.66, so the answer is reasonable.

5. $62.16 \times 14.8 = 4.2$
$60 \times 15 = 4$
4 is close to 4.2 so the answer is reasonable.

7.
$$\begin{array}{r} 69.2 \\ 32.1 \\ +\ 48.5 \\ \hline 149.7 \end{array} \qquad \begin{array}{r} 70 \\ 30 \\ +\ 50 \\ \hline 150 \end{array}$$
149.8 is close to 150, so the answer is reasonable.

9.
$$\begin{array}{r} 34.92 \\ -12.03 \\ \hline 22.89 \end{array} \qquad \begin{array}{r} 35 \\ -12 \\ \hline 23 \end{array}$$
23 is close to 22.89 so the answer is reasonable.

11. $2(12.2) + 2(5.9) \approx 2(12) + 2(6)$
$= 24 + 12$
$= 36$ inches

13. $11.8 + 12.9 + 14.2 \approx 12 + 13 + 14 = 39$ ft

15. $3.14(7)(2) = 43.96$ meters

17.
$$\begin{array}{r} 51.6 \\ 30\overline{)\ 1550.0} \\ \underline{-150} \\ 50 \\ \underline{-30} \\ 200 \\ \underline{-180} \\ 20 \end{array}$$
Their car will use about 52 gallons.

19. 398.79 is approximately 400
5 years is 5 × 12 = 60 months.
60 × 400 = 124000
They will pay about $24,000.

21. 19.9 + 15.1 + 10.9 + 6.7 = ?
Estimate:
20 + 15 + 11 + 7 = 53 miles
The distance is about 53 miles.

23. $600.8 million → $600 million
$461.0 million → $500 million
$435.0 million → $400 million
$431.1 million → $400 million
$403.7 million → $400 million
$357.1 million → <u>$400 million</u>
The estimate is $2700 million

25. 501 rounded to the nearest 10 is 500.
271 rounded to the nearest 10 is 270.
$$\begin{array}{r} 00 \\ \times\ \ 270 \\ \hline 0 \\ 35000 \\ \underline{100000} \\ 135{,}000 \end{array}$$
The population is about 135,000 people.

27. $9 \times 40 = 360$
c.

29. $78.6 \div 100 = 0.786$
b.

31. $100 \times 40 = 4000$
Not reasonable

33. $1000 - 100 = 900$
Reasonable

35. $(0.4)^2 = (0.4)(0.4) = 0.16$

37. $\frac{1+0.8}{-0.6} = \frac{1.8}{-0.6} = \frac{18}{-6} = -3$

39. $1.4(2-1.8) = 1.4(0.2) = 0.28$

41. $4.83 \div 2.1 = 2.3$

43. $(-2.3)^2(0.3+0.7) = (-2.3)^2(1)$
$= 5.29(1)$
$= 5.29$

45. $(3.1+0.7)(2.9-0.9) = (3.8)(2.0) = 7.6$

47. $\frac{(4.5)^2}{100} = \frac{20.25}{100} = 0.2025$

49. $\frac{7+0.74}{-6} = \frac{7.74}{-6} = -1.29$

51. $z^2 = (-2.4)^2 = 5.76$

53. $x - y = 6 - (0.3) = 5.7$

55. $4y - z = 4(0.3) - (-2.4) = 1.2 + 2.4 = 3.6$

57.
$$7x + 2.1 = -7$$
$$7(-1.3) + 2.1 = -7$$
$$-9.1 + 2.1 = -7$$
$$-7 = -7 \quad \text{True}$$
Yes, −1.3 is a solution.

59.
$$x - 6.5 = 2x + 1.8$$
$$-4.7 - 6.5 = 2(-4.7) + 1.8$$
$$-11.2 = -9.4 + 1.8$$
$$-11.2 = -7.6 \quad \text{False}$$
No, −4.7 is not a solution.

61. $\frac{3}{4} \cdot \frac{5}{12} = \frac{3 \cdot 5}{4 \cdot 3 \cdot 4} = \frac{5}{16}$

63.
$$-\frac{36}{56} \div \frac{30}{35} = -\frac{36}{56} \cdot \frac{35}{30}$$
$$= -\frac{2 \cdot 2 \cdot 3 \cdot 3 \cdot 5 \cdot 7}{2 \cdot 2 \cdot 2 \cdot 7 \cdot 2 \cdot 3 \cdot 5}$$
$$= -\frac{3}{4}$$

65. $\frac{5}{12} - \frac{1}{3} = \frac{5}{12} - \frac{4}{12} = \frac{1}{12}$

67.
$$1.96(7.852 - 3.147)^2 = 1.96(4.705)^2$$
$$= 1.96(22.137025)$$
$$= 43.388569$$
Estimate: $2(8-3)^2 = 2(5)^2 = 2(25) = 50$
The result is reasonable.

69. Answers may vary.

71. Square first; answers may vary.

Section 5.6

Practice Problems

1. a. $\frac{2}{5} = 2 \div 5$

$$\begin{array}{r} 0.4 \\ 5 \overline{)\ 2.0} \\ \underline{-2\,0} \\ 0 \end{array}$$

$\frac{2}{5} = 0.4$

b. $\frac{9}{40} = 9 \div 40$

$$\begin{array}{r} 0.225 \\ 40 \overline{)\ 9.000} \\ \underline{-8\,0} \\ 100 \\ \underline{-80} \\ 200 \\ \underline{-200} \\ 0 \end{array}$$

$\frac{9}{40} = 0.225$

2.
$$\begin{array}{r} 0.375 \\ 8 \overline{)\ 3.000} \\ \underline{-24} \\ 60 \\ \underline{-56} \\ 40 \\ \underline{-40} \\ 0 \end{array}$$

$-\frac{3}{8} = -0.375$

3. a.
$$\begin{array}{r} 0.833\ldots \\ 6\overline{)\ 5.000} \\ \underline{-4\ 8} \\ 20 \\ \underline{-18} \\ 20 \\ \underline{-18} \\ 2 \end{array}$$

$\frac{5}{6} = 0.8\overline{3} \approx 0.83$

b.
$$\begin{array}{r} 0.22\ldots \\ 9\overline{)\ 2.00} \\ \underline{-1\ 8} \\ 20 \\ \underline{-18} \\ 2 \end{array}$$

$\frac{2}{9} = 0.\overline{2} \approx 0.2$

4.
$$\begin{array}{r} 0.3636 \\ 11\overline{)\ 4.0000} \\ \underline{-33} \\ 70 \\ \underline{-66} \\ 40 \\ \underline{-33} \\ 70 \\ \underline{-66} \\ 4 \end{array}$$

$\frac{4}{11} = -0.\overline{36} \approx 0.364$

5.
$$\begin{array}{r} 0.1111\ldots \\ 9\overline{)1.0000} \\ \underline{-9} \\ 10 \\ \underline{-9} \\ 10 \end{array}$$

$\frac{1}{9} = 0.\overline{1} \approx 0.111$

6. $\frac{1}{5} = 1 \div 5$
$$\begin{array}{r} 0.2 \\ 5\overline{)\ 1.0} \\ \underline{-1\ 0} \\ 0 \end{array}$$

$\frac{1}{5} = 0.20$

Since $0.20 < 0.25$, $\frac{1}{5} < 0.25$.

7. a.
$$\begin{array}{r} 0.5 \\ 2\overline{)\ 1.0} \\ \underline{-1\ 0} \\ 0 \end{array}$$

$\frac{1}{2} = 0.50$

Since $0.50 < 0.54$, $\frac{1}{2} < 0.54$.

b. Since $\frac{2}{9} = 0.\overline{2}$, $0.\overline{2} = \frac{2}{9}$.

c.
$$\begin{array}{r} 0.714 \\ 7\overline{)\ 5.000} \\ \underline{-4\ 9} \\ 10 \\ \underline{-7} \\ 30 \\ \underline{-28} \\ 2 \end{array}$$

Since $\frac{5}{7} \approx 0.714$ and $0.714 < 0.72$,
$\frac{5}{7} < 0.72$.

8. a.

Original number	$\frac{1}{3}$	0.302	$\frac{3}{8}$
Decimals	0.333...	0.302	0.375
Compare in order	2nd	1st	3rd

Then, written in order: 0.302, $\frac{1}{3}$, $\frac{3}{8}$

b.

Original number	1.26	$1\frac{1}{4}$	$1\frac{2}{5}$
Decimals	1.26	1.25	1.40
Compare in order	2nd	1st	3rd

Then, written in order: $1\frac{1}{4}$, 1.26, $1\frac{2}{5}$

c.

Original number	0.4	0.41	$\frac{5}{7}$
Decimals	0.40	0.41	≈0.714
Compare in order	1st	2nd	3rd

Then, written in order: 0.4, 0.41, $\frac{5}{7}$

9. $\text{area} = \frac{1}{2} \cdot \text{base} \cdot \text{height}$

$$= \frac{1}{2} \cdot 7 \cdot 2.1$$
$$= 0.5 \cdot 7 \cdot 2.1$$
$$= 7.35$$

The area is 7.35 square meters.

Exercise Set 5.6

1. $\frac{1}{5} = 0.2$

$$\begin{array}{r} 0.2 \\ 5\overline{)\ 1.0} \\ \underline{-1\ 0} \\ 0 \end{array}$$

3. $\frac{4}{8} = 0.5$

$$\begin{array}{r} 0.5 \\ 8\overline{)\ 4.0} \\ \underline{-4\ 0} \\ 0 \end{array}$$

5. $\frac{3}{4} = 0.75$

$$\begin{array}{r} 0.75 \\ 4\overline{)\ 3.00} \\ \underline{-2\ 8} \\ 20 \\ \underline{-20} \\ 0 \end{array}$$

7. $-\frac{2}{25} = -0.08$

$$\begin{array}{r} 0.08 \\ 25\overline{)\ 2.00} \\ \underline{-2\ 00} \\ 0 \end{array}$$

9. $\frac{3}{8} = 0.375$

$$\begin{array}{r} 0.375 \\ 8\overline{)\ 3.000} \\ \underline{-2\ 4}\ \ \\ 60\ \\ \underline{-56}\ \\ 40 \\ \underline{-40} \\ 0 \end{array}$$

11. $\frac{11}{12} = 0.91\overline{6}$

$$\begin{array}{r} 0.9166\ldots \\ 12\overline{)\ 11.0000} \\ \underline{-10\ 8}\ \ \ \ \\ 20\ \ \ \\ \underline{-12}\ \ \ \\ 80\ \ \\ \underline{-72}\ \ \\ 80\ \\ \underline{-72}\ \\ 8\ \end{array}$$

13. $\frac{17}{40} = 0.425$

$$\begin{array}{r} 0.425 \\ 40\overline{)\ 17.000} \\ -16\ 0 \\ \hline 1\ 00 \\ -80 \\ \hline 200 \\ -200 \\ \hline 0 \end{array}$$

15. $\frac{9}{20} = 0.45$

$$\begin{array}{r} 0.45 \\ 20\overline{)\ 9.00} \\ -8\ 0 \\ \hline 1\ 00 \\ -1\ 00 \\ \hline 0 \end{array}$$

17. $-\frac{1}{3} = -0.\overline{3}$

$$\begin{array}{r} 0.33\ldots \\ 3\overline{)1.00} \\ -9 \\ \hline 10 \\ -9 \\ \hline 1 \end{array}$$

19. $\frac{7}{16} = 0.4375$

$$\begin{array}{r} 0.4375 \\ 16\overline{)\ 7.0000} \\ -6\ 4 \\ \hline 60 \\ -48 \\ \hline 120 \\ -112 \\ \hline 80 \\ -80 \\ \hline 0 \end{array}$$

21. $\frac{2}{9} = 0.\overline{2}$

$$\begin{array}{r} 0.22\ldots \\ 9\overline{)\ 2.00} \\ -18 \\ \hline 20 \\ -18 \\ \hline 2 \end{array}$$

23. $\frac{5}{3} = 1.\overline{6}$

$$\begin{array}{r} 1.66\ldots \\ 3\overline{)\ 5.00} \\ -3 \\ \hline 2\ 0 \\ -1\ 8 \\ \hline 20 \\ -18 \\ \hline 2 \end{array}$$

25. $0.\overline{3} \approx 0.333\ldots \approx 0.33$

27. $0.4375 \approx 0.44$

29. $0.\overline{2} = 0.222\ldots \approx 0.2$

31. $1.\overline{6} = 1.666\ldots \approx 1.7$

33.

$$\begin{array}{r} 0.668 \\ 1048\overline{)\ 701.000} \\ -6288 \\ \hline 7220 \\ -6288 \\ \hline 9320 \\ -8384 \\ \hline 936 \end{array}$$

$\frac{701}{1048} \approx 0.67$

35.

$$\begin{array}{r} 0.44 \\ 25\overline{)\ 11.00} \\ -10\ 0 \\ \hline 1\ 00 \\ -1\ 00 \\ \hline 0 \end{array}$$

$\frac{11}{25} = 0.44$

37.
$$\begin{array}{r} 0.615 \\ 91\overline{)\ 56.000} \\ \underline{-546} \\ 140 \\ \underline{-\ 91} \\ 490 \\ \underline{-455} \\ 35 \end{array}$$
$\frac{56}{91} \approx 0.62$

39. $2 < 9$, so $0.562 < 0.569$

41. $2 > 1$, so $0.823 > 0.813$

43. $-0.0923 > -0.0932$

45. $\frac{2}{3} = \frac{4}{6}$ and $\frac{4}{6} < \frac{5}{6}$, so $\frac{2}{3} < \frac{5}{6}$

47. $\frac{5}{9} = 0.\overline{5} = 0.555\cdots$
$\frac{51}{91} \approx 0.5604$
$0.5\overline{5} < 0.5604$, so $\frac{5}{9} < \frac{51}{91}$.

49. $\frac{4}{7} \approx 0.5714$ and $0.5714 > 0.14$,
so $\frac{4}{7} > 0.14$.

51. $\frac{18}{13} \approx 1.3846$
$1.38 < 1.3846$, so $1.38 < \frac{18}{13}$.

53. $\frac{456}{64} = 7.125$
$7.123 < 7.125$, so $7.123 < \frac{456}{64}$

55. 0.32, 0.34, 0.35

57. $0.49 = 0.490$
0.49, 0.491, 0.498

59. $\frac{3}{4} = 0.75$
0.73, $\frac{3}{4}$, 0.78

61. $\frac{4}{7} \approx 0.571$
0.412, 0.453, $\frac{4}{7}$

63. $\frac{42}{8} = 5.25$
5.23, $\frac{42}{8}$, 5.34

65. $\frac{12}{5} = 2.4$, $\frac{17}{8} = 2.125$
$\frac{17}{8}$, 2.37, $\frac{12}{5}$

67.
$$\begin{aligned} \text{Area} &= \frac{1}{2} \cdot \text{base} \cdot \text{height} \\ &= \frac{1}{2} \times 5.7 \times 9 \\ &= 0.5 \times 5.7 \times 9 \\ &= 25.65 \end{aligned}$$
The area is 25.65 square inches.

69.
$$\begin{aligned} \text{Area} &= \frac{1}{2} \cdot \text{base} \cdot \text{height} \\ &= \frac{1}{2} \cdot 5.2 \cdot 3.6 \\ &= 0.5 \cdot 5.2 \cdot 3.6 \\ &= 9.36 \end{aligned}$$
The area is 9.36 square centimeters.

71.
$$\begin{aligned} \text{Area} &= \text{base} \cdot \text{height} \\ &= 0.62 \cdot \frac{2}{5} \\ &= 0.62 \cdot 0.4 \\ &= 0.248 \end{aligned}$$
The area is 0.248 square yards.

73. $2^3 = 2 \cdot 2 \cdot 2 = 8$

75. $6^2 \cdot 2 = 6 \cdot 6 \cdot 2 = 72$

77. $\left(\frac{1}{3}\right)^4 = \frac{1}{3} \cdot \frac{1}{3} \cdot \frac{1}{3} \cdot \frac{1}{3} = \frac{1}{81}$

79. $\left(\frac{3}{5}\right)^2 = \frac{3}{5} \cdot \frac{3}{5} = \frac{9}{25}$

81. $\left(\frac{2}{5}\right)\left(\frac{5}{2}\right)^2 = \frac{2}{5} \cdot \frac{5}{2} \cdot \frac{5}{2} = \frac{5}{2}$

83. $\frac{2321}{10,569} \approx 0.202$

85.

	Estimate
2131	2100
1179	1800
813	800
713	700
603	600
+ 547	+ 500
	5900 stations

87.
$$\begin{array}{r} 0.625 \\ 8\overline{)\,5.000} \\ \underline{-4\,8} \\ 20 \\ \underline{-16} \\ 40 \\ \underline{-40} \\ 0 \end{array}$$

You should enter 0.625 as the margin width.

89. Answers may vary.

91. $\frac{3}{4}-(9.6)(5) = 0.75-48$
$= -47.25$

93. $\left(\frac{1}{10}\right)^2 + (1.6)(2.1) = \frac{1}{100}+(1.6)(2.1)$
$= 0.01+3.36$
$= 3.37$

95. $\frac{3}{8}(4.7-5.9) = 0.375(4.7-5.9)$
$= 0.375 \cdot -12$
$= -0.45$

Section 5.7

Practice Problems

1. $z+0.9 = 1.3$
$z+0.9-0.9 = 1.3-0.9$
$z = 0.4$

2. $0.17x = -0.34$
$\frac{0.17x}{0.17} = \frac{-0.34}{0.17}$
$x = -2$

3. $2.9 = 1.7+0.3x$
$2.9-1.7 = 1.7+0.3x-1.7$
$1.2 = 0.3x$
$\frac{1.2}{0.3} = \frac{0.3x}{0.3}$
$4 = x$ or $x = 4$

4. $8x+4.2 = 10x+11.6$
$8x+4.2-10x = 10x+11.6-10x$
$-2x+4.2 = 11.6$
$-2x+4.2-4.2 = 11.6-4.2$
$-2x = 7.4$
$\frac{-2x}{-2} = \frac{7.4}{-2}$
$x = -3.7$

5. $6.3-5x = 3(x+2.9)$
$6.3-5x = 3x+8.7$
$6.3-5x-6.3 = 3x+8.7-6.3$
$-5x = 3x+2.4$
$-5x-3x = 3x+2.4-3x$
$-8x = 2.4$
$\frac{-8x}{-8} = \frac{2.4}{-8}$
$x = -0.3$

6. $0.2y+2.6 = 4$
$10(0.2y+2.6) = 10(4)$
$2y+26 = 40$
$2y+26-26 = 40-26$
$2y = 14$
$\frac{2y}{2} = \frac{14}{2}$
$y = 7$

Exercise Set 5.7

1. $x+1.2 = 7.1$
$x+1.2-1.2 = 7.1-1.2$
$x = 5.9$

3. $-5y = 2.15$
$\frac{-5y}{-5} = \frac{2.15}{-5}$
$y = -0.43$

5. $6.2 = y-4$
$6.2+4 = y-4+4$
$10.2 = y$

7. $3.1x = -13.95$
$$\frac{3.1x}{3.1} = \frac{-13.95}{3.1}$$
$$x = -4.5$$

9.
$$\begin{aligned} 2(x-1.3) &= 5.8 \\ 2x - 2.6 &= 5.8 \\ -3.5x + 2.8 &= -11.2 \\ -3.5x + 2.8 - 2.8 &= -11.2 - 2.8 \\ -3.5x &= -14 \\ \frac{-3.5x}{-3.5} &= \frac{-14}{-3.5} \\ x &= 4 \end{aligned}$$

11.
$$\begin{aligned} 6x + 8.65 &= 3x + 10 \\ 6x + 8.65 - 8.65 &= 3x + 10 - 8.65 \\ 6x &= 3x + 1.35 \\ 6x - 3x &= 3x - 3x + 1.35 \\ 3x &= 1.35 \\ \frac{3x}{3} &= \frac{1.35}{3} \\ x &= 0.45 \end{aligned}$$

13.
$$\begin{aligned} 2(x-1.3) &= 5.8 \\ 2x - 2.6 &= 5.8 \\ 2x - 2.6 + 2.6 &= 5.8 + 2.6 \\ 2x &= 8.4 \\ \frac{2x}{2} &= \frac{8.4}{2} \\ x &= 4.2 \end{aligned}$$

15.
$$\begin{aligned} 0.4x + 0.7 &= -0.9 \\ 4x + 7 &= -9 \\ 4x + 7 - 7 &= -9 - 7 \\ 4x &= -16 \\ \frac{4x}{4} &= \frac{-16}{4} \\ x &= -4 \end{aligned}$$

17.
$$\begin{aligned} 7x - 10.8 &= x \\ 70x - 108 &= 10x \\ 70x - 108 + 108 &= 10x + 108 \\ 70x &= 10x + 108 \\ 70x - 10x &= 10x - 10x + 108 \\ 60x &= 108 \\ \frac{60x}{60} &= \frac{108}{60} \\ x &= 1.8 \end{aligned}$$

19.
$$\begin{aligned} 2.1x + 5 - 1.6x &= 10 \\ 21x + 50 - 16x &= 100 \\ 5x + 50 &= 100 \\ 5x + 50 - 50 &= 100 - 50 \\ 5x &= 50 \\ \frac{5x}{5} &= \frac{50}{5} \\ x &= 10 \end{aligned}$$

21.
$$\begin{aligned} y - 3.6 &= 4 \\ y - 3.6 + 3.6 &= 4 + 3.6 \\ y &= 7.6 \end{aligned}$$

23.
$$\begin{aligned} -0.02x &= -1.2 \\ -2x &= -120 \\ \frac{-2x}{-2} &= \frac{-120}{-2} \\ x &= 60 \end{aligned}$$

25.
$$\begin{aligned} 6.5 &= 10x + 7.2 \\ 65 &= 100x + 72 \\ 65 - 72 &= 100x + 72 - 72 \\ -7 &= 100x \\ -0.07 &= x \end{aligned}$$

27.
$$\begin{aligned} 2.7x - 25 &= 1.2x + 5 \\ 2.7x - 25 - 1.2x &= 1.2x + 5 - 1.2x \\ 1.5x - 25 &= 5 \\ 1.5x - 25 + 25 &= 5 + 25 \\ 1.5x &= 30 \\ \frac{1.5x}{1.5} &= \frac{30}{1.5} \\ x &= 20 \end{aligned}$$

29.
$$\begin{aligned} 200x - 0.67 &= 100x + 0.81 \\ 200x - 0.67 + 0.67 &= 100x + 0.81 + 0.67 \\ 200x &= 100x + 1.48 \\ 200x - 100x &= 100x - 100x + 1.48 \\ 100x &= 1.48 \\ x &= 0.0148 \end{aligned}$$

31.
$$\begin{aligned} 3(x + 2.71) &= 2x \\ 3x + 8.13 &= 2x \\ 3x - 2x &= -8.13 \\ x &= -8.13 \end{aligned}$$

33.
$$\begin{aligned} 8x - 5 &= 10x - 8 \\ 8x - 5 - 10x &= 10x - 8 - 10x \\ -2x - 5 &= -8 \\ -2x - 5 + 5 &= -8 + 5 \\ -2x &= -3 \\ \frac{-2x}{-2} &= \frac{-3}{-2} \\ x &= 1.5 \end{aligned}$$

35.
$$\begin{aligned} 1.2+0.3x &= 0.9 \\ 12+3x &= 9 \\ 12-12+3x &= 9-12 \\ 3x &= -3 \\ \frac{3x}{3} &= \frac{-3}{3} \\ x &= -1 \end{aligned}$$

37.
$$\begin{aligned} 0.9x+2.65 &= 0.5x+5.45 \\ 90x+265 &= 50x+545 \\ 90x+265-265 &= 50x+545-265 \\ 90x-50x &= 50x-50x+280 \\ 40x &= 280 \\ x &= 7 \end{aligned}$$

39.
$$\begin{aligned} 4x+7.6 &= 2(3x-3.2) \\ 4x+7.6 &= 6x-6.4 \\ 4x-6x+7.6-7.6 &= 6x-6x-6.4-7.6 \\ -2x &= -14 \\ x &= 7 \end{aligned}$$

41.
$$\begin{aligned} 0.7x+13.8 &= x-2.16 \\ 0.7x+13.8-x &= x-2.16-x \\ -0.3x+13.8 &= x-2.16-x \\ -0.3x+13.8-13.8 &= -2.16-13.8 \\ -0.3x &= -15.96 \\ \frac{-0.3x}{-0.3} &= \frac{-15.96}{-0.3} \\ x &= 53.2 \end{aligned}$$

43. $2x-6+4x-10 = (2x+4x)+(-6-10) = 6x-16$

45. $3(x-5)+10 = 3x-15+10 = 3x-5$

47.
$$\begin{aligned} 5y-1.2-7y+8 &= (5y-7y)+(8-1.2) \\ &= -2y+6.8 \end{aligned}$$

49. Answers may vary.

51.
$$\begin{aligned} -5.25x &= -40.33575 \\ \frac{-5.25x}{-5.25} &= \frac{-40.33575}{-5.25} \\ x &= 7.683 \end{aligned}$$

53.
$$\begin{aligned} 1.95y+6.834 &= 7.65y-19.8591 \\ 19.8591+6.834 &= 7.65y-1.95y \\ 26.6931 &= 5.7y \\ \frac{26.6931}{5.7} &= \frac{5.7y}{5.7} \\ 4.683 &= y \end{aligned}$$

Section 5.8

Practice Problems

1. $\sqrt{100} = 10$ because $10^2 = 100$ and 10 is positive.

2. $\sqrt{64} = 8$ because $8^2 = 64$ and 8 is positive.

3. $\sqrt{121} = 11$ because $11^2 = 121$ and 11 is positive.

4. $\sqrt{0} = 0$ because $0^2 = 0$.

5. $\sqrt{\frac{1}{4}} = \frac{1}{2}$ because $\frac{1}{2}\cdot\frac{1}{2} = \frac{1}{4}$.

6. $\sqrt{\frac{9}{16}} = \frac{3}{4}$

7. $\sqrt{11} \approx 3.317$

8. $\sqrt{29} \approx 5.385$

9.
$$\begin{aligned} a^2+b^2 &= c^2 \\ 12^2+16^2 &= c^2 \\ 144+256 &= c^2 \\ 400 &= c^2 \\ c &= \sqrt{400} \\ c &= 20 \end{aligned}$$

The hypotenuse is 20 feet.

10.
$$\begin{aligned} a^2+b^2 &= c^2 \\ 9^2+7^2 &= c^2 \\ 81+49 &= c^2 \\ 130 &= c^2 \\ c &= \sqrt{130} \\ c &\approx 11 \end{aligned}$$

The length of the hypotenuse is exactly $\sqrt{130}$ kilometers, which is approximately 11 kilometers.

11.
$$\begin{aligned} a^2+b^2 &= c^2 \\ a^2+7^2 &= 11^2 \\ a^2+49 &= 121 \\ a^2 &= 72 \\ a &= \sqrt{72} \\ a &\approx 8.49 \end{aligned}$$

The length of the leg is exactly $\sqrt{72}$ feet, which is approximately 8.49 feet.

12. 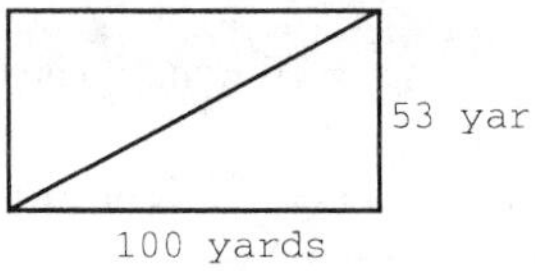

$$a^2 + b^2 = c^2$$
$$100^2 + 53^2 = c^2$$
$$10,000 + 2809 = c^2$$
$$12,809 = c$$
$$c = \sqrt{12,809}$$
$$c \approx 113$$

The diagonal of the football field is exactly $\sqrt{12,809}$ yards, which is approximately 113 yards.

Calculator Explorations

Depending on what type of calculator you have, you will either press the $\boxed{\sqrt{\ }}$ key before or after the number of which you wish to take the square root. Then press $\boxed{= \text{or ENTER}}$.

1. $\sqrt{1024} = 32$

2. $\sqrt{676} = 26$

3. $\sqrt{15} \approx 3.872983346 \approx 3.873$

4. $\sqrt{19} \approx 4.358898944 \approx 4.359$

5. $\sqrt{97} \approx 9.848857802 \approx 9.849$

6. $\sqrt{56} \approx 7.483314774 \approx 7.483$

Exercise Set 5.8

1. $\sqrt{4} = 2$ because $2^2 = 4$.

3. $\sqrt{625} = 25$ because $25^2 = 625$.

5. $\sqrt{\frac{1}{81}} = \frac{1}{9}$ because $\frac{1}{9} \cdot \frac{1}{9} = \frac{1}{81}$.

7. $\sqrt{\frac{144}{64}} = \frac{12}{8} = \frac{3}{2}$ because $\frac{12}{8} \cdot \frac{12}{8} = \frac{144}{64}$.

9. $\sqrt{256} = 16$ because $16^2 = 256$.

11. $\sqrt{\frac{9}{4}} = \frac{3}{2}$ because $\frac{3}{2} \cdot \frac{3}{2} = \frac{9}{4}$.

13. $\sqrt{3} \approx 1.732$

15. $\sqrt{15} \approx 3.873$

17. $\sqrt{14} \approx 3.742$

19. $\sqrt{47} \approx 6.856$

21. $\sqrt{8} \approx 2.828$

23. $\sqrt{26} \approx 5.099$

25. $\sqrt{71} \approx 8.426$

27. $\sqrt{7} \approx 2.646$

29.
$$a^2 + b^2 = c^2$$
$$5^2 + 12^2 = c^2$$
$$25 + 144 = c^2$$
$$169 = c^2$$
$$c = \sqrt{169}$$
$$c = 13$$

The length of the hypotenuse is 13 inches.

31.
$$a^2 + b^2 = c^2$$
$$10^2 + b^2 = 12^2$$
$$100 + b^2 = 144$$
$$b^2 = 44$$
$$b = \sqrt{44}$$
$$b \approx 6.633$$

The length of the leg is approximately 6.633 centimeters.

33. 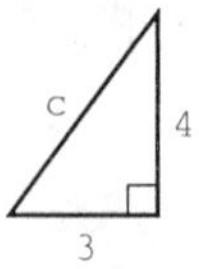

$$a^2+b^2=c^2$$
$$3^2+4^2=c^2$$
$$9+16=c^2$$
$$25=c^2$$
$$c=\sqrt{25}$$
$$c=5$$

35.

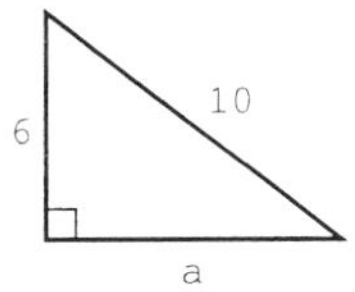

$$a^2+b^2=c^2$$
$$a^2+6^2=10^2$$
$$a^2+36=100$$
$$a^2=64$$
$$a=\sqrt{64}$$
$$a=8$$

37.

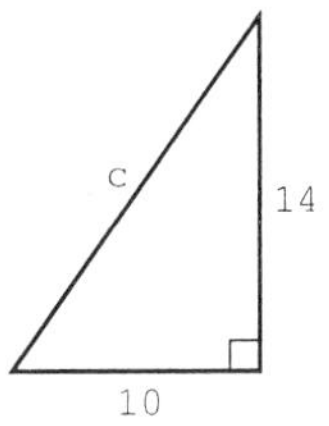

$$a^2+b^2=c^2$$
$$10^2+14^2=c^2$$
$$100+196=c^2$$
$$296=c^2$$
$$c=\sqrt{296}$$
$$c\approx 17.205$$

39.

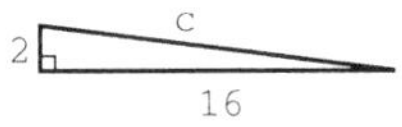

$$a^2+b^2=c^2$$
$$2^2+16^2=c^2$$
$$4+256=c^2$$
$$260=c^2$$
$$c=\sqrt{260}$$
$$c\approx 16.125$$

41.

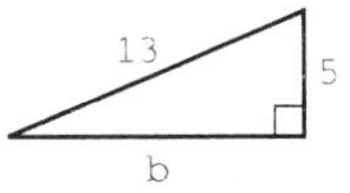

$$a^2+b^2=c^2$$
$$5^2+b^2=13^2$$
$$25+b^2=169$$
$$b^2=144$$
$$b=12$$

43.

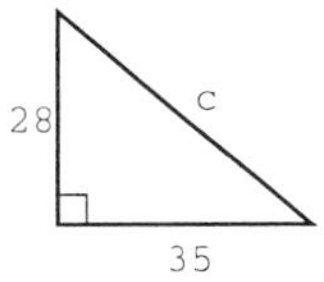

$$a^2+b^2=c^2$$
$$35^2+28^2=c^2$$
$$1225+784=c^2$$
$$2009=c^2$$
$$c=\sqrt{2009}$$
$$c\approx 44.822$$

45.

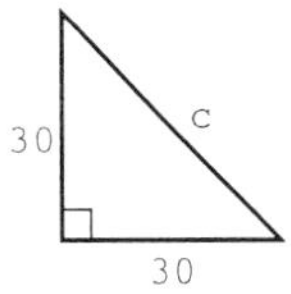

$$a^2+b^2=c^2$$
$$30^2+30^2=c^2$$
$$900+900=c^2$$
$$1800=c^2$$
$$c=\sqrt{1800}$$
$$c\approx 42.426$$

47.

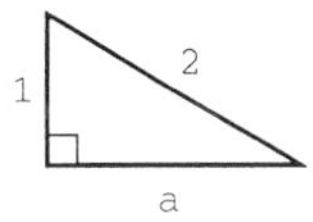

$$a^2+b^2=c^2$$
$$a^2+1^2=2^2$$
$$a^2+1=4$$
$$a^2=3$$
$$a=\sqrt{3}$$
$$a\approx 1.732$$

49.

$$a^2+b^2=c^2$$
$$100^2+100^2=c^2$$
$$10,000+10,000=c^2$$
$$20,000=c^2$$
$$c=\sqrt{20,000}$$
$$c\approx 141.42$$

The length is approximately 141.42 yards.

51.
$$a^2 + b^2 = c^2$$
$$20^2 + b^2 = 32^2$$
$$400 + b^2 = 1024$$
$$b^2 = 624$$
$$b = \sqrt{624}$$
$$b \approx 25.0$$

The height is approximately 25.0 feet.

53.
$$a^2 + b^2 = c^2$$
$$300^2 + 160^2 = c^2$$
$$90,000 + 25,600 = c^2$$
$$115,600 = c^2$$
$$c = \sqrt{115,600}$$
$$c = 340$$

The length is 340 feet.

55. $\frac{10}{12} = \frac{2 \cdot 5}{2 \cdot 6} = \frac{5}{6}$

57. $\frac{24}{60} = \frac{2 \cdot 2 \cdot 2 \cdot 3}{2 \cdot 3 \cdot 2 \cdot 5} = \frac{2}{5}$

59. $\frac{30}{72} = \frac{2 \cdot 3 \cdot 5}{2 \cdot 36} = \frac{2 \cdot 3 \cdot 5}{2 \cdot 6 \cdot 6} = \frac{2 \cdot 3 \cdot 5}{2 \cdot 2 \cdot 3 \cdot 2 \cdot 3} = \frac{5}{12}$

61. $\sqrt{38}$ is between 6 and 7.
$\sqrt{38} \approx 6.164$

63. $\sqrt{101}$ is between 10 and 11.
$\sqrt{101} \approx 10.050$

65. Answers may vary.

Chapter 5 Review

1. 23.45
↑
tenths

2. 0.000345
↑
hundred thousandths

3. -23.45 is negative twenty-three and forty-five hundredths.

4. 0.00345 is three hundred forty-five hundred thousandths.

5. 109.23 is one hundred nine and twenty-three hundredths.

6. 200.000032 is two hundred and thirty-two millionths

7. 2.15

8. –503.102

9. 16,025.0014

10. $0.16 = \frac{16}{100} = \frac{4}{25}$

11. $-12.023 = -12\frac{23}{1000}$

12. $1.0045 = 1\frac{45}{10,000} = 1\frac{9}{2000}$

13. $0.00231 = \frac{231}{100,000}$

14. $25.25 = 25\frac{25}{100} = 25\frac{1}{4}$

15. 0.49 0.43
↑ ↑
9 > 3
0.49 > 0.43

16. 0.973 = 0.9730

17. –402.00032 < –402.000032

18. –0.230505 > –0.23505

19. 0.623 to the nearest tenth is 0.6.

20. 0.9384 to the nearest hundredth is 0.94.

21. 42.895 to the nearest hundredth is 42.90.

22. 16.34925 to the nearest thousandth is 16.349.

23. 13,490.5 people rounded to the nearest hundred is 13,500 people.

24. $10.75 = 10\frac{75}{100} = 10\frac{3}{4}$ teaspoons

25. $$\begin{array}{r} 2.4 \\ +\ 7.1 \\ \hline 9.5 \end{array}$$

26. $$\begin{array}{r} 3.9 \\ +\ 1.2 \\ \hline 5.1 \end{array}$$

27. $-6.4 + (-0.88)$
Add the absolute values.
$$\begin{array}{r} 6.40 \\ +\ 0.88 \\ \hline 7.28 \end{array}$$
Attach the common sign.
-7.28

28. Subtract the absolute values.
$$\begin{array}{r} 19.02 \\ -6.98 \\ \hline 12.04 \end{array}$$
Since $19.02 > 6.98$, the answer is negative. The answer is -12.04.

29. $$\begin{array}{r} 200.490 \\ 16.820 \\ +\ 103.002 \\ \hline 320.312 \end{array}$$

30. $$\begin{array}{r} 100.45000 \\ 48.29000 \\ +\ \ 0.00236 \\ \hline 148.74236 \end{array}$$

31. $$\begin{array}{r} 4.9 \\ -3.2 \\ \hline 1.7 \end{array}$$

32. $$\begin{array}{r} 5.23 \\ -2.74 \\ \hline 2.49 \end{array}$$

33. Add the absolute values.
$$\begin{array}{r} 892.1 \\ +432.4 \\ \hline 1324.5 \end{array}$$
Attach the common sign.
-1324.5

34. Subtract the absolute values.
$$\begin{array}{r} 10.200 \\ -\ 0.064 \\ \hline 10.136 \end{array}$$
Since $10.2 > 0.064$, the answer is negative. The answer is -10.136.

35. $$\begin{array}{r} 100.00 \\ -34.98 \\ \hline 65.02 \end{array}$$

36. $$\begin{array}{r} 200.00000 \\ -\ \ 0.00198 \\ \hline 199.99802 \end{array}$$

37. $$\begin{array}{r} 8920.70 \\ +\ \ 684.81 \\ \hline 9605.51 \end{array}$$
The DJIA opened at 9605.51.

38. $x - y = 1.2 - 6.9 = -5.7$

39. $$\begin{aligned} 2.3x + 6.5 + 1.9x + 6.3 &= 2.3x + 1.9x + 6.5 + 6.3 \\ &= 4.2x + 12.8 \end{aligned}$$

40. $8.6y - 7.61 + 1.29y + 3.44$
$= 8.6y + 1.29y - 7.61 + 3.44$
$= 9.89y - 4.17$

41. $7.2 \times 10 = 72$

42. $9.345 \times 1000 = 9345$

43. $$\begin{array}{rl} 34.02 & \text{2 decimal places} \\ \times\ \ 2.3 & \text{1 decimal place} \\ \hline 10206 & \\ 68040 & \\ \hline 78.246 & \text{3 decimal places} \end{array}$$
The answer is negative.
$-34.02 \times 2.3 = -78.246$

44. $$\begin{array}{rl} -839.02 & \text{2 decimal places} \\ \times\ (-87.3) & \text{1 decimal place} \\ \hline 251706 & \\ 5873140 & \\ +67121600 & \\ \hline 73246446 & \text{3 decimal places} \end{array}$$

45. $C = 2 \cdot \pi \cdot r = 2 \cdot \pi \cdot 7 = 14\pi$ meters
$C \approx 14(3.14) = 43.96$ meters

46. $$\begin{array}{r} 0.625 \\ \times\ \ 102 \\ \hline 1250 \\ +\ 62\ 500 \\ \hline \end{array}$$
63.750 rounded to the nearest tenth is 63.8 miles.

47. $21 \div 0.3$
$$\frac{21}{0.3} = \frac{210}{3} = 70$$

48. $0.03\overline{)0.0063}$

Move decimal points 2 places.

$$\begin{array}{r} 0.21 \\ 3.\overline{)0.63} \\ \underline{-6} \\ 03 \\ \underline{-3} \\ 0 \end{array}$$

The answer is negative.
$-0.0063 \div 0.03 = -0.21$

49. $0.005\overline{)24.5}$

Move decimal point 3 places.

$$\begin{array}{r} 4900 \\ 5.\overline{)\ 24500.} \\ \underline{-20} \\ 45 \\ \underline{-45} \\ 00 \\ \underline{-0} \\ 00 \\ \underline{-0} \\ 0 \end{array}$$

The answer is negative.
$24.5 \div (-0.005) = -4900$

50. $2.3\overline{)54.98}$

Move decimal points 1 place.

$$\begin{array}{r} 23.9043 \approx 23.904 \\ 23.\overline{)\ 549.8000} \\ \underline{-46} \\ 89 \\ \underline{-69} \\ 208 \\ \underline{-207} \\ 10 \\ \underline{-0} \\ 100 \\ \underline{-92} \\ 80 \\ \underline{-69} \\ 11 \end{array}$$

$54.98 \div 2.3 \approx 23.904$

51.

$$\begin{array}{r} 8.0588 \approx 8.059 \\ 34\overline{)\ 274.0000} \\ \underline{-272} \\ 20 \\ \underline{-0} \\ 200 \\ \underline{-170} \\ 300 \\ \underline{-272} \\ 280 \\ \underline{-272} \\ 8 \end{array}$$

52.

$$\begin{array}{r} 158.25 \\ 20\overline{)\ 3165.00} \\ \underline{-20} \\ 116 \\ \underline{-100} \\ 165 \\ \underline{-160} \\ 50 \\ \underline{-40} \\ 100 \\ \underline{-100} \\ 0 \end{array}$$

$-3165 \div (-20) = 158.25$

53. $3.28\overline{)24.00}$

Move decimal points 2 places.

$$\begin{array}{r} 7.31 \approx 7.3 \\ 328.\overline{)\ 2400.00} \\ \underline{-2296} \\ 1040 \\ \underline{-984} \\ 560 \\ \underline{-328} \\ 232 \end{array}$$

There are about 7.3 meters in 24 feet.

54. $69.71\overline{)3136.95}$

Move decimal points 2 places.

$$\begin{array}{r} 45 \\ 6971\overline{)\ 313695} \\ \underline{-27884} \\ 34855 \\ \underline{-34855} \\ 0 \end{array}$$

The loan will be paid off in 45 months.

55.
$$\begin{array}{r}2.4\\6.7\\+9.1\\\hline 18.2\end{array}\qquad\begin{array}{r}2\\7\\+9\\\hline 18\end{array}$$

56.
$$\begin{array}{r}15.9\\+34.1\\\hline 50.0\end{array}\qquad\begin{array}{r}16\\+34\\\hline 50\end{array}$$

57.
$$\begin{array}{r}340.03\\-240.98\\\hline 99.05\end{array}\qquad\begin{array}{r}340\\-241\\\hline 99\end{array}$$

58.
$$\begin{array}{r}100.0\\-\ 45.9\\\hline 54.1\end{array}\qquad\begin{array}{r}100\\-46\\\hline 54\end{array}$$

59.
$$\begin{array}{r}6.02\\\times\ 5.91\\\hline 602\\5\ 4180\\30\ 1000\\\hline 35.5782\end{array}\qquad\begin{array}{r}6\\\times 6\\\hline 36\end{array}$$

60.
$$\begin{array}{r}0.205\\\times\ 1.72\\\hline 410\\14350\\20500\\\hline 0.35260\end{array}\qquad\begin{array}{r}0.2\\\times 1.7\\\hline 0.34\end{array}$$

61. $1.9\overline{)62.13}$

becomes

$$\begin{array}{r}32.7\\19.\overline{)\ 621.3}\\-57\\\hline 51\\-38\\\hline 13\ 3\\-13\ 3\\\hline 0\end{array}\qquad\begin{array}{r}31\\2\overline{)\ 62}\\-6\\\hline 02\\-2\\\hline 0\end{array}$$

62. $19.8\overline{)601.92}$

becomes

$$\begin{array}{r}30.4\\198.\overline{)\ 6019.2}\\-594\\\hline 79\\-0\\\hline 79\ 2\\-79\ 2\\\hline 0\end{array}\qquad\begin{array}{r}30.1\\20\overline{)\ 602.0}\\-60\\\hline 02\\-0\\\hline 2\,0\\-2\,0\\\hline 0\end{array}$$

63.
$$\begin{array}{r}99\\37\\28\\22\\+14\\\hline 200\end{array}$$

The total average consumption is 200 quadrillion BTU.

64. $77.3\times 115.9\approx 77\times 116=8932$
The area is about 8932 square feet.

65.
$$\begin{array}{r}1.07\\1.89\\+\ \ 0.99\end{array}\quad\text{Estimate}\quad\begin{array}{r}1\\2\\+1\\\hline 4\end{array}$$

Yes, \$5 is enough.

66. $(-7.6)(1.9)+2.5=-14.44+2.5=-11.94$

67. $2.3^2-1.4=5.29-1.4=3.89$

68. $\dfrac{(-3.2)^2}{100}=\dfrac{10.24}{100}=0.1024$

69. $(2.6+1.4)(4.5-3.6)=4(0.9)=3.6$

70.
$$\begin{array}{r}0.8\\5\overline{)\ \ 4.0}\\-4\,0\\\hline 0\end{array}$$

$\dfrac{4}{5}=0.8$

71.
$$\begin{array}{r}0.9230\approx 0.923\\13\overline{)\ 12.0000}\\-117\\\hline 30\\-26\\\hline 40\\-39\\\hline 10\\-0\\\hline 10\end{array}$$

$-\dfrac{12}{13}\approx -0.923$

72.
$$\begin{array}{r} 0.4285 \approx 0.429 \\ 7\overline{)\ 3.0000} \\ \underline{-2\ 8} \\ 20 \\ \underline{-14} \\ 60 \\ \underline{-56} \\ 40 \\ \underline{-35} \\ 5 \end{array}$$
$-\frac{3}{7} \approx -0.429$

73.
$$\begin{array}{r} 0.2166\ldots = 0.21\overline{6} \\ 60\overline{)\ 13.0000} \\ \underline{-12\,0} \\ 1\ 00 \\ \underline{-60} \\ 400 \\ \underline{-360} \\ 400 \\ \underline{-360} \\ 40 \end{array}$$
$\frac{13}{60} = 0.21\overline{6} \approx 0.217$

74.
$$\begin{array}{r} 0.1125 \approx 0.113 \\ 80\overline{)\ 9.0000} \\ \underline{-8\ 0} \\ 1\ 00 \\ \underline{-80} \\ 200 \\ \underline{-160} \\ 400 \\ \underline{-400} \\ 0 \end{array}$$
$\frac{9}{80} = 0.1125 \approx 0.113$

75.
$$\begin{array}{r} 51.0571 \approx 51.057 \\ 175\overline{)\ 8935.0000} \\ \underline{-875} \\ 185 \\ \underline{-175} \\ 100 \\ \underline{-0} \\ 1000 \\ \underline{-875} \\ 1250 \\ \underline{-1225} \\ 250 \\ \underline{-175} \\ 75 \end{array}$$
$\frac{8935}{175} \approx 51.057$

76. $0.3920 = 0.392$

77. $\frac{4}{7} \approx 0.5714$
$\frac{5}{8} = 0.625$
$\frac{4}{7} < \frac{5}{8}$

78. $\frac{5}{17} \approx 0.294$
$0.293 < \frac{5}{17}$

79. $\frac{6}{11} \approx 0.545$
$\frac{6}{11} < 0.55$

80. 0.832, 0.837, 0.839

81. $\frac{3}{7} \approx 0.4286$
$0.42,\ \frac{3}{7},\ 0.43$

82. $\frac{18}{11} \approx 1.636,\ \frac{19}{12} \approx 1.583$
$\frac{19}{12},\ 1.63,\ \frac{18}{11}$

83. $\frac{6}{7} \approx 0.8571,\ \frac{8}{9} = 0.\overline{8} \approx 0.8889,\ \frac{3}{4} = 0.75$
$\frac{3}{4},\ \frac{6}{7},\ \frac{8}{9}$

84. $\text{Area} = \frac{1}{2} \cdot \text{base} \cdot \text{height}$
$= 0.5 \cdot 4.6 \cdot 3$
$= 6.9$
The area is 6.9 square feet.

85. $\text{Area} = \frac{1}{2} \cdot \text{base} \cdot \text{height}$
$= 0.5 \cdot 5.2 \cdot 2.1$
$= 5.46$
The area is 5.46 square inches.

86.
$$\begin{aligned} x + 3.9 &= 4.2 \\ x + 3.9 - 3.9 &= 4.2 - 3.9 \\ x &= 0.3 \end{aligned}$$

87.
$$\begin{aligned} 70 &= y + 22.81 \\ 70 - 22.81 &= y + 22.81 - 22.81 \\ 47.19 &= y \end{aligned}$$

88.
$$\begin{aligned} 2x &= 17.2 \\ \frac{2x}{2} &= \frac{17.2}{2} \\ x &= 8.6 \end{aligned}$$

89.
$$\begin{aligned} 1.1y &= 88 \\ 10(1.1y) &= 10(88) \\ 11y &= 880 \\ \frac{11y}{11} &= \frac{880}{11} \\ y &= 80 \end{aligned}$$

90.
$$\begin{aligned} \frac{x}{4} &= 0.12 \\ 4\left(\frac{x}{4}\right) &= 4(0.12) \\ x &= 0.48 \end{aligned}$$

91.
$$\begin{aligned} 6.8 &= \frac{y}{5} \\ (6.8)5 &= \frac{y}{5} \cdot 5 \\ 34.0 &= y \end{aligned}$$

92.
$$\begin{aligned} x + 0.78 &= 1.2 \\ x + 0.78 - 0.78 &= 1.2 - 0.78 \\ x &= 0.42 \end{aligned}$$

93.
$$\begin{aligned} 0.56 &= 2x \\ \frac{0.56}{2} &= \frac{2x}{2} \\ 0.28 &= x \end{aligned}$$

94.
$$\begin{aligned} 1.3x - 9.4 &= 0.4x + 8.6 \\ 1.3x - 0.4x - 9.4 &= 0.4x - 0.4x + 8.6 \\ 0.9x - 9.4 + 9.4 &= 8.6 + 9.4 \\ 0.9x &= 18 \\ \frac{0.9x}{0.9} &= \frac{18}{0.9} \\ x &= 20 \end{aligned}$$

95.
$$\begin{aligned} 3(x - 1.1) &= 5x - 5.3 \\ 3x - 3.3 &= 5x - 5.3 \\ 3x - 3.3 + 3.3 &= 5x - 5.3 + 3.3 \\ 3x &= 5x - 2 \\ 3x - 5x &= 5x - 5x - 2 \\ -2x &= -2 \\ x &= 1 \end{aligned}$$

96. $\sqrt{64} = 8$ since $8^2 = 64$.

97. $\sqrt{144} = 12$ since $12^2 = 144$.

98. $\sqrt{36} = 6$ since $6^2 = 36$.

99. $\sqrt{1} = 1$ since $1^2 = 1$.

100. $\sqrt{\frac{4}{25}} = \frac{2}{5}$ since $\left(\frac{2}{5}\right)^2 = \frac{4}{25}$.

101. $\sqrt{\frac{1}{100}} = \frac{1}{10}$ since $\left(\frac{1}{10}\right)^2 = \frac{1}{100}$.

102.
$$\begin{aligned} a^2 + b^2 &= c^2 \\ 12^2 + 5^2 &= c^2 \\ 144 + 25 &= c^2 \\ 169 &= c^2 \\ \sqrt{169} &= c \\ 13 &= c \end{aligned}$$

103.
$$\begin{aligned} a^2 + b^2 &= c^2 \\ 20^2 + 21^2 &= c^2 \\ 400 + 441 &= c^2 \\ 841 &= c^2 \\ \sqrt{841} &= c \\ 29 &= c \end{aligned}$$

104. $a^2 + b^2 = c^2$
$9^2 + b^2 = 14^2$
$81 + b^2 = 196$
$b^2 = 115$
$b = \sqrt{115}$
$b \approx 10.7$

105. $a^2 + b^2 = c^2$
$124^2 + b^2 = 155^2$
$15,376 + b^2 = 24,025$
$b^2 = 8649$
$b = \sqrt{8649}$
$b = 93$

106. $a^2 + b^2 = c^2$
$66^2 + 56^2 = c^2$
$4356 + 3136 = c^2$
$7492 = c^2$
$\sqrt{7492} = c$
$86.6 \approx c$

107. $a^2 + b^2 = c^2$
$20^2 + 20^2 = c^2$
$400 + 400 = c^2$
$800 = c^2$
$\sqrt{800} = c$
$28.28 \approx c$
The diagonal is approximately 28.28 centimeters.

108. $a^2 + b^2 = c^2$
$90^2 + b^2 = 126^2$
$8100 + b^2 = 15,876$
$b^2 = 7776$
$b = \sqrt{7776}$
$b \approx 88.2$
The height of the building is approximately 88.2 feet.

Chapter 5 Test

1. 45.092 is forty-five and ninety-two thousandths.

2. Three thousand and fifty-nine thousandths is 3000.059.

3. $$\begin{array}{r} 2.893 \\ 4.210 \\ +\ 10.492 \\ \hline 17.595 \end{array}$$

4. $$\begin{array}{r} -47.92 \\ -\ 3.28 \\ \hline -51.20 \end{array}$$

5. $9.83 - 30.25 = 9.83 + (-30.25)$
Subtract the absolute values.
$$\begin{array}{r} 30.25 \\ \underline{-9.83} \\ 20.42 \end{array}$$
Since $30.25 > 9.83$, the answer is negative.
-20.42

6. $$\begin{array}{r} 10.2 \\ \times\ 4.01 \\ \hline 102 \\ 0 \\ 40\ 800 \\ \hline 40.902 \end{array}$$

7. $0.23\overline{)0.00843}$
becomes
$$\begin{array}{r} 0.0366\ldots \approx 0.037 \\ 23\overline{)0.8430} \\ \underline{-69} \\ 153 \\ \underline{-138} \\ 150 \\ \underline{-138} \\ 15 \end{array}$$
$(-0.00843) \div (-0.23) \approx 0.037$

8. 34.8923 rounded to the nearest tenth is 34.9.

9. 0.8623 rounded to the nearest thousandth is 0.862.

10. $25.0909 < 25.9090$

11. $\frac{4}{9} = 0.444\ldots$
$\frac{4}{9} < 0.445$

12. $0.345 = \frac{345}{1000} = \frac{69}{200}$

13. $-24.73 = -24\frac{73}{100}$

14. $-\frac{13}{26} = -\frac{1}{2} = -0.5$

15. $\frac{16}{17} \approx 0.941$

$$\begin{array}{r} 0.9411 \\ 17\overline{)\ 16.0000} \\ \underline{-153} \\ 70 \\ \underline{-68} \\ 20 \\ \underline{-17} \\ 30 \\ \underline{-17} \\ 13 \end{array}$$

16. $(-0.6)^2 + 1.57 = 0.36 + 1.57 = 1.93$

17.
$$\begin{aligned} \frac{0.23+1.63}{-0.3} &= \frac{1.86}{-0.3} \\ &= -\frac{186}{30} \\ &= -\frac{62\cdot 3}{10\cdot 3} \\ &= -\frac{62}{10} \\ &= -6.2 \end{aligned}$$

18. $2.4x - 3.6 - 1.9x - 9.8$
$= (2.4 - 1.9)x - 3.6 - 9.8$
$= 0.5x - 13.4$

19. $\sqrt{49} = 7$

20. $\sqrt{157} = 12.530$

21. $\sqrt{\frac{64}{100}} = \frac{8}{10} = \frac{4}{5}$

22.
$$\begin{aligned} 0.2x + 1.3 &= 0.7 \\ 10(0.2x + 1.3) &= 10(0.7) \\ 2x + 13 &= 7 \\ 2x + 13 - 13 &= 7 - 13 \\ 2x &= -6 \\ x &= -3 \end{aligned}$$

23.
$$\begin{aligned} 2(x + 5.7) &= 6x - 3.4 \\ 2x + 11.4 &= 6x - 3.4 \\ 2x - 2x + 11.4 &= 6x - 2x - 3.4 \\ 11.4 &= 4x - 3.4 \\ 11.4 + 3.4 &= 4x - 3.4 + 3.4 \\ 14.8 &= 4x \\ 3.7 &= x \end{aligned}$$

24.
$$\begin{aligned} a^2 + b^2 &= c^2 \\ 4^2 + 4^2 &= c^2 \\ 16 + 16 &= c^2 \\ 32 &= c^2 \\ \sqrt{32} &= c \\ 5.66 &\approx c \end{aligned}$$

The length of the hypotenuse is approximately 5.66 centimeters.

25.
$$\begin{aligned} \text{Area } &= \frac{1}{2}\cdot \text{base}\cdot \text{height} \\ &= 0.5\cdot 4.2\cdot 1.1 \\ &= 2.31 \end{aligned}$$

The area is 2.31 square miles.

26. $A = 123.8(80) = 9904$
9904 square feet of lawn
$9904 \times 0.02 = 198.08$
She needs 198.08 ounces of insecticide.

27.
$$\begin{aligned} \text{Circumference } &= 2\cdot \pi \cdot \text{radius} \\ &= 2\cdot \pi \cdot 9 \\ &= 18\pi \\ &\approx 18(3.14) \\ &= 56.52 \end{aligned}$$

The circumference is 18π miles $\approx$ 56.52 miles.

28.
$$\begin{array}{r} 12.4 \approx 12 \\ 700\overline{)\ 8740.0} \\ \underline{-700} \\ 1740 \\ \underline{-1400} \\ 3400 \\ \underline{-2800} \\ 600 \end{array}$$

It takes 12 CDs to hold as much data as a DVD.

29.
$$\begin{array}{r} 14.2 \\ 16.1 \\ \underline{+\ 23.7} \end{array} \quad \text{Estimate} \quad \begin{array}{r} 14 \\ 16 \\ \underline{+\ 24} \\ 54 \end{array}$$

The total distance is about 54 miles.

Cumulative Review

1.
$$\begin{array}{r} 34,285 \\ +149,761 \\ \hline 184,046 \end{array}$$

2.
$$\begin{array}{r} 5,785 \\ +210,199 \\ \hline 215,984 \end{array}$$

3.
$$\begin{array}{r} 300 \\ 600 \\ 1100 \\ +300 \\ \hline 2300 \end{array}$$

4.
$$\begin{array}{r} 200 \\ 400 \\ 900 \\ +1400 \\ \hline 2900 \end{array}$$

5.
$$\begin{array}{r} 401 \text{ R } 2 \\ 17\overline{)\ 6819} \\ -68 \\ \hline 01 \\ 0 \\ \hline 19 \\ -17 \\ \hline 2 \end{array}$$

6.
$$\begin{array}{r} 146 \text{ R } 3 \\ 14\overline{)\ 2047} \\ -14 \\ \hline 64 \\ 56 \\ \hline 87 \\ -84 \\ \hline 3 \end{array}$$

7. $\frac{21-5(3)}{3} = \frac{21-15}{3} = \frac{6}{3} = 2$

8. $\frac{2(7)+4}{3} = \frac{14+4}{3} = \frac{18}{3} = 6$

9. **a.** -11
b. 2
c. 0

10. **a.** 7
b. -4
c. 1

11. $-2+(-21)=-23$

12. $-7+(-15)=-22$

13. $2 \cdot 5^2 = 2.25 = 50$

14. $4 \cdot 2^3 = 4 \cdot 8 = 32$

15. $-3^2 = -(3)(3) = -9$

16. $(-2)^5 = (-2)(-2)(-2)(-2)(-2) = -32$

17. $(-3)^2 = (-3)(-3) = 9$

18. $-7^2 = -(7)(7) = -49$

19. **a.** $3x+2x=5x$
b. $y-7y=-6y$
c. $3x^2+5x^2-2=8x^2-2$

20. **a.** $2a-5a=-3a$
b. $-3z^2-z^2=-4z^2$
c. $4k+2+7k=4k+7k+2=11k+2$

21.
$$\begin{aligned} 5x+2-4x &= 7-9 \\ x+2 &= -2 \\ x+2-2 &= -2-2 \\ x &= -4 \end{aligned}$$

22.
$$\begin{aligned} 7x-3 &= 6x+2 \\ 7x-3-6x &= 6x+2-6x \\ x-3 &= 2 \\ x-3+3 &= 2+3 \\ x &= 5 \end{aligned}$$

23.
$$\begin{aligned} -5x &= 15 \\ \frac{-5x}{-5} &= \frac{15}{-5} \\ x &= -3 \end{aligned}$$

24.
$$\begin{aligned}-21 &= -7x\\ \frac{-21}{-7} &= \frac{-7x}{-7}\\ 3 &= x\end{aligned}$$

25.
$$\begin{aligned}7(x-2) &= 9x-6\\ 7x-14 &= 9x-6\\ 7x-14-9x &= 9x-6-9x\\ -2x-14 &= -6\\ -2x-14+14 &= -6+14\\ -2x &= 8\\ \frac{-2x}{-2} &= \frac{8}{-2}\\ x &= -4\end{aligned}$$

26.
$$\begin{aligned}2(x+4) &= -x-1\\ 2x+8 &= -x-1\\ 2x+8+x &= -x-1+x\\ 3x+8 &= -1\\ 3x+8-8 &= -1-8\\ 3x &= -9\\ \frac{3x}{3} &= \frac{-9}{3}\\ x &= -3\end{aligned}$$

27. Let x = votes received by Thomas' challenger. Then x + 110,280 = Thomas' votes.
$$\begin{aligned}x+x+110{,}280 &= 204{,}358\\ 2x+110{,}280 &= 204{,}358\\ 2x+110{,}280-110{,}280 &= 204{,}358-110{,}280\\ 2x &= 94{,}078\\ \frac{2x}{x} &= \frac{94{,}078}{2}\\ x &= 47{,}039\end{aligned}$$
Thomas' votes = 47,039 + 110,280 = 157,319.

28.
$$\begin{aligned}84+3x &= 153\\ 84+3x-84 &= 153-84\\ 3x &= 79\\ x &= 23\end{aligned}$$

29. numerator = 3
denominator = 7

30. numerator = 2
denominator = $5a$

31. numerator = $13x$
denominator = 5

32. numerator = $7y$
denominator = $3x$

33. $\frac{12}{20} = \frac{2 \cdot 6}{5 \cdot 6} = \frac{2}{5}$

34. $\frac{64}{112} = \frac{4 \cdot 16}{7 \cdot 16} = \frac{4}{7}$

35. $-\frac{1}{4} \cdot \frac{1}{2} = -\frac{1}{8}$

36. $\left(-\frac{1}{3}\right)\left(-\frac{1}{4}\right) = \frac{1}{12}$

37. $\frac{2}{7} + \frac{3}{7} = \frac{5}{7}$

38. $\frac{2}{5} + \frac{3}{5} = \frac{5}{5} = 1$

39. $\frac{7}{8} + \frac{6}{8} + \frac{3}{8} = \frac{16}{8} = 2$

40. $\frac{2}{3} + \frac{1}{3} + \frac{2}{3} = \frac{5}{3}$ or $1\frac{2}{3}$

41.
$$\begin{aligned}\frac{2}{5} + \frac{4}{15} &= \frac{2 \cdot 3}{5 \cdot 3} + \frac{4}{15}\\ &= \frac{6}{15} + \frac{4}{15}\\ &= \frac{10}{15}\\ &= \frac{2}{3}\end{aligned}$$

42.
$$\begin{aligned}\frac{3}{4} + \frac{5}{12} &= \frac{3 \cdot 3}{4 \cdot 3} + \frac{5}{12}\\ &= \frac{9}{12} + \frac{5}{12}\\ &= \frac{14}{12}\\ &= \frac{7}{6} \text{ or } 1\frac{1}{6}\end{aligned}$$

43. $\frac{\frac{x}{4}}{\frac{3}{2}} = \frac{x}{4} \div \frac{3}{2} = \frac{x}{4} \cdot \frac{2}{3} = \frac{x \cdot 2}{2 \cdot 2 \cdot 3} = \frac{x}{6}$

44. $$\frac{\frac{2}{3}}{\frac{4x}{9}} = \frac{2}{3} \div \frac{4x}{9} = \frac{2}{3} \cdot \frac{9}{4x} = \frac{2 \cdot 3 \cdot 3}{3 \cdot 2 \cdot 2x} = \frac{3}{2x}$$

45. $$\begin{aligned} \frac{3}{5}a &= 9 \\ \frac{5}{3} \cdot \frac{3}{5}a &= 9 \cdot \frac{5}{3} \\ a &= \frac{3 \cdot 3 \cdot 5}{3} \\ a &= 15 \end{aligned}$$

46. $$\begin{aligned} \frac{2}{3}y &= 12 \\ \frac{3}{2} \cdot \frac{2}{3}y &= 12 \cdot \frac{3}{2} \\ y &= \frac{2 \cdot 6 \cdot 3}{2} \\ y &= 18 \end{aligned}$$

47. $$\begin{array}{r} 763.7651 \\ 22.0010 \\ \underline{+43.8900} \\ 829.6561 \end{array}$$

48. $$\begin{array}{r} 89.2700 \\ 14.3610 \\ \underline{+127.2318} \\ 230.8628 \end{array}$$

49. $$\begin{array}{r} 23.6 \\ \underline{\times 0.78} \\ 1888 \\ \underline{16520} \\ 18.408 \end{array}$$

50. $$\begin{array}{r} 43.8 \\ \underline{\times 0.645} \\ 2190 \\ 17520 \\ \underline{262800} \\ 27.2510 \end{array}$$

Answer: 27.251

Chapter 6

Pretest

1. The ratio of 15 to 19 is $\frac{15}{19}$.

2. The ratio of $3\frac{4}{5}$ to $9\frac{1}{8}$ is $\frac{3\frac{4}{5}}{9\frac{1}{8}}$.

3. $\frac{5.1}{7.9} = \frac{5.1 \cdot 10}{7.9 \cdot 10} = \frac{51}{79}$

4. $\frac{\$30}{\$20} = \frac{3 \cdot \$10}{2 \cdot \$10} = \frac{3}{2}$

5. $\frac{\$6}{3\text{ pounds}} = \frac{3}{3 \cdot 1\text{ pound}} = \frac{\$2}{1\text{ pound}}$

6. $\frac{292.5\text{ miles}}{15\text{ gallons}} = \frac{19.5\text{ miles}}{1\text{ gallon}} = 19.5\text{ miles per gallon}$

7. $\frac{\$3.27}{3\text{ boxes}} = \frac{\$1.09}{1\text{ box}} = \$1.09\text{ per box}$

8. $\frac{\text{credits}}{\text{classes}} = \frac{\text{credits}}{\text{classes}}$
   $\frac{18}{6} = \frac{15}{5}$

9. $\frac{\text{days}}{\text{weeks}} = \frac{\text{days}}{\text{weeks}}$
   $\frac{49}{7} = \frac{35}{5}$

10. $\frac{3}{5} = \frac{21}{34}?$
    $5 \cdot 21 = 3 \cdot 34?$
    $105 \neq 102$
    Since the cross products are not equal, the proportion is not true.

11. $\frac{72}{9} = \frac{216}{27}?$
    $9 \cdot 216 = 72 \cdot 27?$
    $1944 = 1944$
    Since the cross products are equal, the proportion is true.

12. $\frac{22}{x} = \frac{66}{12}$
    $66x = 22 \cdot 12$
    $66x = 264$
    $\frac{66x}{66} = \frac{264}{66}$
    $x = 4$

13. $\frac{x}{8} = \frac{0.6}{2.4}$
    $8 \cdot 0.6 = 2.4x$
    $4.8 = 2.4x$
    $\frac{4.8}{2.4} = \frac{2.4x}{2.4}$
    $2 = x$

14. $\frac{\frac{1}{2}}{8} = \frac{3}{y}$
    $8 \cdot 3 = \frac{1}{2}y$
    $24 = \frac{1}{2}y$
    $2 \cdot 24 = 2 \cdot \frac{1}{2}y$
    $48 = y$

15. $\frac{1\frac{1}{3}}{\frac{6}{5}} = \frac{n}{9}$
    $\frac{6}{5}n = 9 \cdot 1\frac{1}{3}$
    $\frac{6}{5}n = 9 \cdot \frac{4}{3}$
    $\frac{6}{5}n = \frac{3 \cdot 3 \cdot 4}{3}$
    $\frac{6}{5}n = 12$
    $\frac{5}{6} \cdot \frac{6}{5}n = \frac{5}{6} \cdot 12$
    $n = \frac{5 \cdot 6 \cdot 2}{6}$
    $n = 10$

16. $\frac{\text{miles}}{\text{inches}} = \frac{\text{miles}}{\text{inches}}$

$\frac{20 \text{ miles}}{1 \text{ inch}} = \frac{x \text{ miles}}{5\frac{3}{8} \text{ inches}}$

$\frac{20}{1} = \frac{x}{5\frac{3}{8}}$

$1 \cdot x = 20 \cdot 5\frac{3}{8}$

$x = 20 \cdot \frac{43}{8}$

$x = \frac{4 \cdot 5 \cdot 43}{2 \cdot 4}$

$x = \frac{215}{2} = 107\frac{1}{2}$

$5\frac{3}{8}$ inches represents $107\frac{1}{2}$ miles.

17. Since the triangles are similar, we can compare any of the corresponding sides to find the ratio.

$\frac{5}{10} = \frac{1}{2}$

18. $\frac{6}{18} = \frac{2}{n}$

$18 \cdot 2 = 6n$

$36 = 6n$

$\frac{36}{6} = \frac{6n}{6}$

$6 = n$

19. $\frac{3.5}{24.5} = \frac{n}{38.5}$

$24.5n = 3.5 \cdot 38.5$

$24.5n = 134.75$

$\frac{24.5n}{24.5} = \frac{134.75}{24.5}$

$n = 5.5$

20. $\frac{\text{tree height}}{\text{shadow length}} = \frac{\text{tree height}}{\text{shadow length}}$

$\frac{40 \text{ feet}}{22 \text{ feet}} = \frac{36 \text{ feet}}{x \text{ feet}}$

$\frac{40}{22} = \frac{36}{x}$

$22 \cdot 36 = 40x$

$792 = 40x$

$\frac{792}{40} = \frac{40x}{40}$

$19.8 = x$

A 36-foot tree casts a 19.8-foot shadow.

Section 6.1

Practice Problems

1. The ratio is $\frac{20}{23}$.

2. The ratio of 10.3 to 15.1 is $\frac{10.3}{15.1}$.

3. The ratio of $3\frac{1}{3}$ to $12\frac{1}{5}$ is $\frac{3\frac{1}{3}}{12\frac{1}{5}}$.

4. $\frac{\$8}{\$6} = \frac{8}{6} = \frac{4 \cdot 2}{3 \cdot 2} = \frac{4}{3}$

5. $\frac{1.68}{4.8} = \frac{1.68 \cdot 100}{4.8 \cdot 100} = \frac{168}{48} = \frac{7 \cdot 24}{8 \cdot 57} = \frac{7}{2}$

6. $\frac{\text{work miles}}{\text{total miles}} = \frac{4800}{15,000} = \frac{8 \cdot 600}{25 \cdot 600} = \frac{8}{25}$

7. **a.** $\frac{\text{shortest side}}{\text{longest side}} = \frac{6 \text{ m}}{10 \text{ m}} = \frac{3 \cdot 2}{5 \cdot 2} = \frac{3}{5}$

b. $\frac{\text{longest side}}{\text{perimeter}} = \frac{10 \text{ m}}{6 \text{ m} + 8 \text{ m} + 10 \text{ m}}$

$= \frac{10\text{m}}{24 \text{ m}}$

$= \frac{5 \cdot 2}{12 \cdot 2}$

$= \frac{5}{12}$

Exercise Set 6.1

1. The ratio of 11 to 14 is $\frac{11}{14}$.

3. The ratio of 23 to 10 is $\frac{23}{10}$.

5. The ratio of 151 to 201 is $\frac{151}{201}$.

7. The ratio of 2.8 to 7.6 is $\frac{2.8}{7.6}$.

9. The ratio of 5 to $7\frac{1}{2}$ is $\frac{5}{7\frac{1}{2}}$.

11. The ratio of $3\frac{3}{4}$ to $1\frac{2}{3}$ is $\frac{3\frac{3}{4}}{1\frac{2}{3}}$.

13. $\frac{16}{24} = \frac{2 \cdot 8}{3 \cdot 8} = \frac{2}{3}$

15. $\frac{7.7}{10} = \frac{7.7 \cdot 10}{10 \cdot 10} = \frac{77}{100}$

17. $\frac{4.63}{8.21} = \frac{4.63 \cdot 100}{8.21 \cdot 100} = \frac{463}{821}$

19. $\frac{9 \text{ inches}}{12 \text{ inches}} = \frac{3 \cdot 3}{4 \cdot 3} = \frac{3}{4}$

21. $\frac{10 \text{ hours}}{24 \text{ hours}} = \frac{5 \cdot 2}{12 \cdot 2} = \frac{5}{12}$

23. $\frac{\$32}{\$100} = \frac{8 \cdot 4}{25 \cdot 4} = \frac{8}{25}$

25. $\frac{24 \text{ days}}{14 \text{ days}} = \frac{12 \cdot 2}{7 \cdot 2} = \frac{12}{7}$

27. $\frac{32{,}000 \text{ bytes}}{46{,}000 \text{ bytes}} = \frac{16 \cdot 2000}{23 \cdot 2000} = \frac{16}{23}$

29. $\$2 = 200¢$

$\frac{35¢}{200¢} = \frac{7 \cdot 5}{40 \cdot 5} = \frac{7}{40}$

31. $\frac{\text{vacation / other miles}}{\text{total miles}} = \frac{900 \text{ miles}}{15{,}000 \text{ miles}}$

$= \frac{300 \cdot 3}{300 \cdot 50}$

$= \frac{3}{50}$

33. $\frac{\text{length}}{\text{width}} = \frac{94 \text{ feet}}{50 \text{ feet}} = \frac{47 \cdot 2}{25 \cdot 2} = \frac{47}{25}$

35. perimeter = 8 + 15 + 17 = 40 feet

$\frac{\text{longest side}}{\text{perimeter}} = \frac{17 \text{ feet}}{40 \text{ feet}} = \frac{17}{40}$

37. $\frac{\text{calories from fat}}{\text{total calories}} = \frac{200}{450} = \frac{4 \cdot 50}{9 \cdot 50} = \frac{4}{9}$

39. $\frac{\text{women}}{\text{men}} = \frac{125}{100} = \frac{25 \cdot 5}{25 \cdot 4} = \frac{5}{4}$

41. There are 6000 – 4500 = 1500 married students.

$\frac{\text{single students}}{\text{married students}} = \frac{4500}{1500} = \frac{3 \cdot 1500}{1 \cdot 1500} = \frac{3}{1}$

43. $\frac{\text{red blood cells}}{\text{platelet cells}} = \frac{600}{40} = \frac{40 \cdot 15}{40 \cdot 1} = \frac{15}{1}$

45. $\frac{\$5.15}{\$0.25} = \frac{103 \cdot 0.05}{5 \cdot 0.05} = \frac{103}{5}$

47. $\frac{12 \text{ medals}}{234 \text{ medals}} = \frac{2 \cdot 6}{39 \cdot 6} = \frac{2}{39}$

49. $\frac{19 \text{ mountains}}{57 \text{ mountains}} = \frac{19}{3 \cdot 19} = \frac{1}{3}$

51.

```
   2.3
9) 20.7
  -18
    27
   -27
     0
```

53.

```
3.7)0.555   Move the decimal points
   0.15     1 place.
37)5.55
  -37
   185
  -185
     0
```

55. States without bicycle helmet laws

= 50 – 15

= 35

$\frac{15 \text{ states}}{35 \text{ states}} = \frac{3 \cdot 5}{7 \cdot 5} = \frac{3}{7}$

57. $\frac{2\frac{1}{2}}{5\frac{3}{4}} = 2\frac{1}{2} \div 5\frac{3}{4} = \frac{5}{2} \div \frac{23}{4}$

$= \frac{5}{2} \cdot \frac{4}{23}$

$= \frac{5 \cdot 2 \cdot 2}{2 \cdot 23}$

$= \frac{10}{23}$

59. $\frac{\text{bruised}}{\text{total}} = \frac{3}{3+30} = \frac{3}{33} = \frac{1\cdot 3}{11\cdot 3} = \frac{1}{11}$
No, the shipment should not be refused.

61. a. $\frac{\text{19 states with law}}{\text{50 total states}} = \frac{19}{50}$

b. $50 - 19 = 31$ states without law
$\frac{\text{19 states with law}}{\text{31 states without law}} = \frac{19}{31}$

Section 6.2

Practice Problems

1. $\frac{\text{12 commercials}}{\text{45 minutes}} = \frac{3\cdot 4\text{ commercials}}{3\cdot 15\text{ minutes}} = \frac{\text{4 commercials}}{\text{15 minutes}}$

2. $\frac{\text{1680 dollars}}{\text{8 weeks}} = \frac{8\cdot 210\text{ dollars}}{8\cdot 1\text{ week}} = \frac{\text{210 dollars}}{\text{1 week}}$

3. $\frac{\text{236 miles}}{\text{12 gallons}} = \frac{4\cdot 59\text{ miles}}{4\cdot 3\text{ gallons}} = \frac{\text{59 miles}}{\text{3 gallons}}$

4. $\frac{\text{3600 feet}}{\text{12 seconds}} = \frac{12\cdot 300\text{ feet}}{12\cdot 1\text{ second}} = \frac{\text{300 feet}}{\text{1 second}}$ or 300 feet per second

5. $\frac{\text{52 bushels}}{\text{8 trees}} = \frac{\text{6.5 bushels}}{\text{1 tree}}$ or 65 bushels/tree

$$\begin{array}{r} 6.5 \\ 8\overline{)\,52.0} \\ -48 \\ 4\,0 \\ -4\,0 \\ \hline 0 \end{array}$$

6. $\frac{\$170}{\text{5 days}} = \frac{5\cdot \$34}{5\cdot 1\text{ day}} = \frac{\$34}{\text{1 day}}$
The rental agency charges $34 per day.

7. 11-ounce size:
unit price $= \frac{\$2.32}{\text{11 ounces}} \approx \frac{\$0.21}{\text{1 ounce}}$ or $0.21 per ounce
16-ounce size:
unit price $= \frac{\$3.59}{\text{16 ounces}} \approx \frac{\$0.22}{\text{1 ounce}}$ or $0.22 per ounce
Thus, the 11-ounce bag is the better buy.

Exercise Set 6.2

1. $\frac{\text{5 shrubs}}{\text{15 feet}} = \frac{\text{1 shrub}}{\text{3 feet}}$

3. $\frac{\text{15 returns}}{\text{100 sales}} = \frac{\text{3 returns}}{\text{20 sales}}$

5. $\frac{\text{8 phone lines}}{\text{36 employees}} = \frac{\text{2 phone lines}}{\text{9 employees}}$

7. $\frac{\text{18 gallons of pesticide}}{\text{4 acres of crops}} = \frac{\text{9 gallons}}{\text{2 acres}}$

9. $\frac{\text{6 flight attendants}}{\text{200 passengers}} = \frac{\text{3 flight attendants}}{\text{100 passengers}}$

11. $\frac{\text{355 calories}}{\text{10 fluid ounces}} = \frac{\text{71 calories}}{\text{2 fluid ounces}}$

13. $\frac{\text{375 riders}}{\text{5 subway cars}} = \frac{\text{75 riders}}{\text{1 subway car}}$
= 75 riders per car

15. $\frac{\text{330 calories}}{\text{3 ounces}} = \frac{\text{110 calories}}{\text{1 ounce}}$
= 110 calories per ounce

17. 1 minute = 60 seconds
$\frac{\text{5400 wingbeats}}{\text{60 seconds}} = \frac{\text{90 wingbeats}}{\text{1 second}}$
90 wingbeats per second

19. $\frac{\$1,000,000}{\text{20 years}} = \frac{\$50,000}{\text{1 year}} = \$50,000$ per year

21. $\frac{\text{26,600 miles}}{\text{20 days}} = \frac{\text{1330 miles}}{\text{1 day}}$
1330 miles per day

23. $\frac{\text{5,740,020 voters}}{\text{2 senators}} = \frac{\text{2,870,010 voters}}{\text{1 senator}}$
2,870,010 voters per senator

25. $\dfrac{12{,}000 \text{ good}}{40 \text{ defective}} = \dfrac{300 \text{ good}}{1 \text{ defective}}$
$= 300$ good per defective

27. $\dfrac{12 \text{ million tons dust and dirt}}{25 \text{ million acres}}$
$= \dfrac{0.48 \text{ ton dust and dirt}}{1 \text{ acre}}$
$= 0.48$ ton dust and dirt per acre

29. $\dfrac{\$28{,}600{,}000}{500 \text{ species}} = \dfrac{\$57{,}200}{1 \text{ species}}$
$57,200 per species

31. $\dfrac{\$121{,}200{,}000}{60 \text{ shows}} = \dfrac{\$2{,}020{,}000}{1 \text{ show}}$
$2,020,000 per show

33. a. Greer:
$\dfrac{250 \text{ boards}}{8 \text{ hours}}$
$= 31.25$ computer boards per hour

b. Lamont:
$\dfrac{400 \text{ boards}}{12 \text{ hours}} \approx 33.3$ boards per hour

c. Lamont can assemble about 33.3 boards in the same time that Greer assembles 31.25 boards. Thus, Lamont assembles them faster.

35. $\dfrac{\$57.50}{5 \text{ compact disks}} = \dfrac{\$11.50}{1 \text{ compact disk}}$
$= \$11.50$ per compact disk

37. $\dfrac{\$1.19}{7 \text{ bananas}} = \dfrac{\$0.17}{1 \text{ banana}} = \$0.17$ per banana

39. 8-ounce size:
$\dfrac{\$1.19}{8 \text{ ounces}} \approx \$0.149$ per ounce
12-ounce size:
$\dfrac{\$1.59}{12 \text{ ounces}} \approx \$0.133$ per ounce
The 12-ounce size costs less per ounce, thus it is the better buy.

41. 16-ounce size:
$\dfrac{\$1.69}{16 \text{ ounces}} \approx \$0.106$ per ounce
6-ounce size:
$\dfrac{\$0.69}{6 \text{ ounces}} = \$0.115$ per ounce
The 16-ounce size costs less per ounce, thus it is the better buy.

43. 12-ounce size:
$\dfrac{\$2.29}{12 \text{ ounces}} \approx \$0.191$ per ounce
8-ounce size:
$\dfrac{\$1.49}{8 \text{ ounces}} \approx \$0.186$ per ounce
The 8-ounce size costs less per ounce, thus it is the better buy.

45. 100-pack size:
$\dfrac{\$0.59}{100 \text{ napkins}} \approx \$0.006$ per napkin
180-pack size:
$\dfrac{\$0.93}{180 \text{ napkins}} \approx \$0.005$ per napkin
The package of 180 napkins costs less per napkin thus, it is the better buy.

47.
$$\begin{array}{r} 1.7 \\ \times\ 6 \\ \hline 10.2 \end{array}$$

49.
$$\begin{array}{r} 3.7 \\ \times\ 1.2 \\ \hline 74 \\ 370 \\ \hline 4.44 \end{array}$$

51. $2.3\overline{)4.37}$ Move the decimal points 1 place
$$\begin{array}{r} 1.9 \\ 23.\overline{)43.7} \\ -23 \\ \hline 207 \\ -207 \\ \hline 0 \end{array}$$

53.

Miles Driven	Miles per Gallon (round to the nearest tenth)
79,543 – 79,286 = 257	$\frac{257}{13.4} = 19.2$
79,895 – 79,543 = 352	$\frac{352}{15.8} = 22.3$
80,242 – 79,895 = 347	$\frac{347}{16.1} = 21.6$

55. $\frac{11,674 \text{ steps}}{7759 \text{ feet}}$

$$\begin{array}{r} 1.50 \\ 7759\overline{)11,674.00} \\ -7759 \\ 39150 \\ -38795 \\ 3550 \\ -\quad 0 \\ \hline 3550 \end{array}$$

Rounded to the nearest tenth, the unit rate is 1.5 steps per foot.

57. $\frac{481,687 \text{ students}}{22,008 \text{ teachers}}$

$481,687 \div 22,008 \approx 21.89$

Rounded to the nearest whole student, the unit rate is 22 students per teacher.

59. Answers may vary.

Section 6.3

Practice Problems

1. a. $\frac{\text{right}}{\text{wrong}} = \frac{\text{right}}{\text{wrong}}$

$\frac{24}{6} = \frac{4}{1}$

b. $\frac{\text{Cubs fans}}{\text{Mets fans}} = \frac{\text{Cubs fans}}{\text{Met fans}}$

$\frac{32}{18} = \frac{16}{9}$

2. $\frac{3}{6} = \frac{4}{8}$?

$6 \cdot 4 = 3 \cdot 8$?

$24 = 24$

Since the cross products are equal, the proportion is true.

3. $\frac{3.6}{6} = \frac{5.4}{8}$?

$6 \cdot 5.4 = 3.6 \cdot 8$?

$32.4 \neq 28.8$

Since the cross products are not equal, the proportion is not true.

4. $\frac{4\frac{1}{5}}{2\frac{1}{3}} = \frac{3\frac{3}{10}}{1\frac{5}{6}}$?

$2\frac{1}{3} \cdot 3\frac{3}{10} = 4\frac{1}{5} \cdot 1\frac{5}{6}$?

$\frac{7}{3} \cdot \frac{33}{10} = \frac{21}{5} \cdot \frac{11}{6}$?

$\frac{77}{10} = \frac{77}{10}$

Since the cross products are equal, the proportion is true.

5. $\frac{2}{7} = \frac{x}{35}$

$7 \cdot x = 2 \cdot 35$

$7x = 70$

$\frac{7x}{7} = \frac{70}{7}$

$x = 10$

6. $\frac{2}{15} = \frac{y}{60}$

$15y = 2 \cdot 60$

$15y = 120$

$\frac{15y}{15} = \frac{120}{15}$

$y = 8$

Check: $\frac{2}{15} = \frac{y}{60}$

$\frac{2}{15} = \frac{8}{60}$

$\frac{2}{15} = \frac{2}{15}$

Since $\frac{2}{15} = \frac{2}{15}$ is a true statement, 8 is the solution.

7. $\frac{\frac{7}{8}}{z} = \frac{\frac{2}{3}}{\frac{4}{7}}$

$\frac{2}{3} \cdot z = \frac{7}{8} \cdot \frac{4}{7}$

$\frac{2}{3} z = \frac{1}{2}$

$\frac{3}{2} \cdot \frac{2}{3} z = \frac{1}{2} \cdot \frac{3}{2}$

$z = \frac{3}{4}$

8. $\frac{y}{6} = \frac{0.7}{1.2}$
$6(0.7) = 1.2y$
$4.2 = 1.2y$
$\frac{4.2}{1.2} = \frac{1.2y}{1.2}$
$3.5 = y$

9. $\frac{15}{z} = \frac{8}{10}$
$8z = 150$
$\frac{8z}{8} = \frac{150}{8}$
$z = \frac{75}{4}$ or 18.75

10. $\frac{3.4}{1.8} = \frac{y}{3}$
$1.8y = 10.2$
$\frac{1.8y}{1.8} = \frac{10.2}{1.8}$
$y \approx 5.7$

Mental Math

1. Is $1 \cdot 6 = 2 \cdot 3$? Yes
True

2. Is $1 \cdot 15 = 3 \cdot 5$? Yes
True

3. Is $2 \cdot 3 = 1 \cdot 5$? No
False

4. Is $11 \cdot 1 = 2 \cdot 5$? No
False

5. Is $3 \cdot 4 = 2 \cdot 6$? Yes
True

6. Is $4 \cdot 6 = 3 \cdot 8$? Yes
True

Exercise Set 6.3

1. $\frac{10 \text{ diamonds}}{6 \text{ opals}} = \frac{5 \text{ diamonds}}{3 \text{ opals}}$

3. $\frac{3 \text{ printers}}{12 \text{ computers}} = \frac{1 \text{ printer}}{4 \text{ computers}}$

5. $\frac{6 \text{ eagles}}{58 \text{ sparrows}} = \frac{3 \text{ eagles}}{29 \text{ sparrows}}$

7. $\frac{2\frac{1}{4} \text{ cups flour}}{24 \text{ cookies}} = \frac{6\frac{3}{4} \text{ cups flour}}{72 \text{ cookies}}$

9. $\frac{22 \text{ vanilla wafers}}{1 \text{ cup cookie crumbs}}$
$= \frac{55 \text{ vanilla wafers}}{2.5 \text{ cups cookie crumbs}}$

11. $\frac{15}{9} = \frac{5}{3}?$
$9 \cdot 5 = 15 \cdot 3?$
$45 = 45$
Since the cross products are equal, the proportion is true.

13. $\frac{8}{6} = \frac{9}{7}?$
$6 \cdot 9 = 8 \cdot 7?$
$54 \neq 56$
Since the cross products are not equal, the proportion is false.

15. $\frac{9}{36} = \frac{2}{8}?$
$362 = 9 \cdot 8?$
$72 = 72$
Since the cross products are equal, the proportion is true.

17. $\frac{5}{8} = \frac{625}{1000}?$
$8 \cdot 625 = 5 \cdot 1000?$
$5000 = 5000$
Since the cross products are equal, the proportion is true.

19. $\frac{0.8}{0.3} = \frac{0.2}{0.6}?$
$0.3 \cdot 0.2 = 0.8 \cdot 0.6?$
$0.06 \neq 0.48$
Since the cross products are not equal, the proportional is false.

21. $\frac{4.2}{8.4} = \frac{5}{10}?$
$8.4 \cdot 5 = 4.2 \cdot 10?$
$42 = 42$
Since the cross products are equal, the proportion is true.

23. $\dfrac{\frac{3}{4}}{\frac{4}{3}} = \dfrac{\frac{1}{2}}{\frac{8}{9}}?$

$\dfrac{4}{3} \cdot \dfrac{1}{2} = \dfrac{3}{4} \cdot \dfrac{8}{9}?$

$\dfrac{2 \cdot 2 \cdot 1}{3 \cdot 2} = \dfrac{3 \cdot 4 \cdot 2}{4 \cdot 3 \cdot 3}?$

$\dfrac{2}{3} = \dfrac{2}{3}$

Since the cross products are equal, the proportion is true.

25. $\dfrac{2\frac{2}{5}}{\frac{2}{3}} = \dfrac{\frac{10}{9}}{\frac{1}{4}}?$

$\dfrac{2}{3} \cdot \dfrac{10}{9} = 2\dfrac{2}{5} \cdot \dfrac{1}{4}?$

$\dfrac{2}{3} \cdot \dfrac{10}{9} = \dfrac{12}{5} \cdot \dfrac{1}{4}?$

$\dfrac{2 \cdot 10}{3 \cdot 9} = \dfrac{3 \cdot 4 \cdot 1}{5 \cdot 4}?$

$\dfrac{20}{27} = \dfrac{3}{5}?$

$27 \cdot 3 = 20 \cdot 5?$

$81 \neq 100$

Since the cross products are not equal, the proportion is false.

27. $\dfrac{x}{5} = \dfrac{6}{10}$

$30 = 10x$

$\dfrac{30}{10} = \dfrac{10x}{10}$

$3 = x$

29. $\dfrac{30}{10} = \dfrac{15}{y}$

$10 \cdot 15 = 30y$

$150 = 30y$

$\dfrac{150}{30} = \dfrac{30y}{30}$

$5 = y$

31. $\dfrac{z}{8} = \dfrac{50}{100}$

$400 = 100z$

$\dfrac{400}{100} = \dfrac{100z}{400}$

$4 = z$

33. $\dfrac{n}{6} = \dfrac{8}{15}$

$6 \cdot 8 = 15n$

$48 = 15n$

$\dfrac{48}{15} = \dfrac{15n}{15}$

$3.2 = n$

35. $\dfrac{12}{10} = \dfrac{x}{16}$

$10x = 12 \cdot 16$

$10x = 192$

$\dfrac{10x}{10} = \dfrac{192}{10}$

$x = 19.2$

37. $\dfrac{n}{\frac{6}{5}} = \dfrac{4\frac{1}{6}}{6\frac{2}{3}}$

$\dfrac{6}{5} \cdot 4\dfrac{1}{6} = 6\dfrac{2}{3} \cdot n$

$\dfrac{6}{5} \cdot \dfrac{25}{6} = \dfrac{20}{3}n$

$\dfrac{150}{30} = \dfrac{20}{3}n$

$5 = \dfrac{20}{3}n$

$\dfrac{3}{20} \cdot \dfrac{5}{1} = \dfrac{3}{20} \cdot \dfrac{20}{3}n$

$\dfrac{15}{20} = n$

$\dfrac{3}{4} = n$

39. $\dfrac{\frac{3}{4}}{12} = \dfrac{y}{48}$

$12y = \dfrac{3}{4} \cdot 48$

$12y = 36$

$\dfrac{12y}{12} = \dfrac{36}{12}$

$y = 3$

41. $\frac{\frac{2}{3}}{\frac{6}{9}} = \frac{12}{z}$

$\frac{6}{9} \cdot 12 = \frac{2}{3} z$

$\frac{3}{2} \cdot \frac{6}{9} \cdot \frac{12}{1} = \frac{3}{2} \cdot \frac{2}{3} z$

$\frac{3 \cdot 2 \cdot 3 \cdot 12}{2 \cdot 3 \cdot 3 \cdot 1} = z$

$12 = z$

43 $\frac{n}{0.6} = \frac{0.05}{12}$

$0.6 \cdot 0.05 = 12n$

$0.03 = 12n$

$\frac{0.03}{12} = \frac{12n}{12}$

$0.0025 = n$

45. $\frac{3.5}{12.5} = \frac{7}{z}$

$12.5 \cdot 7 = 3.5z$

$87.5 = 3.5z$

$\frac{87.5}{3.5} = \frac{3.5z}{3.5}$

$25 = z$

47. $\frac{3.2}{0.3} = \frac{x}{1.4}$

$0.3x = 3.2 \cdot 1.4$

$0.3x = 4.48$

$\frac{0.3x}{0.3} = \frac{4.48}{0.3}$

$x \approx 14.9$

49. $\frac{z}{5.2} = \frac{0.08}{6}$

$5.2 \cdot 0.08 = 6z$

$0.416 = 6z$

$\frac{0.416}{6} = \frac{6z}{6}$

$0.07 \approx z$

51. $\frac{9}{11} = \frac{x}{4}$

$11x = 36$

$\frac{11x}{11} = \frac{36}{11}$

$x \approx 3.3$

53. $\frac{43}{17} = \frac{8}{z}$

$17 \cdot 8 = 43z$

$136 = 43z$

$\frac{136}{43} = \frac{43z}{43}$

$3.163 \approx z$

55. $-8 < 8$

57. $-2 > -3$

59. $-5 < 0$

61. $-1\frac{1}{2} > -2\frac{1}{2}$

63. $-8.3 < -7.9$

65. $1.23 > 1.039$

67. $\frac{n}{7} = \frac{0}{8}$

$7 \cdot 0 = 8n$

$0 = 8n$

$\frac{0}{8} = \frac{8n}{8}$

$0 = n$

69. $\frac{n}{1150} = \frac{588}{483}$

$1150 \cdot 588 = 483n$

$676,200 = 483n$

$\frac{676,200}{483} = \frac{483n}{483}$

$1400 = n$

71. $\frac{222}{1515} = \frac{37}{n}$

$1515 \cdot 37 = 222n$

$56,055 = 222n$

$\frac{52,055}{222} = \frac{222n}{222}$

$252.5 = n$

73. Answers may vary.

Integrated Review

1. $\frac{18}{20} = \frac{9 \cdot 2}{10 \cdot 2} = \frac{9}{10}$

2. $\frac{36}{100} = \frac{9 \cdot 4}{25 \cdot 4} = \frac{9}{25}$

3. $\frac{8.6}{10} = \frac{86}{100} = \frac{43 \cdot 2}{50 \cdot 2} = \frac{43}{50}$

4. $\frac{1.6}{4.6} = \frac{16}{46} = \frac{8 \cdot 2}{23 \cdot 2} = \frac{8}{23}$

5. $\frac{8.65}{6.95} = \frac{865}{695} = \frac{173 \cdot 5}{139 \cdot 5} = \frac{173}{139}$

6. $\frac{7.2}{8.4} = \frac{72}{84} = \frac{6 \cdot 12}{7 \cdot 12} = \frac{6}{7}$

7. $\frac{3\frac{1}{2}}{13} = \frac{3.5}{13} = \frac{35}{130} = \frac{7 \cdot 5}{26 \cdot 5} = \frac{7}{26}$

8. $\frac{1\frac{2}{3}}{2\frac{3}{4}} = \frac{5}{3} \div \frac{11}{4} = \frac{5}{3} \cdot \frac{4}{11} = \frac{5 \cdot 4}{3 \cdot 11} = \frac{20}{33}$

9. $\frac{8 \text{ inches}}{12 \text{ inches}} = \frac{8}{12} = \frac{2 \cdot 4}{3 \cdot 4} = \frac{2}{3}$

10. $\frac{3 \text{ hours}}{24 \text{ hours}} = \frac{3}{24} = \frac{1 \cdot 3}{8 \cdot 3} = \frac{1}{8}$

11. $\frac{12 \text{ inches}}{18 \text{ inches}} = \frac{12}{18} = \frac{2 \cdot 6}{3 \cdot 6} = \frac{2}{3}$

12. $\frac{\$26 \text{ hundred million}}{\$8 \text{ hundred million}} = \frac{26}{8} = \frac{13 \cdot 2}{4 \cdot 2} = \frac{13}{4}$

13. $\frac{5 \text{ offices}}{20 \text{ graduate assistants}}$
$= \frac{1 \text{ office}}{4 \text{ graduate assistants}}$

14. $\frac{6 \text{ lights}}{15 \text{ feet}} = \frac{2 \text{ lights}}{5 \text{ feet}}$

15. $\frac{100 \text{ U.S. Senators}}{50 \text{ states}} = \frac{2 \text{ U.S. Senators}}{1 \text{ state}}$

16. $\frac{5 \text{ teachers}}{140 \text{ students}} = \frac{1 \text{ teacher}}{28 \text{ students}}$

17. $\frac{20 \text{ inches}}{2 \text{ feet}} = \frac{10 \text{ inches}}{1 \text{ foot}}$

18. $\frac{40 \text{ cents}}{3 \text{ dollars}}$

19. $\frac{64 \text{ households with computers}}{100 \text{ household}}$
$= \frac{16 \text{ households with computers}}{25 \text{ households}}$

20. $\frac{538 \text{ electoral votes}}{50 \text{ states}} = \frac{269 \text{ electoral votes}}{25 \text{ states}}$

21. $\frac{165 \text{ miles}}{3 \text{ hours}} = \frac{55 \text{ miles}}{1 \text{ hour}}$

$$\begin{array}{r} 55 \\ 3\overline{)165} \\ \underline{-15} \\ 15 \\ \underline{15} \\ 0 \end{array}$$

55 miles per hour or 55 mph

22. $\frac{560 \text{ feet}}{4 \text{ seconds}} = \frac{140 \text{ feet}}{1 \text{ second}}$

$$\begin{array}{r} 140 \\ 4\overline{)560} \\ \underline{-4} \\ 16 \\ \underline{-16} \\ 00 \\ \underline{-0} \\ 0 \end{array}$$

140 feet per second

23. $\frac{63 \text{ employees}}{3 \text{ fax lines}} = \frac{21 \text{ employees}}{1 \text{ fax line}}$

$$\begin{array}{r} 21 \\ 3\overline{)63} \\ \underline{-6} \\ 03 \\ \underline{-3} \\ 0 \end{array}$$

21 employees per fax line

24. $\frac{85 \text{ phone calls}}{5 \text{ teenagers}} = \frac{17 \text{ phone calls}}{1 \text{ teenager}}$

$$\begin{array}{r} 17 \\ 5\overline{)\,85} \\ \underline{-5} \\ 35 \\ \underline{-35} \\ 0 \end{array}$$

17 phone calls per teenager

25. $\frac{115 \text{ miles}}{5 \text{ gallons}} = \frac{23 \text{ miles}}{1 \text{ gallon}}$
23 miles per gallon

26. $\frac{112 \text{ teachers}}{7 \text{ computers}} = \frac{16 \text{ teachers}}{1 \text{ computer}}$
16 teachers per computer

27. $\frac{7524 \text{ books}}{1254 \text{ college students}} = \frac{6 \text{ books}}{1 \text{ college student}}$
6 books per college student

28. $\frac{2002 \text{ pounds}}{13 \text{ adults}} = \frac{154 \text{ pounds}}{1 \text{ adult}}$
154 pounds per adult

29. $\text{8-pound unit price} = \frac{\$2.16}{8 \text{ pounds}} = \$0.27 \text{ per pound}$

$\text{18-pound unit price} = \frac{\$4.99}{18 \text{ pounds}} \approx \$0.28 \text{ per pound}$

The 8-pound size is the better buy.

30. $\text{100-plate unit price} = \frac{\$1.98}{100 \text{ plates}} \approx \$0.020 \text{ per plate}$

$\text{500-plate unit price} = \frac{\$8.99}{500 \text{ plates}} \approx \$0.018 \text{ per plate}$

The 500-plate size is the better buy.

31. $\text{3-pack unit price} = \frac{\$2.39}{3 \text{ packs}} \approx \$0.80 \text{ per pack}$

$\text{8-pack unit price} = \frac{\$5.99}{8 \text{ packs}} \approx \$0.75 \text{ per pack}$

The 8-pack size is the better buy.

32. $\text{4-battery unit price} = \frac{\$3.69}{4 \text{ batteries}} \approx \$0.92 \text{ per battery}$

$\text{10-battery unit price} = \frac{\$9.89}{10 \text{ batteries}} \approx \$0.99 \text{ per battery}$

The 4 batteries are the better buy.

Section 6.4

Practice Problems

1. $\frac{12 \text{ feet}}{1 \text{ inch}} = \frac{n \text{ feet}}{3\frac{1}{2} \text{ inches}}$

$$\frac{12}{1} = \frac{n}{3\frac{1}{2}}$$

$$1 \cdot n = 12 \cdot 3\frac{1}{2}$$

$$n = \frac{12}{1} \cdot \frac{7}{2}$$

$$n = 42$$

$3\frac{1}{2}$ inches corresponds to 42 feet.

2. $\frac{14 \text{ gallons}}{3 \text{ ounces}} = \frac{n \text{ gallons}}{16 \text{ ounces}}$

$$\frac{14}{3} = \frac{n}{16}$$

$$3 \cdot n = 14 \cdot 16$$

$$3n = 224$$

$$\frac{3n}{3} = \frac{224}{3}$$

$$n = 74\frac{2}{3}$$

$74\frac{2}{3}$ gallons of gas can be treated with a 16-ounce bottle of alcohol.

3. area = 260 feet · 4 feet = 1040 square feet

$$\frac{1 \text{ gallon}}{400 \text{ square feet}} = \frac{n \text{ gallons}}{1040 \text{ square feet}}$$
$$\frac{1}{400} = \frac{n}{1040}$$
$$400 \cdot n = 1 \cdot 1040$$
$$400n = 1040$$
$$\frac{400n}{400} = \frac{1040}{400}$$
$$n = 2.6$$

Since we must buy full gallons, 3 gallons is needed.

Exercise Set 6.4

1. Let x = the number of completed passes.

$$\frac{4 \text{ completed}}{9 \text{ attempted}} = \frac{x \text{ completed}}{27 \text{ attempted}}$$
$$9x = 27 \cdot 4$$
$$9x = 108$$
$$\frac{9x}{9} = \frac{108}{9}$$
$$x = 12$$

He completed 12 passes.

3. Let x = the amount of time.

$$\frac{30 \text{ min}}{4 \text{ pages}} = \frac{x \text{ min}}{22 \text{ pages}}$$
$$4x = 660$$
$$\frac{4x}{4} = \frac{660}{4}$$
$$x = 165$$

It takes 165 minutes to do 22 pages.

5. Let x = the number of students accepted.

$$\frac{2 \text{ accepts}}{7 \text{ applicants}} = \frac{x \text{ accepts}}{630 \text{ applicants}}$$
$$7x = 1260$$
$$\frac{7x}{7} = \frac{1260}{7}$$
$$x = 180$$

180 students were accepted.

7. Let x = the length of the wall.

$$\frac{1 \text{ inch}}{8 \text{ feet}} = \frac{2\frac{7}{8} \text{ inches}}{x \text{ feet}}$$
$$x = 8 \cdot 2\frac{7}{8}$$
$$x = 8 \cdot \frac{23}{8}$$
$$x = 23$$

The wall is 23 feet long.

9. Let x = the amount of floor space.

$$\frac{9 \text{ sq. ft}}{1 \text{ student}} = \frac{x \text{ sq. ft}}{30 \text{ students}}$$
$$x = 270$$

270 square feet is required.

11. Let x = the number of miles.

$$\frac{450 \text{ mi}}{12 \text{ gal}} = \frac{x}{1\frac{1}{2} \text{ gal}}$$
$$450 \cdot 1\frac{1}{2} = 12x$$
$$450 \cdot \frac{3}{2} = 12x$$
$$675 = 12x$$
$$\frac{675}{12} = \frac{12x}{12}$$
$$56.25 = x$$

To the nearest mile, Dave can go 56 miles.

13. Let x = the distance from Milan to Rome.

$$\frac{1 \text{ cm}}{30 \text{ km}} = \frac{15 \text{ cm}}{x \text{ km}}$$
$$450 = x$$

It is 450 km from Milan to Rome.

15. Let x = the number of ounces of grapefruit juice.

$$\frac{3 \text{ grapefruit}}{4 \text{ cranberry}} = \frac{x \text{ ounces grapefruit}}{32 \text{ ounces cranberry}}$$
$$4x = 96$$
$$\frac{4x}{4} = \frac{96}{4}$$
$$x = 24$$

24 ounces of grapefruit juice should be used.

17. Let x = the number of bags of fertilizer.

Area of lawn = 260 feet · 180 feet
= 46,800 square feet

$$\frac{1 \text{ bag}}{3000 \text{ sq. ft}} = \frac{x}{46{,}800 \text{ sq. ft}}$$
$$3000x = 46{,}800$$
$$\frac{3000x}{3000} = \frac{46{,}800}{3000}$$
$$x = 15.6$$

Since whole bags must be purchased, 16 bags are needed.

19. Let x = the value of Janet's home.

$$\frac{\$1.45 \text{ taxes}}{\$100 \text{ value}} = \frac{\$2349 \text{ taxes}}{x \text{ value}}$$
$$1.45x = 234,900$$
$$\frac{1.45x}{1.45} = \frac{234,900}{1.45}$$
$$x = 162,000$$

The value of her house if \$162,000.

21. Let x = the number of hits expected.

$$\frac{3 \text{ hits}}{8 \text{ at bats}} = \frac{x \text{ hits}}{40 \text{ at bats}}$$
$$8x = 120$$
$$\frac{8x}{8} = \frac{120}{8}$$
$$x = 15$$

He would be expected to make 15 hits.

23. Let x = the number of people who prefer Coke.

$$\frac{2 \text{ Coke}}{3 \text{ people}} = \frac{x \text{ Coke}}{40 \text{ people}}$$
$$3x = 80$$
$$\frac{3x}{3} = \frac{80}{3}$$
$$x = 26\frac{2}{3}$$

Rounded to the nearest person, 27 people are likely to prefer Coke.

25. Let x = the number of weeks it will last.

$$\frac{5 \text{ boxes}}{3 \text{ weeks}} = \frac{144 \text{ boxes}}{x \text{ weeks}}$$
$$432 = 5x$$
$$\frac{432}{5} = \frac{5x}{5}$$
$$86.4 = x$$
$$x = 86.4$$

The envelopes will last 86 weeks.

27. Let n = the number of people.

$$\frac{1 \text{ person}}{625 \text{ square feet of lawn}} = \frac{n \text{ people}}{3750 \text{ square feet of lawn}}$$
$$625n = 3750$$
$$\frac{625n}{625} = \frac{3750}{625}$$
$$n = 6$$

The lawn supplies enough oxygen for 6 people.

29. Let n = the estimated height of Statue of Liberty.

$$\frac{42 \text{ feet}}{2 \text{ feet}} = \frac{n \text{ feet}}{5\frac{1}{3} \text{ feet}}$$
$$2n = 42 \cdot 5\frac{1}{3}$$
$$2n = \frac{42}{1} \cdot \frac{16}{3}$$
$$2n = 224$$
$$\frac{2n}{2} = \frac{224}{2}$$
$$n = 112$$

The estimate height is 112 feet. The actual height is 111 feet 1 inch. The difference in the estimated height and the actual height is

$112 - 111\frac{1}{2} = \frac{11}{12}$ of a foot or 11 inches.

31. Let n = the number of pounds of sugar.

$$\frac{1 \text{ pound of sugar}}{2\frac{1}{4} \text{ cups packed sugar}} = \frac{n \text{ pounds sugar}}{6 \text{ cups packed sugar}}$$
$$2\frac{1}{4} \cdot n = 1 \cdot 6$$
$$\frac{9}{4} \cdot n = 6$$
$$\frac{4}{9} \cdot \frac{9}{4} \cdot n = \frac{4}{9} \cdot \frac{6}{1}$$
$$n = \frac{8}{3}$$
$$n = 2\frac{2}{3}$$

$2\frac{2}{3}$ pounds of sugar will be required.

33. Let xn= men who blame fast food.

$$\frac{2}{5} = \frac{n}{40}$$
$$5n = 40 \cdot 2$$
$$5n = 80$$
$$\frac{5n}{5} = \frac{80}{5}$$
$$n = 16$$

16 men blame fast food.

35. Let n = the number of visits including a prescription.

$$\frac{7 \text{ prescriptions}}{10 \text{ visits}} = \frac{n \text{ prescriptions}}{620 \text{ visits}}$$
$$10n = 7 \cdot 620$$
$$10n = 4340$$
$$\frac{10n}{10} = \frac{4340}{10}$$
$$n = 434$$

434 emergency room visits included a prescription.

37. Let n = the number of calories.

$$\frac{4}{190} = \frac{9}{n}$$
$$9 \cdot 190 = 4n$$
$$1710 = 4n$$
$$\frac{1710}{4} = \frac{4n}{4}$$
$$427.5 = n$$

There are 427.5 calories in the 9-piece.

39. Let n = the number of cups of rock salt.

$$\frac{5}{1} = \frac{12}{n}$$
$$1 \cdot 12 = 5n$$
$$12 = 5n$$
$$\frac{12}{5} = \frac{5n}{5}$$
$$2.4 = n$$

Mix 2.4 cups of rock salt with the ice.

41. a. $\frac{50}{1} = \frac{5}{x}$

$$50x = 5$$
$$\frac{50x}{50} = \frac{5}{50}$$
$$x = \frac{1}{10} \text{ or } 0.1 \text{ gallon}$$

b. $\frac{1 \text{ gal}}{128 \text{ fl. oz.}} = \frac{0.1 \text{ gal}}{x}$

$x = 12.8$

When rounded to the nearest whole ounces, the answer is 13 fluid oz.

43. a. $\frac{150 \text{ mg}}{20 \text{ lb}} = \frac{x}{275 \text{ lb}}$

$$20x = 150 \cdot 275$$
$$20x = 41{,}250$$
$$\frac{20x}{20} = \frac{41{,}250}{20}$$
$$x = 2062.5 \text{ mg}$$

b. 24 hours $\div$ 8 = 3 doses a day

3 doses $\times$ 500 mg = 1500 mg

He is not receiving the proper dosage.

45. $15 = 3 \cdot 5$

47. $20 = 4 \cdot 5$

$$= 2 \cdot 2 \cdot 5$$
$$= 2^2 \cdot 5$$

49. $200 = 2 \cdot 100$

$$= 2 \cdot 4 \cdot 25$$
$$= 2 \cdot 2 \cdot 2 \cdot 5 \cdot 5$$
$$= 2^3 \cdot 5^2$$

51. $32 = 4 \cdot 8$

$$= 2 \cdot 2 \cdot 2 \cdot 4$$
$$= 2 \cdot 2 \cdot 2 \cdot 2 \cdot 2$$
$$= 2^5$$

53. $\frac{15 \text{ mg}}{1 \text{ mL}} = \frac{12 \text{ mg}}{x}$

$$15x = 12$$
$$\frac{15x}{15} = \frac{12}{15}$$
$$x = 0.8 \text{ mL}$$

55. $\frac{8 \text{ mg}}{1 \text{ mL}} = \frac{10 \text{ mg}}{x}$

$$8x = 10$$
$$\frac{8x}{8} = \frac{10}{8}$$
$$x = 1.25 \text{ mL}$$

57. $\frac{40\text{ pounds}}{n\text{ feet}} = \frac{60\text{ pounds}}{7\text{ feet}}$

$60n = 40 \cdot 7$

$60n = 280$

$\frac{60n}{60} = \frac{280}{60}$

$n = \frac{14}{3}$

$n = 4\frac{2}{3}$

The board will balance when the distance is $4\frac{2}{3}$ feet.

59. Answers may vary.

Section 6.5

Practice Problems

1. MNO is congruent to RQS because of Side-Angle-Side (SAS).

2. We are given the lengths of two corresponding sides. Their ratio is $\frac{9\text{ meters}}{13\text{ meters}} = \frac{9}{13}$.

3. Since the triangles are similar, corresponding sides are in proportion.

$\frac{10}{5} = \frac{n}{4}$

$5n = 40$

$\frac{5n}{5} = \frac{40}{5}$

$n = 8$

The missing length is 8 units.

4. The triangles formed are similar triangles, so

$\frac{5}{n} = \frac{8}{200}$

$8n = 1000$

$n = \frac{1000}{8}$

$n = 125$ feet

The height of the building is 125 feet.

Exercise Set 6.5

1. congruent; Side-Side-Side (SSS)

3. congruent; Angle-Side-Angle (ASA)

5. Since the triangles are similar, we can compare any of the corresponding sides to find the ratio.

$\frac{22}{11} = \frac{2}{1}$

7. Since the triangles are similar, we can compare any of the corresponding sides to find the ratio.

$\frac{12}{8} = \frac{3}{2}$

9. $\frac{3}{n} = \frac{6}{9}$

$6n = 27$

$\frac{6n}{6} = \frac{27}{6}$

$n = 4.5$

11. $\frac{12}{4} = \frac{18}{n}$

$72 = 12n$

$\frac{72}{12} = \frac{12n}{12}$

$6 = n$

13. $\frac{n}{3.75} = \frac{12}{9}$

$45 = 9n$

$\frac{45}{9} = \frac{9n}{9}$

$5 = n$

15. $\frac{18}{n} = \frac{40}{30}$

$40n = 540$

$\frac{40n}{40} = \frac{540}{40}$

$n = 13.5$

17. $\frac{n}{3.25} = \frac{17.5}{3.25}$

$56.875 = 3.25n$

$\frac{56.875}{3.25} = \frac{3.25n}{3.25}$

$17.5 = n$

19.
$$\frac{n}{2}=\frac{8\frac{1}{2}}{2\frac{1}{8}}$$
$$\left(2\frac{1}{8}\right)n=(2)8\frac{1}{2}$$
$$\frac{17}{8}n=2\cdot\frac{17}{2}$$
$$\frac{8}{17}\cdot\frac{17}{8}n=\frac{8}{17}\cdot\frac{17}{1}$$
$$n=8$$

21.
$$\frac{34}{n}=\frac{16}{10}$$
$$16n=340$$
$$\frac{16n}{16}=\frac{340}{16}$$
$$n=21.25$$

23.
$$\frac{\text{height of building}}{\text{height of flagpole}}=\frac{\text{shadow of building}}{\text{shadow of flagpole}}$$
$$\frac{n}{40}=\frac{25}{2}$$
$$2n=40\cdot 25$$
$$2n=1000$$
$$\frac{2n}{2}=\frac{1000}{2}$$
$$n=500$$
The height of the building is 500 feet.

25.
$$\frac{5}{4}=\frac{x}{48}$$
$$4x=5\cdot 48$$
$$4x=240$$
$$x=60$$
The height of the tree is 60 feet.

27.
$$\frac{30}{24}=\frac{18}{x}$$
$$30x=432$$
$$x=14.4$$
The shadow is 14.4 feet long.

29. $\frac{14+17+21+18}{4}=\frac{70}{4}=17.5$

31. $\frac{76+79+88}{3}=\frac{243}{3}=81$

33.
$$\frac{5.2}{n}=\frac{7.8}{12.6}$$
$$7.8n=65.52$$
$$n=8.4$$

35. Answers may vary.

37.
$$\frac{3\text{ in}}{x}=\frac{\frac{1}{4}\text{ in}}{1\text{ ft}}\quad;\quad\frac{4\frac{1}{2}\text{ in}}{x}=\frac{\frac{1}{4}\text{ in}}{1\text{ ft}}$$
$$\frac{1}{4}x=3 \qquad \frac{1}{4}x=4\frac{1}{2}$$
$$4\cdot\frac{1}{4}x=3\cdot 4 \qquad 4\cdot\frac{1}{4}x=\frac{9}{2}\cdot\frac{4}{1}$$
$$x=12 \qquad x=18$$
$$3\text{ in}=12\text{ ft} \qquad 4\frac{1}{2}\text{ in}=18\text{ ft}$$

The dimensions of the deck are 12 ft by 18 ft.

Chapter 6 Review

1. $\frac{6000\text{ people}}{4800\text{ people}}=\frac{6000}{4800}=\frac{60}{48}=\frac{5}{4}$

2. $\frac{121\text{ births}}{143\text{ births}}=\frac{121}{143}=\frac{11}{13}$

3.
$$\frac{2\frac{1}{4}\text{ days}}{10\text{ days}}=\frac{2\frac{1}{4}}{10}$$
$$=\frac{\frac{9}{4}}{10}$$
$$=\frac{9}{4}\div 10$$
$$=\frac{9}{4}\cdot\frac{1}{10}$$
$$=\frac{9}{40}$$

4. $\frac{14\text{ quarters}}{5\text{ quarters}}=\frac{14}{5}$

5. $\frac{4\text{ weeks}}{15\text{ weeks}}=\frac{4}{15}$

6. $\frac{4\text{ yards}}{8\text{ yards}}=\frac{1}{2}$

7. $\frac{3\frac{1}{2}\text{ dollars}}{7\text{ dollars}} = \frac{3\frac{1}{2}}{7}$
$= \frac{\frac{7}{2}}{7}$
$= \frac{7}{2} \div 7$
$= \frac{7}{2} \cdot \frac{1}{7}$
$= \frac{1}{2}$

8. $\frac{3.5\text{ cm}}{75\text{ cm}} = \frac{3.5}{75} = \frac{7}{150}$

9. $\frac{8\text{ stillborn births}}{1000\text{ live births}} = \frac{1\text{ stillborn birth}}{125\text{ live births}}$

10. $\frac{6\text{ professors}}{20\text{ assistants}} = \frac{3\text{ professors}}{10\text{ assistants}}$

11. $\frac{15\text{ pages}}{6\text{ minutes}} = \frac{5\text{ pages}}{2\text{ minutes}}$

12. $\frac{8\text{ computers}}{6\text{ hours}} = \frac{4\text{ computers}}{3\text{ hours}}$

13. $\frac{468\text{ miles}}{9\text{ hours}} = \frac{52\text{ miles}}{1\text{ hour}} = 52$ miles per hour
or 52 mph

14. $\frac{180\text{ ft}}{12\text{ sec}} = \frac{15\text{ ft}}{1\text{ sec}} = 15$ ft per sec

15. $\frac{\$0.93}{3\text{ pears}} = \frac{\$0.31}{1\text{ pear}}$
$= \$0.31$ per pear

16. $\frac{\$6.96}{4\text{ diskettes}} = \frac{\$1.74}{1\text{ diskette}}$
$= \$1.74$ per diskette

17. $\frac{260\text{ kilometers}}{4\text{ hours}} = \frac{65\text{ kilometer}}{1\text{ hour}}$
$= 65$ km per hour

18. $\frac{8\text{ gal}}{6\text{ acres}} = \frac{1\frac{1}{3}\text{ gal}}{1\text{ acre}} = 1\frac{1}{3}$ gal per acre

19. $\frac{\$184\text{ for books}}{5\text{ college courses}} = \frac{\$36.80}{1\text{ college course}}$
$= \$36.80$ per college course

20. $\frac{52\text{ bushels}}{4\text{ trees}} = \frac{13\text{ bushels}}{1\text{ tree}}$
$= 13$ bushels per tree

21. 8-ounce size:
$\frac{\$0.99}{8\text{ oz}} \approx \frac{\$0.124}{1\text{ oz}} = \$0.124$ per ounce
12-ounce size:
$\frac{\$1.69}{12\text{ oz}} \approx \frac{\$0.141}{1\text{ oz}} = \$0.141$ per ounce
The 8-ounce size is the better buy.

22. 18-ounce size:
$\frac{\$1.49}{18\text{ oz}} \approx \frac{\$0.083}{1\text{ oz}} = \$0.083$ per ounce
28-ounce size:
$\frac{\$2.39}{28\text{ oz}} \approx \frac{\$0.085}{1\text{ oz}} = \$0.085$ per ounce
The 18-ounce size is the better buy.

23. 16-ounce size:
$\frac{\$0.59}{16\text{ oz}} \approx \frac{\$0.037}{1\text{ oz}} = \$0.037$ per ounce
$\frac{1}{2}$-gallon size:
$\frac{1}{2}$ gallon = 64 ounces
$\frac{\$1.69}{\frac{1}{2}\text{ gallon}} = \frac{\$1.69}{64\text{ oz}} \approx \frac{\$0.026}{1\text{ oz}} = \$0.026$ per ounce
1-gallon size:
1-gallon = 128 ounces
$\frac{\$2.26}{1\text{ gallon}} = \frac{\$2.26}{128\text{ oz}} \approx \frac{\$0.018}{1\text{ oz}} = \$0.018$ per ounce
The 1-gallon size is the better buy.

24. 12-ounce size:
$\frac{\$0.59}{12\text{ oz}} \approx \frac{\$0.0492}{1\text{ oz}} = \$0.0492$ per ounce
16-ounce size:
$\frac{\$0.79}{16\text{ oz}} \approx \frac{\$0.0494}{1\text{ oz}} = \$0.0494$ per ounce
32-ounce size:
$\frac{\$1.19}{32\text{ oz}} \approx \frac{\$0.0372}{1\text{ oz}} = \$0.0372$ per ounce
The 32-oz size is the better buy.

25. $\frac{20\text{ men}}{14\text{ women}} = \frac{10\text{ men}}{7\text{ women}}$

26. $\frac{50 \text{ tries}}{4 \text{ successes}} = \frac{25 \text{ tries}}{2 \text{ successes}}$

27. $\frac{16 \text{ sandwiches}}{8 \text{ players}} = \frac{2 \text{ sandwiches}}{1 \text{ player}}$

28. $\frac{12 \text{ tires}}{3 \text{ cars}} = \frac{4 \text{ tires}}{1 \text{ car}}$

29. $\frac{21}{8} = \frac{16}{4}$?
$8 \cdot 16 = 21 \cdot 4$?
$128 \neq 84$
Since the cross products are not equal, the proportion is false.

30. $\frac{3}{5} = \frac{60}{100}$?
$5 \cdot 60 = 3 \cdot 100$?
$300 = 300$
Since the cross products are equal, the proportion is true.

31. $\frac{3.1}{6.2} = \frac{0.8}{0.16}$?
$62 \cdot 0.8 = 3.1 \cdot 0.16$?
$4.96 \neq 0.496$
Since the cross products are not equal, the proportion is false.

32. $\frac{3.75}{3} = \frac{7.5}{6}$?
$3 \cdot 7.5 = 3.75 \cdot 6$?
$22.5 = 22.5$
Since the cross products are equal, the proportion is true.

33. $\frac{x}{6} = \frac{15}{18}$
$15 \cdot 6 = 18x$
$90 = 18x$
$\frac{90}{18} = \frac{18x}{18}$
$5 = x$

34. $\frac{y}{9} = \frac{5}{3}$
$9 \cdot 5 = 3y$
$45 = 3y$
$\frac{45}{3} = \frac{3y}{3}$
$15 = y$

35. $\frac{4}{13} = \frac{10}{x}$
$10 \cdot 13 = 4x$
$130 = 4x$
$\frac{130}{4} = \frac{4x}{4}$
$\frac{65}{2} = x$
$32.5 = x$

36. $\frac{8}{5} = \frac{9}{z}$
$5 \cdot 9 = 8z$
$45 = 8z$
$\frac{45}{8} = \frac{8z}{8}$
$5.625 = z$

37. $\frac{16}{3} = \frac{y}{6}$
$3y = 16 \cdot 6$
$3y = 96$
$\frac{3y}{3} = \frac{96}{3}$
$y = 32$

38. $\frac{x}{3} = \frac{9}{2}$
$3 \cdot 9 = 2x$
$27 = 2x$
$\frac{27}{2} = \frac{2x}{2}$
$13.5 = x$

39. $\frac{x}{5} = \frac{27}{2\frac{1}{4}}$
$5 \cdot 27 = \left(2\frac{1}{4}\right)x$
$135 = \frac{9}{4}x$
$\frac{4}{9} \cdot 135 = \frac{4}{9} \cdot \frac{9}{4}x$
$\frac{4 \cdot 9 \cdot 15}{9} = x$
$60 = x$

40.
$$\frac{2\frac{1}{2}}{6} = \frac{3}{z}$$
$$6 \cdot 3 = \left(2\frac{1}{2}\right)z$$
$$18 = \frac{5}{2}z$$
$$\frac{2}{5} \cdot 18 = \frac{2}{5} \cdot \frac{5}{2}z$$
$$\frac{36}{5} = z$$
$$7\frac{1}{5} = z$$

41.
$$\frac{x}{0.4} = \frac{4.7}{3}$$
$$3x = (4.7)(0.4)$$
$$3x = 1.88$$
$$\frac{3x}{3} = \frac{1.88}{3}$$
$$x = \frac{1.88}{3}$$
$$x \approx 0.63$$

42.
$$\frac{0.07}{0.3} = \frac{7.2}{n}$$
$$(0.3)(7.2) = 0.07n$$
$$2.16 = 0.07n$$
$$\frac{2.16}{0.07} = \frac{0.07n}{0.07}$$
$30.9 \approx n$ rounded to the nearest tenth

43. Let x = the number of completed passes.
$$\frac{3 \text{ completed passes}}{7 \text{ attempted passes}} = \frac{x \text{ completed passes}}{32 \text{ attempted passes}}$$
$$\frac{3}{7} = \frac{x}{32}$$
$$7x = 3 \cdot 32$$
$$7x = 96$$
$$\frac{7x}{7} = \frac{96}{7}$$
$$x \approx 13.7$$
$$x \approx 14$$

44. Let x = the number of attempts.
$$\frac{3 \text{ passes}}{7 \text{ attempts}} = \frac{15 \text{ passes}}{x \text{ attempts}}$$
$$\frac{3}{7} = \frac{15}{x}$$
$$7 \cdot 15 = 3x$$
$$105 = 3x$$
$$\frac{105}{3} = \frac{3x}{3}$$
$$35 = x$$

45. Let x = the number of bags of pesticide.
Garden area = 180 · 175 = 31,500 square feet
$$\frac{1 \text{ bag}}{4000 \text{ sq. feet}} = \frac{x \text{ bags}}{31{,}500 \text{ sq. feet}}$$
$$\frac{1}{4000} = \frac{x}{31{,}500}$$
$$4000x = 31{,}500$$
$$\frac{4000x}{4000} = \frac{31{,}500}{4000}$$
$$x = 7.875$$
Purchase 8 bags of pesticide.

46. Let x = the number of bags of pesticide.
Garden area = 250 · 250 = 62,500 square feet
$$\frac{1 \text{ bag}}{4000 \text{ sq. feet}} = \frac{x \text{ bags}}{62{,}500 \text{ sq. feet}}$$
$$4000x = 62{,}500$$
$$\frac{4000x}{4000} = \frac{62{,}500}{4000}$$
$$x = 15.625$$
Purchase 16 bags of pesticide.

47. Let x = the number of miles.
$$\frac{420 \text{ miles}}{11 \text{ gallons}} = \frac{x \text{ miles}}{1\frac{1}{2} \text{ gallons}}$$
$$\frac{420}{11} = \frac{x}{1\frac{1}{2}}$$
$$11x = 420 \cdot 1\frac{1}{2}$$
$$11x = 420 \cdot \frac{3}{2}$$
$$11x = 630$$
$$\frac{11x}{11} = \frac{630}{11}$$
$$x = 57\frac{3}{11}$$
Tom can only drive $57\frac{3}{11}$ miles on $1\frac{1}{2}$ gallons of gas so he will not be able to drive to a gas station 65 miles away.

48. Let x = the number of gallons of gas.

$$\frac{11 \text{ gal}}{420 \text{ miles}} = \frac{x \text{ gal}}{3000 \text{ miles}}$$
$$\frac{11}{420} = \frac{x}{3000}$$
$$33,000 = 420x$$
$$\frac{33,000}{420} = \frac{420x}{420}$$
$$78.5 \approx x$$

Tom will burn about 79 gallons.

49. Let x = the house value.

$$\frac{\$100 \text{ house value}}{\$1.15 \text{ tax}} = \frac{x \text{ house value}}{\$627.90 \text{ tax}}$$
$$\frac{100}{1.15} = \frac{x}{627.90}$$
$$(100)\cdot(627.90) = 1.15x$$
$$62,790 = 1.15x$$
$$\frac{62,790}{1.15} = \frac{1.15x}{1.15}$$
$$54,600 = x$$

The house value is \$54,600.

50.
$$\frac{1.15}{\$100} = \frac{\$x}{\$89,000}$$
$$\frac{1.15}{100} = \frac{x}{89,000}$$
$$100x = 1.15\cdot 89,000$$
$$100x = 102,350$$
$$\frac{100x}{100} = \frac{102,350}{100}$$
$$x = 1023.50$$

The property tax is \$1023.50.

51. Let x = the length in feet.

$$\frac{1 \text{ inch}}{12 \text{ feet}} = \frac{3\frac{3}{8} \text{ inch}}{x \text{ feet}}$$
$$\frac{1}{12} = \frac{3\frac{3}{8}}{x}$$
$$\left(3\frac{3}{8}\right)(12) = x$$
$$\left(\frac{27}{8}\right)\cdot 12 = x$$
$$\frac{27\cdot 4\cdot 3}{4\cdot 2} = x$$
$$\frac{81}{2} = x$$
$$40\frac{1}{2} = x$$

The wall is $40\frac{1}{2}$ feet.

52. Let x = the blueprint measurement in inches.

$$\frac{1 \text{ inch}}{12 \text{ feet}} = \frac{x \text{ inches}}{99 \text{ feet}}$$
$$\frac{1}{12} = \frac{x}{99}$$
$$12x = 99\cdot 1$$
$$\frac{12x}{12} = \frac{99}{12}$$
$$x = \frac{33}{4}$$
$$x = 8\frac{1}{4}$$

The blueprint measurement should be $8\frac{1}{4}$ inches.

53.
$$\frac{20}{8} = \frac{x}{15}$$
$$20\cdot 15 = 8x$$
$$300 = 8x$$
$$\frac{300}{8} = \frac{8x}{4}$$
$$\frac{75}{2} = x$$
$$37.5 = x$$

54.
$$\frac{x}{20} = \frac{16}{24}$$
$$20 \cdot 16 = 24x$$
$$320 = 24x$$
$$\frac{320}{24} = \frac{24x}{24}$$
$$\frac{40}{3} = x$$
$$13\frac{1}{3} = x$$

55.
$$\frac{x}{5.8} = \frac{24}{8}$$
$$8x = (5.8)(24)$$
$$8x = 139.2$$
$$\frac{8x}{8} = \frac{139.2}{8}$$
$$x = 17.4$$

56.
$$\frac{8\frac{2}{3}}{n} = \frac{12\frac{1}{2}}{9\frac{3}{8}}$$
$$\frac{\frac{26}{3}}{n} = \frac{\frac{25}{2}}{\frac{75}{8}}$$
$$\left(\frac{26}{3}\right)\left(\frac{75}{8}\right) = \left(\frac{25}{2}\right)n$$
$$\frac{325}{4} = \frac{25}{2}x$$
$$\frac{2}{25} \cdot \frac{325}{4} = \frac{2}{25} \cdot \frac{25}{2}x$$
$$\frac{13}{2} = x$$
$$6\frac{1}{2} = x$$

57. Let x = building height.
$$\frac{\text{man shadow}}{\text{building shadow}} = \frac{\text{man height}}{\text{building height}}$$
$$\frac{7 \text{ feet}}{42 \text{ feet}} = \frac{5\frac{1}{2} \text{ feet}}{x \text{ feet}}$$
$$\frac{7}{42} = \frac{5\frac{1}{2}}{x}$$
$$7x = \left(5\frac{1}{2}\right)(42)$$
$$7x = \frac{11}{2} \cdot 42$$
$$7x = 231$$
$$\frac{7x}{7} = \frac{231}{7}$$
$$x = 33$$
The building is 33 feet tall.

58.
$$\frac{2 \text{ inches}}{24 \text{ feet}} = \frac{x \text{ inches}}{10 \text{ feet}} = \frac{y \text{ inches}}{26 \text{ feet}}$$
$$\frac{2}{24} = \frac{x}{10}$$
$$2 \cdot 10 = 24x$$
$$20 = 24x$$
$$\frac{20}{24} = \frac{24x}{24}$$
$$\frac{5}{6} = x$$
$$\frac{2}{24} = \frac{y}{26}$$
$$2 \cdot 26 = 24y$$
$$52 = 24y$$
$$\frac{52}{24} = \frac{24y}{24}$$
$$\frac{13}{6} = y$$
$$2\frac{1}{6} = y$$

x is $\frac{5}{6}$ inches and y is $2\frac{1}{6}$ inches.

59. They are congruent because of Angle-Side-Angle (ASA).

60. They are not congruent.

Chapter 6 Test

1. $\frac{4500 \text{ trees}}{6500 \text{ trees}} = \frac{9 \cdot 500}{13 \cdot 500} = \frac{9}{13}$

2. $\frac{\$75}{\$10} = \frac{15 \cdot 5}{2 \cdot 5} = \frac{15}{2}$

3. $\frac{28 \text{ men}}{4 \text{ women}} = \frac{7 \text{ men}}{1 \text{ woman}}$

4. $\frac{9 \text{ inches of rain}}{30 \text{ days}} = \frac{3 \text{ inches of rain}}{10 \text{ days}}$

5. $\frac{650 \text{ kilometers}}{8 \text{ hours}} = 81.25$ kilometers per hour

$$\begin{array}{r} 81.25 \\ 8\overline{)650.00} \\ \underline{-64} \\ 10 \\ \underline{-8} \\ 20 \\ \underline{-16} \\ 40 \\ \underline{-40} \\ 0 \end{array}$$

6. $\frac{8 \text{ inches of rain}}{12 \text{ hours}} = \frac{2}{3}$ inches rain per hour

$$\begin{array}{r} 0.66\ldots \\ 12\overline{)\ 8.00} \\ \underline{-\,7\,2} \\ 80 \\ \underline{-72} \\ 8 \end{array}$$

7. $\frac{140 \text{ students}}{5 \text{ teachers}} = \frac{28 \text{ students}}{1 \text{ teacher}}$

$= 28$ students per teacher

8. 8-ounce size:
$\frac{\$1.19}{8 \text{ oz}} \approx \$0.149$ per ounce
12-ounce size:
$\frac{\$1.89}{12 \text{ oz}} \approx \$0.158$ per ounce
The 8-ounce size costs less per ounce, thus, it is a better buy.

9. 16-ounce size:
$\frac{\$1.49}{16 \text{ oz}} \approx \$0.093$ per ounce
24-ounce size:
$\frac{\$2.39}{24 \text{ oz}} \approx \$0.100$ per ounce
The 16-ounce size costs less per ounce, thus it is the better buy.

10. $\frac{28}{16} = \frac{14}{8}?$

$16 \cdot 14 = 28 \cdot 8?$

$224 = 224$

Since the cross products are equal, the proportion is true.

11. $\frac{3.6}{2.2} = \frac{1.9}{1.2}?$

$2.2 \cdot 1.9 = 3.6 \cdot 1.2?$

$4.18 \neq 4.32$

Since the cross products are not equal, the proportion is false.

12. $\frac{n}{3} = \frac{15}{9}$

$3 \cdot 15 = 9n$

$45 = 9n$

$\frac{45}{9} = \frac{9n}{9}$

$5 = n$

13. $\frac{8}{x} = \frac{11}{6}$

$11 \cdot x = 8 \cdot 6$

$11x = 48$

$\frac{11x}{11} = \frac{48}{11}$

$x = \frac{48}{11} = 4\frac{4}{11}$

14. $\frac{4}{\frac{3}{7}} = \frac{y}{\frac{1}{4}}$

$\frac{3}{7}y = 4 \cdot \frac{1}{4}$

$\frac{3}{7}y = 1$

$\frac{7}{3} \cdot \frac{3}{7}y = \frac{7}{3} \cdot 1$

$y = \frac{7}{3}$

15.
$$\frac{1.5}{5} = \frac{2.4}{n}$$
$$1.5n = 2.4 \cdot 5$$
$$1.5n = 12$$
$$\frac{1.5n}{1.5} = \frac{12}{1.5}$$
$$n = 8$$

16. Let n = the number of feet.
$$\frac{2}{9} = \frac{11}{n}$$
$$2n = 99$$
$$\frac{2n}{2} = \frac{99}{2}$$
$$n = 49\frac{1}{2}$$
The home is $49\frac{1}{2}$ feet long.

17. Let x = the length of time.
$$\frac{3}{80} = \frac{x}{100}$$
$$80x = 300$$
$$\frac{80x}{80} = \frac{300}{80}$$
$$x = \frac{15}{4} = 3\frac{3}{4}$$
It will take $3\frac{3}{4}$ hours.

18. Let n = the number of grams of medicine.
$$\frac{10}{15} = \frac{n}{80}$$
$$15n = 800$$
$$\frac{15n}{15} = \frac{800}{15}$$
$$n = \frac{160}{3} = 53\frac{1}{3}$$
The standard dose is $53\frac{1}{3}$ grams.

19. Let n = the number of cartons.
$$\frac{6}{86} = \frac{8}{n}$$
$$6n = 688$$
$$\frac{6n}{6} = \frac{688}{6}$$
$$n = \frac{344}{3}$$
$$n = 114\frac{2}{3}$$
He can pack $114\frac{2}{3}$ cartons.

20. Let n = amount of people that prefer Maxwell House.
$$\frac{2}{25} = \frac{n}{3200}$$
$$25n = 6400$$
$$n = 256$$
256 coffee drinkers prefer Maxwell House.

21.
$$\frac{5}{8} = \frac{n}{12}$$
$$8n = 5 \cdot 12$$
$$8n = 60$$
$$\frac{8n}{8} = \frac{60}{8}$$
$$n = 7.5$$

22.
$$\frac{\text{tower's shadow}}{\text{Tamara's shadow}} = \frac{\text{tower's height}}{\text{Tamara's height}}$$
$$\frac{48 \text{ feet}}{4 \text{ feet}} = \frac{x \text{ feet}}{5\frac{3}{4} \text{ feet}}$$
$$4x = 48 \cdot 5\frac{3}{4}$$
$$4x = 48 \cdot \frac{23}{4}$$
$$4x = 276$$
$$\frac{4x}{4} = \frac{276}{4}$$
$$x = 69$$
The tower is 69 feet tall.

Cumulative Review

1.
$$\begin{array}{r} 128 \text{ R } 16 \\ 403\overline{)\ 51,600} \\ \underline{-403} \\ 1130 \\ \underline{-806} \\ 3240 \\ \underline{-3224} \\ 16 \end{array}$$

2.
$$\begin{array}{r} 122 \text{ R } 17 \\ 194\overline{)\ 23,685} \\ \underline{-194} \\ 428 \\ \underline{-388} \\ 405 \\ \underline{-388} \\ 17 \end{array}$$

3. **a.** $7+x$
b. $15-x$
c. $2x$
d. $x \div 5 = \frac{x}{5}$
e. $x-2$

4. **a.** $y+3$
b. $10 \div y = \frac{10}{y}$
c. $4-y$
d. $7y$

5. **a.** 4
b. -5
c. -6

6. **a.** -3
b. -2
c. 1

7. $-10-5=-10+(-5)=-15$

8. $-7-3=-7+(-3)=-10$

9.
$$\begin{aligned} 7+(-12)-3-(-8) &= -4-3-(-8) \\ &= -7+9 \\ &= 1 \end{aligned}$$

10.
$$\begin{aligned} -7+(-4)+3-(-11) &= -11+3-(-11) \\ &= -8+11 \\ &= 3 \end{aligned}$$

11. $6x+2x-5=8x-5$

12.
$$\begin{aligned} & -7x+6+9x \\ &= -7x+9x+6=2x+6 \end{aligned}$$

13.
$$\begin{aligned} & 2x-5+3y+4x-10y+11 \\ &= 2x+4x+3y-10y-5+11 \\ &= 6x-7y+6 \end{aligned}$$

14.
$$\begin{aligned} & 3x+2z-4z+2+7x-5 \\ &= 3x+7x+2z-4z+2-5 \\ &= 10x-2z-3 \end{aligned}$$

15.
$$\begin{aligned} 4(6-3) &= 12 \\ 4(3) &= 12 \\ 12 &= 12 \quad \text{True} \end{aligned}$$
6 is a solution.

16.
$$\begin{aligned} -3(7+2\cdot 2) &= -33 \\ -3(7+4) &= -33 \\ -3(11) &= -33 \\ -33 &= -33 \quad \text{True} \end{aligned}$$
2 is a solution.

17.
$$\begin{aligned} -8 &= 2y \\ \frac{-8}{2} &= \frac{2y}{2} \\ -4 &= y \end{aligned}$$

18.
$$\begin{aligned} -3k &= 12 \\ \frac{-3k}{-3} &= \frac{12}{-3} \\ k &= -4 \end{aligned}$$

19.
$$\begin{aligned} 20-x &= 21 \\ 20-x-20 &= 21-20 \\ -x &= 1 \\ \frac{-1x}{-1} &= \frac{1}{-1} \\ x &= -1 \end{aligned}$$

20.
$$\begin{aligned} 21-2x &= -9x \\ 21-2x+2x &= -9x+2x \\ 21 &= -7x \\ \frac{21}{-7} &= \frac{-7x}{-7} \\ -3 &= x \end{aligned}$$

21. $\frac{2\cdot 3}{5\cdot 3}=\frac{6}{15}$

22. $\frac{3\cdot 8}{7\cdot 8}=\frac{24}{56}$

23. $80=2\cdot 2\cdot 2\cdot 2\cdot 5$ or $2^4\cdot 5$

24. $44=2\cdot 2\cdot 11$ or $2^2\cdot 11$

25. $\frac{3x}{4}\cdot\frac{8}{5x}=\frac{3x\cdot 2\cdot 4}{4\cdot 5x}=\frac{6}{5}$

26. $\frac{2a}{3}\cdot\frac{9}{4a}=\frac{2a\cdot 3\cdot 3}{3\cdot 2\cdot 2a}=\frac{3}{2}$

27. $\frac{8}{9}-\frac{1}{9}=\frac{7}{9}$

28. $\frac{3}{5}-\frac{1}{5}=\frac{2}{5}$

29. $\frac{7}{8}-\frac{5}{8}=\frac{2}{8}=\frac{1}{4}$

30. $\frac{7}{12}-\frac{5}{12}=\frac{2}{12}=\frac{1}{6}$

31.
$$\begin{aligned}2-\frac{x}{3}&=\frac{2\cdot 3}{1\cdot 3}-\frac{x}{3}\\&=\frac{6}{3}-\frac{x}{3}\\&=\frac{6-x}{3}\end{aligned}$$

32.
$$\begin{aligned}\frac{x}{10}-\frac{4}{5}&=\frac{x}{10}-\frac{4\cdot 2}{5\cdot 2}\\&=\frac{x}{10}-\frac{8}{10}\\&=\frac{x-8}{10}\end{aligned}$$

33.
$$\begin{aligned}\frac{\frac{y}{5}-2}{\frac{3}{10}}&=\frac{10\left(\frac{y}{5}-2\right)}{10\left(\frac{3}{10}\right)}\\&=\frac{2y-20}{3}\end{aligned}$$

34.
$$\begin{aligned}\frac{\frac{3x}{2}+5}{\frac{3}{8}}&=\frac{8\left(\frac{3x}{2}+5\right)}{8\left(\frac{3}{8}\right)}\\&=\frac{12x+40}{3}\end{aligned}$$

35.
$$\begin{aligned}\frac{1}{3}x&=7\\3\cdot\frac{1}{3}x&=7\cdot 3\\x&=21\end{aligned}$$

36.
$$\begin{aligned}\frac{2}{5}x&=8\\\frac{5}{2}\cdot\frac{2}{5}x&=\frac{8}{1}\cdot\frac{5}{2}\\x&=\frac{2\cdot 4\cdot 5}{1\cdot 2}\\x&=20\end{aligned}$$

37.
$$\begin{aligned}3\frac{1}{3}\cdot\frac{7}{8}&=\frac{10}{3}\cdot\frac{7}{8}=\frac{2\cdot 5\cdot 7}{3\cdot 2\cdot 4}\\&=\frac{35}{12}\text{ or }2\frac{11}{12}\end{aligned}$$

38. $2\frac{4}{5}\cdot\frac{1}{9}=\frac{14}{5}\cdot\frac{1}{9}=\frac{14}{45}$

39. $\frac{43}{100}$

40. $\frac{65}{100}=\frac{5\cdot 13}{5\cdot 20}=\frac{13}{20}$

41. $2.3\overline{)10.764}$

Move decimal point 1 place

$$\begin{array}{r}4.68\\23\overline{)107.64}\\\underline{-92}\\156\\\underline{-138}\\184\\\underline{-184}\\0\end{array}$$

42. $9.6\overline{)22.752}$

Move decimal point 1 place

$$\begin{array}{r} 2.37 \\ 96\overline{)\ 227.52} \\ \underline{-192} \\ 355 \\ \underline{-288} \\ 672 \\ \underline{-672} \\ 0 \end{array}$$

43. $-0.5(8.6-1.2)$
$= -0.5(7.4) = -3.7$

44. $0.7(5.9-2.3)$
$= 0.7(3.6) = 2.52$

45. $\frac{9}{20}$;

$$\begin{array}{r} 0.45 \\ 20\overline{)\ 9.00} \\ \underline{-8\,0} \\ 100 \\ \underline{-100} \\ 0 \end{array}$$

$\frac{4}{9}$;

$$\begin{array}{r} 0.444\ldots \approx 0.444 \\ 9\overline{)\ 4.000} \\ \underline{-3\,6} \\ 40 \\ \underline{-36} \\ 40 \\ \underline{-36} \\ 4 \end{array}$$

$\frac{4}{9}, \frac{9}{20}, 0.456$

46. $\frac{4}{7}$;

$$\begin{array}{r} 0.5714 \approx 0.571 \\ 7\overline{)\ 4.0000} \\ \underline{-35} \\ 50 \\ \underline{-49} \\ 10 \\ \underline{-7} \\ 30 \\ \underline{-28} \\ 2 \end{array}$$

$\frac{1}{2}$;

$$\begin{array}{r} 0.5 \\ 2\overline{)\ 1.0} \\ \underline{-1\,0} \\ 0 \end{array}$$

$\frac{1}{2}$ 0.531, $\frac{4}{7}$

47.
$$\begin{aligned} x-1.5 &= 8 \\ x-1.5+1.5 &= 8+1.5 \\ x &= 9.5 \end{aligned}$$

48.
$$\begin{aligned} 3x+2.5 &= 13 \\ 3x+2.5-2.5 &= 13-2.5 \\ 3x &= 10.5 \\ \frac{3x}{3} &= \frac{10.5}{3} \\ x &= 3.5 \end{aligned}$$

49.
$$\begin{aligned} \frac{\frac{1}{2}}{\frac{4}{5}} &= \frac{\frac{3}{4}}{y} \\ \frac{1}{2}y &= \frac{4\cdot 3}{5\cdot 4} \\ \frac{1}{2}y &= \frac{3}{5} \\ \frac{2}{1}\cdot\frac{1}{2}y &= \frac{3}{5}\cdot\frac{2}{1} \\ y &= \frac{6}{5} \end{aligned}$$

50.
$$\begin{aligned} \frac{2c}{5} &= \frac{3}{10} \\ 20c &= 15 \\ \frac{20c}{20} &= \frac{15}{20} \\ c &= \frac{15}{20} \\ c &= \frac{3}{4} \end{aligned}$$

Chapter 7

Pretest

1. $\frac{12}{100} = 12\%$

2. $57\% = 57.\% = 0.57$

3. $2.75 = 275\%$

4. $7.5\% = \frac{7.5}{100} - \frac{75}{1000} = \frac{3}{40}$

5. $\frac{3}{20} = \frac{3 \cdot 5}{20 \cdot 5} = \frac{15}{100} = 15\%$

6. $18\% \cdot 50 = x$

7. $4\% \cdot x = 89$

8. $\frac{82}{b} = \frac{90}{100}$

9. $\frac{48}{112} = \frac{p}{100}$

10. $x \cdot 80 = 16$
$\frac{x \cdot 80}{80} = \frac{16}{80}$
$x = 0.2$
$x = 20\%$
16 is 20% of 80.

11. $x = 1.5\% \cdot 220$
$x = 0.015 \cdot 220$
$x = 3.3$
3.3 is 1.5% of 220.

12. $32 = 16\% \cdot x$
$32 = 0.16 \cdot x$
$\frac{32}{0.16} = \frac{0.16 \cdot x}{0.16}$
$200 = x$
32 is 16% of 200.

13. What number is 1.2% of 250?
$x = 1.2\% \cdot 250$
$x = 0.012 \cdot 250$
$x = 3$
3 lightbulbs were defective.

14. What number is 2% of 4200?
$x = 2\% \cdot 4200$
$x = 0.02 \cdot 4200$
$x = 84$
The enrollment decreased by 84 students. The current enrollment is 4200 – 84 = 4316 students.

15. $\$34.93 = r \cdot \$499$
$\frac{\$34.93}{\$499} = \frac{r \cdot \$499}{\$499}$
$0.07 = r$
$7\% = r$
The sales tax rate is 7%.

16. $\$448 = 2\% \cdot x$
$\$448 = 0.02 \cdot x$
$\frac{\$448}{0.02} = \frac{0.02 \cdot x}{0.02}$
$\$22,400 = x$
His sales were $22,400.

17. $\text{discount} = 12\% \cdot \$650$
$= 0.12 \cdot \$650$
$= \$78$
sales price = $650 – 78 = $572

18. $\text{simple interest} = \text{principal} \cdot \text{rate} \cdot \text{time}$
$= \$600 \cdot 8\% \cdot 3$
$= \$600 \cdot (0.08) \cdot 3$
$= \$144$

19. The compound interest factor for 6 years at 6% compounded quarterly is 1.42950.
total amount = $5000 · 1.42950 = $7147.50

20. $\text{monthly payment} = \frac{\text{principal interest}}{\text{number of payments}}$
$= \frac{\$700 + \$196}{2 \cdot 12}$
$= \frac{\$896}{24}$
$\approx \$37.33$

Section 7.1

Practice Problems

1. $\frac{23}{100} = 23\%$

2. $\frac{29}{100} = 29\%$

3. $89\% = 89.\% = 0.89$

4. $2.7\% = 0.027$

5. $150\% = 150.\% = 1.5$

6. $0.69\% = 0.0069$

7. $500\% = 500.\% = 5$

8. $0.19 = 19.\% = 19\%$

9. $1.75 = 175.\% = 175\%$

10. $0.044 = 004.4\% = 4.4\%$

11. $0.7 = 070.\% = 70\%$

12. $25\% = \frac{25}{100} = \frac{1 \cdot 25}{4 \cdot 25} = \frac{1}{4}$

13. $2.3\% = \frac{2.3}{100} = \frac{2.3 \cdot 10}{100 \cdot 10} = \frac{23}{1000}$

14. $150\% = \frac{150}{100} = \frac{3 \cdot 50}{2 \cdot 50} = \frac{3}{2}$

15. $$66\frac{2}{3}\% = \frac{66\frac{2}{3}}{100} = \frac{\frac{200}{3}}{100} = \frac{200}{3} \div 100 = \frac{200}{3} \cdot \frac{1}{100} = \frac{2}{3}$$

16. $8\% = \frac{8}{100} = \frac{2 \cdot 4}{25 \cdot 4} = \frac{2}{25}$

17. $\frac{1}{2} = \frac{1}{2} \cdot 100\% = \frac{100}{2}\% = 50\%$

18. $\frac{7}{40} = \frac{7}{40} \cdot 100\% = \frac{700}{40}\% = \frac{35}{2}\% = 17\frac{1}{2}\%$

19. $2\frac{1}{4} = \frac{9}{4} \cdot 100\% = \frac{900}{4}\% = 225\%$

20. $\frac{3}{17} = \frac{3}{17} \cdot 100\% = \frac{300}{17}\% \approx 17.65\%$

$$\begin{array}{r} 17.647 \approx 17.65 \\ 17\overline{)\,300.000} \\ \underline{-17} \\ 130 \\ \underline{-119} \\ 11\,0 \\ \underline{-10\,2} \\ 80 \\ \underline{-68} \\ 120 \\ \underline{-119} \\ 1 \end{array}$$

21. $25\% = 25.\% = 0.25$

22. $1\frac{1}{4} = \frac{5}{4} \cdot 100\% = \frac{500}{4}\% = 125\%$

Mental Math

1. $\frac{13}{100} = 13\%$

2. $\frac{92}{100} = 92\%$

3. $\frac{87}{100} = 87\%$

4. $\frac{71}{100} = 71\%$

5. $\frac{1}{100} = 1\%$

6. $\frac{2}{100} = 2\%$

Exercise Set 7.1

1. $\frac{81}{100} = 81\%$

3. $\frac{9}{100} = 9\%$

5. The largest section of the circle graph is chocolate chip. Therefore, chocolate chip was the most preferred cookie.
$\frac{52}{100} = 52\%$

7. $\frac{12}{100} = 12\%$

9. $48\% = 48.\% = 0.48$

11. $6\% = 6.\% = 0.06$

13. $100\% = 100.\% = 1.00 = 1$

15. $61.3\% = 0.613$

17. $2.8\% = 0.028$

19. $64\frac{1}{4}\% = 6.25\% = 0.625$

21. $300\% = 300.\% = 3.00 = 3$

23. $32.58\% = 0.3258$

25. $73.7\% = 0.737$

27. $25\% = 25.\% = 0.25$

29. $11.1\%=0.111$

31. $46.2\% = 0.462$

33. $3.1 = 3.10 = 310.\% = 310\%$

35. $29 = 29.00 = 2900.\% = 2900\%$

37. $0.003 = 000.3\% = 0.3\%$

39. $0.22 = 022.\% = 22\%$

41. $0.056 = = 005.6\% = 5.6\%$

43. $0.3328 = 033.28\% = 33.28\%$

45. $3.00 = 300.\% = 300\%$

47. $0.7 = 0.70 = 070.\% = 70\%$

49. $0.10 = 010.\% = 10\%$

51. $0.324 = 32.4\%$

53. $0.38 = 038.\% = 38\%$

55. $4\% = \frac{4}{100} = \frac{4 \cdot 1}{4 \cdot 25} = \frac{1}{25}$

57. $4.5\% = \frac{4.5}{100} = \frac{45}{1000} = \frac{5 \cdot 9}{5 \cdot 200} = \frac{9}{200}$

59. $175\% = \frac{175}{100} = \frac{25 \cdot 7}{25 \cdot 4} = \frac{7}{4} = 1\frac{3}{4}$

61. $73\% = \frac{73}{100}$

63. $12.5\% = \frac{12.5}{100} = \frac{125}{1000} = \frac{125 \cdot 1}{125 \cdot 8} = \frac{1}{8}$

65. $6.25\% = \frac{6.25}{100} = \frac{625}{10,000} = \frac{625}{625 \cdot 16} = \frac{1}{16}$

67.
$$\begin{aligned} 10\frac{1}{3}\% &= \frac{10\frac{1}{3}}{100} \\ &= \frac{\frac{31}{3}}{100} \\ &= \frac{31}{3} \div 100 \\ &= \frac{31}{3} \cdot \frac{1}{100} \\ &= \frac{31}{300} \end{aligned}$$

69.
$$\begin{aligned} 22\frac{3}{8}\% &= \frac{22\frac{3}{8}}{100} \\ &= \frac{\frac{179}{8}}{100} \\ &= \frac{179}{8} \div 100 \\ &= \frac{179}{8} \cdot \frac{1}{100} \\ &= \frac{179}{800} \end{aligned}$$

71. $\frac{3}{4} = \frac{3}{4} \cdot 100\% = \frac{300}{4}\% = 75\%$

73. $\frac{7}{10} = \frac{7}{10} \cdot 100\% = \frac{700}{10}\% = 70\%$

75. $\frac{2}{5} = \frac{2}{5} \cdot 100\% = \frac{200}{5}\% = 40\%$

77. $\frac{59}{100} = \frac{59}{100} \cdot 100\% = \frac{59 \cdot 100}{100}\% = 59\%$

79. $\frac{17}{50} = \frac{17}{50} \cdot 100\% = \frac{1700}{50}\% = 34\%$

81. $\frac{3}{8} = \frac{3}{8} \cdot 100\%$
$= \frac{300}{8}\%$
$= \frac{4 \cdot 75}{4 \cdot 2}\%$
$= \frac{75}{2}\%$
$= 37\frac{1}{2}\%$

83. $\frac{5}{16} = \frac{5}{16} \cdot 100\% = \frac{500}{16}\% = 31\frac{1}{4}\%$

85. $\frac{2}{3} = \frac{2}{3} \cdot 100\% = \frac{200}{3}\% = 66\frac{2}{3}\%$

87. $2\frac{1}{2} = \frac{5}{2} \cdot 100\% = \frac{500}{2}\% = 250\%$

89. $1\frac{9}{10} = \frac{19}{10} \cdot 100\% = \frac{1900}{10}\% = 190\%$

91. $\frac{7}{11} = \frac{7}{11} \cdot 100\% = \frac{700}{11}\% \approx 63.64\%$

$$\begin{array}{r} 63.636 \approx 63.64 \\ 11\overline{)\ 700.000} \\ \underline{-66} \\ 40 \\ \underline{-33} \\ 70 \\ \underline{-66} \\ 40 \\ \underline{-33} \\ 70 \\ \underline{-66} \\ 4 \end{array}$$

93. $\frac{4}{15} = \frac{4}{15} \cdot 100\% = \frac{400}{15}\% \approx 26.67\%$

$$\begin{array}{r} 26.666 \approx 26.67 \\ 15\overline{)400.00} \\ \underline{-30} \\ 100 \\ \underline{-90} \\ 100 \\ \underline{-90} \\ 100 \\ \underline{-90} \\ 10 \end{array}$$

95. $\frac{1}{7} = \frac{1}{7} \cdot 100\% = \frac{100}{7}\% \approx 14.29\%$

$$\begin{array}{r} 14.285 \approx 14.29 \\ 7\overline{)\ 100.000} \\ \underline{-7} \\ 30 \\ \underline{-28} \\ 20 \\ \underline{-14} \\ 60 \\ \underline{-56} \\ 40 \\ \underline{-35} \\ 5 \end{array}$$

97. $\frac{11}{12} = \frac{11}{12} \cdot 100\% = \frac{1100}{12}\% \approx 91.67\%$

$$\begin{array}{r} 91.666 \approx 91.67 \\ 12\overline{)\ 1100.000} \\ \underline{-108} \\ 20 \\ \underline{-12} \\ 80 \\ \underline{-72} \\ 80 \\ \underline{-72} \\ 80 \\ \underline{-72} \\ 8 \end{array}$$

99.

Percent	Decimal	Fraction
35%	0.35	$\frac{7}{20}$
20%	0.2	$\frac{1}{5}$
50%	0.5	$\frac{1}{2}$
70%	0.7	$\frac{7}{10}$
37.5%	0.375	$\frac{3}{8}$

101.

Percent	Decimal	Fraction
40%	0.4	$\frac{2}{5}$
23.5%	0.235	$\frac{47}{200}$
80%	0.8	$\frac{4}{5}$
$33\frac{1}{3}\%$	$0.333\bar{3}$	$\frac{1}{3}$
87.5%	0.875	$\frac{7}{8}$
7.5%	0.075	$\frac{3}{40}$

103. $24.9\% = 0.249 = \dfrac{249}{1000}$

105. $\dfrac{17}{200} = \dfrac{17}{200} \cdot 100\% = \dfrac{1700}{200}\% = \dfrac{17}{2}\% = 8.5\%$

$$\begin{array}{r} 8.5 \\ 2\overline{)17.0} \\ -16 \\ \hline 10 \\ -10 \\ \hline 0 \end{array}$$

107. $20.7\% = 0.207 = \dfrac{207}{1000}$

109. $\dfrac{1}{4} = \dfrac{1}{4} \cdot 100\% = \dfrac{100}{4}\% = 25\%$

111. $0.4\% = 0.004 = \dfrac{4}{1000} = \dfrac{1}{250}$

113. $12\% = \dfrac{12}{100} = \dfrac{3}{25}$

115. $7.1\% = 0.071 = \dfrac{71}{1000}$

117. $3n = 45$

$\dfrac{3n}{3} = \dfrac{45}{3}$

$n = 15$

119. $-8n = 80$

$\dfrac{-8n}{-8} = \dfrac{80}{-8}$

$n = -10$

121. $-6n = -72$

$\dfrac{-6n}{-6} = \dfrac{-72}{-6}$

$n = 12$

123. $\dfrac{3}{4} = \dfrac{75}{100} = 75\%$

125. $\dfrac{4}{5} = \dfrac{80}{100} = 80\%$

127. $\dfrac{850}{736} \approx 1.155 = 115.5\%$

129. A fraction written as a percent is greater than 100% when the numerator is <u>greater</u> than the denominator.

131. Answers may vary.

133. Computer software engineers applications is predicted to be the fastest growing occupation.

135. $62\% = 62.\% = 0.62$

Section 7.2

Practice Problems

1. $6 = x \cdot 24$

2. $1.8 = 20\% \cdot x$

3. $x = 40\% \cdot 3.6$

4. $42\% \cdot 50 = x$

5. $15\% \cdot x = 9$

6. $x \cdot 150 = 90$

7. $x = 20\% \cdot 85$

$x = 0.2 \cdot 85$

$x = 17$

The number is 17.

8. $90\% \cdot 150 = x$

$0.9 \cdot 150 = x$

$135 = x$

The number is 135.

9. $15\% \cdot x = 1.2$

$0.15 \cdot x = 1.2$

$\dfrac{0.15 \cdot x}{0.15} = \dfrac{1.2}{0.15}$

$x = 8$

The number is 8.

10. $27 = 4\frac{1}{2}\% \cdot x$
$27 = 0.045 \cdot x$
$\frac{27}{0.045} = \frac{0.045 \cdot x}{0.045}$
$600 = x$
The number is 600.

11. $x \cdot 80 = 8$
$\frac{x \cdot 80}{80} = \frac{8}{80}$
$x = 0.10$
$x = 10\%$
The percent is 10%.

12. $35 = x \cdot 25$
$\frac{35}{25} = \frac{x \cdot 25}{25}$
$1.4 = x$
$140\% = x$
The percent is 140%.

Mental Math

1. percent: 42
   base: 50
   amount: 21

2. percent: 30
   base: 65
   amount: 19.5

3. percent: 125
   base: 86
   amount: 107.5

4. percent: 110
   base: 90
   amount: 99

Exercise Set 7.2

1. $15\% \cdot 72 = x$

3. $30\% \cdot x = 80$

5. $x \cdot 90 = 20$

7. $1.9 = 40\% \cdot x$

9. $x = 9\% \cdot 43$

11. $10\% \cdot 35 = x$
$0.10 \cdot 35 = x$
$3.5 = x$

13. $x = 14\% \cdot 52$
$x = 0.14 \cdot 52$
$x = 7.28$

15. $3000 = 5\% \cdot x$
$30 = 0.05x$
$\frac{30}{0.05} = \frac{0.05x}{0.05}$
$600 = x$

17. $1.2 = 12\% \cdot x$
$1.2 = 0.12x$
$\frac{1.2}{0.12} = \frac{0.12x}{0.12}$
$10 = x$

19. $66 = x \cdot 60$
$\frac{66}{60} = \frac{x \cdot 60}{60}$
$1.1 = x$
$110\% = x$

21. $16 = x \cdot 50$
$\frac{16}{50} = \frac{x \cdot 50}{50}$
$0.32 = x$
$32\% = x$

23. $0.1 = 10\% \cdot x$
$0.1 = 0.10x$
$\frac{0.1}{0.10} = \frac{0.10x}{0.10}$
$1 = x$

25. $125\% \cdot 36 = x$
$1.25 \cdot 36 = x$
$45 = x$

27. $82.5 = 16\frac{1}{2}\% \cdot x$
$82.5 = 0.165 \cdot x$
$\frac{82.5}{0.165} = \frac{0.165 \cdot x}{0.165}$
$500 = x$

29. $2.58 = x \cdot 50$
$\frac{2.58}{50} = \frac{x \cdot 50}{50}$
$0.0516 = x$
$5.16\% = x$

31. $x = 42\% \cdot 60$
$x = 0.42 \cdot 60$
$x = 25.2$

33. $x \cdot 150 = 67.5$
$\frac{x \cdot 150}{150} = \frac{67.5}{150}$
$x = 0.45$
$x = 45\%$

35. $120\% \cdot x = 42$
$1.2 \cdot x = 42$
$\frac{1.2 \cdot x}{1.2} = \frac{42}{1.2}$
$x = 35$

37. $\frac{27}{n} = \frac{9}{10}$
$9 \cdot n = 27 \cdot 10$
$\frac{9 \cdot n}{9} = \frac{270}{9}$
$n = 30$

39. $\frac{n}{5} = \frac{8}{11}$
$5 \cdot 8 = 11 \cdot n$
$\frac{40}{11} = \frac{11 \cdot n}{11}$
$3\frac{7}{11} = n$

41. $\frac{17}{12} = \frac{n}{20}$

43. $\frac{8}{9} = \frac{14}{n}$

45. $1.5\% \cdot 45,775 = x$
$0.015 \cdot 45,775 = x$
$686.625 = x$

47. $22,113 = 180\% \cdot x$
$22,113 = 1.8 \cdot x$
$\frac{22,113}{1.8} = \frac{1.8 \cdot x}{1.8}$
$12,285 = x$

Section 7.3

Practice Problems

1. $\frac{55}{b} = \frac{15}{100}$

2. $\frac{35}{70} = \frac{p}{100}$

3. $\frac{a}{68} = \frac{25}{100}$

4. $\frac{520}{b} = \frac{65}{100}$

5. $\frac{65}{50} = \frac{p}{100}$

6. $\frac{a}{80} = \frac{36}{100}$

7. $\frac{a}{120} = \frac{8}{100}$
$a \cdot 100 = 120 \cdot 8$
$a \cdot 100 = 960$
$\frac{a \cdot 100}{100} = \frac{960}{100}$
$a = 9.6$
Therefore, 9.6 is 8% of 120.

8. $\frac{60}{b} = \frac{75}{100}$
$b \cdot 75 = 6000$
$\frac{b \cdot 75}{75} = \frac{6000}{75}$
$b = 80$
Therefore, 75% of 80 is 60.

9. $\frac{15}{b} = \frac{5}{100}$
$5 \cdot b = 1500$
$\frac{5 \cdot b}{5} = \frac{1500}{5}$
$b = 300$
Therefore, 15 is 5% of 300.

10. $\frac{5}{40} = \frac{p}{100}$
$40 \cdot p = 500$
$\frac{40 \cdot p}{40} = \frac{500}{40}$
$p = 12.5$
Therefore, 12.5% of 40 is 5.

11. $\frac{336}{160} = \frac{p}{100}$
$160 \cdot p = 33,600$
$\frac{160 \cdot p}{160} = \frac{33,600}{160}$
$p = 210$
Therefore, 210% of 160 is 336.

Mental Math

1. amount: 12.6
base: 42
percent: 30

2. amount: 201
base: 300
percent: 67

3. amount: 102
base: 510
percent: 20

4. amount: 248
base: 620
percent: 40

Exercise Set 7.3

1. $\frac{a}{65} = \frac{32}{100}$

3. $\frac{75}{b} = \frac{40}{100}$

5. $\frac{70}{200} = \frac{p}{100}$

7. $\frac{2.3}{b} = \frac{58}{100}$

9. $\frac{a}{130} = \frac{19}{100}$

11. $$\begin{aligned} \frac{a}{55} &= \frac{10}{100} \\ \frac{a}{55} &= \frac{1}{10} \\ a \cdot 10 &= 55 \cdot 1 \\ a \cdot 10 &= 55 \\ \frac{a \cdot 10}{10} &= \frac{55}{10} \\ a &= 5.5 \end{aligned}$$
Therefore, 10% of 55 is 5.5.

13. $$\begin{aligned} \frac{a}{105} &= \frac{18}{100} \\ \frac{a}{105} &= \frac{9}{50} \\ a \cdot 50 &= 105 \cdot 9 \\ \frac{a \cdot 50}{50} &= \frac{945}{50} \\ a &= 18.9 \end{aligned}$$
Therefore, 18% of 105 is 18.9.

15. $$\begin{aligned} \frac{60}{b} &= \frac{15}{100} \\ \frac{60}{b} &= \frac{3}{20} \\ 60 \cdot 20 &= b \cdot 3 \\ 1200 &= b \cdot 3 \\ \frac{1200}{3} &= \frac{b \cdot 3}{3} \\ 400 &= b \end{aligned}$$
Therefore, 15% of 400 is 60.

17. $$\begin{aligned} \frac{7.8}{b} &= \frac{78}{100} \\ \frac{7.8}{b} &= \frac{39}{50} \\ 7.8 \cdot 50 &= b \cdot 39 \\ 390 &= b \cdot 39 \\ \frac{390}{39} &= \frac{b \cdot 39}{39} \\ 10 &= b \end{aligned}$$
Therefore, 78% of 10 is 7.8.

19. $$\begin{aligned} \frac{105}{84} &= \frac{p}{100} \\ \frac{5}{4} &= \frac{p}{100} \\ 5 \cdot 100 &= 4 \cdot p \\ 500 &= 4 \cdot p \\ \frac{500}{4} &= \frac{4 \cdot p}{4} \\ 125 &= p \end{aligned}$$
Therefore, 125% of 84 is 105.

21. $$\begin{aligned} \frac{14}{50} &= \frac{p}{100} \\ \frac{7}{25} &= \frac{p}{100} \\ 7 \cdot 100 &= 25 \cdot p \\ 700 &= 25 \cdot p \\ \frac{700}{25} &= \frac{25 \cdot p}{25} \\ 28 &= p \end{aligned}$$
Therefore, 28% of 50 is 14.

23. $$\begin{aligned} \frac{2.9}{b} &= \frac{10}{100} \\ \frac{2.9}{b} &= \frac{1}{10} \\ 2.9 \cdot 10 &= b \cdot 1 \\ 29 &= b \end{aligned}$$
Therefore, 10% of 29 is 2.9.

25. $$\begin{aligned} \frac{a}{80} &= \frac{2.4}{100} \\ a \cdot 100 &= 80 \cdot 2.4 \\ a \cdot 100 &= 192 \\ \frac{a \cdot 100}{100} &= \frac{192}{100} \\ a &= 1.92 \end{aligned}$$
Therefore, 2.4% of 80 is 1.92.

27. $\frac{160}{b} = \frac{16}{100}$
$\frac{160}{b} = \frac{4}{25}$
$160 \cdot 25 = b \cdot 4$
$4000 = b \cdot 4$
$\frac{4000}{4} = \frac{b \cdot 4}{4}$
$1000 = b$

Therefore, 16% of 1000 is 160.

29. $\frac{348.6}{166} = \frac{p}{100}$
$348.6 \cdot 100 = 166 \cdot p$
$34,860 = 166 \cdot p$
$\frac{34,860}{166} = \frac{166 \cdot p}{166}$
$210 = p$

Therefore, 210% of 166 is 348.6.

31. $\frac{a}{62} = \frac{89}{100}$
$a \cdot 100 = 62 \cdot 89$
$a \cdot 100 = 5518$
$\frac{a \cdot 100}{100} = \frac{5518}{100}$
$a = 55.18$

Therefore, 89% of 62 is 55.18.

33. $\frac{3.6}{8} = \frac{p}{100}$
$3.6 \cdot 100 = 8 \cdot p$
$360 = 8 \cdot p$
$\frac{360}{8} = \frac{8 \cdot p}{8}$
$45 = p$

Therefore, 45% of 8 is 3.6.

35. $\frac{119}{b} = \frac{140}{100}$
$\frac{119}{b} = \frac{7}{5}$
$119 \cdot 5 = b \cdot 7$
$595 = b \cdot 7$
$\frac{595}{7} = \frac{b \cdot 7}{7}$
$85 = b$

Therefore, 140% of 85 is 119.

37. $\frac{11}{16} + \frac{3}{16} = \frac{11+3}{16} = \frac{14}{16} = \frac{7 \cdot 2}{8 \cdot 2} = \frac{7}{8}$

39.
$$\begin{array}{rcr} 3\frac{1}{2} & = & 3\frac{15}{30} \\ -\frac{11}{30} & = & -\frac{11}{30} \\ \hline & & 3\frac{4}{30} = 3\frac{2}{15} \end{array}$$

41.
$$\begin{array}{r} \overset{1}{0.41} \\ +\ 0.29 \\ \hline 0.70 \end{array}$$ or 0.7

43.
$$\begin{array}{r} 2.38 \\ -\ 0.19 \\ \hline 2.19 \end{array}$$

Check:
$$\begin{array}{r} \overset{1}{2.19} \\ +\ 0.19 \\ \hline 2.38 \end{array}$$

45. $\frac{a}{53,862} = \frac{22.3}{100}$
$a \cdot 100 = 53,862 \cdot 22.3$
$a \cdot 100 = 1,201,122.6$
$\frac{a \cdot 100}{100} = \frac{1,201,122.6}{100}$
$a = 12,011.226$

Therefore, 22.3% of 53,862 rounded to the nearest tenth is 12,011.2.

47. $\frac{8652}{b} = \frac{119}{100}$
$8652 \cdot 100 = b \cdot 119$
$865,200 = b \cdot 119$
$\frac{865,200}{119} = \frac{b \cdot 119}{119}$
$7270.6 \approx b$

Therefore, to the nearest tenth 8625 is 119% of 7270.6.

Integrated Review

1. $0.12 = 12\%$
2. $0.68 = 68\%$
3. $\frac{1}{4} = 0.25 = 25\%$
4. $\frac{1}{2} = 0.50 = 50\%$
5. $5.2 = 520\%$
6. $7.8 = 780\%$

7. $\frac{3}{50} = \frac{3}{50} \cdot \frac{2}{2} = \frac{6}{100} = 6\%$

8. $\frac{11}{25} = \frac{11}{25} \cdot \frac{4}{4} = \frac{44}{100} = 44\%$

9. $2\frac{1}{2} = \frac{5}{2} = \frac{5}{2} \cdot \frac{50}{50} = \frac{250}{100} = 250\%$

10. $3\frac{1}{4} = \frac{13}{4} = \frac{3}{14} \cdot \frac{25}{25} = \frac{325}{100} = 325\%$

11. $0.03 = 3\%$

12. $0.05 = 5\%$

13. $65\% = 65.\% = 0.65$

14. $31\% = 31.\% = 0.31$

15. $8\% = 8.\% = 0.08$

16. $7\% = 7.\% = 0.07$

17. $142\% = 142.\% = 1.42$

18. $538\% = 538.\% = 5.38$

19. $2.9\% = 0.029$

20. $6.6\% = 0.066$

21. $3\% = \frac{3}{100}$

22. $8\% = \frac{8}{100} = \frac{2}{25}$

23. $5.25\% = \frac{5.25}{100} = \frac{525}{10,000} = \frac{21}{400}$

24. $12.75\% = \frac{12.75}{100} = \frac{1275}{10,000} = \frac{51}{400}$

25. $38\% = \frac{38}{100} = \frac{19}{50}$

26. $45\% = \frac{45}{100} = \frac{9}{20}$

27. $12\frac{1}{3}\% = \frac{37}{3}\% = \frac{37}{3} \div 100 = \frac{37}{3} \cdot \frac{1}{100} = \frac{37}{300}$

28. $$\begin{aligned} 16\frac{2}{3} &= \frac{50}{3}\% \\ &= \frac{50}{3} \div 100 \\ &= \frac{50}{3} \cdot \frac{1}{100} \\ &= \frac{50}{300} \\ &= \frac{1}{6} \end{aligned}$$

29. $$\begin{aligned} \frac{a}{70} &= \frac{12}{100} \\ \frac{a}{70} &= \frac{3}{25} \\ a \cdot 25 &= 70 \cdot 3 \\ a \cdot 25 &= 210 \\ \frac{a \cdot 25}{25} &= \frac{210}{25} \\ a &= 8.4 \end{aligned}$$
12% of 70 is 8.4.

30. $$\begin{aligned} \frac{36}{b} &= \frac{36}{100} \\ \frac{36}{b} &= \frac{9}{25} \\ 36 \cdot 25 &= b \cdot 9 \\ 900 &= b \cdot 9 \\ \frac{900}{9} &= \frac{b \cdot 9}{9} \\ 100 &= b \end{aligned}$$
36 is 36% of 100.

31. $$\begin{aligned} \frac{212.5}{b} &= \frac{85}{100} \\ \frac{212.5}{b} &= \frac{17}{20} \\ 212.5 \cdot 20 &= b \cdot 17 \\ 4250 &= b \cdot 17 \\ \frac{4250}{17} &= \frac{b \cdot 17}{17} \\ 250 &= b \end{aligned}$$
212.5 is 85% of 250.

32. $$\begin{aligned} \frac{66}{55} &= \frac{p}{100} \\ 66 \cdot 100 &= 55 \cdot p \\ 6600 &= 55 \cdot p \\ \frac{6600}{55} &= \frac{55 \cdot p}{55} \\ 120 &= p \end{aligned}$$
66 is 120% of 55.

33. $\frac{23.8}{85} = \frac{p}{100}$
$23.8 \cdot 100 = 85 \cdot p$
$2380 = 85 \cdot p$
$\frac{2380}{85} = \frac{85 \cdot p}{85}$
$28 = p$
23.8 is 28% of 85.

34. $\frac{a}{200} = \frac{38}{100}$
$\frac{a}{200} = \frac{19}{50}$
$a \cdot 50 = 200 \cdot 19$
$a \cdot 50 = 3800$
$\frac{a \cdot 50}{50} = \frac{3800}{50}$
$a = 76$
38% of 200 is 76.

35. $\frac{a}{44} = \frac{25}{100}$
$\frac{a}{44} = \frac{1}{4}$
$a \cdot 4 = 44 \cdot 1$
$a \cdot 4 = 44$
$\frac{a \cdot 4}{4} = \frac{44}{4}$
$a = 11$
11 is 25% of 44.

36. $\frac{128.7}{99} = \frac{p}{100}$
$128.7 \cdot 100 = 99 \cdot p$
$12,870 = 99 \cdot p$
$\frac{12,870}{99} = \frac{99 \cdot p}{99}$
$130 = p$
130% of 99 is 128.7.

37. $\frac{215}{250} = \frac{p}{100}$
$\frac{43}{50} = \frac{p}{100}$
$43 \cdot 100 = 50 \cdot p$
$4300 = 50 \cdot p$
$\frac{4300}{50} = \frac{50 \cdot p}{50}$
$86 = p$
86% of 250 is 215.

38. $\frac{a}{84} = \frac{45}{100}$
$\frac{a}{84} = \frac{9}{20}$
$a \cdot 20 = 84 \cdot 9$
$a \cdot 20 = 756$
$\frac{a \cdot 20}{20} = \frac{756}{2}$
$a = 37.8$
37.8 is 45% of 84.

39. $\frac{63}{b} = \frac{42}{100}$
$\frac{63}{b} = \frac{21}{50}$
$63 \cdot 50 = b \cdot 21$
$3150 = b \cdot 21$
$\frac{3150}{21} = \frac{b \cdot 21}{21}$
$150 = b$
63 is 42% of 150.

40. $\frac{58.9}{b} = \frac{95}{100}$
$\frac{58.9}{b} = \frac{19}{20}$
$58.9 \cdot 20 = b \cdot 19$
$1178 = b \cdot 19$
$\frac{1178}{19} = \frac{b \cdot 19}{19}$
$62 = b$
58.9 is 95% of 62.

Section 7.4

Practice Problems

1. 61 is what percent of 106%?
$61 = x \cdot 106$
$\frac{61}{106} = \frac{x \cdot 106}{106}$
$0.575 \approx x$
About 58% of Ohio nursing schools have RN degrees.

2. 775 is 31% of what number?
$775 = 31\% \cdot x$
$775 = 0.31 \cdot x$
$\frac{775}{0.31} = \frac{0.31 \cdot x}{0.31}$
$2500 = x$
There are 2500 students that go to Euclid University.

3. 130 is what percent of 190?

$130 = x \cdot 190$

$\frac{130}{190} = \frac{x \cdot 190}{190}$

$0.684 \approx x$

$68.4\% \approx x$

About 68.4% of the calories are from fat.

4. What number is 10% of 122 million?

$x = 10\% \cdot 122$

$x = 0.10 \cdot 122$

$x = 12.2$

The increase in vehicles is 12.2 million. The number of vehicles in 2000 is 122 million + 12.2 million = 134.2 million.

5.
$$\begin{aligned} \text{percent increase} &= \frac{\text{amount of increase}}{\text{original amount}} \\ &= \frac{333-285}{285} \\ &= \frac{48}{285} \\ &\approx 0.168 \\ &= 16.8\% \end{aligned}$$

The attendance increased by about 16.8%.

6.
$$\begin{aligned} \text{percent decrease} &= \frac{\text{amount of decrease}}{\text{original amount}} \\ &= \frac{20,145-18,430}{20,145} \\ &= \frac{1715}{20,145} \\ &\approx 0.085 \\ &= 8.5\% \end{aligned}$$

The population decreased by about about 8.5%.

Exercise Set 7.4

1. Let n = the number of bolts inspected.

$1.5\% \cdot n = 24$

$0.015 \cdot n = 24$

$\frac{0.015 \cdot n}{0.015} = \frac{24}{0.015}$

$n = 1600$

1600 bolts were inspected.

3. Let x = the hours billed per 40 hour week.

$x = 75\% \cdot 40$

$x = (0.75)(40)$

$x = 30$

The owner can bill 30 hours.

5. Let x = the percent of income spent on food.

$\$300 = x \cdot \$2000$

$\frac{300}{2000} = \frac{x \cdot 2000}{2000}$

$0.15 = x$

$0.15 \cdot 100\% = x$

$15\% = x$

She spends 15% of her monthly income on food.

7. Let x = the number of defective components.

$x = 1.04\% \cdot 28,350$

$x = 0.0104 \cdot 28,350$

$x = 294.84$

$x \approx 295$

295 defective components are expected.

9. Let x = the percent of the members of the 108th Congress that attended a community college.

$73 = x \cdot 535$

$\frac{73}{535} = \frac{x \cdot 535}{535}$

$0.136 \approx x$

$0.136 \cdot 100\% = x$

$13.6\% = x$

13.6% of the members of the 108th Congress have attended a community school.

11. Let n = the number of registered dental hygienists in the U.S.

$98.3\% \cdot n = 98,400$

$0.983 \cdot n = 98,400$

$\frac{0.983n}{0.983} = \frac{98,400}{0.983}$

$n \approx 100,102$

There are 100,102 dental hygienists in the U.S.

13. Let x = the percent of calories from fat.

$35 = x \cdot 120$

$\frac{35}{120} = \frac{x \cdot 120}{120}$

$0.292 = x$

$0.292 \cdot 100\% = x$

$29.2\% = x$

29.2% of the food's total calories is from fat.

15. $x = 8\% \cdot 6200$

$x = 0.08 \cdot 6200$

$x = 496$

Ace Furniture Company increased production by 496 chairs.

$6200 + 496 = 6696$

The new number of chairs produced each month is 6696.

17. 20% of \$170 is what number?

$$20\% \cdot \$170 = n$$
$$0.2 \cdot \$170 = n$$
$$\$34.00 = n$$

Their new bill is \$170 – \$34 = \$136.

19. 4.5% of \$19,286 is what number?

$$4.5\% \cdot \$19,286 = n$$
$$0.045 \cdot \$19,286 = n$$
$$\$867.87 = n$$

The increase is \$867.87. The new price is \$19,286 + \$867.87 = \$20,153.87.

21. 33% of 26.8 million is what number?

$$33\% \cdot 26.8 \text{ million} = n$$
$$0.33 \cdot 26,800,000 = n$$
$$8,844,000 = n$$

projected population:
26.8 million + 8.844 million
= 35.644 million
The increase is 8.844 million. The projected population is 35.644 million.

	Original Amount	New Amount	Amount of Increase	Percent Increase
23.	40	50	50 – 40 = 10	$\frac{10}{40} = 0.25 = 25\%$
25.	85	187	187 – 85 = 102	$\frac{102}{85} = 1.2 = 120\%$

	Original Amount	New Amount	Amount of Decrease	Percent Decrease
27.	8	6	8 – 6 = 2	$\frac{2}{8} = 0.25 = 25\%$
29.	160	40	160 – 40 = 120	$\frac{120}{160} = 0.75 = 75\%$

31. $\text{percent decrease} = \frac{150-84}{150} = \frac{66}{150} = 0.44 = 44\%$

33. $\text{percent increase} = \frac{23.7-19.5}{19.5} = \frac{4.2}{19.5} \approx 0.215 = 21.5\%$

35. $\text{percent decrease} = \frac{10,845-10,700}{10,845} = \frac{145}{10,845} \approx 0.013 = 1.3\%$

37. $\text{percent decrease} = \frac{52.1-6.7}{52.1} = \frac{45.4}{52.1} \approx 0.871 = 87.1\%$

39. $\text{percent increase} = \frac{300,000-75,000}{75,000} = \frac{225,000}{75,000} = 3 = 300\%$

41. $\text{percent increase} = \frac{29,000-16,000}{16,000} = \frac{13,000}{16,000} = 0.8125 = 81.25\%$ or 81.3% when rounded to the nearest tenth

43. $\text{percent decrease} = \frac{272.6-76}{272.6} = \frac{196.6}{272.6} \approx 0.721 = 72.1\%$

45. $\text{percent increase} = \frac{110{,}000{,}000-16{,}000{,}000}{16{,}000{,}000} = \frac{94{,}000{,}000}{16{,}000{,}000} = 5.875 = 587.5\%$

47. $\text{percent increase} = \frac{28{,}700-26{,}518}{26{,}518} = \frac{2182}{26{,}518} \approx 0.082 = 8.2\%$

49.
```
  0.12
×  38
   96
  360
 4.56
```

51.
```
  9.20
+ 1.98
 11.18
```

53.
```
  78.00
- 19.46
  58.54
```

55. The increased number is double the original number. Answers may vary.

Section 7.5

Practice Problems

1. $\text{tax} = 6\% \cdot \$29.90 = 0.06 \cdot \$29.9 = \$1.79$

$\text{total} = \$29.90 + \$1.79 = \$31.69$

The tax is \$1.79 and the total is \$31.69.

2. $\$1080 = r \cdot \$13{,}500$

$\frac{\$1080}{\$13{,}500} = \frac{r \cdot 13{,}500}{13{,}500}$

$0.08 = r$

$8\% = r$

The sales tax rate is 8%.

3. $\text{commission} = 6.6\% \cdot \$37{,}632 = 0.066 \cdot \$37{,}632 = \$2483.712$

His commission is \$2483.71.

4. $\$1290 = r \cdot \$8600$

$\frac{\$1290}{\$8600} = \frac{r \cdot 8600}{8600}$

$0.15 = r$

$15\% = r$

The commission rate is 15%.

5. $\text{discount} = 15\% \cdot \$700 = 0.15 \cdot \$700 = \$105$

$\text{sale price} = \$700 - \$105 = \$595$

The discount is \$105 and the sale price is \$595.

Exercise Set 7.5

1. $\text{tax} = 5\% \cdot \$150.00 = 0.05 \cdot \$150.00 = \$7.50$

The sales tax is \$7.50.

3. $\text{tax} = 7.5\% \cdot \$799 = 0.075 \cdot \$799 = \$59.925$

$\text{total} = \$799 + \$59.925 = \$858.925$

The total price is \$858.93.

5. $\$54 = r \cdot \$600$

$\frac{\$54}{\$600} = r$

$0.09 = r$

$9\% = r$

The sales tax rate is 9%.

7. $\text{tax} = 8.5\% \cdot \$220 = 0.085 \cdot \$220 = \$18.70$

$\text{total} = \$220 + \$18.70 = \$238.70$

The total price is \$238.70.

9. $\text{tax} = 6.5\% \cdot \$1800 = 0.065 \cdot \$1800 = \$117$

$\text{total} = \$1800 + \$117 = \$1917$

The total price is \$1917.

11. $\$920 = 8\% \cdot n$
$\$920 = 0.08 \cdot n$
$\frac{\$920}{0.08} = n$
$\$11,500 = n$
The purchase price is $11,500.

13. total purchase $= \$90 + \$15 = \$105$
tax $= 7\% \cdot \$105$
$= 0.07 \cdot \$105$
$= \$7.35$
total $= \$105 + \$7.35 = \$112.35$
The total price is $112.35.

15. $\$98.70 = r \cdot \$1645$
$\frac{\$98.70}{\$1645} = r$
$0.06 = r$
$6\% = r$
The sales tax rate is 6%.

17. commission $= 4\% \cdot \$1,236,856$
$= 0.04 \cdot \$1,236,856$
$= \$49,474.24$
Her commission was $49,474.24.

19. $\$1380.40 = r \cdot \$9860.00$
$\frac{\$1380.40}{\$9860.00} = r$
$0.14 = r$
$14\% = r$
The commission rate is 14%.

21. commission $= 1.5\% \cdot \$125,900$
$= 0.015 \cdot \$125,900$
$= \$1888.50$
His commission is $1888.50.

23. $2565 = 3\% \cdot x$
$2565 = 0.03 \cdot x$
$\frac{2565}{0.03} = x$
$85,500 = x$
$85,500 is the selling price of the house.

	Original Price	Discount Rate	Amount of Discount	Sale Price
25.	$68.00	10%	$68.00 · 10% = $68.00 · 0.10 = $6.80	$68.00 – $6.80 = $61.20
27.	$96.50	50%	$96.50 · 50% = $9650 · 0.5 = $48.25	$96.50 – $48.25 = $48.25
29.	$215.00	35%	$215.00 · 35% = $215.00 · 0.35 = $75.25	$215.00 – $75.25 = $139.75
31.	$21,700.00	15%	$21,700.00 · 15% = $21,700· 0.15 =$3255.00	$21,700.00 – $3255.00 = $18,445.00

33. discount $= 15\% \cdot \$300$
$= 0.15 \cdot \$300$
$= \$45$
sale price $= \$300 - \$45$
$= \$255$

	Original Price	Discount Rate	Amount of Discount	Sale Price
35.	$75.00	20%	$75 \cdot 0.2 = \$15$	75.00 – 15.00 = $60.00
37.	$120.00	$\frac{39.60}{120} = 33\%$	$39.60	120.00 – 39.60 = $80.40
39.	$\frac{370}{0.40} = \$925$	40%	$370.00	$925 – $370 = $555.00

41. $2000 \cdot 0.3 \cdot 2 = 600 \cdot 2 = 1200$

43. $400 \cdot 0.03 \cdot 11 = 12 \cdot 11 = 132$

45.
$$\begin{aligned} 600 \cdot 0.04 \cdot \frac{2}{3} &= 24 \cdot \frac{2}{3} \\ &= \frac{24}{1} \cdot \frac{2}{3} \\ &= \frac{24 \cdot 2}{3} \\ &= \frac{48}{3} \\ &= 16 \end{aligned}$$

47.
$$\begin{aligned} \text{discount} &= \$24{,}966 \cdot 15\% \\ &= 24{,}966 \cdot 0.15 \\ &= \$3744.90 \end{aligned}$$

$$\begin{aligned} \text{discount price} &= \$24{,}966 - \$3744.90 \\ &= \$21{,}221.10 \end{aligned}$$

$$\begin{aligned} \text{tax} &= \$21{,}221.10 \cdot 7.5\% \\ &= 21{,}221.10 \cdot 0.075 \\ &= \$1591.58 \end{aligned}$$

total price = $21,221.10 + $1591.58 = $22,812.68

49. 60% discount:
$50 · 60% = $50 · 0.6 = $30
discount price = $50 – $30 = $20
30% discount followed by a 35% discount
$50 · 30% = $50 · 0.3 = $15
$50 – $15 = $35
$35 · 35% = $35 · 0.35 = $12.25
discount price = $35 – $12.25 = $22.75
A discount of 60% is better.

	Bill Amount	10%	15%	20%
51.	$15.89	$1.60	$2.40	$3.20
53.	$9.33	$0.90	$1.35	$1.80

Section 7.6

Practice Problems

1.
$$\begin{aligned} I &= P \cdot R \cdot T \\ &= \$750 \cdot 8\% \cdot 3 \\ &= \$750 \cdot 0.08 \cdot 3 \\ &= \$180 \end{aligned}$$

2. time = 9 months = $\frac{9}{12}$ year = $\frac{3}{4}$ year
$$\begin{aligned} I &= P \cdot R \cdot T \\ &= \$800 \cdot 20\% \cdot \frac{3}{4} \\ &= \$800 \cdot 0.2 \cdot \frac{3}{4} \\ &= \$120 \end{aligned}$$
She paid $120 in interest.

3. time = 6 months = $\frac{6}{12}$ year = $\frac{1}{2}$ year
$$\begin{aligned} I &= P \cdot R \cdot T \\ &= \$500 \cdot 12\% \cdot \frac{1}{2} \\ &= \$500 \cdot 0.12 \cdot \frac{1}{2} \\ &= \$30 \end{aligned}$$
$$\begin{aligned} \text{total amount} &= \$500 + \$30 \\ &= \$530 \end{aligned}$$

4. total amount
= original principal · compound interest factor
= $5500 · 1.41902
= $7804.61

5. interest earned
= total amount – original principal
= $9933.14 – $5500
= $4433.14

6. monthly payment
$$\begin{aligned} &= \frac{\text{principal + interest}}{\text{total number of payments}} \\ &= \frac{\$3000 + \$1123.58}{3 \cdot 12} \\ &\approx \$114.54 \end{aligned}$$

The monthly payment is $114.54

Calculator Explorations

1. $\left(1 + \frac{0.09}{4}\right)^{(4 \cdot 5)} \approx 1.56051$

2. $\left(1+\frac{0.14}{365}\right)^{(365\cdot 15)} \approx 8.16288$

3. $\left(1+\frac{0.11}{1}\right)^{(1\cdot 20)} \approx 8.06231$

4. $\left(1+\frac{0.07}{2}\right)^{(2\cdot 1)} \approx 1.07123$

5. Compound interest factor $= \left(1+\frac{0.06}{4}\right)^{(4\cdot 4)} \approx 1.26899$

$\$500 \cdot 1.26899 \approx \$634.50$

6. Compound interest factor $= \left(1+\frac{0.05}{365}\right)^{(365\cdot 19)} \approx 2.58554$

$\$2500 \cdot 2.58554 = \$6463.85$

Exercise Set 7.6

1. simple interest $=$ principal $\cdot$ rate $\cdot$ time
$= \$200 \cdot 8\% \cdot 2$
$= \$200 \cdot (0.08) \cdot 2$
$= \$32$

3. simple interest $=$ principal $\cdot$ rate $\cdot$ time
$= \$160 \cdot 11.5\% \cdot 4$
$= \$160 \cdot (0.115) \cdot 4$
$= \$73.60$

5. simple interest $=$ principal $\cdot$ rate $\cdot$ time
$= \$5000 \cdot 10\% \cdot 1\frac{1}{2}$
$= \$5000 \cdot (0.10) \cdot 1.5$
$= \$750$

7. simple interest $=$ principle $\cdot$ rate $\cdot$ time
$= \$375 \cdot 18\% \cdot \frac{6}{12}$
$= \$375 \cdot (0.18) \cdot (0.5)$
$= \$33.75$

9. simple interest $=$ principal $\cdot$ rate $\cdot$ time
$= \$2500 \cdot 16\% \cdot \frac{21}{12}$
$= \$2500 \cdot (0.16) \cdot 1.75$
$= \$700$

11. simple interest $=$ principal $\cdot$ rate $\cdot$ time
$= \$62,500 \cdot 12.5\% \cdot 2$
$= \$62,500 \cdot (0.125) \cdot 2$
$= \$15,625$

total = \$62,500 + \$15,625 = \$78,125.
The total amount paid is \$78,125.

13. simple interest $=$ principal $\cdot$ rate $\cdot$ time
$= \$5000 \cdot 9\% \cdot \frac{15}{12}$
$= \$5000 \cdot (0.09) \cdot 1.25$
$= \$562.50$

total = \$5000 + \$562.50 = \$5562.50
The total amount received is \$5562.50

15. simple interest $=$ principal $\cdot$ rate $\cdot$ time
$= \$8500 \cdot 12\% \cdot 4$
$= \$8500 \cdot (0.12) \cdot 4$
$= \$4080$

total = \$8500 + \$4080 = \$12,580
She pays back a total of \$12,580.

17. total $=$ principal $\cdot$ compound interest factor
$= \$6150(7.61226)$
$= \$46,815.399$

The total amount is \$46,815.40.

19. total $=$ principal $\cdot$ compound interest factor
$= \$1560(1.49176)$
$= \$2327.1456$

The total amount is \$2327.15.

21. total $=$ principal $\cdot$ compound interest factor
$= \$10,000(5.81636)$
$= \$58,163.60$

The total amount is \$58,163.60.

23. total $=$ principal $\cdot$ compound interest factor
$= \$2675(1.09000)$
$= \$2915.75$

compound interest
$=$ total amount $-$ original principal
$= \$2915.75 - \$2675$
$= \$240.75$

The interest earned is \$240.75.

25. total = original principal · compound interest factor
$= \$2000(1.46933)$
$= \$2938.66$
compound interest = total amount − original principal
$= \$2938.66 - \$2000$
$= \$938.66$
The interest earned is \$938.66.

27. total = original principal · compound interest factor
$= \$2000(1.48595)$
$= \$2971.90$
compound interest = total amount − original principal
$= \$2971.90 - \$2000$
$= \$971.90$
The interest earned is \$971.90.

29. $\text{monthly payment} = \dfrac{\text{principal} + \text{interest}}{\text{number of payments}} = \dfrac{\$1500 + \$61.88}{6} = \dfrac{\$1561.88}{6} \approx \$260.31$

The monthly payment is \$260.31.

31. $\text{monthly payment} = \dfrac{\text{principal} + \text{interest}}{\text{number of payments}} = \dfrac{\$20,000 + \$10,588.70}{48} = \dfrac{\$30,588.70}{48} \approx \$637.26$

The monthly payment is \$637.26.

33. $-5 + (-24) = -29$

35. $(-5)(-10) = 50$

37. $\dfrac{7-10}{3} = \dfrac{-3}{3} = -1$

39. Answers may vary.

41. Answers may vary.

Chapter 7 Review

1. $\frac{37}{100} = 37\%$

2. $\frac{77}{100} = 77\%$

3. $83\% = 0.83$

4. $75\% = 0.75$

5. $73.5\% = 0.735$

6. $1.5\% = 0.015$

7. $125\% = 1.25$

8. $145\% = 1.45$

9. $0.5\% = 0.005$

10. $0.7\% = 0.007$

11. $200\% = 2.00$ or 2

12. $400\% = 4.00$ or 4

13. $26.25\% = 0.2625$

14. $85.34\% = 0.8534$

15. $2.6 = 260\%$

16. $0.055 = 5.5\%$

17. $0.35 = 35\%$

18. $1.02 = 102\%$

19. $0.725 = 72.5\%$

20. $0.25 = 25\%$

21. $0.076 = 7.6\%$

22. $0.085 = 8.5\%$

23. $0.75 = 75\%$

24. $0.65 = 65\%$

25. $4.00 = 400\%$

26. $9.00 = 900\%$

27. $1\% = \frac{1}{100}$

28. $10\% = \frac{10}{100} = \frac{1}{10}$

29. $25\% = \frac{25}{100} = \frac{1}{4}$

30. $8.5\% = \frac{8.5}{100} = \frac{85}{1000} = \frac{17}{200}$

31. $10.2\% = \frac{10.2}{100} = \frac{102}{1000} = \frac{51}{500}$

32.
$$\begin{aligned}16\frac{2}{3}\% &= \frac{16\frac{2}{3}}{100}\\ &= 16\frac{2}{3} \div 100\\ &= \frac{50}{3} \cdot \frac{1}{100}\\ &= \frac{50}{300}\\ &= \frac{1}{6}\end{aligned}$$

33. $33\frac{1}{3}\% = \frac{33\frac{1}{3}}{100} = 33\frac{1}{3} \div 100 = \frac{100}{3} \cdot \frac{1}{100} = \frac{1}{3}$

34. $110\% = \frac{110}{100} = \frac{11}{10}$ or $1\frac{1}{10}$

35. $\frac{1}{5} = \frac{1}{5} \cdot 100\% = \frac{100\%}{5} = 20\%$

36. $\frac{7}{10} = \frac{7}{10} \cdot 100\% = 70\%$

37. $\frac{5}{6} \cdot 100\% = \frac{500\%}{6} = \frac{250\%}{3} = 83\frac{1}{3}\%$

38.
$$\begin{aligned}\frac{5}{8} &= \frac{5}{8} \cdot 100\%\\ &= \frac{500\%}{8}\\ &= \frac{125}{2}\%\\ &= 62\frac{1}{2}\% \text{ or } 62.5\%\end{aligned}$$

39. $1\frac{2}{3} = \frac{5}{3} = \frac{5}{3} \cdot 100\% = \frac{500\%}{3} = 166\frac{2}{3}\%$

40. $1\frac{1}{4} = \frac{5}{4} = \frac{5}{4} \cdot 100\% = 125\%$

41. $\frac{3}{5} = \frac{3}{5} \cdot 100\% = \frac{300\%}{5} = 60\%$

42.
$$\begin{aligned}\frac{1}{16} &= \frac{1}{16} \cdot 100\%\\ &= \frac{100\%}{16}\\ &= \frac{25}{4}\%\\ &= 6\frac{1}{4}\% \text{ or } 6.25\%\end{aligned}$$

43. $90\% = \frac{90}{100} = \frac{9}{10}$; $10\% = \frac{10}{100} = \frac{1}{10}$

44. $96\% = \frac{96}{100} = \frac{24}{25}$

45. $\frac{7}{10} = \frac{7}{10} \cdot 100\% = 70\%$

46. $150\% = 1.50$ or 1.5

47.
$$\begin{aligned}1250 &= 1.25\% \cdot n\\ 1250 &= 0.0125n\\ \frac{1250}{0.0125} &= n\\ 100{,}000 &= n\end{aligned}$$

48.
$$\begin{aligned}n &= 33\frac{1}{3}\% \cdot 24{,}000\\ n &= \frac{33\frac{1}{3}}{100} \cdot 24{,}000\\ n &= 33\frac{1}{3} \cdot 240\\ n &= \frac{100}{3} \cdot 240\\ n &= 8000\end{aligned}$$

49.
$$\begin{aligned}124.2 &= n \cdot 540\\ \frac{124.2}{540} &= n\\ 0.23 &= n\\ 23\% &= n\end{aligned}$$

50.
$$\begin{aligned}22.9 &= 20\% \cdot n\\ 22.9 &= 0.2n\\ \frac{22.9}{0.2} &= n\\ 114.5 &= n\end{aligned}$$

51. $n = 40\% \cdot 7500$
$n = (0.40)(7500)$
$n = 3000$

52. $693 = n \cdot 462$
$\frac{693}{462} = n$
$1.5 = n$
$150\% = n$

53. $\frac{104.5}{b} = \frac{25}{100}$
$b \cdot 25 = 104.5 \cdot 100$
$b \cdot 25 = 10,450$
$b = \frac{10,450}{25}$
$b = 418$
Therefore, 25% of 418 is 104.5.

54. $\frac{16.5}{b} = \frac{5.5}{100}$
$b \cdot 5.5 = 16.5 \cdot 100$
$b \cdot 5.5 = 1650$
$b = \frac{1650}{5.5}$
$b = 300$
Therefore, 5.5% of 300 is 16.5.

55. $\frac{a}{180} = \frac{36}{100}$
$a \cdot 100 = 36 \cdot 180$
$a \cdot 100 = 6480$
$a = \frac{6480}{100}$
$a = 64.8$
Therefore, 36% of 180 is 64.8.

56. $\frac{63}{35} = \frac{p}{100}$
$63 \cdot 100 = 35 \cdot p$
$6300 = 35 \cdot p$
$\frac{6300}{35} = p$
$180 = p$
Therefore, 180% of 35 is 63.

57. $\frac{93.5}{85} = \frac{p}{100}$
$93.5 \cdot 100 = 85 \cdot p$
$9350 = 85 \cdot p$
$\frac{9350}{85} = p$
$110 = p$
Therefore, 110% of 85 is 93.5.

58. $\frac{a}{500} = \frac{33}{100}$
$a \cdot 100 = 500 \cdot 33$
$a \cdot 100 = 16,500$
$a = \frac{16,500}{100}$
$a = 165$
Therefore, 33% of 500 is 165.

59. What percent of 2000 is 1320?
$n \cdot 2000 = 1320$
$n = \frac{1320}{2000}$
$n = 0.66$
$n = 66\%$

60. What percent of 12,360 is 2000?
$n \cdot 12,360 = 2000$
$n = \frac{2000}{12,360} \approx 0.16$
About 16% of entering freshmen are enrolled in Basic College Mathematics.

61. $\text{percent increase} = \frac{\text{amount of increase}}{\text{original amount}}$
$= \frac{33-16}{16}$
$= \frac{17}{16}$
$= 1.0625$
$= 106.25\%$

62. $\text{percent decrease} = \frac{\text{amount of decrease}}{\text{original amount}}$
$= \frac{675-534}{675}$
$= \frac{141}{675}$
$= 0.208\overline{8}$
$\approx 20.9\%$

63. decrease $= 4\% \cdot \$215,000$
$= 0.04 \cdot 215,000 = \$8600$
Next year = this year − decrease
$= \$215,000 - \$8600 = \$206,400$

64. 15% of \$11.50 is what number?
$(0.15)(\$11.50) = n$
$\$1.725 = n$
New hourly rate is
$\$11.50 + \$1.725 = \$13.225 \approx \$13.23$

65. Sales tax is
$(5.5\%)(\$250) = (0.055)(\$250) = \$13.75.$

Total price of the coat is
$\$250 + \$13.75 = \$263.75$.

66. Sales tax is
$$(4.5\%)(\$25.50) = (0.045)(\$25.50) = \$1.1475 \approx \$1.15$$

67. $$\text{Commission} = 5\% \cdot \$100,000 = 0.05 \cdot \$100,000 = \$5000$$

68. $$\text{Commission} = (7.5\%)(\$4005) = (0.075)(\$4005) = \$300.375 \approx \$300.38$$

69. $$\text{discount} = 30\% \cdot \$3000 = 0.3 \cdot \$3000 = \$900$$
$$\text{sale price} = \$3000 - \$900 = \$2100$$
The discount is \$900 and the sale price is \$2100.

70. $$\text{discount} = 10\% \cdot \$90 = 0.1 \cdot \$90 = \$9$$
$$\text{sale price} = \$90 - \$9 = \$81$$
The discount is \$9 and the sale price is \$81.

71. $$\text{simple interest} = \text{principal} \cdot \text{rate} \cdot \text{time} = \$4000 \cdot 12\% \cdot \frac{3}{12} = \$4000 \cdot 0.12 \cdot 0.25 = \$120$$

72. $$\text{simple interest} = \text{principle} \cdot \text{rate} \cdot \text{time} = \$1200 \cdot 15\% \cdot \frac{8}{12} = \$1200 \cdot 0.15 \cdot \frac{2}{3} = \$120$$
total due = \$1200 + \$120 = \$1320

73. The compound interest factor for 15 years at 12% compounded annually is 5.47357.
$$\text{total amount} = \$5500 \cdot 5.47357 = \$30,104.635$$
The total is \$30,104.64.

74. The compound interest factor for 10 years at 11% compounded semiannually is 2.91776.
$$\text{total amount} = \$6000 \cdot 2.91776 = \$17,506.56$$
The total is \$17,506.56.

75. The compound interest factor for 5 years at 12% compounded quarterly is 1.80611.
total amount = \$100 · 1.80611 ≈ \$180.61
Interest earned
= total amount – original principal
= \$180.61 – \$100 = \$80.61

76. The compound interest factor for 20 years at 18% compounded quarterly is 33.83010.
$$\text{Total amount} = \$1000 \cdot 33.83010 = \$33,830.10$$
$$\text{Interest earned} = \$33,830.10 - \$1000 = \$32,830.10$$

Chapter 7 Test

1. $85\% = 85.\% = 0.85$

2. $500\% = 500.\% = 5$

3. $0.6\% = 0.006$

4. $0.056 = 5.6\%$

5. $6.1 = 6.10 = 610.\% = 610\%$

6. $0.35 = 35\%$

7. $120\% = \frac{120}{100} = \frac{6}{5}$

8. $38.5\% = \frac{38.5}{100} = \frac{385}{1000} = \frac{77}{200}$

9. $0.2\% = \frac{0.2}{100} = \frac{2}{1000} = \frac{1}{500}$

10. $\frac{11}{20} = \frac{11}{20} \cdot \frac{5}{5} = \frac{55}{100} = 55\%$

11. $\frac{3}{8} = 0.375 = 37.5\%$

12. $1\frac{3}{4} = \frac{7}{4} = \frac{7}{4} \cdot \frac{25}{25} = \frac{175}{100} = 175\%$

13. $\frac{1}{5} = \frac{1}{5} \cdot 100\% = \frac{100}{5}\% = 20\%$

14. $64\% = \frac{64}{100} = \frac{16}{25}$

15. $n = 42\% \cdot 80$
$n = (0.42)(80)$

$n = 33.6$
Therefore, 42% of 80 is 33.6.

16. $0.6\% \cdot n = 7.5$
$0.006 \cdot n = 7.5$
$n = \frac{7.5}{0.006}$
$n = 1250$
Therefore, 0.6% of 1250 is 7.5.

17. $567 = x \cdot 756$
$\frac{567}{756} = \frac{x \cdot 756}{x}$
$0.75 = x$
$75\% = x$
Therefore, 75% of 756 is 567.

18. 12% of 320 is the amount of copper.
$12\% \cdot 320 = n$
$0.12 \cdot 320 = n$
$38.4 = n$
The alloy contains 38.4 pounds of copper.

19. 20% of what is $11,350?
$0.20n = \$11,350$
$n = \frac{\$11,350}{0.20}$
$n = \$56,750$
The value is $56,750.

20. $\text{tax} = 1.25\% \cdot \$354$
$= (0.0125)(\$354)$
$= \$4.425$
$\approx \$4.43$
Total price is $354 + $4.43 = $358.43.

21. $\text{percent increase} = \frac{26,460 - 25,200}{25,200}$
$= \frac{1260}{25,200}$
$= 0.05$
$= 5\%$
The population increased 5%.

22. $\text{discount} = 15\% \cdot \$120$
$= 0.15 \cdot \$120$
$= \$18$
$\text{sale price} = \$120 - \$18$
$= \$102$

23. $\text{commission} = 4\% \cdot \$9875$
$= 0.04 \cdot \$9875$
$= \$395$
His commission is $395.

24. $\$1.53 = r \cdot \$152.99$
$\frac{\$1.53}{\$152.99} = r$
$0.01 \approx r$
$1\% = r$

25. $\text{simple interest} = \text{principal} \cdot \text{rate} \cdot \text{time}$
$= \$2000 \cdot 9.25\% \cdot 3\frac{1}{2}$
$= \$2000 \cdot (0.0925) \cdot 3.5$
$= \$647.50$

26. The compound interest factor for 5 years at 8% compounded annually is 1.46933.
$\text{total amount} = \$1365 \cdot 1.46933$
$= \$2005.63545$
The total amount is $2005.64.

27. $\text{interest} = \text{principal} \cdot \text{rate} \cdot \text{time}$
$\text{interest} = \$400 \cdot 13.5\% \cdot \frac{6}{12}$
$= \$400 \cdot (0.135) \cdot 0.5$
$= \$27.00$
Total amount due the bank = $400 + $27
= $427

28. $\text{percent decrease} = \frac{125,587 - 118,346}{125,587}$
$= \frac{7241}{125,587}$
≈ 0.058
$= 5.8\%$
The percent decrease is about 5.8%.

Cumulative Review

1.
$$\begin{array}{r} 236 \\ \times 86 \\ \hline 1416 \\ 18880 \\ \hline 20,296 \end{array}$$

2.
$$\begin{array}{r} 409 \\ \times 76 \\ \hline 2454 \\ +28630 \\ \hline 31,084 \end{array}$$

3. $-3 - 7 = -10$

4. $8 - (-2) = 10$

5. $$\begin{aligned} x-2&=1 \\ x-2+2&=1+2 \\ x&=3 \end{aligned}$$

6. $$\begin{aligned} x+4&=3 \\ x+4-4&=3-4 \\ x&=-1 \end{aligned}$$

7. $$\begin{aligned} 3(2x-6)+6&=0 \\ 6x-18+6&=0 \\ 6x-12&=0 \\ 6x-12+12&=0+12 \\ 6x&=12 \\ \frac{6x}{6}&=\frac{12}{6} \\ x&=2 \end{aligned}$$

8. $$\begin{aligned} 5(x-2)&=3x \\ 5x-10&=3x \\ 5x-10-5x&=3x-5x \\ -10&=-2x \\ \frac{-10}{-2}&=\frac{-2x}{-2} \\ 5&=x \end{aligned}$$

9. $$3=\frac{3\cdot 7}{1\cdot 7}=\frac{21}{7}$$

10. $$8=\frac{8\cdot 5}{1\cdot 5}=\frac{40}{5}$$

11. $$\frac{84x}{90}=\frac{14\cdot 6x}{15\cdot 6}=\frac{14x}{15}$$

12. $$\frac{10y}{32}=\frac{5\cdot 2y}{16\cdot 2}=\frac{5y}{16}$$

13. $$-\frac{5}{16}\div\left(-\frac{3}{4}\right)=-\frac{5}{16}\cdot\left(-\frac{4}{3}\right)=\frac{5\cdot 4}{4\cdot 4\cdot 3}=\frac{5}{12}$$

14. $$-\frac{2}{5}\div\frac{7}{10}=-\frac{2}{5}\cdot\frac{10}{7}=-\frac{2\cdot 2\cdot 5}{5\cdot 7}=-\frac{4}{7}$$

15. $$-\frac{8}{10}-\left(-\frac{3}{10}\right)=\frac{-8+3}{10}=-\frac{-5}{10}=-\frac{1}{2}$$

16. $$\begin{aligned} 2\left(\frac{2}{5}\right)+3\left(-\frac{1}{5}\right)&=\frac{2\cdot 2}{1\cdot 5}-\frac{3\cdot 1}{1\cdot 5} \\ &=\frac{4}{5}-\frac{3}{5} \\ &=\frac{1}{5} \end{aligned}$$

17. $$\begin{aligned} -\frac{3}{4}-\frac{1}{14}+\frac{6}{7}&=-\frac{3\cdot 7}{4\cdot 7}-\frac{1\cdot 2}{14\cdot 2}+\frac{6\cdot 4}{7\cdot 4} \\ &=\frac{-21-2+24}{28} \\ &=\frac{1}{28} \end{aligned}$$

18. $$\begin{aligned} \frac{2}{9}+\frac{7}{15}-\frac{1}{3}&=\frac{2\cdot 5}{9\cdot 5}+\frac{7\cdot 3}{15\cdot 3}-\frac{1\cdot 15}{3\cdot 15} \\ &=\frac{10+21-15}{45} \\ &=\frac{16}{45} \end{aligned}$$

19. $$\frac{\frac{1}{2}+\frac{3}{8}}{\frac{3}{4}-\frac{1}{6}}=\frac{24\left(\frac{1}{2}+\frac{3}{8}\right)}{24\left(\frac{3}{4}-\frac{1}{6}\right)}=\frac{12+9}{18-4}=\frac{21}{14}=\frac{3}{2}$$

20. $$\frac{\frac{2}{3}+\frac{1}{6}}{\frac{3}{4}-\frac{3}{5}}=\frac{60\left(\frac{2}{3}+\frac{1}{6}\right)}{60\left(\frac{3}{4}-\frac{3}{5}\right)}=\frac{40+10}{45-36}=\frac{50}{9}$$

21. $$\begin{aligned} \frac{x}{2}&=\frac{x}{3}+\frac{1}{2} \\ \left(\frac{x}{2}\right)&=6\left(\frac{x}{3}+\frac{1}{2}\right) \\ 3x&=2x+3 \\ 3x-2x&=2x+3-2x \\ y&=3 \end{aligned}$$

22.
$$\frac{x}{2}+\frac{1}{5}=3-\frac{x}{5}$$
$$10\left(\frac{x}{2}+\frac{1}{5}\right)=10\left(3-\frac{x}{5}\right)$$
$$5x+2=30-2x$$
$$5x+2+2x=30-2x+2x$$
$$7x+2=30$$
$$7x+2-2=30-2$$
$$7x=28$$
$$\frac{7x}{7}=\frac{28}{7}$$
$$x=4$$

23. **a.** $4\frac{2}{9}=\frac{9\cdot 4+2}{9}=\frac{38}{9}$

b. $1\frac{8}{11}=\frac{11\cdot 1+8}{11}=\frac{19}{11}$

24. **a.** $3\frac{2}{5}=\frac{5\cdot 3+2}{5}=\frac{17}{5}$

b. $6\frac{2}{7}=\frac{7\cdot 6+2}{7}=\frac{44}{7}$

25. $0.125=\frac{125}{1000}=\frac{1}{8}$

26. $0.85=\frac{85}{100}=\frac{17}{20}$

27. $-105.083=-105\frac{83}{1000}$

28. $17.015=17\frac{15}{1000}=17\frac{3}{200}$

29.
$$\begin{array}{r} 85.00 \\ \underline{-17.31} \\ 67.69 \end{array}$$

30.
$$\begin{array}{r} 38.00 \\ \underline{-10.06} \\ 27.94 \end{array}$$

31. $7.68\times 10=76.8$

32. $12.483\times 100=1248.3$

33. $(-76.3)(1000)=-76,300$

34. $-853.75\times 10=-8537.5$

35. $\frac{720}{100}=7.2$
$7.2=7.2$ True
720 is a solution

36. $\frac{470}{100}=4.75$
$4.70=4.75$ False
470 is not a solution

37. $\sqrt{\frac{4}{25}}=\frac{2}{5}$

38. $\sqrt{\frac{9}{16}}=\frac{3}{4}$

39. $\frac{2.5}{3.15}=\frac{250}{315}=\frac{50}{63}$

40. $\frac{5.8}{7.6}=\frac{58}{76}=\frac{29}{38}$

41. $\frac{\$3.36}{16 \text{ ounces}}=\frac{\$0.21}{1 \text{ ounce}}$
The unit price is $0.21 per ounce.

42. $\frac{\$90}{40 \text{ square feet}}=\frac{\$2.25}{1 \text{ square foot}}$
The unit price is $2.25 per square foot.

43. $\frac{4.1}{7}=\frac{2.9}{5}$
$4.1(5)=2.9(7)$
$20.5=20.3$ False
Not a proportion

44. $\frac{6.3}{9}=\frac{3.5}{5}$
$6.3(5)=3.5(9)$
$31.5=31.5$ True
Is a proportion

45. $\frac{5}{2}=\frac{x}{7}$
$2x=35$
$x=17.5$
17.5 miles

46. $\frac{7}{6}=\frac{x}{30}$
$6x=210$
$x=35$
35 problems

47. $1.9\%=\frac{1.9}{100}=\frac{19}{1000}$

48. $2.3\%=\frac{2.3}{100}=\frac{23}{1000}$

49. $33\frac{1}{3}\%=33\frac{1}{3}\%\div 100=\frac{100}{3}\div\frac{100}{1}$
$=\frac{100}{3}\cdot\frac{1}{100}=\frac{1}{3}$

50. $108\%=\frac{108}{100}=1\frac{8}{100}=1\frac{2}{25}$

Chapter 8

Pretest

1. The lowest point occurs at April. The least number of burglaries occurred in April.

2. July had 400 burglaries.

3. September had 700 burglaries.

4. Dawn Miller's Day

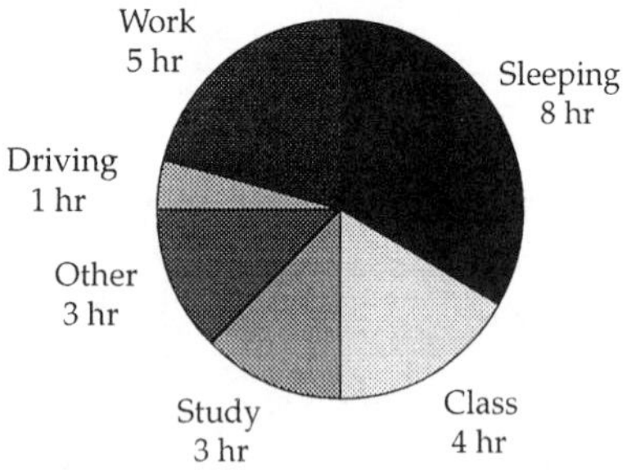

	Class Intervals (Scores)	Tally	Class Frequency (# of Exams)
5.	60 – 69	II	2
6.	70 – 79	IIII	4
7.	80 – 89	IIII	4
8.	90 – 99	~~IIII~~ I	6

9.

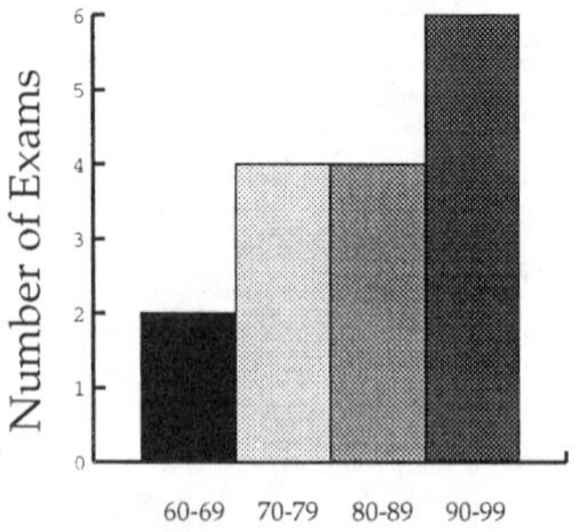

10. $$\begin{aligned} 3x + y &= -1 \\ 3(-2) + 7 &= -1 \\ -6 + 7 &= -1 \\ 1 &= -1 \quad \text{False} \end{aligned}$$

No, (–2, 7) is not a solution.

11. a. $y = 2x - 6$
$y = 2(0) - 6$
$y = 0 - 6$
$y = -6$
The ordered pair is (0, –6).

b. $y = 2x - 6$
$y = 2(-3) - 6$
$y = -6 - 6$
$y = -12$
The ordered pairs is (–3, –12).

c. $y = 2x - 6$
$0 = 2x - 6$
$0 + 6 = 2x - 6 + 6$
$6 = 2x$
$\frac{6}{2} = \frac{2x}{2}$
$3 = x$
The ordered pair is (3, 0).

12. Find 3 ordered pairs that are solutions to $y = 4x - 1$.
Let $x = 0$.
$y = 4x - 1$
$y = 4(0) - 1$
$y = 0 - 1$
$y = -1$
The ordered pair is (0, –1).
Let $x = 1$.
$y = 4x - 1$
$y = 4(1) - 1$
$y = 4 - 1$
$y = 3$
The ordered pair is (1, 3).
Let $x = -1$.
$y = 4x - 1$
$y = 4(-1) - 1$
$y = -4 - 1$
$y = -5$
The ordered pair is (–1, –5).
Plot the 3 ordered pairs. Then draw the line that contains them.

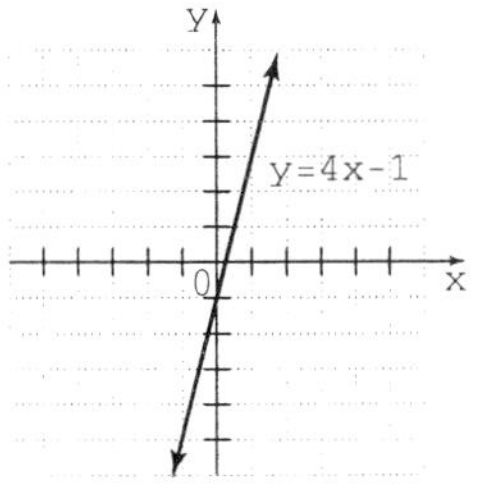

13. mean $= \dfrac{28+36+81+73+28+74+31+74+64+25+74}{11}$

$= \dfrac{588}{11}$

≈ 53.5

median: write the numbers in order to identify the middle number.
25, 28, 28, 31, 36, 64, 73, 74, 74, 74, 81
median = 64
mode: 74 is the mode because it is the number that occurs most often.

14. possible outcomes: 1, 2, 3, 4, 5, 6

probability of a 4 = $\dfrac{1}{6}$

15. possible outcomes: 1, 2, 3, 4, 5, 6

probability of a number greater than 3 = $\dfrac{3}{6} = \dfrac{1}{2}$

16. possible outcomes: 1, 2, 3, 4, 5, 6

probability of a 3 or a 5 = $\dfrac{2}{6} = \dfrac{1}{3}$

Section 8.1

Practice Problems

1. a. Each symbol indicates 50 billion kilowatt hours. Sweden shows 1.5 pictures which would indicate 1.5 × 50 = 75 billion kilowatt hours.

b. Sweden has 1.5 symbols and Russia has 2.5 symbols which make 4 symbols altogether, 40 × 5 = 200 billion kilowatt hours.

2. a. The bar for insects is between 30 and 40. Therefore there are approximately 35 endangered insects.

b. The shortest bars belong to amphibians and arachnids.

3.

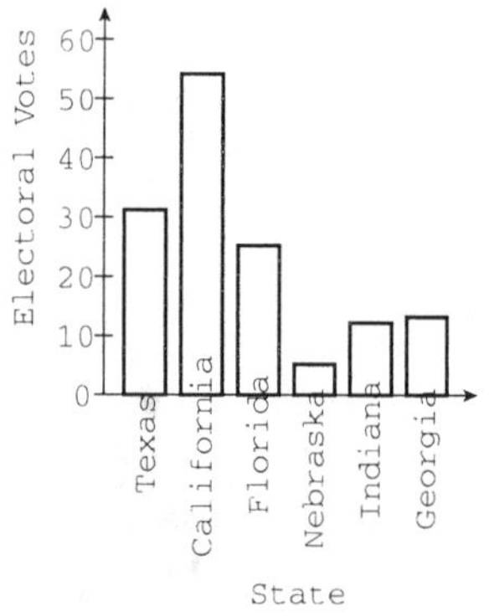

4. Look on the left to locate 70 – 79 under the Student Scores headline. Look to the right and you'll see a frequency of 10.

5. To find the amount of students who socred less than 60, add together the frequencies from the Student Scores 40 – 49 and 50 – 59. 1 + 3 = 4.

6.

Class Intervals (Credit Card Balances)	Tally	Class Frequency (Number of Months)
\$0 – \$49	III	3
\$50 – \$99	IIII	4
\$100 – \$149	II	2
\$150 – \$199	I	1
\$200 – \$249	I	1
\$250 – \$299	I	1

7.

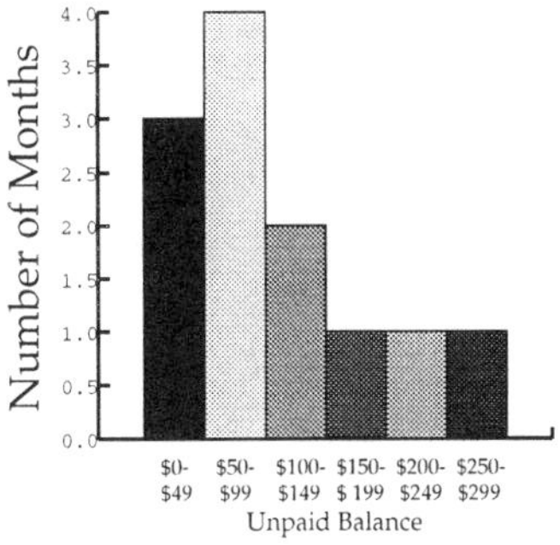

8. **a.** The month with the lowest temperature corresponds to the lowest point. Follow the lowest point down to the horizontal month scale, which reads January.

b. Locate 25°F on the vertical scale and move across horizontally until you reach a darkened point. The month for that point is December.

c. The points above the temperature of 70°F represent the months June, July, and August.

Exercise Set 8.1

1. The year 2002 has the most cars, so the greatest number of automobiles was manufactured in 2002.

3. There are eight cars for 2000, and each car represents 500 automobiles. Approximately $8 \cdot 500 = 4000$ automobiles were manufactured in 2000.

5. Compare each year with the previous year to see that the production of automobiles decreased from the previous year in 1998, 1999, and 2003.

7. The pictograph must show 8 cars for 4000 manufactured automobiles $\left(\frac{4000}{500} = 8\right)$. The years 1997 and 2000 both show 8 cars.

9. The year 1997 has 7.5 chickens and each chicken represents 3 ounces of chicken, so approximately $7.5 \cdot 3 = 22.5$ ounces of chicken were consumed per person per week in 1997.

11. To be greater than 21 ounces, the pictograph must show more than seven chickens $\left(\frac{21}{3} = 7\right)$. The years 1997, 1999, and 2001 have more than seven chickens.

13. There is one more chicken for 2001 than for 1995, so there was an increase of approximately $1 \cdot 3 = 3$ ounces per person per week.

15. The pictograph shows more chickens each year. This indicates a trend of increasing consumption of chicken per person per week in the United States.

17. The tallest bar corresponds to the month of April, so April has the most tornado-related deaths.

19. Draw a horizontal line from the top of the bar above May to the scale on the left. The approximate number of tornado-related deaths is 19.

21. Look for bars that extend above the horizontal line at 5. The months of February, March, April, May, and June have over 5 tornado-related deaths.

23. The longest bar corresponds to Tokyo with an estimated population of 34.5 million or 34,500,000 people.

25. New York City is the largest, with an estimated population of 21.4 million or 21,400,000 people.

27.

Tokyo	=	34.5 million
Sao Paulo	=	−18.5 million
		16.0 million

Tokyo is larger than Sao Paulo by 16 million or 16,000,000 people.

29.

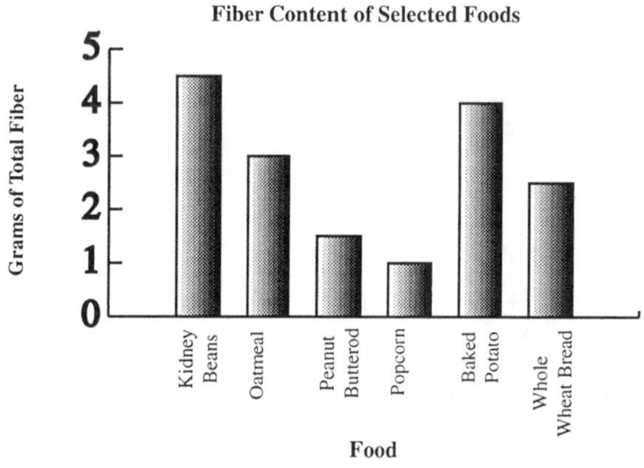

31.

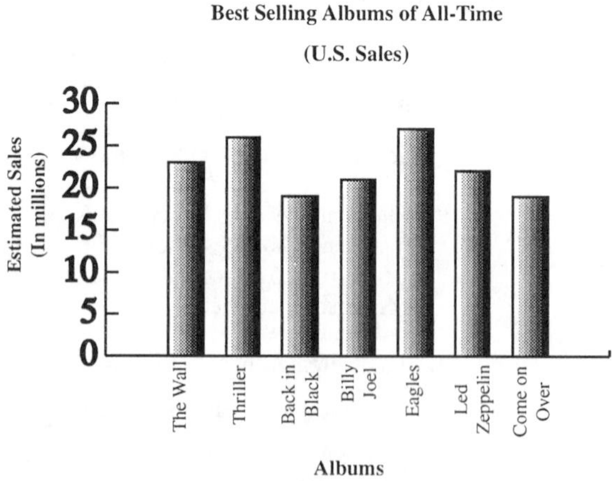

33. The bar goes up to 15. 15 adults drive between 100-149 miles per week.

35. 0 – 49 = 28 adults
50 – 99 = 17 adults
100 – 149 = 15 adults
29 + 17 + 15 = 61 adults drive fewer than 150 miles per week.

37. 100 – 149 = 15 adults
149 – 199 = 9 adults
15 + 9 = 24 adults drive between 100 – 199 miles per week.

39. 250 – 299 = 21 adults
200 – 249 = 9 adults
21 – 9 = 12 adults more drive 250 – 299 miles per week than they drive 200 – 249 miles per week.

41. $\text{ratio} = \dfrac{\text{adults who drive 150 – 199 miles}}{\text{total adults surveyed}} = \dfrac{9}{100}$

43. The highest bar is in the 45 – 54 age range.

45. The 55 – 64 age range bar goes up to 17 million householders.

47. Under 25 = 5 million
25 – 34 = 17 million
35 – 44 = 23 million
5 + 17 + 23 = 45 million householders.

49. Answer may vary.

	Class Intervals (Scores)	Tally	Class Frequency (Number of Games)
51.	70 – 79	I	1
53.	90 – 99	𝍸 III	8

	Class Intervals (Acct. Balances)	Tally	Class Frequency (Number of People)
55.	\$0 – \$99	𝍸 I	6
57.	\$200 – \$299	𝍸 I	6
59.	\$400 – \$499	II	2

61.

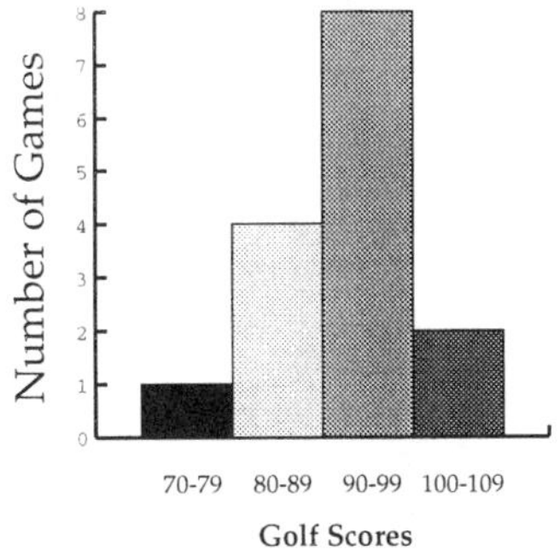

63. In 1994, there was an average of approximately 2.7 field goals per game.

65. 1982 had the highest average number of field goals per game.

67. The average number of field goals per game decreased between 1998 and 2000.

69. $30\% \cdot 12 = 0.3 \cdot 12 = 3.6$

71. $10\% \cdot 62 = 0.1 \cdot 62 = 6.2$

73. $\frac{1}{4} = 0.25 = 25\%$

75. $\frac{17}{50} = 0.34 = 34\%$

77. 83°F was the high temperature reading on Thursday.

79. The lowest temperature occurred on Sunday wit 68°F.

81. The greatest difference between high and low temperatures occurred on Tuesday with a difference of $86 - 73 = 13$°F.

83. Answers may vary.

Section 8.2

Practice Problems

1. $\frac{\text{10 people preferring oatmeal raisin cookies}}{\text{100 people}} = \frac{10}{100} = \frac{1}{10}$

2. Two + Three + Four or More = 15% + 6% + 3% = 24%

3. Four or more = 3%
$= 3\% \cdot 288{,}400{,}000$
$= 0.03 \cdot 288{,}400{,}000$
$= 8{,}652{,}000$ Americans

4. Freshman $30\% \cdot 360° = 108°$
Sophomores $27\% \cdot 360° = 97.2° \approx 97°$
Juniors $25\% \cdot 360° = 90°$
Seniors $18\% \cdot 360° = 64.8° \approx 65°$

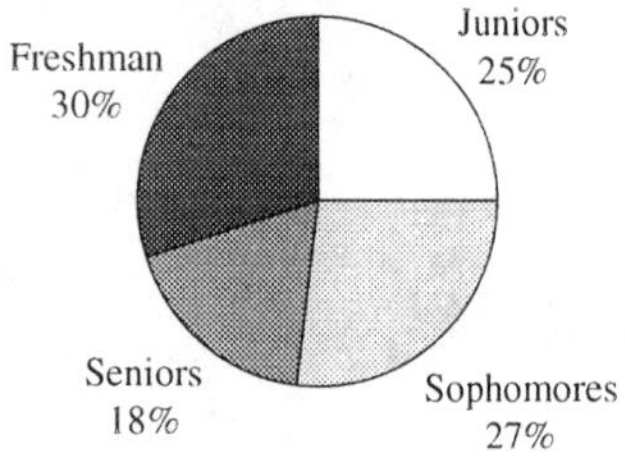

Exercise Set 8.2

1. The largest sector, or 320 students, corresponds to where most college students live. Most college students live at parent or guardian's home.

3. $\frac{\text{Students living in campus housing}}{\text{total students}}$
$= \frac{180}{700} = \frac{9}{35}$

5. $\frac{\text{Students living in campus housing}}{\text{students living at home}}$
$= \frac{180}{320} = \frac{9}{16}$

7. The largest sector is 30% which corresponds to Asia which is the largest continent.

9. Asia + Europe = 30% + 7% = 37%
37% of the land on Earth is accounted for by Asia and Europe.

11. $\text{Asia} = 30\% \cdot 57{,}000{,}000$
$= 0.30 \cdot 57{,}000{,}000$
$= 17{,}100{,}000$ square miles

11. $\text{Austrailia} = 5\% \cdot 57{,}000{,}000$
$= 0.05 \cdot 57{,}000{,}000$
$= 2{,}850{,}000$ square miles

15. The sectors which represent fiction are "Adult Fiction" and Children's Fiction."
percent = 33% + 22% = 55%

17. The second-largest sector is 25% which corresponds to "Nonfiction." Nonfiction is the second-largest category of books.

19. $\text{amount} = 25\% \cdot 125{,}600$
$= 0.25 \cdot 125{,}600$
$= 31{,}400$ books
This library has 31,400 nonfiction books.

21. $\text{amount} = 22\% \cdot 125{,}600$
$= 0.25 \cdot 125{,}600$
$= 31{,}400$ books
This library has 27,632 books in children's fiction.

23. $\text{amount} = (17\% + 3\%) \cdot 125{,}600$
$= 20\% \cdot 125{,}600$
$= 0.2 \cdot 125{,}600$
$= 25{,}120$
This library has 25,120 books in reference or other category.

25.

United States	$75\% \cdot 360° = 270°$
Japan	$11\% \cdot 360° = 40°$
Germany	$6\% \cdot 360° = 20°$
Other Countries	$8\% \cdot 360° = 30°$

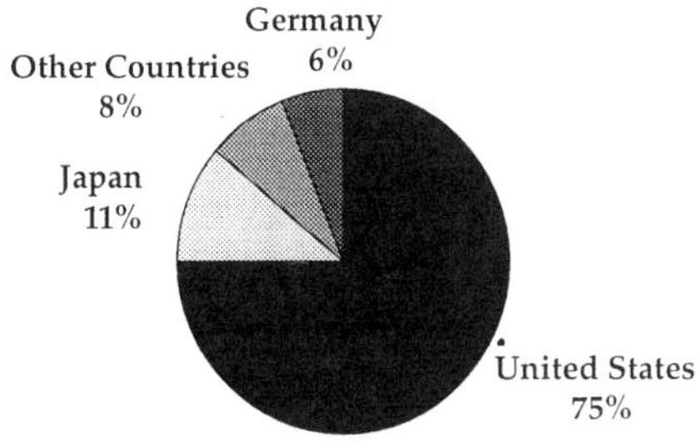

27.

Under 3 days	$7\% \cdot 360° = 25°$
3 – 10 days	$18\% \cdot 360° = 65°$
11 – 20 days	$14\% \cdot 360° = 50°$
21 or more days	$61\% \cdot 360° = 220°$

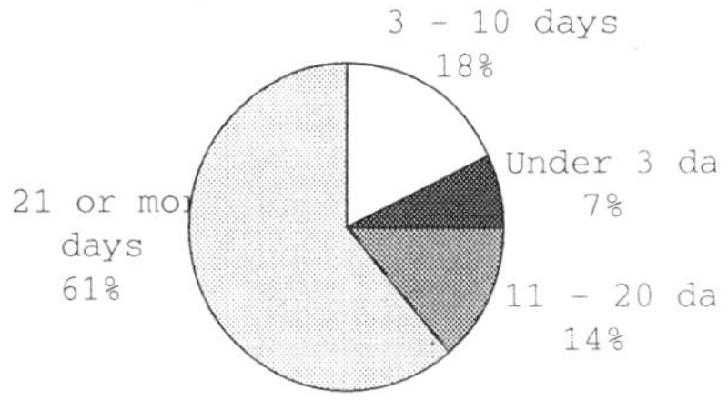

29. $20 = 4 \cdot 5 = 2 \cdot 2 \cdot 5 = 2^2 \cdot 5$

31. $40 = 8 \cdot 5 = 2 \cdot 2 \cdot 2 \cdot 5 = 2^3 \cdot 5$

33. $85 = 5 \cdot 17$

35. Pacific; answers may vary.

37. Pacific Ocean:
$49\% \cdot 264{,}489{,}800 = 0.49 \cdot 264{,}489{,}800$
$= 129{,}600{,}002$
The Pacific Ocean is 129,600,002 square kilometers.

39. Indian Ocean:
$21\% \cdot 264{,}489{,}800 = 0.21 \cdot 264{,}489{,}800$
$= 55{,}542{,}858$
The Indian Ocean is 55,542,858 square kilometers.

41. $21.5\% \cdot 2800 = 0.215 \cdot 2800 = 602$ respondents spend \$0 –\$15 online each month.

43. at least \$15 + over \$175 =\$175
=59.8% + 18.7% = 78.5%
$0.785 \cdot 2800 = 2198$ respondents.

45. $\text{ratio} = \dfrac{\$0-\$15}{\$15-\$75} = \dfrac{602}{1674} = \dfrac{301}{837}$

47. No; answers may vary.

Section 8.3

Practice Problems

1.

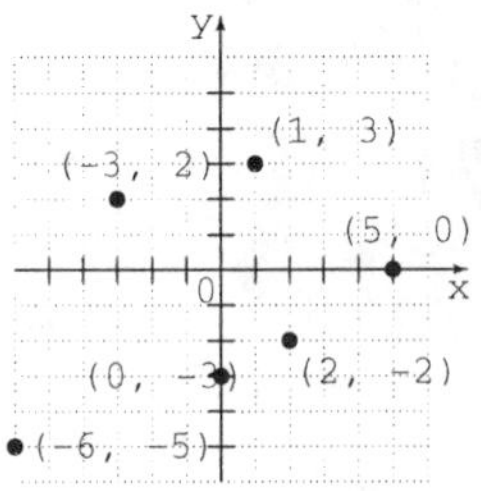

2. Point *A* has coordinates (5, 0).
Point *B* has coordinates (–2, 0).
Point *C* has coordinates (–3, –4).
Point *D* has coordinates (0, –1).
Point *E* has coordinates (2, 1).

3.
$$\begin{aligned} x + 3y &= -12 \\ 0 + 3(-4) &= -12 \\ -12 &= -12 \text{ True} \end{aligned}$$
Yes $(0, -4)$ is a solution.

4.

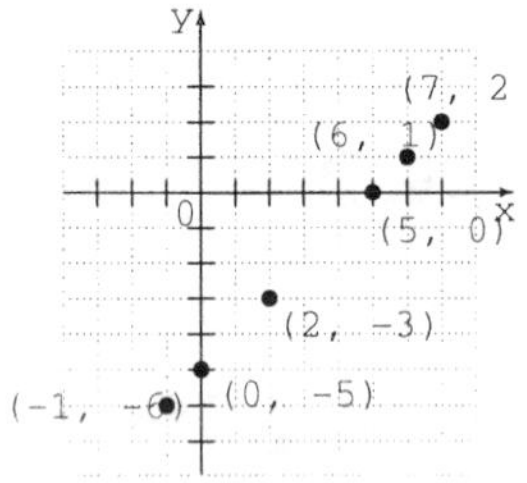

5. a.
$$\begin{aligned} x + y &= 10 \\ 5 + y &= 10 \\ 5 + y - 5 &= 10 - 5 \\ y &= 5 \end{aligned}$$
The solution is (5, 5).

b.
$$\begin{aligned} x + y &= 10 \\ 0 + y &= 10 \\ y &= 10 \end{aligned}$$
The solution is (0, 10).

c.
$$\begin{aligned} x + y &= 10 \\ x + (-2) &= 10 \\ x - 2 &= 10 \\ x - 2 + 2 &= 10 + 2 \\ x &= 12 \end{aligned}$$
The solution is (12, –2).

6. a.
$$\begin{aligned} y &= 5x + 2 \\ y &= 5(0) + 2 \\ y &= 2 \end{aligned}$$
The solution is (0,2).

b.
$$\begin{aligned} y &= 5x + 2 \\ -3 &= 5x + 2 \\ -3 - 2 &= 5x + 2 - 2 \\ -5 &= 5x \\ \frac{-5}{5} &= \frac{5x}{5} \\ -1 &= x \end{aligned}$$
The solution is (-2.-4).

Exercise Set 8.3

1.

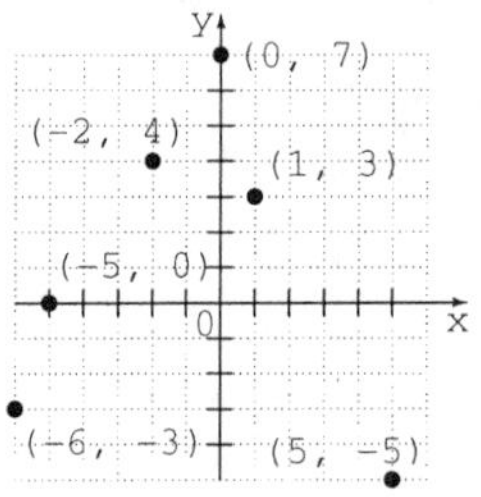

3.

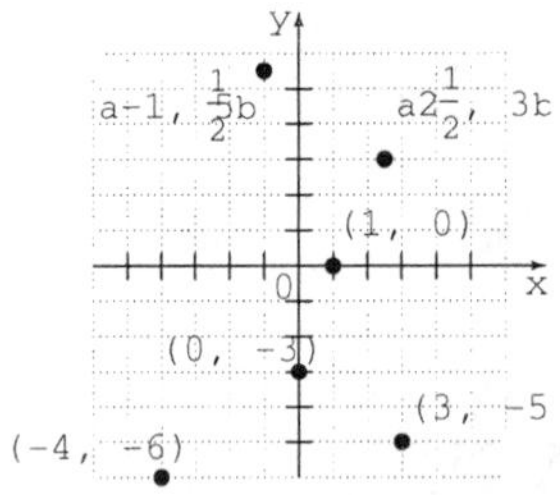

5. Point *A* has coordinates (0, 0).
Point *B* has coordinates $\left(3\frac{1}{2},\ 0\right)$.
Point *C* has coordinates (3, 2).
Point *D* has coordinates (–1, 3).
Point *E* has coordinates (–2, –2).
Point *F* has coordinates (0, –1).
Point *G* has coordinates (2, –1).

7. $y = -10x$

$0 = -10(0)$

$0 = 0$ True

Yes, (0, 0) is a solution.

9. $x - y = 3$

$1 - 2 = 3$

$-1 = 3$ False

No, (1, 2) is not a solution.

11. $y = 2x + 1$

$-3 = 2(-2) + 1$

$-3 = -4 + 1$

$-3 = -3$ True

Yes, (–2, –3) is a solution.

13. $y = -4x$

$-8 = -4 \cdot 2$

$-8 = -8$ True

Yes, (2, –8) is a solution.

15. $2x + 3y = 10$

$2(5) + 3(0) = 10$

$10 + 0 = 10$

$10 = 10$ True

Yes, (5, 0) is a solution.

17. $x - 5y = -1$

$3 - 5(1) = -1$

$3 - 5 = -1$

$-2 = -1$ False

No, (3, 1) is not a solution. of $x - 5y = -1$.

19. $2x + y = 5$; (1, 3), (0, 5), (3, –1)

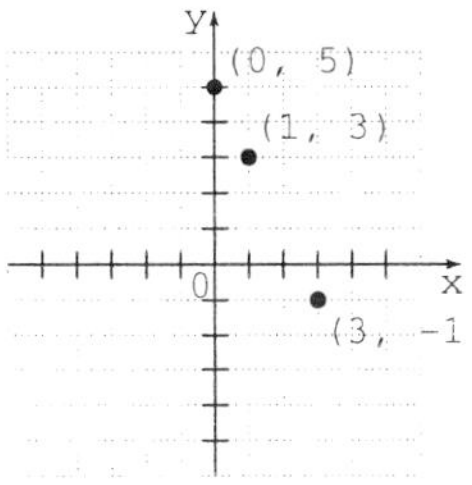

21. $x = 5y$; (5, 1), (0, 0), (–5, –1)

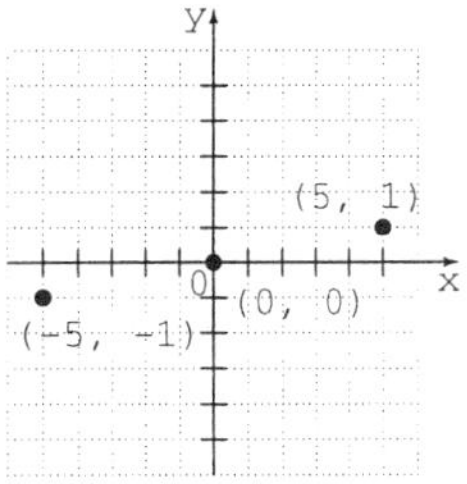

23. $x - y = 7$; (8, 1), (2, –5), (0, –7)

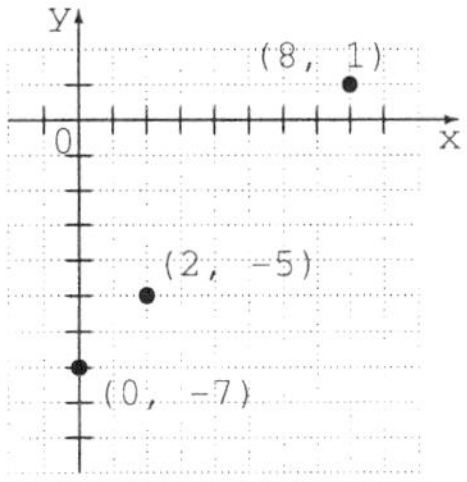

25. $y = 8x$
$y = 8(1)$
$y = 8$
The solution is (1, 8).
$y = 8x$
$y = 8(0)$
$y = 0$
The solution is (0, 0), the origin.
$y = 8x$
$-16 = 8x$
$\frac{-16}{8} = \frac{8x}{8}$
$-2 = x$
The solution is (–2, –16).

27. $x + y = 14$

$2 + y = 14$

$2 + y - 2 = 14 - 2$

$y = 12$

The solution is (2, 12).

$x + y = 14$

$x + (-8) = 14$

$x - 8 + 8 = 14 + 8$

$x = 22$

The solution is (22, –8).

$x + y = 14$

$0 + y = 14$

$y = 14$

The solution is (0, 14).

29. $y = x + 5$
$y = 1 + 5$
$y = 6$
The solution is (1, 6).

$y = x + 5$
$7 = x + 5$
$7 - 5 = x + 5 - 5$
$2 = x$
The solution is (2, 7).
$y = x + 5$
$y = 3 + 5$
$y = 8$
The solution is (3, 8).

31. $y = 3x - 5$
$y = 3(1) - 5$
$y = 3 - 5$
$y = -2$
The solution is (1, –2).
$y = 3x - 5$
$y = 3(2) - 5$
$y = 6 - 5$
$y = 1$
The solution is (2, 1).
$y = 3x - 5$
$y = 3(3) - 5$
$y = 9 - 5$
$y = 4$
The solution is (3, 4).

33. $y = -x$
$0 = -x$
$\frac{0}{-1} = \frac{-x}{-1}$
$0 = x$
The solution is (0, 0).
$y = -x$
$y = -(2)$
$y = -2$
The solution is (2, –2).
$y = -x$
$2 = -x$
$\frac{2}{-1} = \frac{-x}{-1}$
$-2 = x$
The solution is (–2, 2).

35. $x + y = -2$
$-2 + y = -2$
$-2 + y + 2 = -2 + 2$
$y = 0$
The solution is (–2, 0).
$x + y = -2$
$1 + y = -2$
$1 + y - 1 = -2 - 1$
$y = -3$
The solution is (1, –3).
$x + y = -2$
$x + 5 = -2$
$x + 5 - 5 = -2 - 5$
$x = -7$
The solution is (–7, 5).

37. $5.6 - 3.9 = 1.7$

39.
$$\begin{array}{r} 5.6 \\ \times\ 3.9 \\ \hline 5\ 04 \\ 16\ 80 \\ \hline 21.84 \end{array}$$

41. $(0.236)(-100) = -23.6$

43.
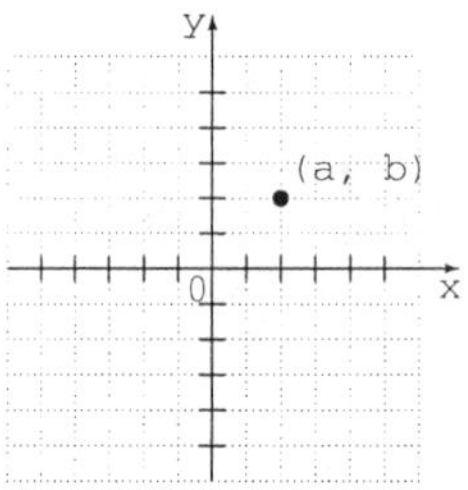

True

45.
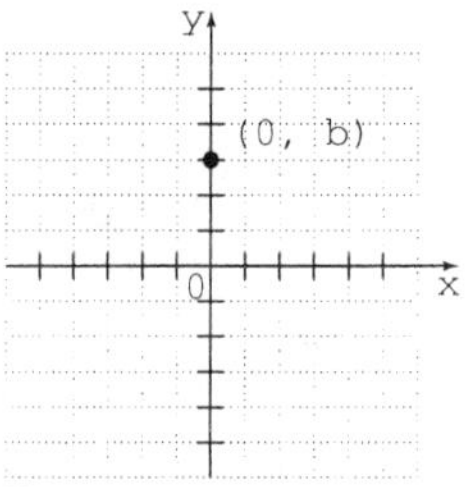

True

47.
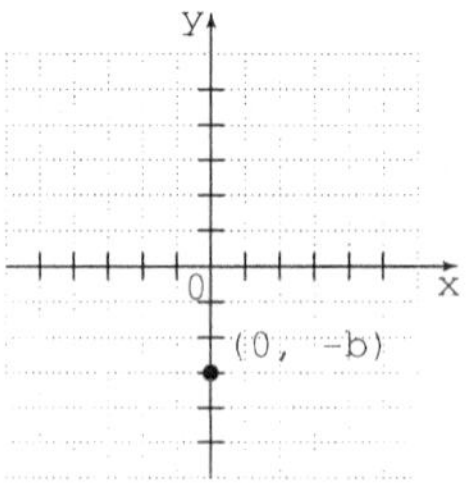

False

49.

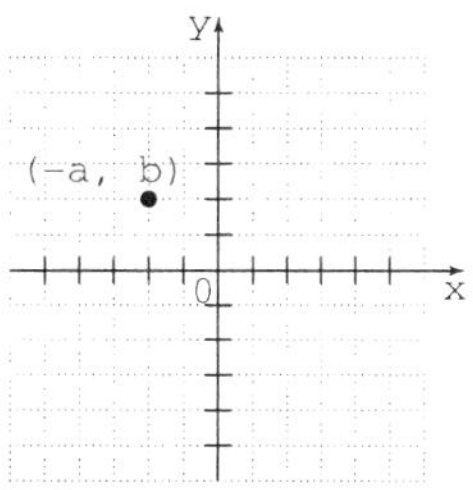

False

51. **a.** The ordered pair is plotted to the right of the y.-axis.
b. The ordered pair is plotted below the x-axis.

53.

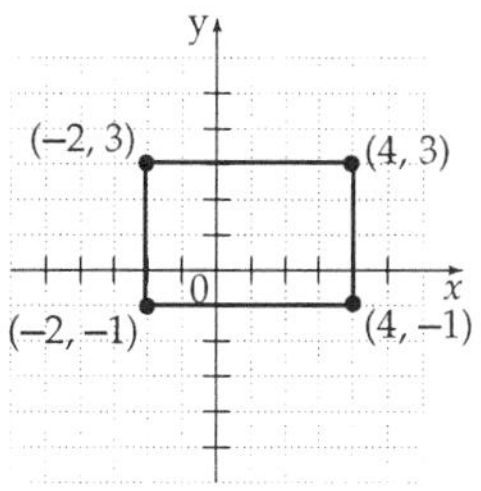

55. Length = 6 units
Width = 4 units
$P = 6 + 6 + 4 + 4 = 20$ units

Integrated Review

1. In 1995 the graph has 6.9 pictures. Each picture represents 10 pounds. The approximate number of pounds of beef and veal consumed per person is $10 \cdot 6 \cdot 9 = 69$ pounds.

2. For the year 1980, the graph has 7.8 pictures. Each picture represents 10 pounds. The approximate number of pounds of beef and veal consumed per person is $10 \cdot 7.8 = 78$ pounds.

3. The number of pounds of beef and veal consumed was the greatest in 1985.

4. The number of pounds of beef and veal consumed was the least in 1995 and 2000.

5. The dam with the greatest height is represented by the tallest bar. The height of this bar is approximately 755 feet. Therefore, the Oroville Dam has the greatest height of approximately 755 feet.

6. The bar with a height between 625 feet and 650 feet is the one representing New Bullards Bar Dam. The New Bullards Bar Dam has a height of approximately 635 feet.

7. Find the difference in the heights of the bars representing these dams.
$725 - 710 = 15$
The Hoover Dam is approximately 15 feet taller than the Glen Canyon Dam.

8. There are 4 bars that have heights over 700 feet. Therefore, there are 4 United States dams that are over 700 feet.

9. Locate the highest points. Thursday and Saturday with temperatures of 100°F are the days with the highest temperature.

10. Locate the lowest point. Monday with a temperature of 82°F is the day with the lowest temperature.

11. There are three points below 90°F. The days corresponding to these points are Sunday, Monday, and Tuesday.

12. There are four points above 90°F. The days corresponding to these points are Wednesday, Thursday, Friday, and Saturday.

13. Whole milk: $35\% \cdot 200 = 70$ quart containers

14. Skim milk: $26\% \cdot 200 = 52$ quart containers

15. Buttermilk: $1\% \cdot 200 = 2$ quart containers

16. Flavored reduced fat and skim milk:
$3\% \cdot 200 = 6$ quart containers

	Class Intervals (Scores)	Tally	Class Frequency (# of Quizzes)
17.	50 – 59	||	2
18.	60 – 69	|	1
19.	70 – 79	|||	3
20.	80 – 89	~~||||~~ |	6
21.	90 – 99	~~||||~~	5

22.

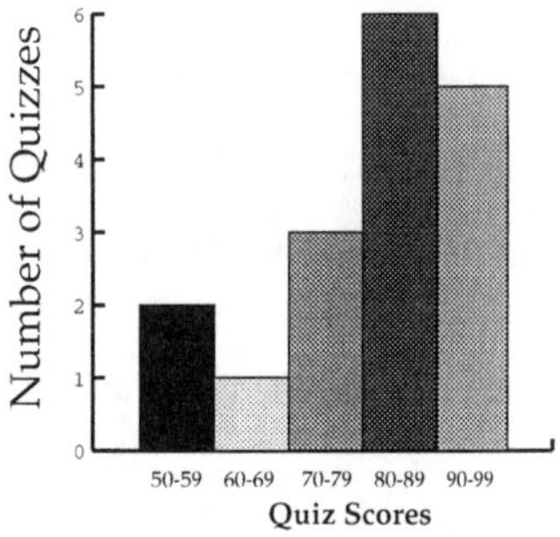

23.

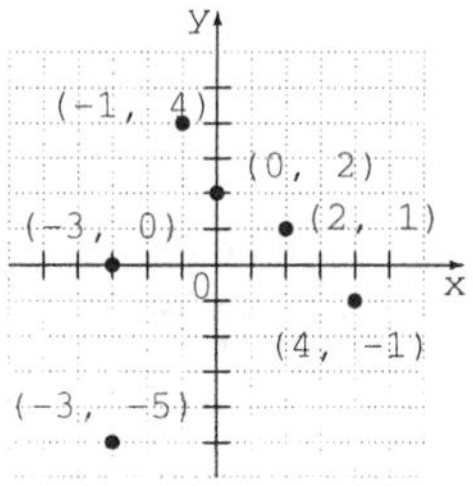

24. $x = 3y$
$1 = 3(3)$
$1 = 9$ False
No, it is not a solution.

25. $x + y = -6$
$-2 + (-4) = -6$
$-6 = -6$ True
Yes, it is a solution.

26. $x - y = 6$
$0 - y = 6$
$-y = 6$
$\frac{-y}{-1} = \frac{6}{-1}$
$y = -6$
The solution is (0, –6).
$x - y = 6$
$x - 0 = 6$
$x = 6$
The solution is (6, 0).
$x - y = 6$
$2 - y = 6$
$2 - y - 2 = 6 - 2$
$-y = 4$
$\frac{-y}{-1} = \frac{4}{-1}$
$y = -4$
The solution is (2, –4).

Section 8.4

Practice Problems

1.

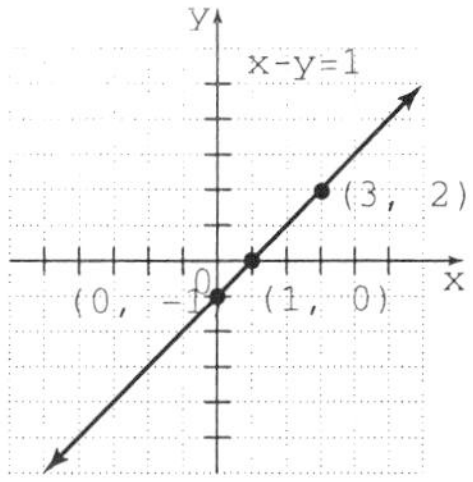

2. Let $x = 0$.
$y - x = 6$
$y - 0 = 6$
$y = 6$
The ordered pair is (0, 6).
Let $y = 0$.
$y - x = 6$
$0 - x = 6$
$-x = 6$
$\frac{-x}{-1} = \frac{6}{-1}$
$x = -6$
The ordered pair is (–6, 0).
Let $x = 4$.
$y - x = 6$
$y - 4 = 6$
$y - 4 + 4 = 6 + 4$
$y = 10$

The ordered pair is (4, 10). Plot the three ordered pairs. Then draw the line through them.

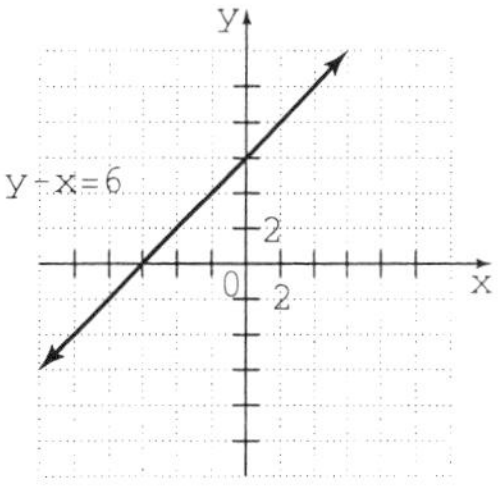

3.

x	$y = -3x + 2$
0	$-3 \cdot 0 + 2 = 2$
1	$-3 \cdot 1 + 2 = -1$
2	$-3 \cdot 2 + 2 = -4$

Plot the three ordered pairs. Then draw the line through them.

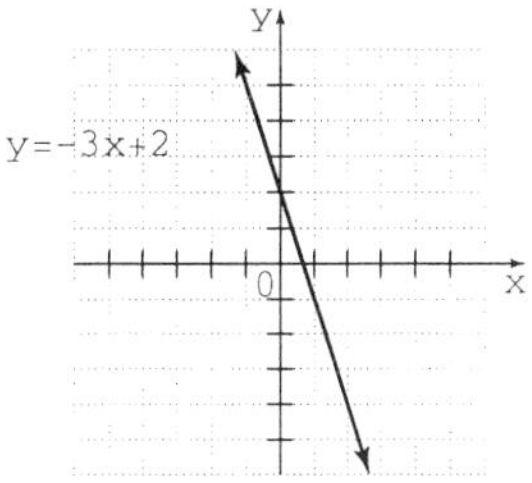

4.

x	$y = -1$
–5	–1
0	–1
5	–1

Plot the three ordered pairs. Then draw the line through them.

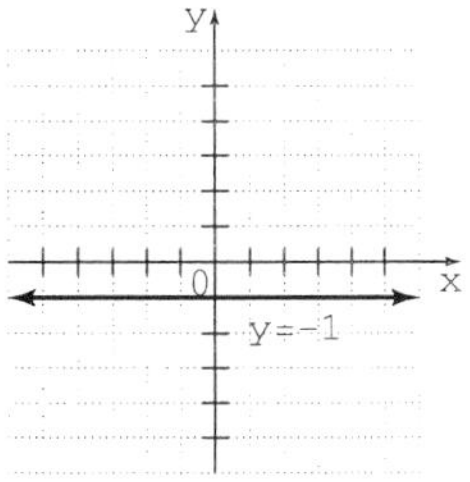

5.

$x = 5$	y
5	–5
5	0
5	5

Plot the three ordered pairs. Then draw the line through them.

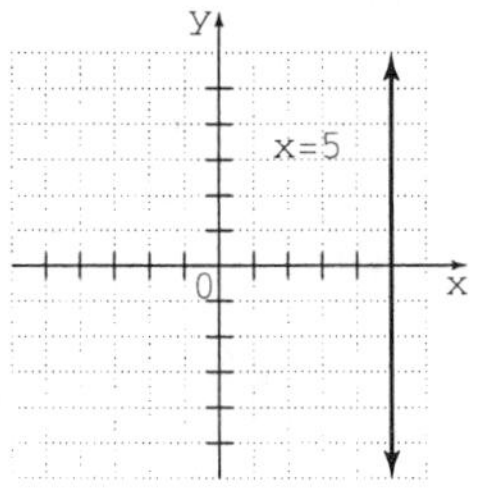

Exercise Set 8.4

1. $x + y = 6$
Find any 3 ordered pair solutions.
Let $x = 0$.

$x + y = 6$

$0 + y = 6$

$y = 6$

(0, 6)
Let $x = 3$.

$x + y = 6$

$3 + y = 6$

$3 + y \cdot 3 = 6 - 3$

$y = 3$

(3, 3)
Let $x = 6$.

$x + y = 6$

$6 + y = 6$

$6 + y - 6 = 6 - 6$

$y = 0$

(6, 0)
Plot (0, 6), (3, 3), and (6, 0). Then draw the line through them.

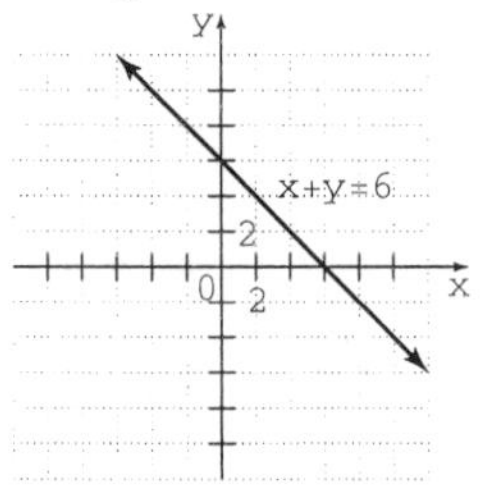

3. $x - y = -2$
Let $x = -2$.

$x - y = -2$

$-2 - y = -2$

$-2 - y + 2 = -2 + 2$

$-y = 0$

$y = 0$

(−2, 0)
Let $x = 0$.

$x - y = -2$

$0 - y = -2$

$-y = -2$

$y = 2$

(0, 2)
Let $x = 2$.

$x - y = -2$

$2 - y = -2$

$2 - y - 2 = -2 - 2$

$-y = -4$

$y = 4$

(2, 4)
Plot (−2, 0), (0, 2), and (2, 4). Then draw the line through them.

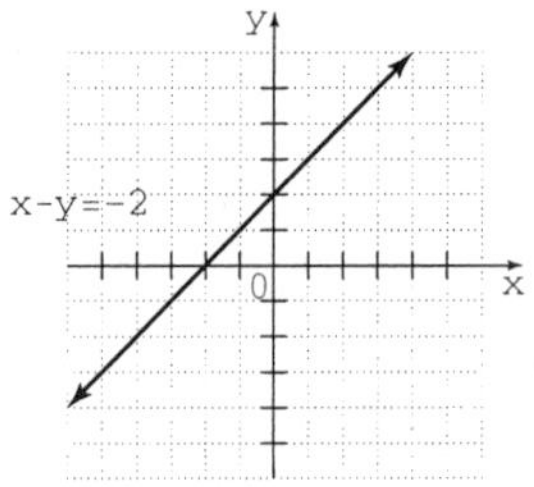

5. $y = 4x$
Find any 3 ordered pair solutions.
Let $x = 0$.

$y = 4x$

$y = 4(0)$

$y = 0$

(0, 0)
Let $x = 1$.

$y = 4x$

$y = 4(1)$

$y = 4$

(1, 4)
Let $x = -1$.
$y = 4x$
$y = 4(-1)$
$y = -4$
(−1, −4)
Plot (0, 0), (1, 4), and (−1, −4). Then draw the

line through them.

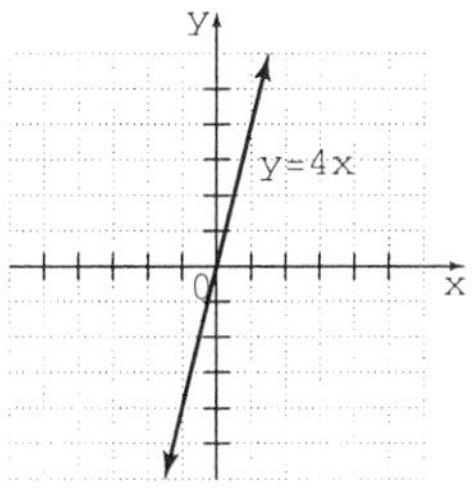

7. $y = 2x - 1$

x	$y = 2x - 1$
−1	$2(-1) - 1 = -2 - 1 = -3$
0	$2(0) - 1 = 0 - 1 = -1$
1	$2(1) - 1 = 2 - 1 = 1$

Plot (−1, −3), (0, −1) and (1, 1). Then draw the line through them.

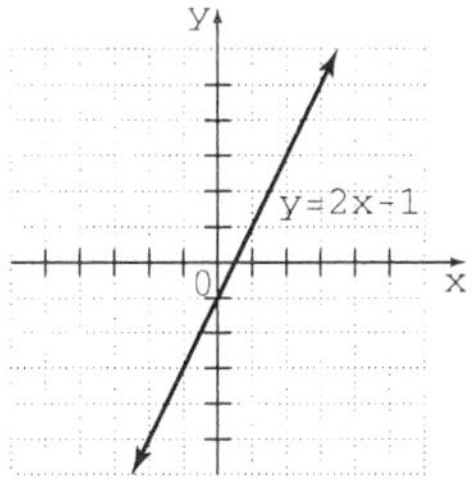

9. $x = 5$
No matter what y-value we choose, x is always 5.

x	y
5	−4
5	0
5	4

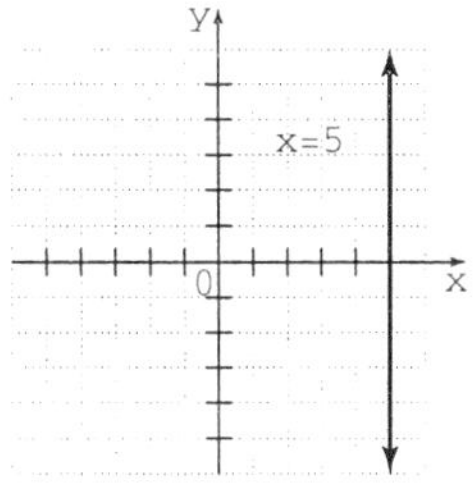

11. $y = -3$
No matter what x-value we choose, y is always −3.

y	y
−5	−3
0	−3
5	−3

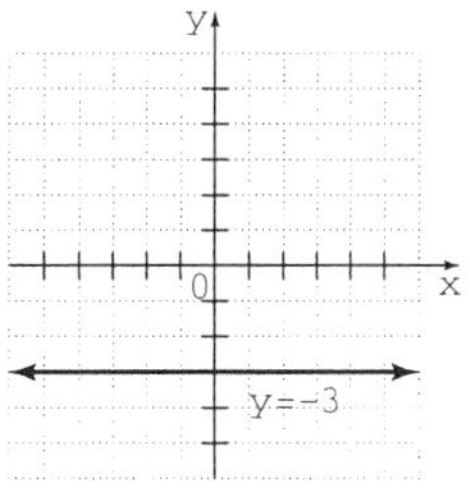

13. $x = 0$
No matter what y-value we choose, x is always 0.

x	y
0	−3
0	0
0	3

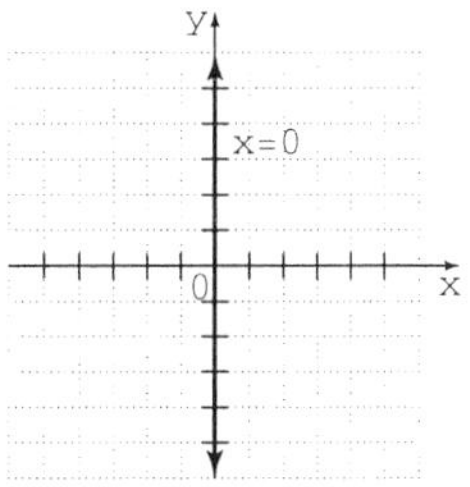

15. $y = -2x$

x	$y = -2x$
−2	$-2(-2) = 4$
0	$-2(0) = 0$
2	$-2(2) = -4$

Plot (−2, 4), (0, 0), and (2, −4). Then draw the line through them.

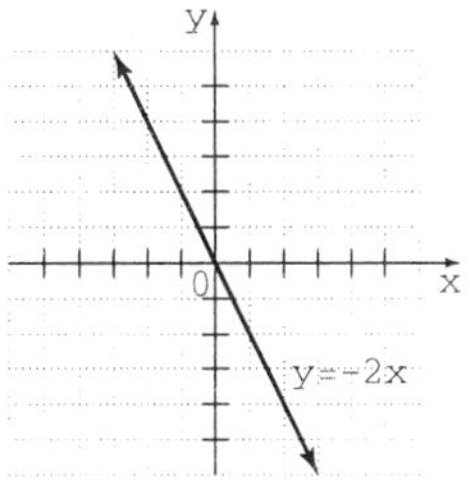

17. $y = -2$
No matter what x-value we choose, y is always −2.

x	y
−4	−2
0	−2

4	–2

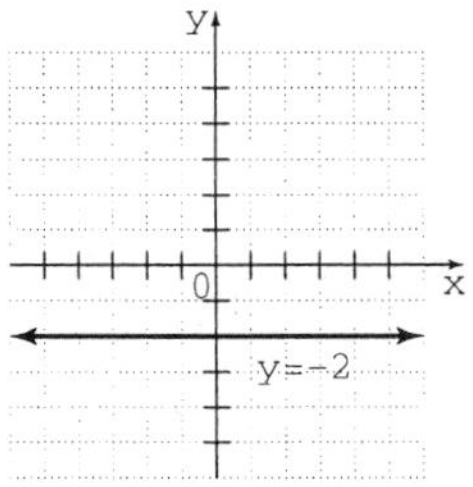

19. $x + 2y = 12$
Let $x = 0$.

$$x + 2y = 12$$
$$0 + 2y = 12$$
$$2y = 12$$
$$y = 6$$

(0, 6)
Let $y = 0$.

$$x + 2y = 12$$
$$x + 2(0) = 12$$
$$x + 0 = 12$$
$$x = 12$$

(12, 0)
Let $x = 6$.

$$x + 2y = 12$$
$$6 + 2y = 12$$
$$6 + 2y - 6 = 12 - 6$$
$$2y = 6$$
$$y = 3$$

(6, 3)
Plot (0, 6), (12, 0), and (6, 3). Then draw the line through them.

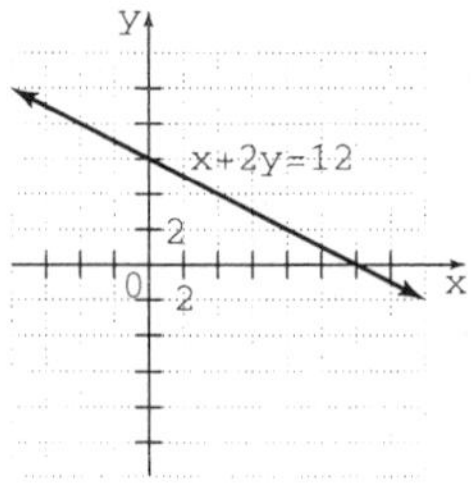

21. $x = 6$
No matter what y-value we choose, x is always 6.

x	y
6	–5
6	0
6	5

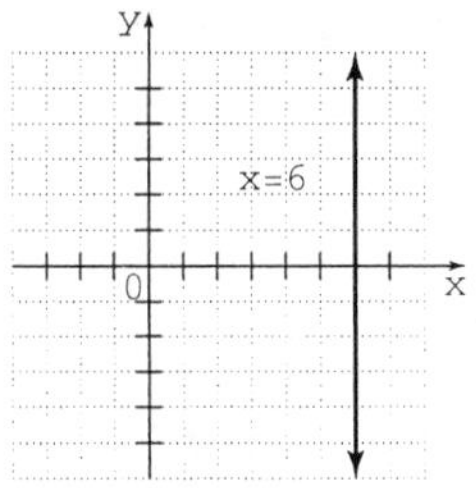

23. $y = x - 3$

x	$y = x - 3$
0	$0 - 3 = -3$
3	$3 - 3 = 0$
6	$6 - 3 = 3$

Plot (0, –3), (3, 0), and (6, 3). Then draw the line through them.

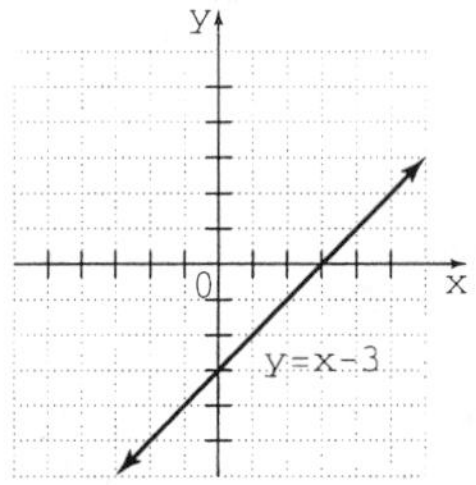

25. $x = y - 4$
Find any 3 ordered pair solutions.
Let $y = 0$.
$x = y - 4$
$x = 0 - 4$
$x = -4$
(–4, 0)
Let $y = 4$.
$x = y - 4$
$x = 4 - 4$
$x = 0$
(0, 4)
Let $y = 6$.
$x = y - 4$
$x = 6 - 4$
$x = 2$
(2, 6)
Plot (–4, 0), (0, 4), and (2, 6). Then draw the line through them.

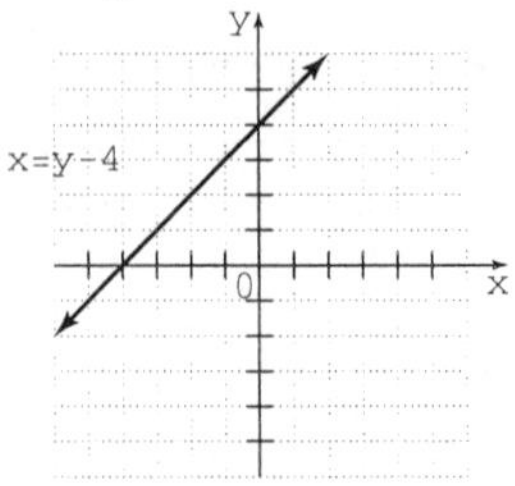

27. $x + 3 = 0$

$x + 3 = 0$

$x + 3 - 3 = 0 - 3$

$x = -3$

No matter what y-value we choose, x is always -3.

x	y
-3	4
-3	0
-3	-4

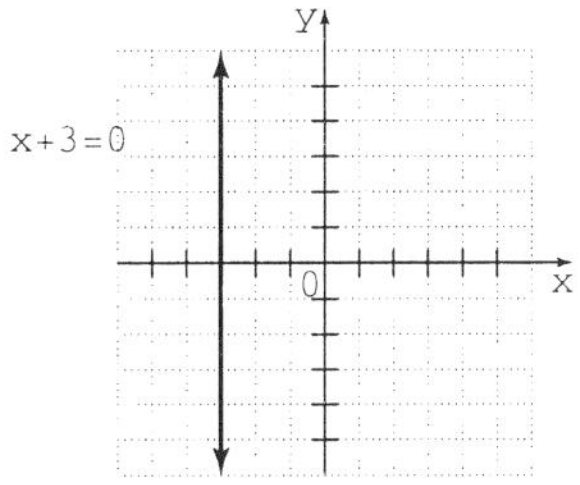

29. $x = 4y$

Find any 3 ordered pair solutions.

Let $y = -1$.

$x = 4y$

$x = 4(-1)$

$x = -4$

$(-4, -1)$

Let $y = 0$.

$x = 4y$

$x = 4(0)$

$x = 0$

$(0, 0)$

Let $y = 1$.

$x = 4y$

$x = 4(1)$

$x = 4$

$(4, 1)$

Plot $(-4, -1)$, $(0, 0)$, and $(4, 1)$. Then draw the line through them.

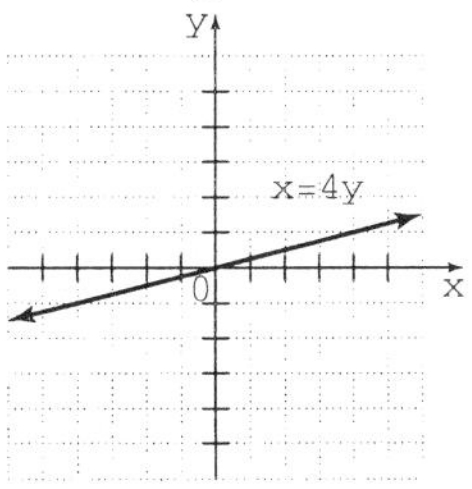

31. $y = \frac{1}{3}x$

x	$y = \frac{1}{3}x$
0	$\frac{1}{3}(0) = 0$
3	$\frac{1}{3}(3) = 1$
6	$\frac{1}{3}(3) = 2$

Plot $(0, 0)$, $(3, 1)$, and $(6, 2)$. Then draw the line thorough them.

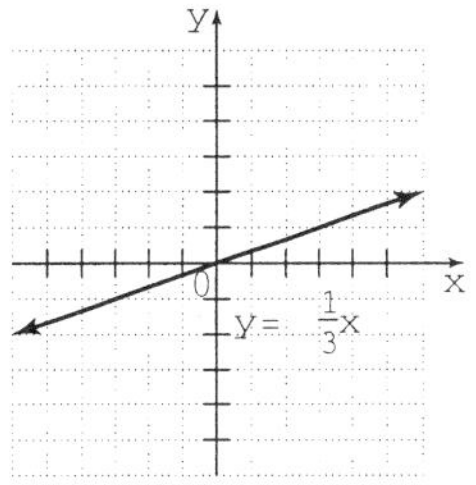

33. $y = 4x + 2$

Find any 3 ordered pair solutions.

$x = -1$

$y = 4x + 2$

$y = 4(-1) + 2$

$y = -4 + 2$

$y = -2$

$(-1, -2)$

$x = 0$

$y = 4x + 2$

$y = 4(0) + 2$

$y = 0 + 2$

$y = 2$

$(0, 2)$

$x = 1$

$y = 4x + 2$

$y = 4(1) + 2$

$y = 4 + 2$

$y = 6$

$(1, 6)$

Plot $(-1, -2)$, $(0, 2)$, and $(1, 6)$. Then draw the line through them.

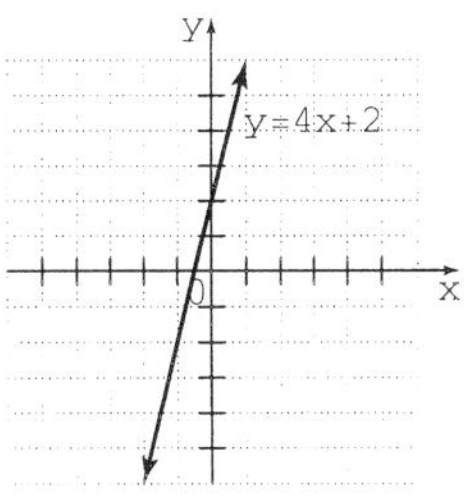

35. $2x + 3y = 6$

Let $x = -3$.

$$\begin{aligned} 2x + 3y &= 6 \\ 2(-3) + 3y &= 6 \\ -6 + 3y &= 6 \\ -6 + 3y + 6 &= 6 + 67 \\ 3y &= 12 \\ y &= 4 \end{aligned}$$

$(-3, 4)$

Let $x = 0$.

$$\begin{aligned} 2x + 3y &= 6 \\ 2(0) + 3y &= 6 \\ 0 + 3y &= 6 \\ 3y &= 6 \\ y &= 2 \end{aligned}$$

$(0, 2)$

Let $y = 0$.

$$\begin{aligned} 2x + 3y &= 6 \\ 2x + 3(0) &= 6 \\ 2x + 0 &= 6 \\ 2x &= 6 \\ x &= 3 \end{aligned}$$

$(3, 0)$

Plot $(-3, 4)$, $(0, 2)$, and $(3, 0)$. Then draw the line through them.

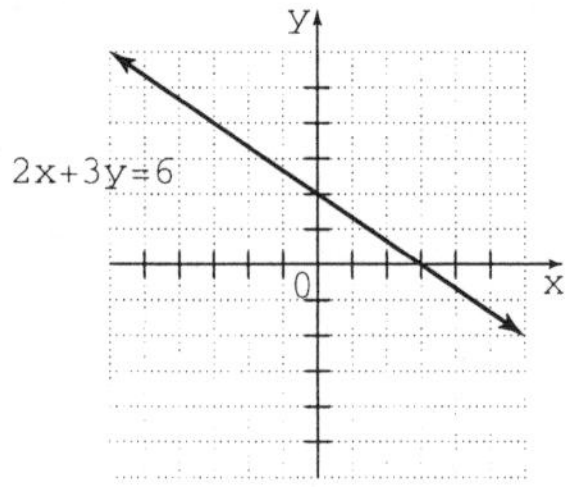

37. $x = -3.5$

No matter what y-value we choose, x is always -3.5.

x	y
−3.5	−3
−3.5	0
−3.5	3

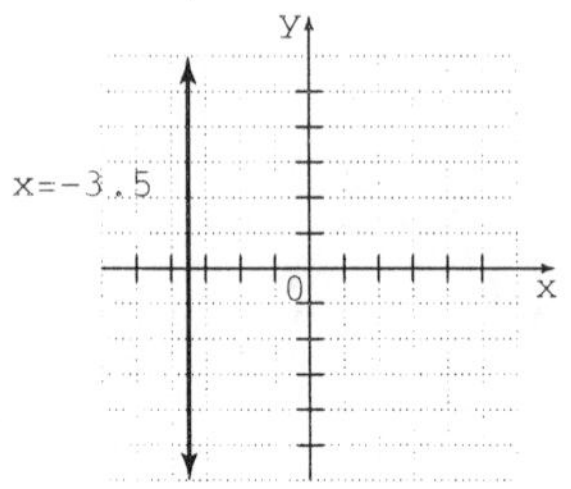

39. $3x - 4y = 24$

Let $x = 0$.

$$\begin{aligned} 3x - 4y &= 24 \\ 3(0) - 4y &= 24 \\ 0 - 4y &= 24 \\ -4y &= 24 \\ y &= -6 \end{aligned}$$

$(0, -6)$

Let $y = 0$.

$$\begin{aligned} 3x - 4y &= 24 \\ 3x - 4(0) &= 24 \\ 3x - 0 &= 24 \\ 3x &= 24 \\ x &= 8 \end{aligned}$$

$(8, 0)$

Let $x = 4$.

$$\begin{aligned} 3x - 4y &= 24 \\ 3(4) - 4y &= 24 \\ 12 - 4y &= 24 \\ 12 - 4y - 12 &= 24 - 12 \\ -4y &= 12 \\ y &= -3 \end{aligned}$$

$(4, -3)$

Plot $(0, -6)$, $(8, 0)$, and $(4, -3)$. Then draw the line through them.

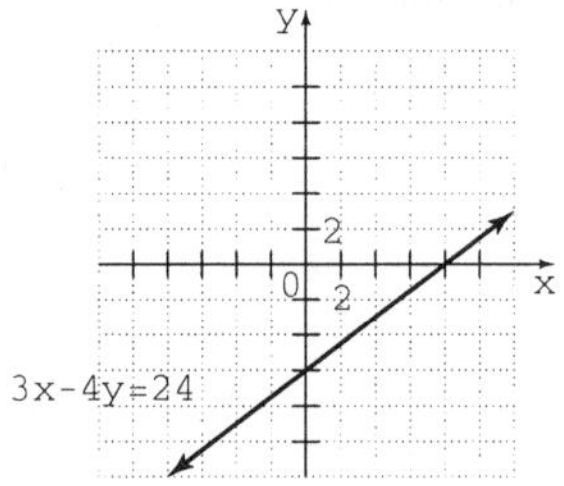

41. $\frac{86 + 94}{2} = \frac{180}{2} = 90$

43. $\frac{12 + 28 + 20}{3} = \frac{60}{3} = 20$

45. $\frac{30 + 22 + 23 + 33}{4} = \frac{108}{4} = 27$

47. $y = |x|$

x	y
−3	3
−2	2
−1	1
0	0
1	1
2	2
3	3

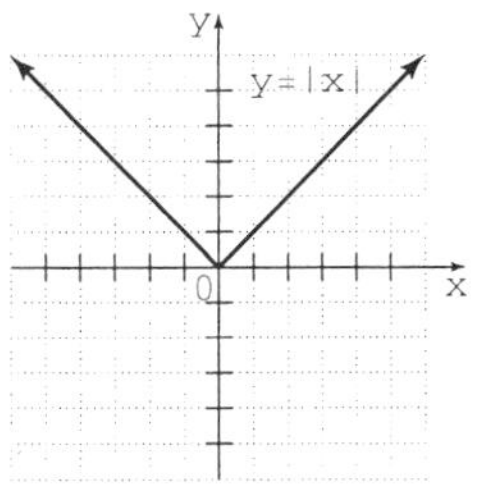

49. Answers may vary.

Section 8.5

Practice Problems

1. mean $= \dfrac{77+85+86+91+88}{5}$
$= \dfrac{427}{5}$
$= 85.4$

2. grade point average
$= \dfrac{4\cdot 2+2\cdot 4+3\cdot 5+1\cdot 2+4\cdot 2}{2+4+5+2+2}$
$= \dfrac{41}{15}$
≈ 2.73

3. Because the list is in numerical order, the median is the middle number, 24.

4. First list the scores in numerical order. Then find the middle number, which will be the mean of the two middle numbers since there is an even number of scores.
43, 65, 71, 78, 88, 89, 95, 95
median $= \dfrac{78+88}{2} = \dfrac{166}{2} = 83$

5. The number 15 occurs most often. Therefore, 15 is the mode.

6. First write the numbers in numerical order.
15, 15, 15, 16, 18, 26, 26, 30, 31, 35
Since there is an even number of items, the median is the mean of the two middle numbers.
median $= \dfrac{18+26}{2} = \dfrac{44}{2} = 22$
The mode is 15, since 15 occurs most often.

Mental Math

1. $\dfrac{3+5}{2} = \dfrac{8}{2} = 4$

2. $\dfrac{10+20}{2} = \dfrac{30}{2} = 15$

3. $\dfrac{1+3+5}{3} = \dfrac{9}{3} = 3$

4. $\dfrac{7+7+7}{3} = \dfrac{21}{3} = 7$

Exercise Set 8.5

1. Mean: $\dfrac{21+28+16+42+38}{5} = \dfrac{145}{5} = 29$
Median: Write the numbers in order.
16, 21, 28, 38, 42
The middle number is 28.
Mode: There is no mode, since there is no number that occurs more often than the others.

3. Mean: $\dfrac{7.6+8.2+8.2+9.6+5.7+9.1}{6} = \dfrac{48.4}{6}$
≈ 8.1
Median: Write the numbers in order.
5.7, 7.6, 8.2, 8.2, 9.1, 9.6
Since there is an even number of items, find the average of the two middle numbers.
$\dfrac{8.2+8.2}{2} = \dfrac{16.4}{2} = 8.2$
Mode: 8.2 occurs most often.

5. Mean: $\dfrac{0.2+0.3+0.5+0.6+0.6+0.9+0.2+0.7+1.1}{9} = \dfrac{5.1}{9}$
≈ 0.6
Median: Write the numbers in order.
0.2, 0.2, 0.3, 0.5, 0.6, 0.6, 0.7, 0.9, 1.1
The middle number is 0.6.
Mode: Since 0.2 and 0.6 occur most often, there are two modes, 0.2 and 0.6.

7. Mean: $\frac{231+543+601+293+588+109+334+268}{8} = \frac{2967}{8}$
≈ 370.9

Median: Write the numbers in order.
109, 231, 268, 293, 334, 543, 588, 601
Since there is an even number of items, find the average of the two middle numbers.
$\frac{293+334}{2} = \frac{627}{2} = 313.5$
Mode: There is no mode since there is no number that occurs more often than the others.

9. Mean: $\frac{1483+1483+1450+1381+1283}{5} = \frac{7080}{5} = 1416$ feet

11. Median: Arrange from smallest to largest. Then, since there is an even number of items, find the average of the two middle numbers: 1227, 1250, 1260, <u>1283</u>, <u>1381</u>, 1450, 1483, 1483

median $= \frac{1283+1381}{2} = \frac{2664}{2} = 1332$ feet

13. Answers may vary.

15.

Grade	Point Value	Credit Hours	$\begin{pmatrix}\text{Point}\\\text{Value}\end{pmatrix}\cdot\begin{pmatrix}\text{Credit}\\\text{Hours}\end{pmatrix}$
B	3	3	9
C	2	3	6
A	4	4	16
C	2	4	8
Totals		14	39

Grade Point Average $= \frac{39}{14} \approx 2.79$

17.

Grade	Point Value	Credit Hours	$\begin{pmatrix}\text{Point}\\\text{Value}\end{pmatrix}\cdot\begin{pmatrix}\text{Credit}\\\text{Hours}\end{pmatrix}$
A	4	3	12
A	4	3	12
B	3	4	12
B	3	1	3
B	3	2	6
Totals		13	45

Grade Point Average $= \frac{45}{13} \approx 3.46$

19. Mean:
$\frac{7.8+6.9+7.5+4.7+6.9+7.0}{6} = \frac{40.8}{6}$
$= 6.8$
The mean time is 6.8 seconds.

21. The most common time is 6.9 seconds.

23. Write the numbers in order.
74, 77, 85, 86, 91, 95
Since there is an even number of scores, find the average of the middle two numbers.
$\text{median} = \frac{85+86}{2} = \frac{171}{2} = 85.5$

25. $\text{mean} = \frac{78+80+66+68+71+64+82+71+70+65+70+75+77+86+72}{15} = \frac{1095}{15} = 73$

27. Since 70 and 71 occur more often than the other numbers, the modes are 70 and 71.

29. Nine: the rates of 66, 68, 71, 64, 71, 70, 65, 70, and 72 are below the mean of 73.

31. $\frac{6}{18} = \frac{2\cdot 3}{2\cdot 3\cdot 3} = \frac{1}{3}$

33. $\frac{18}{30} = \frac{2\cdot 3\cdot 3}{2\cdot 3\cdot 5} = \frac{3}{5}$

35. $\frac{55}{75} = \frac{5\cdot 11}{5\cdot 15} = \frac{11}{15}$

37. There are 5 numbers, so the median is the middle number, 37. The mode is 35 so it must occur two times since the others occur only once. Now we have 35, 35, 37, 40, ___.
Let x = the unknown number.
Since the mean is 38,

$$38 = \frac{35+35+37+40+x}{5}$$
$$5\cdot 38 = 147 + x$$
$$190 = 147 + x$$
$$190 - 147 = 147 + x - 147$$
$$43 = x$$

The list is 35, 35, 37, 40, 43.

39. Yes; answers may vary.

Section 8.6

Practice Problems

1.

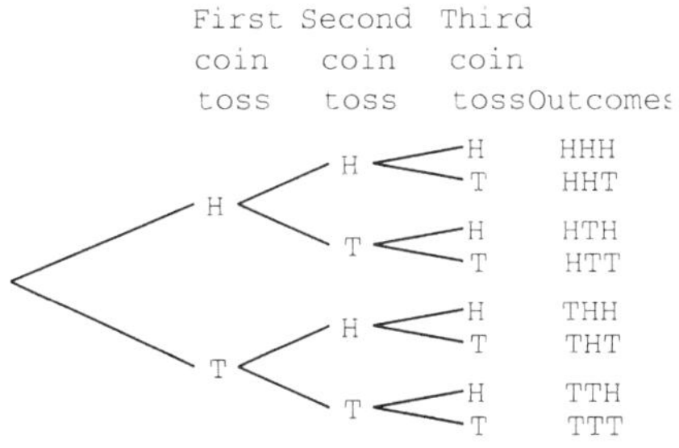

There are 8 outcomes.

2.

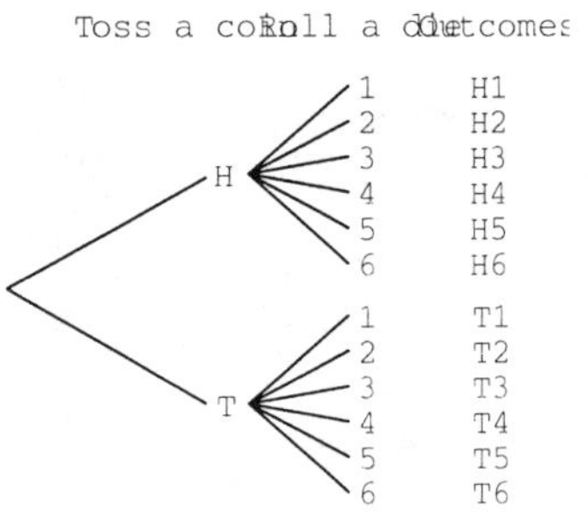

There are 12 outcomes.

3. Possible outcomes: HHH, HHT, HTH, HTT, THH, THT, TTH, TTT

$$\text{probability} = \frac{\text{number of ways the event can occur}}{\text{number of possible outcomes}} = \frac{1}{8}$$

4. Possible outcomes: 1, 2, 3, 4, 5, 6

probability

$$= \frac{\text{number of ways the event can occur}}{\text{number of possible outcomes}} = \frac{2}{6} = \frac{1}{3}$$

5. probability

$$= \frac{\text{number of ways the event can occur}}{\text{number of possible outcomes}} = \frac{2}{4} = \frac{1}{2}$$

Mental Math

1. $\frac{1}{2}$

2. $\frac{1}{2}$

3. $\frac{1}{2}$

4. $\frac{1}{2}$

Exercise Set 8.6

1.

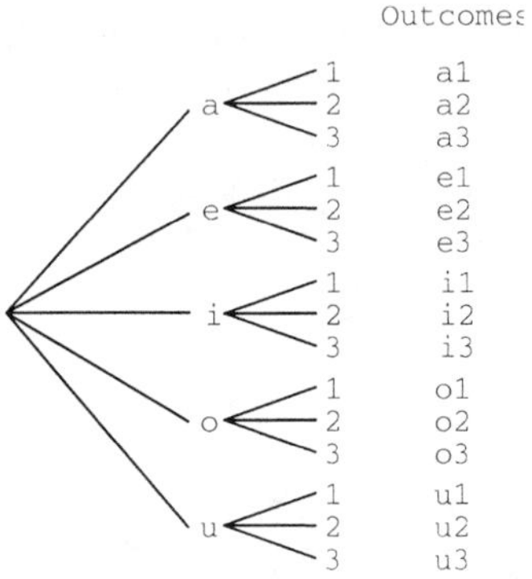

There are 15 outcomes.

3.

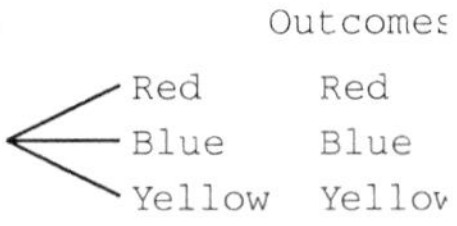

There are 3 outcomes.

5.

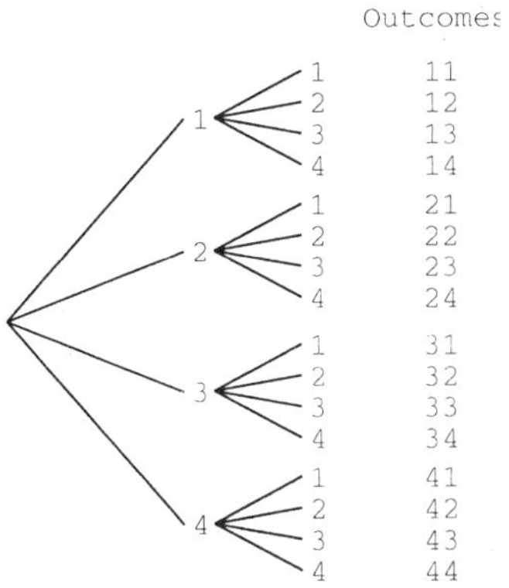

There are 16 outcomes.

7.

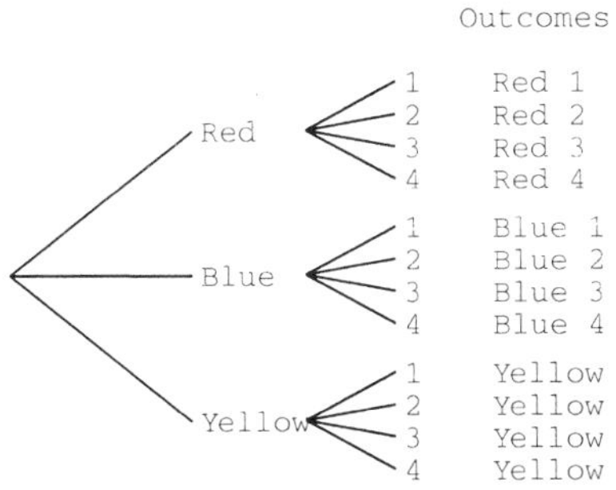

There are 12 outcomes.

9.

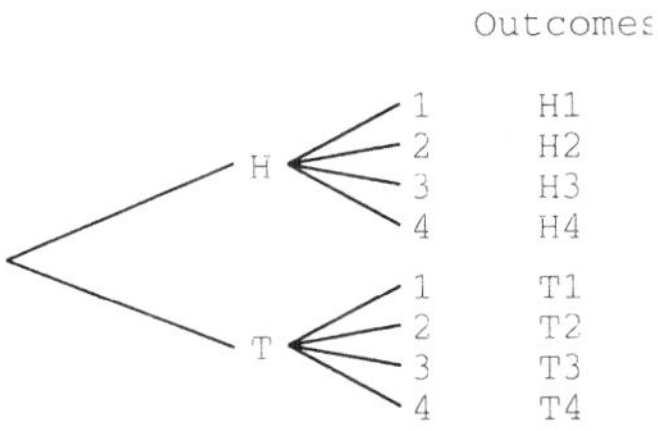

There are 8 outcomes.

11. possible outcomes: 1, 2, 3, 4, 5, 6
probability of a 5 $= \frac{1}{6}$

13. possible outcomes: 1, 2, 3, 4, 5, 6
probability of a 1 or a 4 $= \frac{2}{6} = \frac{1}{3}$

15. possible outcomes: 1, 2, 3, 4, 5, 6
probability of an even number $= \frac{3}{6} = \frac{1}{2}$

17. possible outcomes: 1, 2, 3
probability of a 2 $= \frac{1}{3}$

19. possible outcomes: 1, 2, 3
probability of an odd number $= \frac{2}{3}$

21. possible outcomes: red, blue, yellow, yellow, green, green, green
probability of a red $= \frac{1}{7}$

23. possible outcomes: red, blue, yellow, yellow, green, green, green
probability of yellow $= \frac{2}{7}$

25. probability
$$= \frac{\text{blood pressure higher}}{\text{total participants}} = \frac{38}{200} = \frac{19}{100}$$

27. probability
$$= \frac{\text{blood pressure unchanged}}{\text{total participants}} = \frac{10}{200} = \frac{1}{20}$$

29.
$$\begin{aligned} \frac{1}{2} + \frac{1}{3} &= \frac{1}{2} \cdot \frac{3}{3} + \frac{1}{3} \cdot \frac{2}{2} \\ &= \frac{1 \cdot 3}{2 \cdot 3} + \frac{1 \cdot 2}{3 \cdot 2} \\ &= \frac{3}{6} + \frac{2}{6} \\ &= \frac{5}{6} \end{aligned}$$

31. $\frac{1}{2} \cdot \frac{1}{3} = \frac{1 \cdot 1}{2 \cdot 3} = \frac{1}{6}$

33. $5 \div \frac{3}{4} = \frac{5}{1} \cdot \frac{4}{3} = \frac{5 \cdot 4}{1 \cdot 3} = \frac{20}{3}$ or $6\frac{2}{3}$

35. There are 52 possible outcomes.
There is one King of hearts.
probability of King of Hearts $= \frac{1}{52}$

37. There are 52 possible outcomes.
There are four kings.
probability of a King $= \frac{4}{52} = \frac{1}{13}$

39. There are 52 possible outcomes.
There are 13 hearts.
probability of a heart $= \frac{13}{52} = \frac{1}{4}$

41.

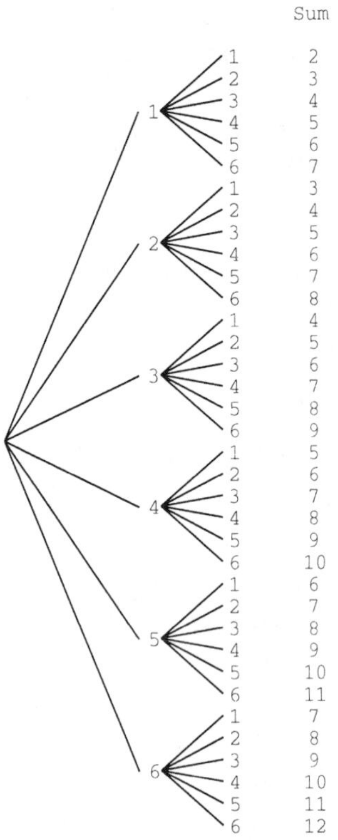

There are 36 possible outcomes. Three outcomes result in a sum of 4.

probability of a sum of 4 $= \frac{3}{36} = \frac{1}{12}$

43. There are 36 possible outcomes. None of the outcomes results is a sum of 0 (see diagram in solution for **37.**)

probability of a sum of 0 $= \frac{0}{36} = 0$

45. Answers may vary.

Chapter 8 Review

1. Each symbol represents 500,000 homes. There are 8 symbols for the Midwest.
$8 \cdot 500{,}000 = 4{,}000{,}000$

2. Each symbol represents 500,000 homes. There are 3.5 symbols for the Northeast.
$3.5 \cdot 500{,}000 = 1{,}750{,}000$

3. The South contains the most symbols.

4. The Northeast contains the least symbols.

5. 4,000,000 or more housing would be at least 8 symbols. The Midwest, South, and West each have more than 8 symbols.

6. The Northeast has less than 8 symbols.

7. The bar above 1960 is approximately 7.5 high, so approximately 7.5% of persons age 25 or more completed 4 or more years of college in 1960.

8. The tallest bar is for the year 2000, so 2000 had the greatest percentage of persons age 25 or more completing 4 or more years of college.

9. The years 1980, 1990, and 2000 all have bars of height 15 or more, so those years had 15% or more persons age 25 or more completing 4 or more years of college.

10. Answers may vary.

11. The line above 2003 is approximately at \$2,100,000.

12. The line above 1997 is at \$1,200,000.

13. The line remains the same between 1991 and 1992. The line decreases between 2000 and 2001 and between 2001 and 2002.

14. The steepest increase is between 1999 and 2000.

15. The line is below \$1,000,000 in 1990, 1991, 1992, 1993, and 1994.

16. At 21 – 25, the bar goes up to 4. 4 employees.

17. At 41 – 45, the bar goes up to 1. 1 employee.

18. At 36 – 40, the bar goes up to 8. At 41 – 45 the bar goes up to 1. $8 + 1 = 9$ employees.

19. At 16 – 20 the bar goes up to 6. At 21 – 25 the bar goes up to 4. At 26 – 30 the bar goes up to 8. $6 + 4 + 8 = 18$ employees.

	Class Intervals (Temperatures)	Tally	Class Frequency (# of Months)
20.	80°–89°	𝍸	5
21.	90° – 99°	III	3
22.	100° – 109°	IIII	4

23.

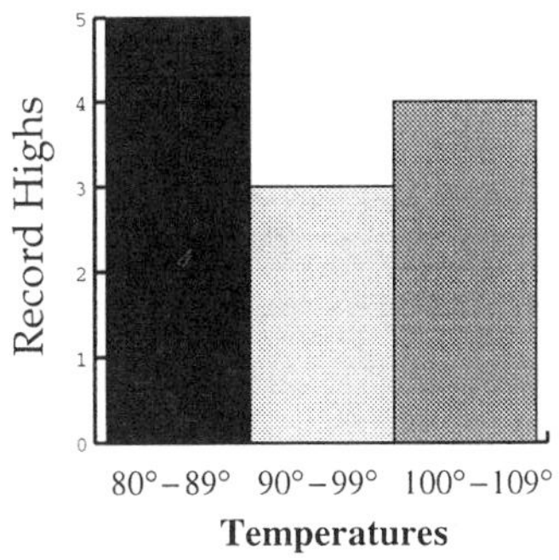

24. The largest sector of the circle graph represents the largest budget item, which is House Mortgage.

25. The smallest sector of the circle graph represents the smallest budget item, which is Utilities.

26. Add the two amounts of the two sectors: \$975 + \$250 = \$1225

27. Add the two amounts of the two sectors: \$400 + \$300 = \$700

28. $\text{ratio} = \frac{\text{house mortgage}}{\text{monthly budget}} = \frac{\$975}{\$4000} = \frac{39}{160}$

29. $\text{ratio} = \frac{\text{food}}{\text{monthly budget}} = \frac{\$700}{\$4000} = \frac{7}{40}$

30. $\text{ratio} = \frac{\text{car expenses}}{\text{food}} = \frac{500}{700} = \frac{5}{7}$

31. amount = 40% · 50 = 20 states

32. amount = 22% · 50 = 11 states

33. amount = 2% · 50 = 1 state

34. $\text{amount} = (22\% + 36\%) \cdot 50$
$= 58\% \cdot 50$
$= 29$ states

35.
$$x = -7y$$
$$0 = -7y$$
$$\frac{0}{-7} = \frac{-7y}{-7}$$
$$0 = y$$
The ordered pair is (0, 0).

$$x = -7y$$
$$x = -7(-1)$$
$$x = 7$$
The ordered pair is (7, –1).

$$x = -7y$$
$$-7 = -7y$$
$$\frac{-7}{-7} = \frac{-7y}{-7}$$
$$1 = y$$
The ordered pair is (–7, 1).

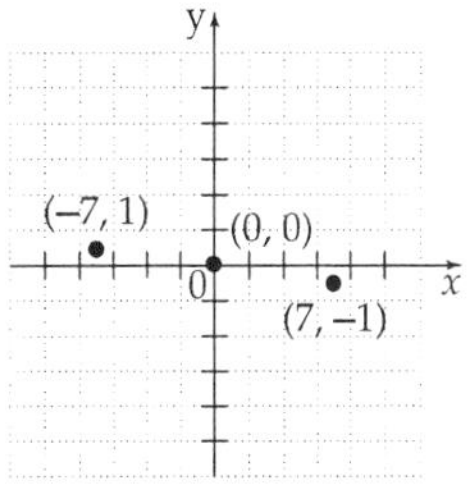

36. $y = 3x - 2$
$y = 3(0) - 2$
$y = -2$
The ordered pair is (0, –2).
$y = 3x - 2$
$y = 3(1) - 2$
$y = 3 - 2$
$y = 1$
The ordered pair is (1, 1).
$y = 3x - 2$
$y = 3(-2) - 2$
$y = -6 - 2$
$y = -8$
The ordered pair is (–2, –8).

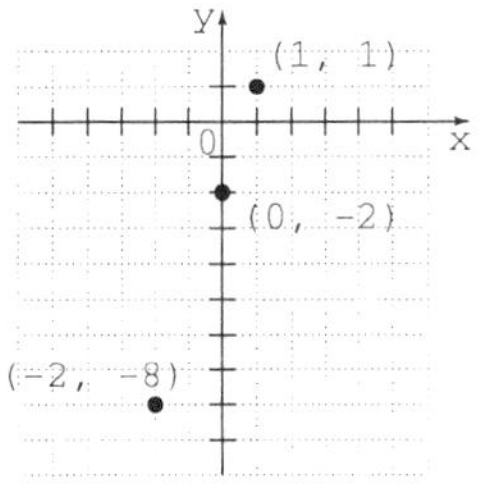

37.
$$x + y = -9$$
$$-1 + y = -9$$
$$-1 + y + 1 = -9 + 1$$
$$y = -8$$
The ordered pair is (–1, –8).

$$x + y = -9$$
$$x + 0 = -9$$
$$x = -9$$
The ordered pair is (–9, 0).

$x + y = -9$
$-5 + y = -9$
$y = -9 + 5$
$y = -4$
The ordered pair is (–5, –4).

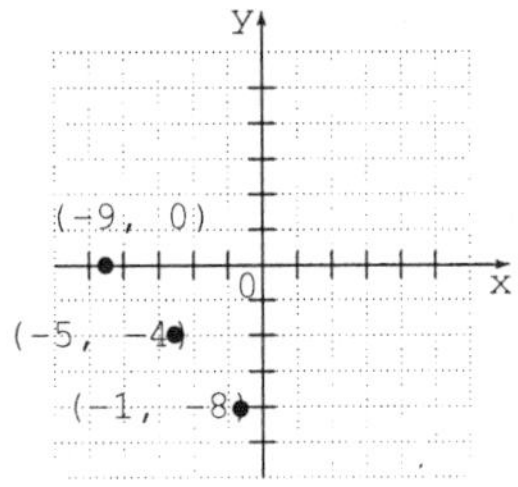

38. $x - y = 3$
$4 - y = 3$
$4 - y - 4 = 3 - 4$
$-y = -1$
$\frac{-y}{-1} = \frac{-1}{-1}$
$y = 1$
The ordered pair is (4, 1).
$x - y = 3$
$0 - y = 3$
$-y = 3$
$\frac{-y}{-1} = \frac{3}{-1}$
$y = -3$
The ordered pair is (0, –3).
$x - y = 3$
$x - 3 = 3$
$x - 3 + 3 = 3 + 3$
$x = 6$
The ordered pair is (6, 3).

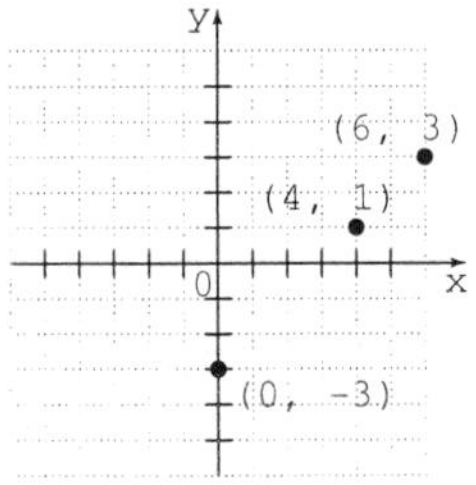

39. $y = 3x$
$y = 3(1)$
$y = 3$
The ordered pair is (1, 3).

$y = 3x$
$y = 3(-2)$
$y = -6$
The ordered pair is (–2, –6).

$y = 3x$
$0 = 3x$
$\frac{0}{3} = \frac{3x}{3}$
$0 = x$
The ordered pair is (0, 0).

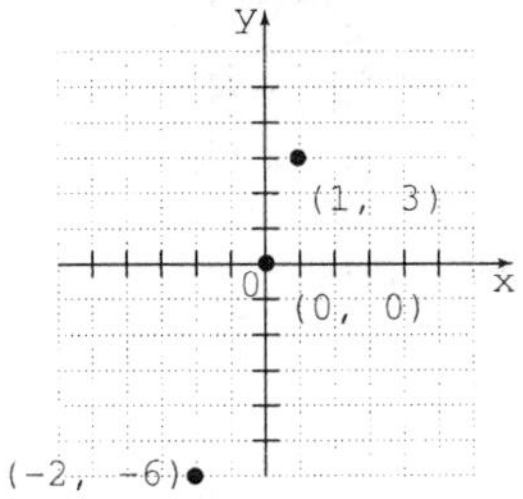

40. $x = y + 6$
$1 = y + 6$
$1 - 6 = y + 6 - 6$
$-5 = y$
The ordered pair is (1, –5).
$x = y + 6$
$6 = y + 6$
$6 - 6 = y + 6 - 6$
$0 = y$
The ordered pair is (6, 0).
$x = y + 6$
$-1 = y + 6$
$-1 - 6 = y + 6 - 6$
$-7 = y$
The ordered pair is (–1, –7).

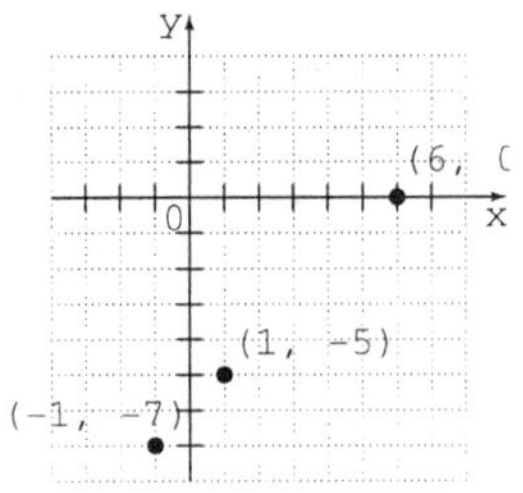

41. $x = -6$

x	y
–6	–5
–6	0
–6	5

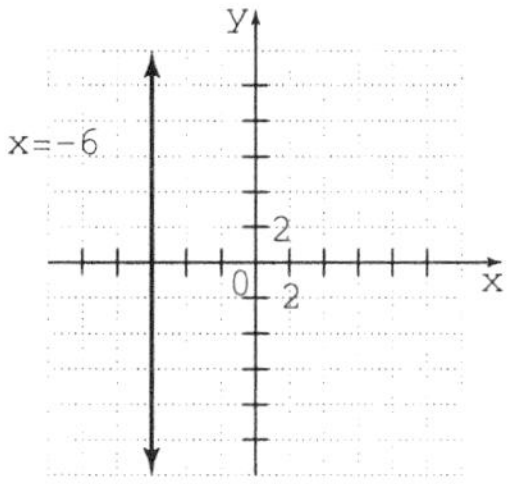

42. $y = 0$

x	y
–5	0
0	0
5	0

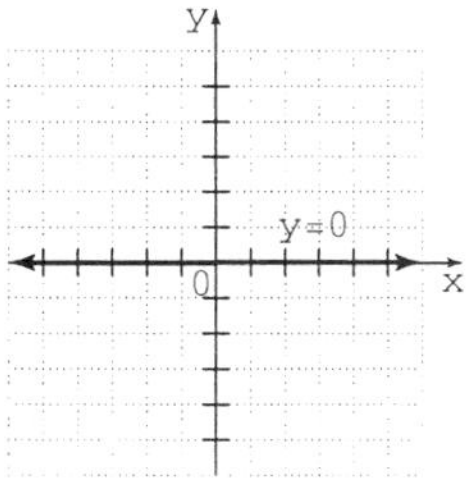

43. $x + y = 11$

x	y
0	11
5	6
11	0

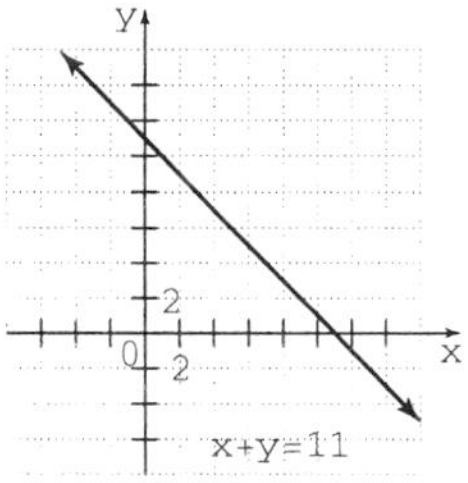

44. $x - y = 11$

x	y
0	–11
5	–6
11	0

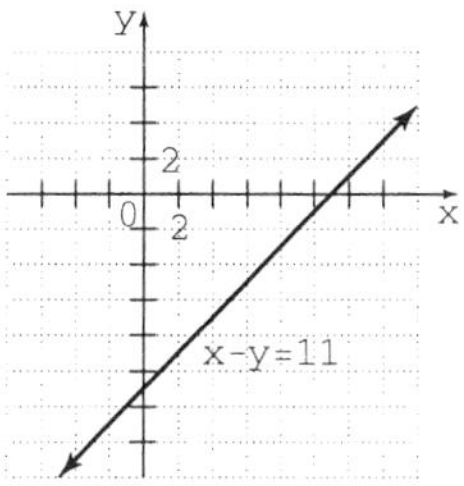

45. $y = 4x - 2$

x	y
–1	–6
0	–2
1	2

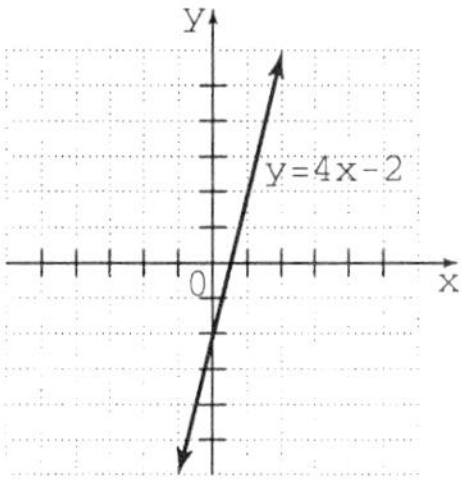

46. $y = 5x$

x	y
–1	–5
0	0
1	5

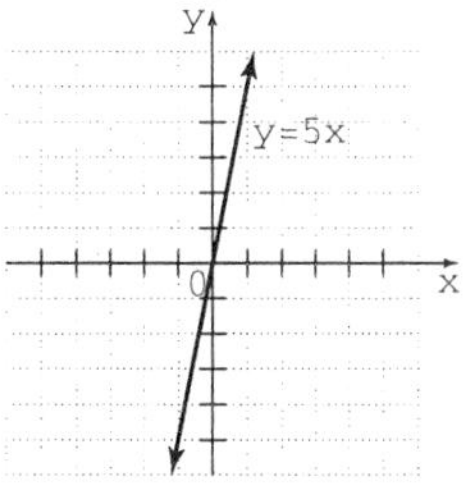

47. $x = -2y$

x	y
2	–1
0	0
–2	1

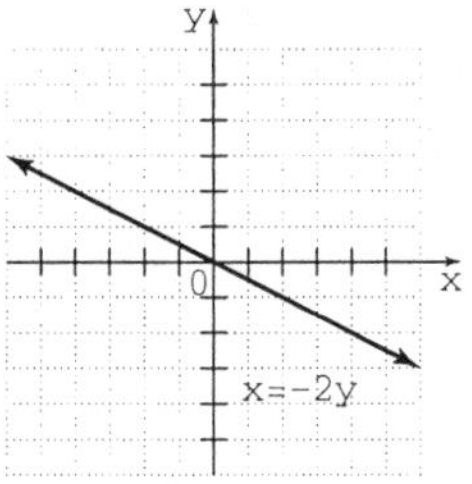

48. $x + y = -1$

x	y
–3	2
–1	0
2	–3

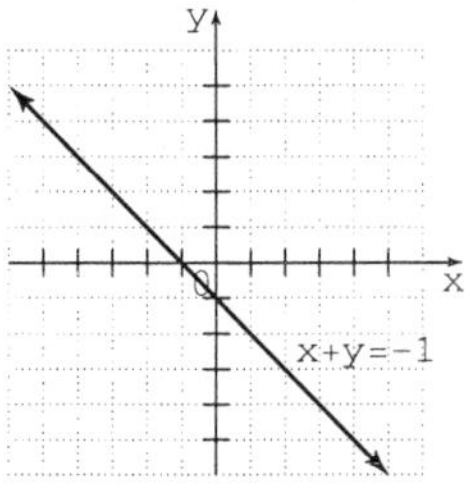

49. $2x - 3y = 12$

x	y
0	–4
3	–2
6	0

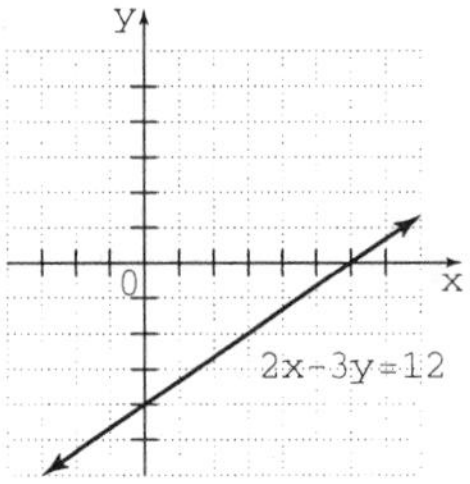

50. $x = \frac{1}{2}y$

x	y
–2	–4
0	0
2	4

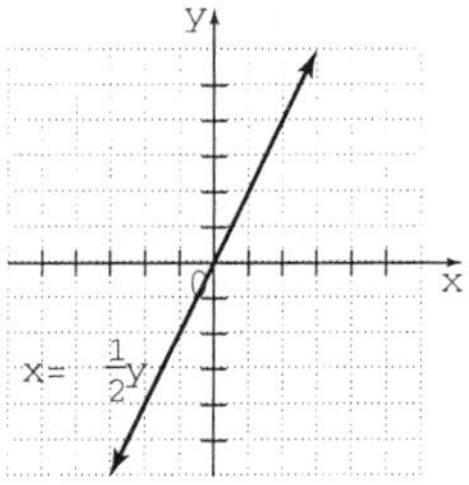

51. $\text{Mean} = \frac{13+23+33+14+6}{5}$
$= \frac{89}{5}$
$= 17.8$

Median: Write the numbers in order to find the middle number. Write the numbers in order.
6, 13, 14, 23, 33
The median is the middle number: Median = 14.
Mode: Since each number occurs only once, there is no mode.

52. $\text{Mean} = \frac{45+21+60+86+64}{5}$
$= \frac{276}{5}$
$= 55.2$

Median: Write the numbers in order to find the middle number. Write the numbers in order.
21, 45, 60, 64, 86
The median is the middle number: Median = 60.
Mode: Since each number occurs only once, there is no mode.

53. $\text{Mean} = \dfrac{\$14,000 + \$20,000 + \$12,000 + \$20,000 + \$36,000 + \$45,000}{6} = \dfrac{\$147,000}{6} = \$24,500$

Median: Write the numbers in order to find the middle number. Write the dollar amounts in order.
\$12,000; \$14,000; \$20,000; \$20,000; \$36,000; \$45,000
The median is the average of the two middle dollar amounts.

$\text{median} = \dfrac{\$20,000 + \$20,000}{2} = \$20,000$

Mode: \$20,000 occurs more often than the other numbers, so \$20,000 is the mode.

54. $\text{Average} = \dfrac{560 + 620 + 123 + 400 + 410 + 300 + 400 + 780 + 430 + 450}{10} = \dfrac{4473}{10} = 447.3$

Median: Write the numbers in order to find the middle number. Write the numbers in order.
123, 300, 400, 400, 410, 430, 450, 560, 620, 780
The median is the average of the two middle numbers.

$\text{median} = \dfrac{410 + 430}{2} = 420$

Mode: The number 400 occurs more often than the other numbers, so 400 is the mode

55.

Grade	Point Value	Credit Hours	$\left(\text{Point Value}\right) \cdot \left(\text{Credit Hours}\right)$
A	4	3	12
A	4	3	12
C	2	2	4
B	3	3	9
C	2	1	2
Totals		12	39

Grade Point Average $= \dfrac{39}{12} = 3.25$

56.

Grade	Point Value	Credit Hours	$\left(\text{Point Value}\right) \cdot \left(\text{Credit Hours}\right)$
B	3	3	9
B	3	4	12
C	2	2	4
D	1	2	2
B	3	3	9
Totals		14	36

Grade Point Average $= \dfrac{36}{14} \approx 2.57$

57.

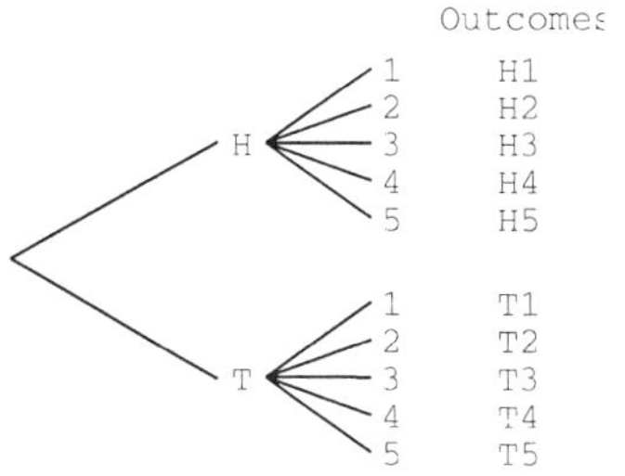

There are 10 outcomes.

58.

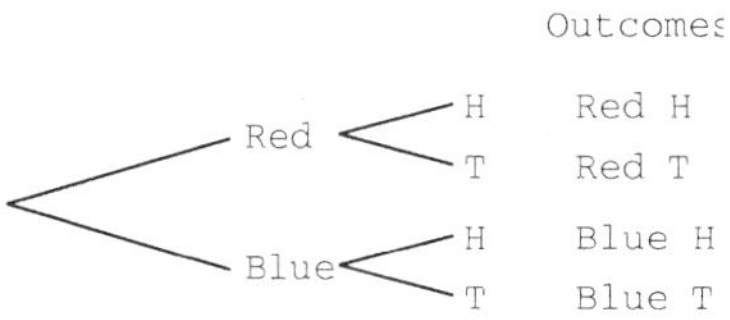

There are 4 outcomes.

59.

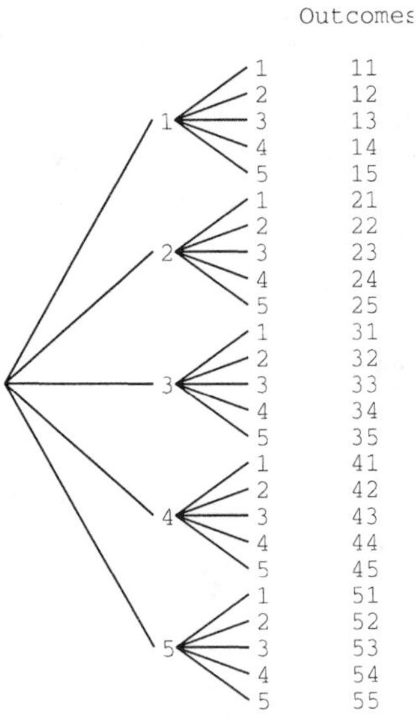

There are 25 outcomes.

60.

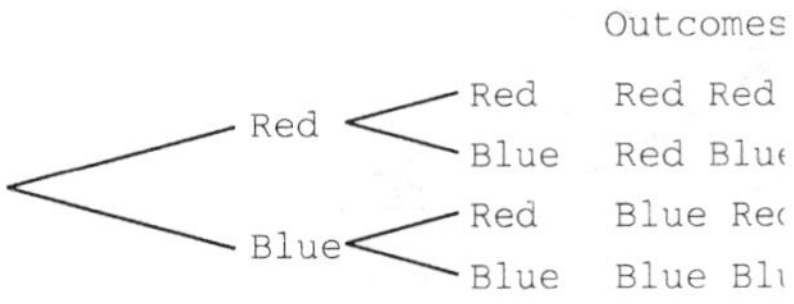

There are 4 outcomes.

61.

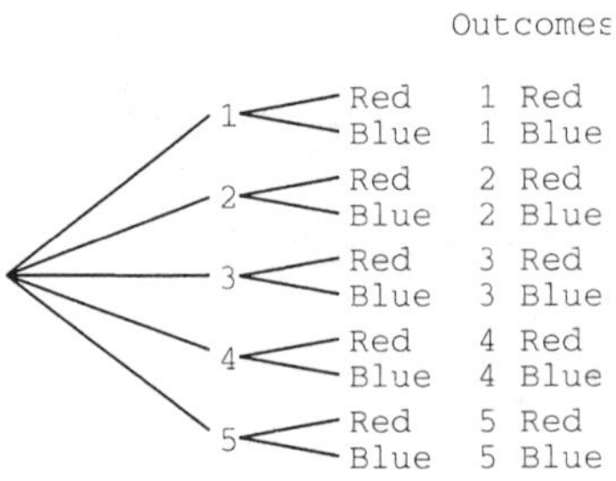

There are 10 outcomes.

62. possible outcomes: 1, 2, 3, 4, 5, 6

probability of a 4 = $\frac{1}{6}$

63. possible outcomes: 1, 2, 3, 4, 5, 6

probability of a 3 = $\frac{1}{6}$

64. possible outcomes: 1, 2, 3, 4, 5

probability of a 4 = $\frac{1}{5}$

65. possible outcomes: 1, 2, 3, 4, 5

probability of a 3 = $\frac{1}{5}$

66. possible outcomes: 1, 2, 3, 4, 5

probability of a 1, 3, or 5 = $\frac{3}{5}$

67. possible outcomes: 1, 2, 3, 4, 5

probability of a 2 or a 4 = $\frac{2}{5}$

Chapter 8 Test

1. The second week has $4\frac{1}{2}$ bills and each bill represents \$50. $4.5 \cdot \$50 = \$225$ was collected during the second week.

2. The most bills are for week 3 with 7 bills. Week 3 took in the most money:
$7 \cdot \$50 = \$350$

3.

Week	Number of Bills	$\left(\begin{array}{c}\text{Number} \\ \text{of Bills}\end{array}\right) \cdot \$50$
1	3	\$150
2	4.5	\$225
3	7	\$350
4	5.5	\$275
5	2	\$100
	Total	\$1100

4. The bars for the months of June, August, and September have heights above 9. June, August, and September normally have more than 9 centimeters of monthly precipitation in Chicago.

5. The shortest bar is above the month of February. February has the least amount of normal monthly precipitation with 3 centimeters.

6. The months of March and November show a normal monthly precipitation of 7 centimeters.

7.

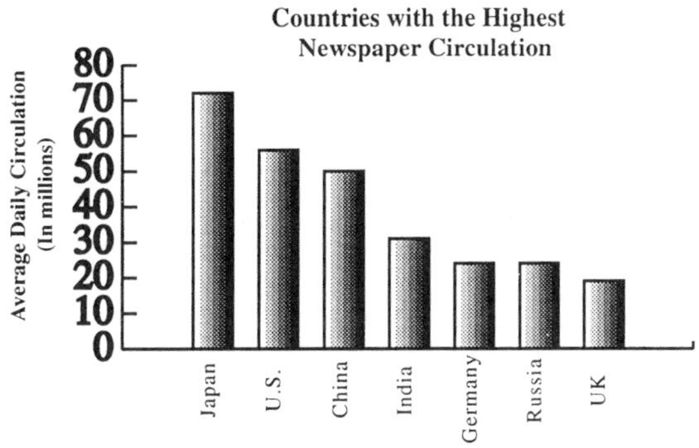

8. $\dfrac{\text{number who prefer rock}}{\text{number surveyed}} = \dfrac{85}{200} = \dfrac{17}{40}$

9. $\dfrac{\text{number who prefer country music}}{\text{number who prefer jazz}} = \dfrac{62}{44} = \dfrac{31}{22}$

10. $\text{amount} = 31\% \cdot 132{,}000{,}000$
$= 40{,}920{,}000$ people

11. $\text{amount} = 16\% \cdot 132{,}000{,}000$
$= 21{,}120{,}000$ people

12. The bar goes up to 9. 9 students.

13. $5 + 6 = 11$

14.

Class Intervals (Scores)	Tally	Class Frequency (# of Students)
40 – 49	I	1
50 – 59	III	3
60 – 69	IIII	4
70 – 79	𝍸	5
80 – 89	𝍸 III	8
90 – 99	IIII	4

15.

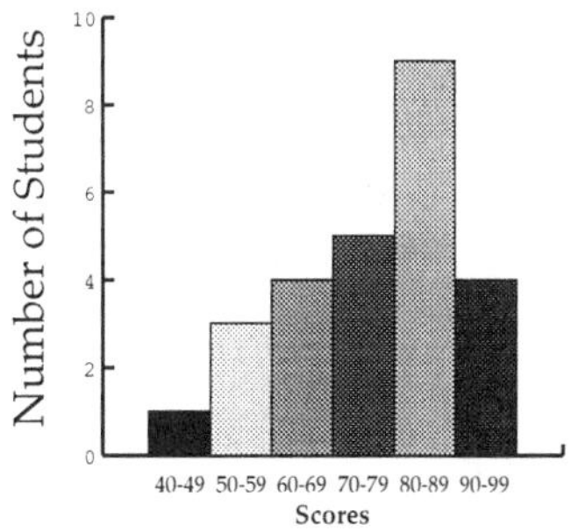

16. (4, 0)

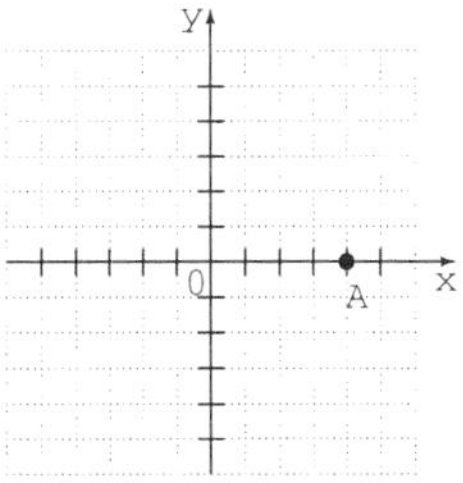

17. (0, –3)

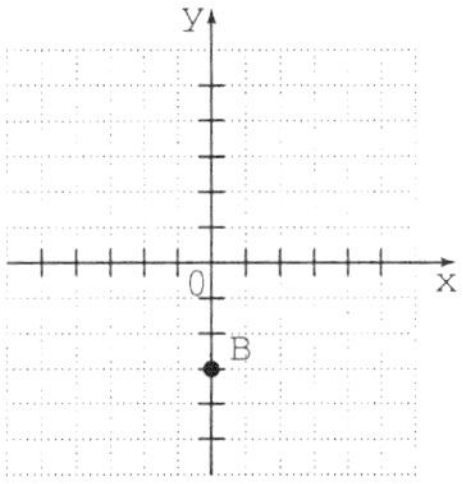

18. (–3, 4)

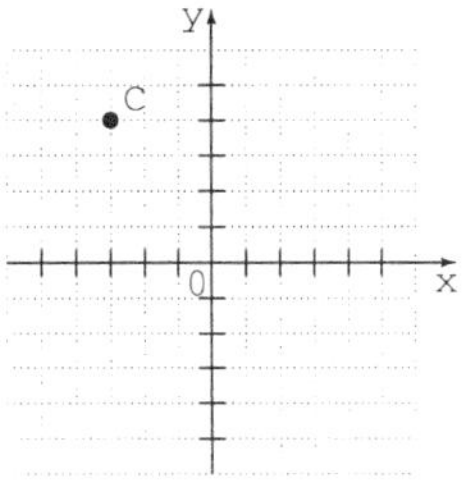

19. (–2, –1)

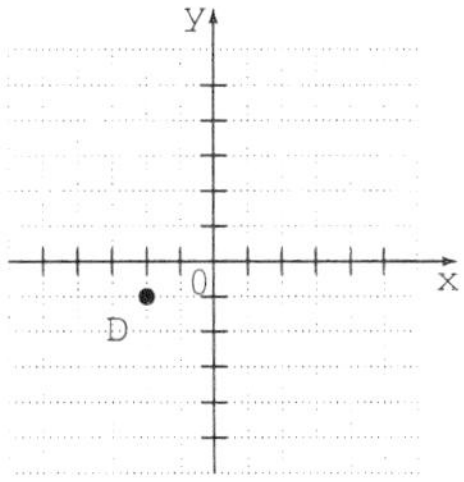

20. $x = -6y$
$0 = -6y$
$0 = y$
The ordered pair is (0, 0).

$x = -6y$
$x = -6(1)$
$x = -6$
The ordered pair is (–6, 1).

$x = -6y$
$12 = -6y$
$-2 = y$
The ordered pair is (12, –2).

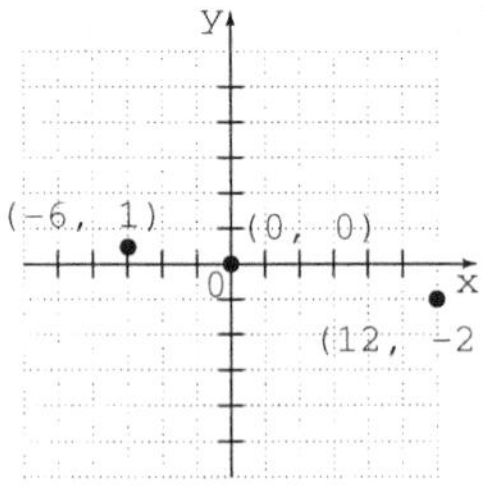

21. $y = 7x - 4$
$y = 7(2) - 4$
$y = 14 - 4$
$y = 10$
The ordered pair is (2, 10).

$y = 7x - 4$
$y = 7(-1) - 4$
$y = -7 - 4$
$y = -11$
The ordered pair is (–1, –11).

$y = 7x - 4$
$y = 7(0) - 4$
$y = 0 - 4$
$y = -4$
The ordered pair is (0, –4).

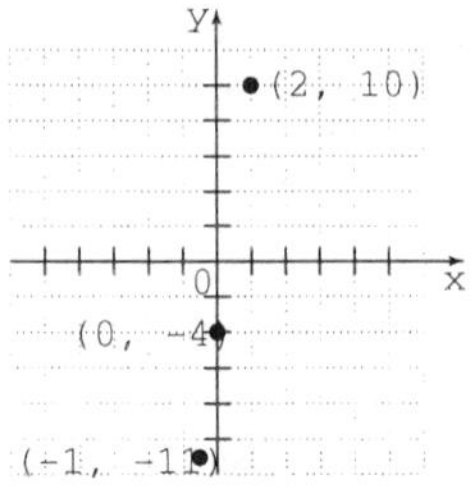

22. $y + x = -4$

x	y
–4	0
–2	–2
0	–4

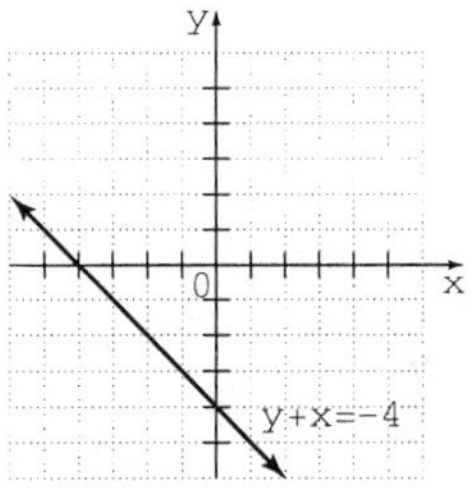

23. $y = -4$

x	y
–5	–4
0	–4
5	–4

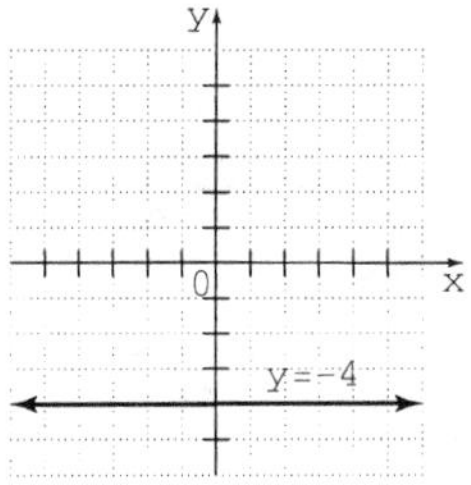

24. $y = 3x - 5$

x	y
0	–5
1	–2
2	1

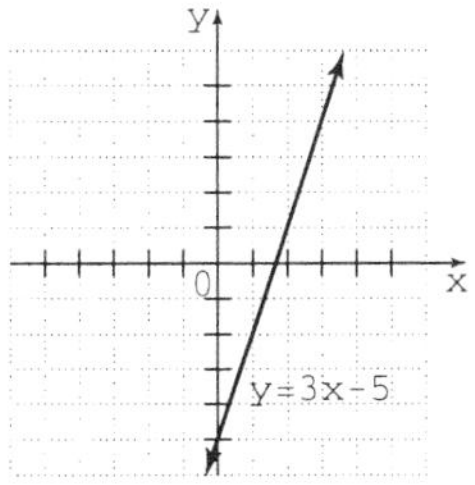

25. $x = 5$

x	y
5	–5
5	0
5	5

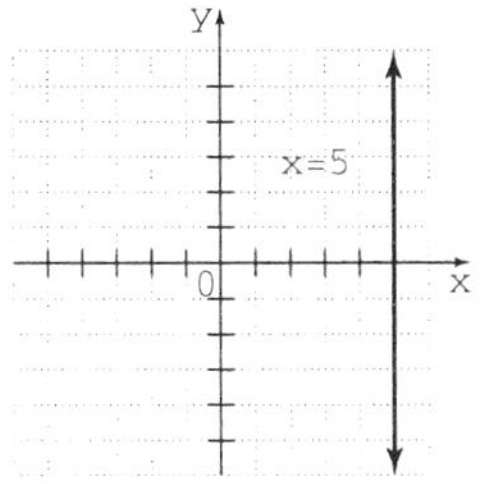

26. $y = -\frac{1}{2}x$

x	y
–4	2
0	0
4	–2

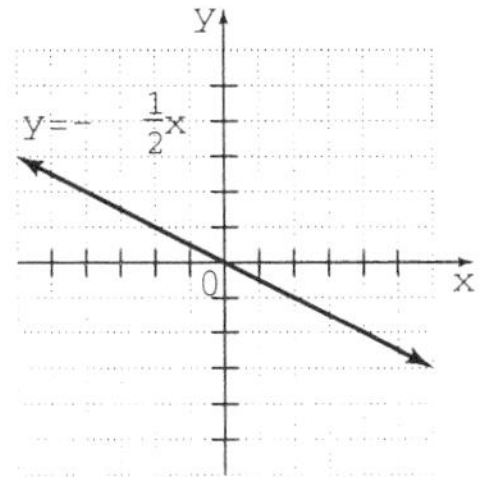

27. $3x - 2y = 12$

x	y
0	–6
2	–3
4	0

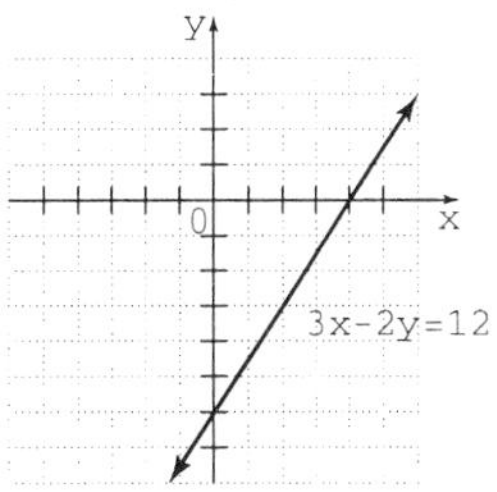

28. $\text{Mean} = \dfrac{26+32+42+43+49}{5}$
$= \dfrac{192}{5}$
$= 38.4$

Median: Write the numbers in order.
26, 32, 42, 43, 49
The median is the middle number, so median = 42.
Mode: Since each number occurs only once, there is no mode.

29. Mean
$= \dfrac{8+10+16+16+14+12+12+13}{8}$
$= \dfrac{101}{8}$
$= 12.625$

Median: Write the numbers in order.
8, 10, 12, 12, 13, 14, 16, 16
The median is the average of the two middle numbers.

$\text{Median} = \dfrac{12+13}{2} = 12.5$

Mode: Since 12 and 16 occur more often than the other numbers, there are two modes: 12 and 16.

30.

Grade	Point Value	Credit Hours	$\begin{pmatrix}\text{Point}\\\text{Value}\end{pmatrix}\cdot\begin{pmatrix}\text{Credit}\\\text{Hours}\end{pmatrix}$
A	4	3	12
B	3	3	9
C	2	3	6
B	3	4	12
A	4	1	4
	Totals	14	43

Grade Point Average $= \frac{43}{14} \approx 3.07$

31.

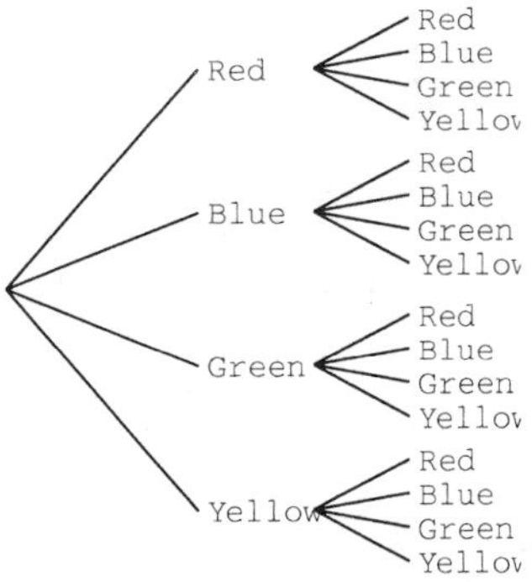

32.

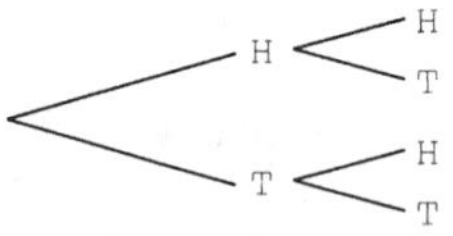

33. possible outcomes: 1, 2, 3, 4, 5, 6, 7, 8, 9, 10
probability of a 6 $= \frac{1}{10}$

34. possible outcomes: 1, 2, 3, 4, 5, 6, 7, 8, 9, 10
probability of a 3 or a 4 $= \frac{2}{10} = \frac{1}{5}$

Cumulative Review

1.
$$\begin{aligned} 4^3 + [3^2 - (10 \div 2) - 7 \cdot 3 &= 4^3[3^2 - 5] - 7 \cdot 3 \\ &= 4^3 + [9 - 5] - 7 \cdot 3 \\ &= 4^3 + 4 - 7 \cdot 3 \\ &= 64 + 4 - 7 \cdot 3 \\ &= 64 + 4 - 21 \\ &= 68 - 21 \\ &= 47 \end{aligned}$$

2.
$$\begin{aligned} 7^2 - \left[5^3 = (6 \div 3)\right] + 4 \cdot 2 &= 7^2 - \left[5^3 + 2\right] + 4 \cdot 2 \\ &= 7^2 - [125 + 2] + 4 \cdot 2 \\ &= 7^2 - 127 + 4 \cdot 2 \\ &= 49 - 127 + 4 \cdot 2 \\ &= 49 - 127 + 8 \\ &= -78 + 8 \\ &= -70 \end{aligned}$$

3. $-3 - 9 = -12$

4. $7 - (-2) = 7 + 2 = 9$

5.
$$\begin{aligned} 3y - 7y &= 12 \\ -4y &= 12 \\ \frac{-4y}{-4} &= \frac{12}{-4} \\ y &= -3 \end{aligned}$$

6.
$$\begin{aligned} 2x - 6x &= 24 \\ -4x &= 24 \\ \frac{-4x}{-4} &= \frac{24}{-4} \\ x &= -6 \end{aligned}$$

7.
$$\begin{aligned} \frac{x}{4} + 1 &= \frac{4}{3} \\ 6\left(\frac{x}{6} + 1\right) &= 6\left(\frac{4}{3}\right) \\ x + 6 &= 8 \\ x + 6 - 6 &= 8 - 6 \\ x &= 2 \end{aligned}$$

8.
$$\begin{aligned} \frac{7}{2} + \frac{a}{4} &= 1 \\ 4\left(\frac{7}{2} + \frac{a}{4}\right) &= 4(1) \\ 14 + a &= 4 \\ 14 + a - 14 &= 4 - 14 \\ a &= -10 \end{aligned}$$

9.
$$\begin{array}{rcr} 2\frac{1}{3} & = & 2\frac{8}{24} \\ +5\frac{3}{8} & = & +5\frac{9}{24} \\ \hline & & 7\frac{17}{24} \end{array}$$

10.
$$\begin{array}{rcr} 3\frac{2}{5} & = & 3\frac{8}{20} \\ +4\frac{3}{4} & = & +4\frac{15}{20} \\ \hline & & 7\frac{23}{20} \end{array}$$

$$\frac{23}{20} = 1\frac{3}{20}$$
$$7 + 1\frac{3}{20} = 8\frac{3}{20}$$

11. $5\frac{6}{10} = 5\frac{3}{5}$

12. $2\frac{8}{10} = 2\frac{4}{5}$

13.
$$\begin{array}{r} 3.500 \\ -0.068 \\ \hline 3.432 \end{array}$$

14.
$$\begin{array}{r} 7.400 \\ -0.073 \\ \hline 7.327 \end{array}$$

15.
$$\begin{array}{r} 0.283 \\ \times 0.3 \\ \hline 0.0849 \end{array}$$

16.
$$\begin{array}{r} 0.147 \\ \times 0.2 \\ \hline 0.0294 \end{array}$$

17.
$$\begin{array}{r} -0.052 \\ 115\overline{)\ 5.980} \\ \underline{-575} \\ 230 \\ \underline{-230} \\ 0 \end{array}$$

18.
$$\begin{array}{r} 0.136 \\ 205\overline{)\ 27.880} \\ \underline{-205} \\ 738 \\ \underline{-615} \\ 1230 \\ \underline{-1230} \\ 0 \end{array}$$

19. $(-1.3)^2 + 2.4 = 1.69 + 2.4 = 4.09$

20. $(-2.7)^2 = 7.29$

21.
$$\begin{array}{r} 0.25 \\ 4\overline{)1.00} \\ \underline{-8} \\ 20 \\ \underline{-20} \\ 0 \end{array}$$

22.
$$\begin{array}{r} 0.375 \\ 8\overline{)\ 3.000} \\ \underline{-24} \\ 60 \\ \underline{-56} \\ 40 \\ \underline{-40} \\ 0 \end{array}$$

23.
$$\begin{aligned} 5(x-0.36) &= -x+2.4 \\ 5x-1.8 &= -x+2.4 \\ 5x-1.8+x &= -x+2.4+x \\ 6x-1.8 &= 2.4 \\ 6x-1.8+1.8 &= 2.4+1.8 \\ 6x &= 4.2 \\ \frac{6x}{6} &= \frac{4.2}{6} \\ x &= 0.7 \end{aligned}$$

24.
$$\begin{aligned} 4(0.35-x) &= x-7 \\ 1.4-4x &= x-7 \\ 1.4-4x-x &= x-7-x \\ 1.4-5x &= -7 \\ 1.4-5x-1.4 &= -7-1.4 \\ -5x &= -8.4 \\ \frac{-5x}{-5} &= \frac{-8.4}{-5} \\ x &= 1.68 \end{aligned}$$

25. $\sqrt{32} \approx 5.657$

26. $\sqrt{60} \approx 7.746$

27. $\frac{12}{17}$

28. $\frac{7}{15}$

29. $\frac{318.5 \text{ miles}}{13 \text{ gallons}} = \frac{24.5 \text{ miles}}{1 \text{ gallon}}$

24.5 miles per gallon

30. $\frac{\$1.59}{3 \text{ ounces}} = \frac{\$0.53}{1 \text{ ounce}}$

$0.53 per ounce

31. $\frac{25}{x} = \frac{20}{4}$
$20x = 100$
$x = 5$
check: $\frac{25}{5} = \frac{20}{4}$
$5 = 5$ True

32. $\frac{8}{5} = \frac{x}{10}$
$5x = 80$
$x = 16$
check: $\frac{8}{5} = \frac{16}{10}$
$\frac{8}{5} = \frac{8}{5}$ True

33. $\frac{12}{17}$

34. $\frac{4}{9}$

35. $4.6\% = 0.046$

36. $32\% = 32.\% = 0.32$

37. $0.74\% = 0.0074$

38. $2.7\% = 0.027$

39. $x = 0.35 \cdot 60$
$x = 21$

40. $x = .40 \cdot 36$
$x = 14.4$

41. $20.8 = 0.40 \cdot x$
$\frac{20.8}{0.40} = x$
$52 = x$

42. $9.5 = 0.25 \cdot x$
$\frac{9.5}{0.25} = x$
$38 = x$

43. cost · rate = sales tax
$300 \cdot \text{x} = 22.50$
$\text{x} = \frac{22.50}{300}$
$x = 0.075$
The sales taxs rate is 7.5%

44. $3.00 \cdot \text{x} = 0.13$
$\text{x} = \frac{0.13}{2.00}$
$x = 0.065$
The sales taxs rate is 6.5%

45. (loan + interest) ÷ how many payments.
$(2000 + 435.88) \div 24 = 2435.88 \div 24 \approx 101.50.$
The monthly payments are \$101.50.

46. $(1600 + 128.60) \div 12 = 1728.60 \div 12 = 144.05.$
The monthly payments are \$144.05.

47. median: middle number or average of the two middle numbers when arranged from lowest to highest.
55, 67, 75, 86, 91, 91
median = $\frac{75+86}{2} = \frac{161}{2} = 80.5$

48. 43, 46, 47, 50, 52, 83
median = $\frac{47+50}{2} = \frac{97}{2} = 48.5$

49. possible outcomes: 1, 2, 3, 4, 5, 6
probability of a 3 or 4 = $\frac{2}{6} = \frac{1}{3}$

50. possible outcomes: 1, 2, 3, 4, 5, 6
probability of an even number (2, 4, or 6) $= \frac{3}{6} = \frac{1}{2}$

Chapter 9

Pretest

1. Since the angle is between 0° and 90°, it is an acute angle.

2. Since the angle is 180°, it is a straight angle.

3. The supplement of an angle that measures 92° is an angle that measures 180° – 92° = 88°.

4. Since $\angle x$ and the 55° angle are vertical angles, $\angle x = 55°$. Since $\angle y$ and the 55° angle are supplementary angles, $\angle y = 180° - 55° = 125°$. Since $\angle y$ and $\angle z$ are vertical angles, $\angle z = 125°$.

5. Since the sum of the measures of the angles of a triangle is 180°, $\angle x = 180° - 40° - 30° = 110°$.

6. $11 \text{ feet} \cdot \frac{1 \text{ yard}}{3 \text{ feet}} = \frac{11 \text{ yards}}{3} = 3\frac{2}{3} \text{ yards}$

7. To convert centimeters to kilometers, move the decimal point 5 places to the left.
6,250,000 cm = 62.5 km

8. $$\begin{aligned} P &= 2l + 2w \\ &= 2 \cdot 24 \text{ inches} + 2 \cdot 6 \text{ inches} \\ &= 48 \text{ inches} + 12 \text{ inches} \\ &= 60 \text{ inches} \end{aligned}$$

9. $$\begin{aligned} C &= 2\pi r \\ &= 2\pi \cdot 9 \text{ yards} \\ &= 18\pi \text{ yards} \\ &\approx 18 \cdot 3.14 \text{ yards} \\ &= 56.52 \text{ yards} \end{aligned}$$

10. $$\begin{aligned} A &= \frac{1}{2}bh \\ &= \frac{1}{2} \cdot 4 \text{ cm} \cdot 3 \text{ cm} \\ &= 6 \text{ square centimeters} \end{aligned}$$

11. $$\begin{array}{r} 7 \text{ lb} \quad 12 \text{ oz} \\ 2\overline{)\ 15 \text{ lb} \quad 8 \text{ oz}} \\ \underline{-14} \qquad\qquad \\ 1 \text{ lb} = \underline{16 \text{ oz}} \\ 24 \text{ oz} \\ \underline{-24 \text{ oz}} \\ 0 \end{array}$$

12. $$\begin{array}{rcr} 9 \text{ gal } 1 \text{ qt} & = & 8 \text{ gal } 5 \text{ qt} \\ \underline{- \qquad 2\text{qt}} & & \underline{- \qquad 2 \text{ qt}} \\ & & 8 \text{ gal } 3 \text{ qt} \end{array}$$

13. To convert liters to milliliters, move the decimal point 3 places to the right.
25 L = 25,000 ml

14. $$\begin{aligned} C &= \frac{5}{9}(F - 32) \\ &= \frac{5}{9}(118 - 32) \\ &= \frac{5}{9}(86) \\ &\approx 47.8 \end{aligned}$$
118°F ≈ 47.8°C

Section 9.1

Practice Problems

1. a. The figure has two endpoints. It is line segment *RS*, or $\overline{RS}$.

   b. The figure is part of a line with one endpoint. It is ray *AB*, or $\overrightarrow{AB}$.

   c. The figure extends indefinitely in two directions. It is line *EF*, or $\overleftrightarrow{EF}$.

   d. The figure is two rays with a common endpoint. It is $\angle HVT$, $\angle TVH$, or $\angle V$.

2. Two other ways to name $\angle z$ are $\angle RTS$ or $\angle STR$.

3. a. $\angle M$ is an acute angle. It measures between 0° and 90°.

   b. $\angle N$ is a straight angle.

   c. $\angle O$ is an obtuse angle. It measures between 90° and 180°.

   d. $\angle P$ is a right angle.

4. The complement of an angle that measures 36° is an angle that measures 90° – 36° = 54°.

5. The supplement of an angle that measures 88° is an angle that measures 180° – 88° = 92°.

6. $\angle y = 136° - 97° = 39°$

7. Since $\angle ABY$ and $\angle ZBC$ are vertical angles, $\angle ABY = 46°$. Since $\angle ABZ$and $\angle YBC$ are vertical angles, $\angle ABZ = 134°$.

8. Since $\angle a$ and the 112° angle are vertical angles, the measure of $\angle a$ is 112°. $\angle a$ and $\angle b$ are supplementary angles, so $\angle b$ measures $180° - 112° = 68°$. $\angle b$ and $\angle c$ are vertical angles, so $\angle c$ measures 68°.

9. Since $\angle w$ and $\angle x$ are vertical angles and $\angle w = 40°$, $\angle x = 40°$. $\angle y$ and $\angle w$ are corresponding angles, so $\angle y = 40°$. $\angle y$ and $\angle z$ are supplementary angles, so
$\angle z = 180° - 40° = 140°$.

Exercise Set 9.1

1. The figure extends indefinitely in two directions. It is line *yz*, or $\overleftrightarrow{yz}$.

3. The figure has two endpoints. It is line segment *LM*, or $\overline{LM}$.

5. The figure has two endpoints. It is line segment *PQ*, or $\overline{PQ}$.

7. The figure is part of a line with one endpoint. It is ray *UW*, or $\overrightarrow{UW}$.

9. $\angle ABC = 15°$

11. $\angle CBD = 50°$

13. $\angle DBA = 50° + 15° = 65°$

15. $\angle CBE = 50° + 45° = 95°$

17. 90°

19. 0°; 90°

21. $\angle S$ is a straight angle.

23. $\angle R$ is a right angle.

25. Since $\angle Q$ measures between 90° and 180°, it is an obtuse angle.

27. $\angle N$ is a right angle.

29. The complement of an angle that measures 17° is an angle that measures
$90° - 17° = 73°$.

31. The supplement of an angle that measures 17° is an angle that measures
$180° - 17° = 163°$.

33. The complement of a 48° angle is an angle that measures $90° - 48° = 42°$.

35. The supplement of a 125° angle is an angle that measures $180° - 125° = 55°$.

37. $\angle MNP$ and $\angle RNO$ are complementary angles since $60° + 30° = 90°$.
$\angle PNQ$ and $\angle QNR$ are complementary angles since $52° + 38° = 90°$.

39. $\angle SPT$ and $\angle TPQ$ are supplementary angles since $45° + 135° = 180°$.
$\angle SPR$ and $\angle RPQ$ are supplementary angles since $135° + 45° = 180°$.
$\angle SPT$ and $\angle SPR$ are supplementary angles since $45° + 135° = 180°$.
$\angle TPQ$ and $\angle QPR$ are supplementary angles since $135° + 45° = 180°$.

41. The supplement of a 125.2° angle is
$180° - 125.2° = 54.8°$.

43. $\angle x = 120° - 88° = 32°$

45. $\angle x = 90° - 15° = 75°$

47. Since $\angle x$ and the 35° angle are vertical angles, $\angle x = 35°$. $\angle x$ and $\angle y$ are supplementary angles, so
$\angle y = 180° - 35° = 145°$. $\angle y$ and $\angle z$ are vertical angles, so $\angle z = 145°$.

49. Since $\angle x$ and the 103° angle are supplementary angles,
$\angle x = 180° - 103° = 77°$. $\angle y$ and the 103° angle are vertical angles, so $\angle y = 103°$. $\angle x$ and $\angle z$ are vertical angles, so $\angle z = 77°$.

51. $\angle x$ and the 80° angle are adjacent angles, so $\angle x = 180° - 80° = 100°$. $\angle y$ and the 80° angle are

alternate interior angles, so
$\angle y = 80°$. $\angle x$ and $\angle z$ are corresponding angles, so $\angle z = 100°$.

53. $\angle x$ and the 46° angle are supplementary angles, so $\angle x = 180° - 46° = 134°$. $\angle y$ and the 46° angle are corresponding angles, so
$\angle y = 46°$. $\angle x$ and $\angle z$ are corresponding angles, so $\angle z = 134°$.

55. $\frac{7}{8}+\frac{1}{4}=\frac{7}{8}+\frac{2}{8}=\frac{9}{8}$ or $1\frac{1}{8}$

57. $\frac{7}{8}\cdot\frac{1}{4}=\frac{7\cdot 1}{8\cdot 4}=\frac{7}{32}$

59. $3\frac{1}{3}-2\frac{1}{2}=\frac{10}{3}-\frac{5}{2}=\frac{20}{6}-\frac{15}{6}=\frac{5}{6}$

61.
$$\begin{aligned} 3\frac{1}{3}\div 2\frac{1}{2} &= \frac{10}{3}\div\frac{5}{2} \\ &= \frac{10}{3}\cdot\frac{2}{5} \\ &= \frac{10\cdot 2}{3\cdot 5} \\ &= \frac{20}{15} \\ &= \frac{4}{3} \text{ or } 1\frac{1}{3} \end{aligned}$$

63. $\angle a$ and the 60° angle are alternate interior angles, so $\angle a = 60°$.
$\angle a$, $\angle b$, and the 70° angle form a straight angle, so
$$\begin{aligned} \angle b &= 180° - 70° - \angle a \\ &= 180° - 70° - 60° \\ &= 50°. \end{aligned}$$
$\angle c$ and the angle that is $\angle a$ and $\angle b$ together are alternate interior angles, so
$\angle c = 60° + 50° = 110°$.
$\angle c$ and $\angle d$ are adjacent angles, so
$\angle d = 180° - 110° = 70°$.
$\angle e$ and the 60° angle are adjacent angles, so
$\angle e = 180° - 60° = 120°$.

65.
$$\begin{aligned} x + x &= 90° \\ 2x &= 90° \\ x &= 45° \end{aligned}$$

67. No; answers may vary.

Section 9.2

Practice Problems

1.
$$\begin{aligned} 5 \text{ ft} &= \frac{5 \text{ ft}}{1}\cdot\frac{12 \text{ in.}}{1 \text{ ft}} \\ &= 5\cdot 12 \text{ in.} \\ &= 60 \text{ in.} \end{aligned}$$

2.
$$\begin{aligned} 7 \text{ yd} &= \frac{7 \text{ yd}}{1}\cdot\frac{3 \text{ ft}}{1 \text{ yd}} \\ &= 7\cdot 3 \text{ ft} \\ &= 21 \text{ ft} \end{aligned}$$

3.
$$\begin{array}{r} 5 \\ 12\overline{)\ 68} \\ \underline{-60} \\ 8 \end{array}$$
68 in. = 5 ft 8 in.

4.
$5 \text{ yd} = \frac{5 \text{ yd}}{1}\cdot\frac{3 \text{ ft}}{1 \text{ yd}} = 15 \text{ ft}$
5 yd 2 ft = 15 ft + 2 ft = 17 ft

5.
$$\begin{array}{l} \quad\ 4 \text{ ft}\ \ 8 \text{ in.} \\ \underline{+\ 8 \text{ ft}\ 11 \text{ in.}} \\ 12 \text{ ft}\ 19 \text{ in.} = 12 \text{ ft} + 1 \text{ ft}\ 7 \text{ in.} \\ \qquad\qquad\qquad = 13 \text{ ft}\ 7 \text{ in.} \end{array}$$

6.
$$\begin{array}{l} \quad\ 4 \text{ ft}\ 7 \text{ in.} \\ \underline{\times \qquad\quad 4} \\ 16 \text{ ft}\ 28 \text{ in.} = 16 \text{ ft} + 2 \text{ ft}\ 4 \text{ in.} \\ \qquad\qquad\qquad = 18 \text{ ft}\ 4 \text{ in.} \end{array}$$

7.
$$\begin{array}{r} 9 \text{ ft}\ 3 \text{ in.} \\ 2\overline{)\ 18 \text{ ft}\ 6 \text{ in.}} \\ \underline{-18 \text{ ft}}\qquad\ \ \\ 0\quad 6 \text{ in.} \\ \underline{-6 \text{ in.}} \\ 0\quad \end{array}$$

8.
$$\begin{array}{rcr} 5 \text{ ft}\ 8 \text{ in.} & = & 4 \text{ ft}\ 20 \text{ in.} \\ \underline{-\ 1 \text{ ft}\ 9 \text{ in.}} & = & \underline{-\ 1 \text{ ft}\ \ 9 \text{ in.}} \\ & & 3 \text{ ft}\ 11 \text{ in.} \end{array}$$

9.
$$\begin{aligned} 3.5 \text{ m} &= \frac{3.5 \text{ m}}{1}\cdot\frac{0.001 \text{ km}}{1 \text{ m}} \\ &= 0.0035 \text{ km} \end{aligned}$$

10. To convert meters to millimeters, move decimal point 3 places to the right.
2.5 m = 2500 mm

11. 640 m = 0.64 km or 2.1 km = 2100 m

$$\begin{array}{r} 2.1\ \text{km} \\ -\ 0.64\ \text{km} \\ \hline 1.46\ \text{km} \end{array} \quad \text{or} \quad \begin{array}{r} 2100\ \text{m} \\ -\ 640\ \text{m} \\ \hline 1460\ \text{m} \end{array}$$

12.
$$\begin{array}{r} 18.3\ \text{hm} \\ \times\ 5 \\ \hline 91.5\ \text{hm} \end{array}$$

13. 0.8 m = 80 cm or 45 cm = 0.45 m

$$\begin{array}{r} 80\ \text{cm} \\ +\ 45\ \text{cm} \\ \hline 125\ \text{cm} \end{array} \quad \text{or} \quad \begin{array}{r} 0.80\ \text{m} \\ 0.45\ \text{m} \\ \hline 1.25\ \text{m} \end{array}$$

The scarf will be 125 cm or 1.25 m long.

Mental Math

1. 12 in. = 1 ft

2. 6 ft. = 2 yd

3. 24 in. = 2 ft

4. 36 in. = 3 ft

5. 36 in. = 1 yd

6. 2 yd = 6 ft = 72 in.

7. No; 30 meters is too long.

8. Yes

9. Yes

10. No; 4 kilometers is much too long.

11. No; 50 kilometers is too long.

12. Yes

Exercise Set 9.2

1. $60\text{ in.} = 60\text{ in.}\cdot\frac{1\text{ ft}}{12\text{ in.}} = \frac{60\text{ ft}}{12} = 5\text{ ft}$

60 inches is 5 feet.

3. $12\text{ yd} = 12\text{ yd}\cdot\frac{3\text{ ft}}{1\text{ yd}} = 12\cdot 3\text{ ft} = 36\text{ ft}$

5.
$$\begin{aligned} 42{,}240\text{ ft} &= 42{,}240\text{ ft}\cdot\frac{1\text{ mi}}{5280\text{ ft}} \\ &= \frac{42{,}240\text{ mi}}{5280} \\ &= 8\text{ mi} \end{aligned}$$

42,240 feet is 8 miles.

7. $102\text{ in.} = 102\text{ in.}\cdot\frac{1\text{ ft}}{12\text{ in.}} = \frac{102\text{ ft}}{12} = 8\frac{1}{2}\text{ ft}$

9. $10\text{ ft} = 10\text{ ft}\cdot\frac{1\text{ yd}}{3\text{ ft}} = \frac{10\text{ yd}}{3} = 3\frac{1}{3}\text{ yd}$

10 feet is $3\frac{1}{3}$ yards.

11.
$$\begin{aligned} 6.4\text{ mi} &= 6.4\text{ mi}\cdot\frac{5280\text{ ft}}{1\text{ mi}} \\ &= 6.4\cdot 5280\text{ ft} \\ &= 33{,}792\text{ ft} \end{aligned}$$

13. 40 ft ÷ 3 = 13 with remainder 1
40 ft = 13 yd 1 ft

15. 41 in. ÷ 12 = 3 with remainder 5
41 in. = 3 ft 5 in.

17. 10,000 ft ÷ 5280 = 1 with remainder 4720
10,000 ft = 1 mi 4720 ft

19. $5\text{ ft} = 5\text{ ft}\cdot\frac{12\text{ in.}}{1\text{ ft}} = 60\text{ in.}$

5 ft 2 in. = 60 in. + 2 in. = 62 in.

21. $5\text{ yd} = 5\text{ yd}\cdot\frac{3\text{ ft}}{1\text{ yd}} = 15\text{ft}$

5 yd 2 ft = 15 ft + 2 ft = 17 ft

23.
$$\begin{aligned} 2\text{ yd} &= 2\text{ yd}\cdot\frac{36\text{ in.}}{1\text{ yd}} = 72\text{ in.} \\ 1\text{ ft} &= 1\text{ ft}\cdot\frac{12\text{ in.}}{1\text{ ft}} = 12\text{ in.} \\ 2\text{ yd }1\text{ ft} &= 72\text{ in.} + 12\text{ in.} = 84\text{ in.} \end{aligned}$$

25.
$$\begin{array}{r} 5\text{ ft }8\text{ in.} \\ +\ 6\text{ ft }7\text{ in.} \\ \hline 11\text{ ft }15\text{ in.} \end{array} = 11\text{ ft} + 1\text{ ft }3\text{ in.} = 12\text{ ft }3\text{ in.}$$

27.
$$\begin{array}{r} 12\text{ yd }2\text{ ft} \\ +\ 9\text{ yd }2\text{ ft} \\ \hline 21\text{ yd }4\text{ ft} \end{array} = 21\text{ yd} + 1\text{ yd }1\text{ ft} = 22\text{ yd }1\text{ ft}$$

29.
$$\begin{array}{r} 24\text{ ft }8\text{ in.} \\ -\ 16\text{ ft }3\text{ in.} \\ \hline 8\text{ ft }5\text{ in.} \end{array}$$

31. $\begin{array}{r} 16 \text{ ft } 3 \text{ in.} \\ -\ 10 \text{ ft } 9 \text{ in.} \\ \hline \end{array} = \begin{array}{r} 15 \text{ ft } 15 \text{ in.} \\ -\ 10 \text{ ft } 9 \text{ in.} \\ \hline 5 \text{ ft } 6 \text{ in.} \end{array}$

33. $\begin{array}{r} 3 \text{ ft } 4 \text{ in.} \\ 2\overline{)\ 6 \text{ ft } 8 \text{ in.}} \\ \underline{-6 \text{ ft}}\phantom{8 \text{ in.}} \\ 0 \quad 8 \text{ in.} \\ \underline{-8 \text{ in.}} \\ 0 \end{array}$

35. $\begin{array}{r} 12 \text{ yd } 2 \text{ ft} \\ \times \quad 4 \\ \hline 48 \text{ yd } 8 \text{ ft} \end{array} \begin{aligned} &= 48 \text{ yd} + 2 \text{ yd } 2 \text{ ft} \\ &= 50 \text{ yd } 2 \text{ ft} \end{aligned}$

37. $\begin{array}{r} 6 \text{ ft } 10 \text{ in.} \\ +\ 3 \text{ ft } \ 8 \text{ in.} \\ \hline 9 \text{ ft } 18 \text{ in.} \end{array} \begin{aligned} &= 9 \text{ ft} + 1 \text{ ft } 6 \text{ in.} \\ &= 10 \text{ ft } 6 \text{ in.} \end{aligned}$

The bamboo is 10 ft 6 in. tall.

39. $\begin{array}{r} 16 \text{ ft } 5 \text{ in} \\ -2 \text{ ft } 6 \text{ in} \\ \hline \end{array} = \begin{array}{r} 15 \text{ ft } 17 \text{ in} \\ -\ 2 \text{ ft } 6 \text{ in} \\ \hline 13 \text{ ft } 11 \text{ in} \end{array}$

The hand is 13 ft 11 in longer than the eye is wide.

41. $\begin{array}{r} 1 \text{ ft } 9 \text{ in.} \\ \times \quad 9 \\ \hline 9 \text{ ft } 81 \text{ in.} \end{array} \begin{aligned} &= 9 \text{ ft} + 6 \text{ ft } 9 \text{ in.} \\ &= 15 \text{ ft } 9 \text{ in.} \end{aligned}$

9 stacks would extend 15 ft 9 in. from the wall.

43. $\begin{array}{r} 3 \text{ ft } 1 \text{ in.} \\ 3\overline{)\ 9 \text{ ft } 3 \text{ in.}} \\ \underline{-9 \text{ ft}}\phantom{3 \text{ in.}} \\ 0 \quad 3 \text{ in.} \\ \underline{-3 \text{ in.}} \\ 0 \end{array}$

Each cut piece will be 3 ft 1 in. long.

45. $\begin{aligned} \text{Perimeter} &= 24 \text{ ft } 9 \text{ in.} + 18 \text{ ft } 6 \text{ in.} + 24 \text{ ft } 9 \text{ in.} + 18 \text{ ft } 6 \text{ in.} \\ &= 84 \text{ ft } 30 \text{ in.} \\ &= 84 \text{ ft} + 2 \text{ ft } 6 \text{ in.} \\ &= 86 \text{ ft } 6 \text{ in.} \end{aligned}$

She must purchase 86 ft 6 in. of fencing material.

47. $79 \text{ ft} = 79 \text{ ft} \cdot \frac{1 \text{ yd}}{3 \text{ ft}} = \frac{79}{3} \text{ yd}$

$\frac{79}{3} \cdot 4 = \frac{316}{3} = 105\frac{1}{3}$

4 trucks are $105\frac{1}{3}$ yd long.

49. To convert meters to centimeters, move the decimal 2 places to the right.
40 m = 4000 cm

51. To convert millimeters to centimeters, move the decimal 1 place to the right.
40 mm = 4.0 cm = 4 cm

53. To convert meters to kilometers, move the decimal 3 places to the left.
300 m = 0.300 km = 0.3 km

55. To convert millimeters to meters, move the decimal 3 places to the left.
1400 mm = 1.4 m

57. To convert centimeters to meters, move the decimal 2 places to the left.
1500 cm = 15 m

59. To convert centimeters to millimeters, move the decimal 1 place to the right.
8.3 cm = 83 mm

61. To convert millimeters to decimeters, move the decimal 2 places to the left.
20.1 mm = 0.201 dm

63. To convert meters to millimeters, move the decimal 3 places to the right.
0.04 m = 0040. mm = 40 mm

65.
$$\begin{array}{r} 8.60 \text{ m} \\ +\ 0.34 \text{ m} \\ \hline 8.94 \text{ m} \end{array}$$

67.
$$\begin{array}{rcl} 2.9 \text{ m} & = & 2.90 \text{ m} \\ +\ 40.0 \text{ mm} & = & 0.04 \text{ m} \\ \hline & & 2.94 \text{ m or } 2940 \text{ mm} \end{array}$$

69.
$$\begin{array}{rcl} 24.8 \text{ mm} & = & 2.48 \text{ cm} \\ -\ 1.19 \text{ cm} & = & -\ 1.19 \text{ cm} \\ \hline & & 1.29 \text{ cm or } 12.9 \text{ mm} \end{array}$$

71.
$$\begin{array}{rcl} 15 \text{ km} & = & 15.000 \text{ km} \\ -\ 2360 \text{ m} & = & -\ 2.360 \text{ km} \\ \hline & & 12.640 \text{ km or } 12{,}640 \text{ m} \end{array}$$

73.
$$\begin{array}{r} 18.3 \text{ m} \\ \times\ 3 \\ \hline 5.49 \text{ m} \end{array}$$

75.
$$\begin{array}{r} 1.55 \\ 4\overline{)\ 6.2} \\ -4 \\ \hline 2.2 \\ -2\,0 \\ \hline 20 \\ -20 \\ \hline 0 \end{array}$$

6.2 km ÷ 4 = 1.55 km

77. 3.4 m + 5.8 m − 8 cm
= 3.4 m + 5.8 m − 0.08 m
= 9.12 m
The tied ropes are 9.12 m long.

79. 80 mm − 5.33 cm
= 80 mm − 53.3 mm
= 26.7 mm
The ice must be 26.7 mm thicker.

81. 25(1 m + 65 cm) = 25(100 cm + 65 cm)
= 25(165 cm)
= 4125 cm or 41.25 m
4125 cm or 41.25 m of wood must be ordered.

83.
$$\begin{array}{r} 3.35 \\ 20\overline{)\ 67.00} \\ -60 \\ \hline 7\,0 \\ -6\,0 \\ \hline 100 \\ -100 \\ \hline 0 \end{array}$$

67 m ÷ 20 = 3.35 m
Each piece will be 3.35 m long.

85. 5.988 km + 21 m = 5988 m + 21 m
= 6009 m or 6.009 km
The elevation is 6009 m or 6.009 km.

87. 3.429 m ÷ 22.86 cm = 3.429 m ÷ 0.2286 m
$0.2286\overline{)3.429}$
Move the decimal points 4 places.
$$\begin{array}{r} 15 \\ 2286.\overline{)\ 34290.} \\ -2286 \\ \hline 11430 \\ -11430 \\ \hline 0 \end{array}$$

15 tiles are needed.

89. 0.86 = 86%

91. $\frac{13}{100} = 13\%$

93. $\frac{1}{4} = \frac{25}{100} = 25\%$

95. Answers may vary.

97. A square has 4 equal sides.
$$\begin{array}{r} 6.575 \\ 4\overline{)\ 26.300} \\ -24 \\ \hline 2\,3 \\ -2\,0 \\ \hline 30 \\ -28 \\ \hline 20 \\ -20 \\ \hline 0 \end{array}$$

Each side will be 6.575 m long.

Section 9.3

Practice Problems

1. Perimeter
$= 60 \text{ feet} + 60 \text{ feet} + 80 \text{ feet} + 80 \text{ feet}$
$= 280 \text{ feet}$

2. $P = 2l + 2w$
$= 2 \cdot 22 \text{ centimeters} + 2 \cdot 10 \text{ centimeters}$
$= 44 \text{ centimeters} + 20 \text{ centimeters}$
$= 64 \text{ centimeters}$

3. $P = 4s = 4 \cdot 50 \text{ yards} = 200 \text{ yards}$

4. $P = a + b + c = 5 \text{ cm} + 9 \text{ cm} + 7 \text{ cm} = 21 \text{ cm}$

5. Perimeter $= 3 \text{ km} + 7 \text{ km} + 3 \text{ km} + 4 \text{ km}$
$= 17 \text{ km}$

6. There are two sides of the room that are unknown. One side is 20 m − 15 m = 5 m, and the other side is 26 m − 7 m = 19 m. The perimeter of the room is
$5 \text{ m} + 19 \text{ m} + 15 \text{ m} + 26 \text{ m} + 20 \text{ m} + 7 \text{ m} = 92 \text{ m}$.

7. First find the perimeter of the room.
$P = 2l + 2w$
$= 2 \cdot 60 \text{ feet} + 2 \cdot 120 \text{ feet}$
$= 120 \text{ feet} + 240 \text{ feet}$
$= 360 \text{ feet}$
The cost for the fencing is
cost $= 1.90 \cdot 360 = 684$
The cost of the fencing is $684.

8. $C = \pi d = \pi \cdot 20 \text{ yards} = 20\pi \text{ yards}$
If we use 3.14 as an approximation of π, then the circumference is approximately
$20 \text{ yards} \cdot 3.14 = 62.8 \text{ yards}$.

Exercise Set 9.3

1. $P = 2l + 2w$
$= 2 \cdot 17 \text{ feet} + 2 \cdot 15 \text{ feet}$
$= 34 \text{ feet} + 30 \text{ feet}$
$= 64 \text{ feet}$

3. $P = 4s = 4(9 \text{ centimeters}) = 36 \text{ centimeters}$

5. $P = a + b + c$
$= 5 \text{ inches} + 7 \text{ inches} + 9 \text{ inches}$
$= 21 \text{ inches}$

7. $P = 2l + 2w$
$= 2(35 \text{ centimeters}) + 2(25 \text{ centimeters})$
$= 70 \text{ centimeters} + 50 \text{ centimeters}$
$= 120 \text{ centimeters}$

9. $P = 10 \text{ feet} + 8 \text{ feet} + 8 \text{ feet} + 15 \text{ feet} + 7 \text{ feet}$
$= 48 \text{ feet}$

11. $P = 12 \text{ inches} + 3 \text{ inches} + 15 \text{ inches} + 24 \text{ inches} + 12 \text{ inches}$
$= 66 \text{ inches}$

13. $P = 5 \text{ feet} + 3 \text{ feet} + 2 \text{ feet} + 7 \text{ feet} + 4 \text{ feet}$
$= 21 \text{ feet}$

15. $P = 4s = 4(15 \text{ feet}) = 60 \text{ feet}$

17. $P = 2l + 2w$
$= 2(120 \text{ yards}) + 2(53 \text{ yards})$
$= 240 \text{ yards} + 106 \text{ yards}$
$= 346 \text{ yards}$

19. $P = 2l + 2w$
$= 2(8 \text{ feet}) + 2(3 \text{ feet})$
$= 16 \text{ feet} + 6 \text{ feet}$
$= 22 \text{ feet}$

21. Since 22 feet of stripping is needed, cost = \$3(22) = \$66.

23. $P = 6(6 \text{ inches}) = 36 \text{ inches}$

25. $P = 4s = 4(7 \text{ inches}) = 28 \text{ inches}$

27. First find the perimeter of the room.
$P = 2l + 2w$
$= 2(6 \text{ feet}) + 2(8 \text{ feet})$
$= 12 \text{ feet} + 16 \text{ feet}$
$= 28 \text{ feet}$
The cost of the wallpaper is
$c = 0.86(28) = \$24.08$.

29. The missing lengths are:
28 meters – 20 meters = 8 meters
20 meters – 17 meters = 3 meters
$P = 8 \text{ meters} + 3 \text{ meters} + 20 \text{ meters} + 20 \text{ meters} + 28 \text{ meters} + 17 \text{ meters}$
$= 96 \text{ meters}$

31. The missing length is: 3 feet + 6 feet + 4 feet = 13 feet
$P = 13 \text{ feet} + 15 \text{ feet} + 3 \text{ feet} + 5 \text{ feet} + 6 \text{ feet} + 5 \text{ feet} + 4 \text{ feet} + 15 \text{ feet}$
$= 66 \text{ feet}$

33. The missing lengths are:
12 miles + 10 miles = 22 miles
8 miles + 34 miles = 42 miles
$P = 12 \text{ miles} + 34 \text{ miles} + 10 \text{ miles} + 8 \text{ miles} + 22 \text{ miles} + 42 \text{ miles}$
$= 128 \text{ miles}$

35. $C = \pi d$
$= \pi 17 \text{ centimeters}$
$\approx 3.14 \cdot 17 \text{ centimeters}$
$= 53.38 \text{ centimeters}$

37. $C = 2\pi r$
$= 2\pi \cdot 8 \text{ miles}$
$= 16\pi \text{ miles}$
$\approx 16 \cdot 3.14 \text{ miles}$
$= 50.24 \text{ miles}$

39. $C = \pi d$
$= \pi \cdot 26 \text{ meters}$
$= 26\pi \text{ meters}$
$\approx 26 \cdot 3.14 \text{ meters}$
$= 81.64 \text{ meters}$

41. $C = 2\pi r$
$= 2\pi \cdot 5 \text{ feet}$
$= 10\pi \text{ feet}$
$\approx 10 \cdot \frac{22}{7} \text{ feet}$
$= \frac{220}{7} \text{ feet}$
$= 31\frac{3}{7} \text{ feet}$

43. $C = \pi d$
$= \pi \cdot 4000 \text{ feet}$
$= 4000\pi \text{ feet}$
$\approx 4000 \cdot 3.14 \text{ feet}$
$= 12,560 \text{ feet}$

45. $5 + 6 \cdot 3 = 5 + 18 = 23$

47. $(20 - 16) \div 4 = 4 \div 4 = 1$

49. $(18 + 8) - (12 + 4) = 26 - 16 = 10$

51. $(72 \div 2) \cdot 6 = 36 \cdot 6 = 216$

57.
$$\begin{aligned} P &= 2L + 2W \\ 30 &= 2 \cdot 9 + 2W \\ 30 &= 18 + 2W \\ 12 &= 2W \\ 6 &= W \end{aligned}$$
The width of the rectangle is 6 feet.

59. Perimeter = add the 3 sides of the square to half of the circumference of the circular part.
$$\begin{aligned} P &= 6 + 6 + 6 + \frac{1}{2}(2 \cdot 3.14 \cdot 3) \\ &= 18 + \frac{1}{2}(18.84) \\ &= 18 + 9.42 \\ &\approx 27.4 \text{ meters} \end{aligned}$$

53. a. Circumference of the smaller circle:
$$\begin{aligned} C &= 2\pi r \\ &= 2\pi \cdot 10 \text{ meters} \\ &= 20\pi \text{ meters} \\ &\approx 20 \cdot 3.14 \text{ meters} \\ &= 62.8 \text{ meters} \end{aligned}$$
Circumference of the larger circle:
$$\begin{aligned} C &= 2\pi r \\ &= 2\pi \cdot 20 \text{ meters} \\ &= 40\pi \text{ meters} \\ &\approx 40 \cdot 3.14 \text{ meters} \\ &= 125.6 \text{ meters} \end{aligned}$$

b. Yes, the circumference is doubled.

55. The perimeter of the skating rink is equal to the circumference of a circle with radius 5 m plus two sides of a rectangle, each of length 22 m.
$$\begin{aligned} \text{Perimeter} &= 2\pi \cdot 5 \text{ m} + 2 \cdot 22 \text{ m} \\ &= 10\pi \text{ m} + 44 \text{ m} \\ &\approx 10 \cdot 3.14 \text{ m} + 44 \text{ m} \\ &= 75.4 \text{ m} \end{aligned}$$

Section 9.4

Practice Problems

1.
$$\begin{aligned} A &= \frac{1}{2}bh \\ &= \frac{1}{2} \cdot 8 \text{ in.} \cdot 6\frac{1}{4} \text{ in.} \\ &= \frac{1}{2} \cdot \frac{8}{1} \cdot \frac{25}{4} \text{ square inches} \\ &= 25 \text{ square inches} \end{aligned}$$

2.
$$\begin{aligned} A &= \frac{1}{2}(b + B)h \\ &= \frac{1}{2} \cdot (4 \text{ yd} + 10 \text{ yd}) \cdot 4.1 \text{ yd} \\ &= \frac{1}{2} \cdot 14 \text{ yd} \cdot 4.1 \text{ yd} \\ &= 28.7 \text{ square yards} \end{aligned}$$

3. Split the figure into two rectangles, and find the sum of the areas of the rectangles.

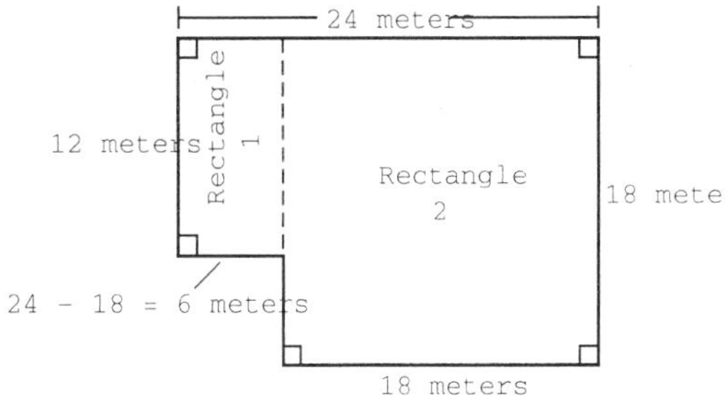

The area of rectangle 1
= (6 meters)(12 meters)
= 72 square meters

The area of rectangle 2
= (18 meters)(18 meters)
= 324 square meters

The area of the figure
= 324 square meters + 72 square meters
= 396 square meters

4.
$$\begin{aligned} A &= \pi r^2 \\ &= \pi \cdot (7 \text{ centimeters})^2 \\ &= 49\pi \text{ square centimeters} \\ &\approx 49 \cdot 3.14 \text{ square centimeters} \\ &= 153.86 \text{ square centimeters} \end{aligned}$$

5.

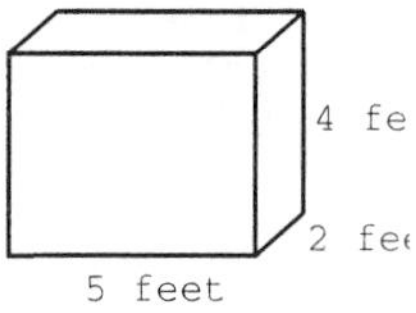

$$V = lwh$$
$$= 5 \text{ feet} \cdot 2 \text{ feet} \cdot 4 \text{ feet}$$
$$= 40 \text{ cubic feet}$$

6.

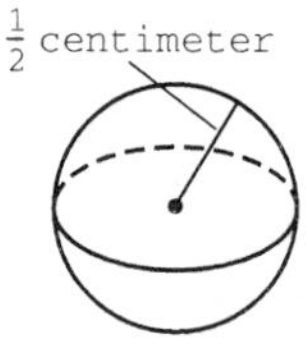

$$V = \frac{4}{3}\pi r^3$$
$$= \frac{4}{3}\pi \cdot \left(\frac{1}{2} \text{ centimeter}\right)^3$$
$$= \frac{1}{8} \cdot \frac{4}{3}\pi \text{ cubic centimeters}$$
$$= \frac{1}{6}\pi \text{ cubic centimeters}$$
$$\approx \frac{1}{6} \cdot \frac{22}{7} \text{ cubic centimeters}$$
$$= \frac{11}{21} \text{ cubic centimeters}$$

7. $V = \pi r^2 h$
$$= \pi \cdot (5 \text{ inches})^2 \cdot 7 \text{ inches}$$
$$= 25 \cdot 7 \cdot \pi \text{ cubic inches}$$
$$= 175\pi \text{ cubic inches}$$
$$\approx 175 \cdot 3.14 \text{ cubic inches}$$
$$= 549.5 \text{ cubic inches}$$

8. $V = \frac{1}{3}s^2 h$
$$= \frac{1}{3} \cdot (3 \text{ meters})^2 \cdot 5.1 \text{ meters}$$
$$= \frac{1}{3} \cdot 9 \cdot 5.1 \text{ cubic meters}$$
$$= 15.3 \text{ cubic meters}$$

Exercise Set 9.4

1. $A = lw$
$$= 3.5 \text{ meters} \cdot 2 \text{ meters}$$
$$= 7 \text{ square meters}$$

3. $A = \frac{1}{2}bh$
$$= \frac{1}{2} \cdot 6\frac{1}{2} \text{ yards} \cdot 3 \text{ yards}$$
$$= \frac{1}{2} \cdot \frac{13}{2} \cdot \frac{3}{1} \text{ square yards}$$
$$= \frac{39}{4} \text{ or } 9\frac{3}{4} \text{ square yards}$$

5. $A = \frac{1}{2}bh$
$$= \frac{1}{2} \cdot 6 \text{ yards} \cdot 5 \text{ yards}$$
$$= \frac{1}{2} \cdot 6 \cdot 5 \text{ square yards}$$
$$= 15 \text{ square yards}$$

7. $r = \frac{d}{2}$
$$= \frac{3 \text{ inches}}{2}$$
$$= 1.5 \text{ inches}$$
$$A = \pi r^2$$
$$= \pi(1.5 \text{ inches})^2$$
$$= 2.25\pi \text{ square inches}$$
$$\approx 2.25(3.14) \text{ square inches}$$
$$= 7.065 \text{ square inches}$$

9. $A = bh$
$$= 7 \text{ feet} \cdot 5.25 \text{ feet}$$
$$= 36.75 \text{ square feet}$$

11. $A = \frac{1}{2}(b + B)h$
$$= \frac{1}{2} \cdot (5 \text{ meters} + 9 \text{ meters}) \cdot 4 \text{ meters}$$
$$= \frac{1}{2} \cdot 14 \cdot 4 \text{ square meters}$$
$$= 28 \text{ square meters}$$

13. $A = \frac{1}{2}(b + B)h$
$$= \frac{1}{2} \cdot (4 \text{ yards} + 7 \text{ yards}) \cdot 4 \text{ yards}$$
$$= \frac{1}{2} \cdot 11 \text{ yards} \cdot 4 \text{ yards}$$
$$= \frac{1}{2} \cdot 11 \cdot 4 \text{ square yards}$$
$$= 22 \text{ square yards}$$

15. $A = bh$

$= 7 \text{ feet} \cdot 5\frac{1}{4} \text{ feet}$

$= 7 \cdot \frac{21}{4} \text{ square feet}$

$= \frac{147}{4} \text{ or } 36\frac{3}{4} \text{ square feet}$

17. $A = bh$

$= 5 \text{ inches} \cdot 4\frac{1}{2} \text{ inches}$

$= 5 \cdot \frac{9}{2} \text{ square inches}$

$= \frac{45}{2} \text{ or } 22\frac{1}{2} \text{ square inches}$

19. Area of rectangle $= bh$

$= 7 \text{ centimeters} \cdot 3 \text{ centimeters}$

$= 21 \text{ square centimeters}$

Area of triangle $= \frac{1}{2}bh$

$= \frac{1}{2} \cdot \left(7 - 1\frac{1}{2} - 1\frac{1}{2}\right) \text{ centimeters} \cdot 2 \text{ centimeters}$

$= \frac{1}{2} \cdot \left(\frac{14}{2} - \frac{3}{2} - \frac{3}{2}\right) \cdot 2 \text{ square centimeters}$

$= \frac{1}{2} \cdot \frac{8}{2} \cdot 2 \text{ square centimeters}$

$= 4 \text{ square centimeters}$

Total area $= 21 \text{ square centimeters} + 4 \text{ square centimeters}$

$= 25 \text{ square centimeters}$

21.

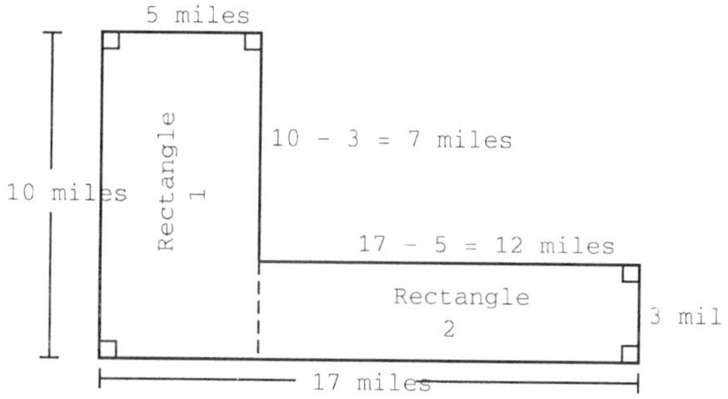

Area of rectangle 1 $= bh$

$= 5 \text{ miles} \cdot 10 \text{ miles}$

$= 50 \text{ square miles}$

Area of rectangle 2 $= bh$

$= 12 \text{ miles} \cdot 3 \text{ miles}$

$= 36 \text{ square miles}$

Total area $= 50 \text{ square miles} + 36 \text{ square miles}$

$= 86 \text{ square miles}$

23. Area of square $= s^2$

$= (3 \text{ centimeters})^2$

$= 9 \text{ square centimeters}$

Area of parallelogram $= b \cdot h$

$= (3 \text{ centimeters})(5 \text{ centimeters})$

$= 15 \text{ square centimeters}$

Total area = 9 square centimeters + 15 square centimeters = 24 square centimeters

25. $A = \pi r^2$

$= \pi(6 \text{ inches})^2$

$= 36\pi \text{ square inches}$

$\approx 36 \cdot \frac{22}{7} \text{ square inches}$

$\approx 113.1 \text{ square inches}$

27. $V = lwh$

$= 6 \text{ inches} \cdot 4 \text{ inches} \cdot 3 \text{ inches}$

$= 72 \text{ cubic inches}$

29. $V = s^3$

$= (8 \text{ centimeters})^3$

$= 512 \text{ cubic centimeters}$

31. $V = \frac{1}{3}\pi r^2 h$
$= \frac{1}{3} \cdot \pi \cdot (2 \text{ yards})^2 \cdot (3 \text{ yards})$
$= 4\pi$ cubic yards
$\approx 4 \cdot \frac{22}{7}$ cubic yards
$= \frac{88}{7}$ or $12\frac{4}{7}$ cubic yards

33. $V = \frac{4}{3}\pi r^3$
$= \frac{4}{3} \cdot \pi \cdot \left(\frac{10 \text{ inches}}{2}\right)^3$
$= \frac{4}{3} \cdot 125 \cdot \pi$ cubic inches
$= \frac{500}{3}\pi$ cubic inches
$\approx \frac{500}{3} \cdot \frac{22}{7}$ cubic inches
$= \frac{11,000}{21}$ cubic inches
$= 523\frac{17}{21}$ cubic inches

35. $V = \frac{1}{3}s^2 h$
$= \frac{1}{3} \cdot (5 \text{ centimeters})^2 \cdot 9$ centimeters
$= 75$ cubic centimeters

37. $V = s^3$
$= \left(1\frac{1}{3} \text{ inches}\right)^3$
$= \left(\frac{4}{3}\right)^3$ cubic inches
$= \frac{64}{27}$ cubic inches
$= 2\frac{10}{27}$ cubic inches

39. $V = lwh$
$= 2 \text{ feet} \cdot 1.4 \text{ feet} \cdot 3 \text{ feet}$
$= 8.4$ cubic feet

41. $A = lw$
$= 500 \text{ feet} \cdot 225 \text{ feet}$
$= 113,625$ square feet

43. Area of one panel $= lw$
$= 6 \text{ feet} \cdot 7 \text{ feet}$
$= 42$ square feet
Area of four panels $= 4 \cdot 42$ square feet
$= 168$ square feet

45. $V = \frac{1}{3}s^2 h$
$= \frac{1}{3} \cdot (12 \text{ centimeters})^2 \cdot 20$ centimeters
$= \frac{2880}{3}$ cubic centimeters
$= 960$ cubic centimeters

47. $A = \frac{1}{2}(b + B)h$
$= \frac{1}{2} \cdot (90 \text{ feet} + 140 \text{ feet}) \cdot 80 \text{ feet}$
$= \frac{1}{2} \cdot 230 \cdot 80$ square feet
$= 9200$ square feet

49. Area of shaded part
$= \frac{1}{2}(b + B)h$
$= \frac{1}{2} \cdot (25 \text{ feet} + 36 \text{ feet}) \cdot 12\frac{1}{2}$ feet
$= \frac{1}{2} \cdot 61 \text{ feet} \cdot \frac{25}{2}$ feet
$= \frac{1}{2} \cdot \frac{61}{1} \cdot \frac{25}{2}$ square feet
$= \frac{1525}{4}$ square feet
$= 381\frac{1}{4}$ square feet
The area of the shaded part to the nearest foot, is 381 square feet.

51. $V = \frac{4}{3}\pi r^3$
$= \frac{4}{3}\pi(7 \text{ inches})^3$
$= \frac{1372}{3}\pi$ cubic inches or $457\frac{1}{3}\pi$ cubic inches

53. $V = lwh$
$= 2 \text{ feet} \cdot 2\frac{1}{2} \text{ feet} \cdot 1\frac{1}{2}$ feet
$= 7\frac{1}{2}$ cubic feet

55. $V = \frac{1}{3}\pi r^2 h;\ r = \frac{1}{2}d$
$= \frac{1}{3} \cdot \frac{22}{7} \cdot (2 \text{ feet})^2 \cdot 3 \text{ feet}$
$= \frac{264}{21}$ cubic feet
$= 12\frac{4}{7}$ cubic feet

57. $V = \frac{4}{3}\pi r^3$
$= \frac{4}{3}\pi(3 \text{ inches})^3$
$= 36\pi$ cubic inches
$= 36(3.14)$ cubic inches
≈ 113.04 cubic inches

59. $V = \frac{1}{3}s^2 h$
$= \frac{1}{3}(5 \text{ inches})^2 \cdot 1.3 \text{ inches}$
$= 10\frac{5}{6}$ cubic inches

61. $5^2 = 25$

63. $3^2 = 9$

65. $1^2 + 2^2 = 1 + 4 = 5$

67. $4^2 + 2^2 = 16 + 4 = 20$

69. perimeter.

71. area

73. area

75. perimeter

77. Area of a 12-inch pizza
$= \pi r^2$
$= \pi\left(\frac{12}{2} \text{ inches}\right)^2$
$= \pi(6 \text{ inches})^2$
$= 36\pi$ square inches

Area of two 8-inch pizzas
$= 2(\pi r^2)$
$= 2 \cdot \pi\left(\frac{8}{2} \text{ inches}\right)^2$
$= 2\pi(4 \text{ inches})^2$
$= 2\pi \cdot 16$ square inches
$= 32\pi$ square inches
The 12-inch pizza is
$\frac{\$10}{36\pi \text{ square inches}} \approx \$0.08$ per square inch.
The two 8-inch pizzas are $\frac{\$9}{32\pi \text{ square inches}} \approx \$0.09$ per square inch.
The 12-inch pizza is the better buy.

79. 8 inches $= \frac{8}{12}$ feet $= \frac{2}{3}$ feet

$A = lw$

$= 2 \text{ feet} \cdot \frac{2}{3} \text{ feet}$

$= \frac{4}{3}$ or $1\frac{1}{3}$ square feet

2 feet = 24 inches

$A = lw$

$= 24 \text{ inches} \cdot 8 \text{ inches}$

$= 192$ square inches

81. Area of skating rink = area of rectangle + area of circle

$A = lw + \pi r^2$

$= 22 \text{ meters} \cdot 10 \text{ meters} + 3.14\,(5 \text{ meters})^2$

$= 220$ square meters $+ 78.5$ square meters

$= 298.5$ square meters

83. $V = \frac{1}{3}s^2h$

$= \frac{1}{3} \cdot (230 \text{ meters})^2 \cdot 146.5 \text{ meters}$

$\approx 2{,}583{,}283$ cubic meters

85. $V = \frac{1}{3}s^2h$

$= \frac{1}{3} \cdot (344 \text{ meters})^2 \cdot 65.5 \text{ meters}$

$\approx 2{,}583{,}669$ cubic meters

87. $V = \pi r^2 h$

$= (3.14)(16.3 \text{ feet})^2(32 \text{ feet})$

$\approx 26{,}695.5$ cubic feetw

89. No; answers may vary.

Integrated Review

1. The supplement of a 27° angle is 180° – 27° = 153°. The complement of a 27° angle is 90° – 27° = 63°.

2. Since $\angle x$ and the 105° angle are supplementary angles, $\angle x$ = 180° – 105° = 75°. $\angle y$ and the 105° angle are vertical angles, so $\angle y$ = 105°. $\angle x$ and $\angle z$ are vertical angles, so $\angle z$ = 75°.

3. Since $\angle x$ and the 52° angle are supplementary angles, $\angle x$ = 180° – 52° = 128°. $\angle y$ and the 52° angle are corresponding angles, so $\angle y$ = 52°. $\angle y$ and $\angle z$ are supplementary angles, so $\angle z$ = 180° – 52° = 128°.

4. $\angle x$ = 180° – 90° – 38° = 52°

5. $36 \text{ in.} = \frac{36 \text{ in.}}{1} \cdot \frac{1 \text{ ft}}{12 \text{ in.}} = 3 \text{ ft}$

6. $10{,}560 \text{ ft} = \frac{10{,}560 \text{ ft}}{1} \cdot \frac{1 \text{ mi}}{5280 \text{ ft}} = 2 \text{ mi}$

7. $20 \text{ ft} = \frac{20 \text{ ft}}{1} \cdot \frac{1 \text{ yd}}{3 \text{ ft}} = \frac{20}{3} \text{ yd} = 6\frac{2}{3} \text{ yd}$

8. $6 \text{ yd} = \frac{6 \text{ yd}}{1} \cdot \frac{3 \text{ ft}}{1 \text{ yd}} = 18 \text{ ft}$

9. $2.1 \text{ mi} = \frac{2.1 \text{ mi}}{1} \cdot \frac{5280 \text{ ft}}{1 \text{ mi}} = 11,088 \text{ ft}$

10. $3.2 \text{ ft} = \frac{3.2 \text{ ft}}{1} \cdot \frac{12 \text{ in.}}{1 \text{ ft}} = 38.4 \text{ in.}$

11. 30 m = 3000 cm

12. 24 mm = 2.4 cm

13. 2000 mm = 2 m

14. 18 m = 1800 cm

15. 7.2 cm = 72 mm

16. 600 m = 0.6 km

17. $P = 4s = 4 \cdot (5 \text{ meters}) = 20 \text{ meters}$
$A = s^2 = (5 \text{ meters})^2 = 25 \text{ square meters}$

18.
$$\begin{aligned} P &= a+b+c \\ &= 3 \text{ feet} + 4 \text{ feet} + 5 \text{ feet} \\ &= 12 \text{ feet} \\ A &= \frac{1}{2}bh \\ &= \frac{1}{2} \cdot 4 \text{ feet} \cdot 3 \text{ feet} \\ &= 6 \text{ square feet} \end{aligned}$$

19.
$$\begin{aligned} C &= 2\pi r \\ &= 2 \cdot \pi \cdot (3 \text{ centimeters}) \\ &= 6\pi \text{ centimeters} \\ &\approx 6 \cdot 3.14 \text{ centimeters} \\ &= 18.84 \text{ centimeters} \\ A &= \pi r^2 \\ &= \pi \cdot (3 \text{ centimeters})^2 \\ &= 9\pi \text{ square centimeters} \\ &\approx 9 \cdot 3.14 \text{ square centimeters} \\ &= 28.26 \text{ square centimeters} \end{aligned}$$

20. Perimeter
= 11 miles + 5 miles + 11 miles + 5 miles
= 32 miles

$$\begin{aligned} A &= bh \\ &= 11 \text{ miles} \cdot 4 \text{ miles} \\ &= 44 \text{ square miles} \end{aligned}$$

21.
$$\begin{aligned} P &= 2l + 2w \\ &= 2 \cdot 14 \text{ feet} + 2 \cdot 17 \text{ feet} \\ &= 28 \text{ feet} + 34 \text{ feet} \\ &= 62 \text{ feet} \\ A &= lw \\ &= 14 \text{ feet} \cdot 17 \text{ feet} \\ &= 238 \text{ square feet} \end{aligned}$$

22.
$$\begin{aligned} V &= s^3 \\ &= (4 \text{ inches})^3 \\ &= 64 \text{ cubic inches} \end{aligned}$$

23.
$$\begin{aligned} V &= lwh \\ &= 2 \text{ feet} \cdot 3 \text{ feet} \cdot 5.1 \text{ feet} \\ &= 30.6 \text{ cubic feet} \end{aligned}$$

24.
$$\begin{aligned} V &= \frac{1}{3}s^2h \\ &= \frac{1}{3} \cdot (10 \text{ centimeters})^2 \cdot 12 \text{ centimeters} \\ &= 400 \text{ cubic centimeters} \end{aligned}$$

25.
$$\begin{aligned} V &= \frac{4}{3}\pi r^3 \\ &= \frac{4}{3} \cdot \pi \cdot \left(\frac{16 \text{ miles}}{2}\right)^3 \\ &= \frac{4}{3} \cdot 512 \cdot \pi \text{ cubic miles} \\ &= \frac{2048}{3}\pi \text{ cubic miles} \\ &\approx \frac{2048}{3} \cdot \frac{22}{7} \text{ cubic miles} \\ &= \frac{45,056}{21} \text{ or } 2145\frac{11}{21} \text{ cubic miles} \end{aligned}$$

Section 9.5

Practice Problems

1.
$$\begin{aligned} 4500 \text{ lb} &= \frac{4500 \text{ lb}}{1} \cdot \frac{1 \text{ ton}}{2000 \text{ lb}} \\ &= \frac{4500 \text{ tons}}{2000} \\ &= \frac{9}{4} \text{ tons} \\ &= 2\frac{1}{4} \text{ tons} \end{aligned}$$

2. $$56\text{ oz} = \frac{56\text{ oz}}{1}\cdot\frac{1\text{ lb}}{16\text{ oz}} = \frac{56\text{ lb}}{16} = \frac{7}{2}\text{ lb} = 3\frac{1}{2}\text{ lb}$$

3.
$$\begin{array}{r} 8\text{ tons }\ 100\text{ lb} \\ -\ 5\text{ tons } 1200\text{ lb} \\ \hline \end{array} = \begin{array}{r} 7\text{ tons } 2100\text{ lb} \\ -\ 5\text{ tons } 1200\text{ lb} \\ \hline 2\text{ tons }\ 900\text{ lb} \end{array}$$

4.
$$\begin{array}{r} 4\text{ lb } 11\text{ oz} \\ \times\quad 8 \\ \hline 32\text{ lb } 88\text{ oz} \end{array} = 32\text{ lb} + 5\text{ lb } 8\text{ oz} = 37\text{ lb } 8\text{ oz}$$

$$\begin{array}{r} 5 \\ 16\overline{)\ 88} \\ -80 \\ \hline 8 \end{array}$$

5.
$$\begin{array}{r} 1\text{ lb } 6\text{ oz} \\ 4\overline{)\ 5\text{ lb } 8\text{ oz}} \\ -4\qquad\quad \\ \hline 1 = 16\text{ oz} \\ 24\text{ oz} \\ -24\quad \\ \hline 0\quad \end{array}$$

6.
$$\begin{array}{r} 5\text{ lb } 14\text{ oz} \\ +\quad 6\text{ oz} \\ \hline 5\text{ lb } 20\text{ oz} \end{array} = 5\text{ lb} + 1\text{ lb } 4\text{ oz} = 6\text{ lb } 4\text{ oz}$$

7. $$3.41\text{ g} = \frac{3.41\text{ g}}{1}\cdot\frac{1000\text{ mg}}{1\text{ g}} = 3140\text{ mg}$$

8. To convert centigrams to grams, move the decimal point 2 places to the left.
$$56.2\text{ cg} = \frac{56.2\text{ cg}}{1}\cdot\frac{1\text{ g}}{100\text{ cg}} = 0.562\text{ g}$$

9. 3.1 dg = 0.31 g or 2.5 g = 25 dg
$$\begin{array}{r} 2.50\text{ g} \\ -\ 0.31\text{ g} \\ \hline 2.19\text{ g} \end{array} \text{ or } \begin{array}{r} 25.0\text{ dg} \\ -\ 3.1\text{ dg} \\ \hline 21.9\text{ dg} \end{array}$$

10.
$$\begin{array}{r} 12.6\text{ kg} \\ \times\ 4 \\ \hline 50.4\text{ kg} \end{array}$$

11.
$$\begin{array}{r} 22.9 \approx 23 \\ 24\overline{)\ 550.0} \\ -48\quad \\ \hline 70\quad \\ -48\quad \\ \hline 220 \\ -216 \\ \hline 4 \end{array}$$
Each bag weighs approximately 23 kg.

Mental Math

1. 16 ounces = 1 lb
2. 32 ounces = 2 lb
3. 1 ton = 2000 lb
4. 2 tons = 4000 lb
5. 1 pound = 16 oz
6. 6 pounds = 96 oz
7. 2000 pounds = 1 ton
8. 4000 pounds = 2 tons
9. No
10. No
11. Yes
12. Yes
13. No
14. No

Exercise Set 9.5

1. $$2\text{ lb} = 2\text{ lb}\cdot\frac{16\text{ oz}}{1\text{ lb}} = 2\cdot 16\text{ oz} = 32\text{ oz}$$

3. $$5\text{ tons} = 5\text{ tons}\cdot\frac{2000\text{ lb}}{1\text{ ton}} = 5\cdot 2000\text{ lb} = 10{,}000\text{ lb}$$

5. $$12{,}000\text{ lb} = 12{,}000\text{ lb}\cdot\frac{1\text{ ton}}{2000\text{ lb}} = \frac{12{,}000\text{ tons}}{2000} = 6\text{ tons}$$

7. $60 \text{ oz} = 60 \text{ oz} \cdot \dfrac{1 \text{ lb}}{16 \text{ oz}}$
$= \dfrac{60 \text{ lb}}{16}$
$= \dfrac{15}{4} \text{ lb}$
$= 3\dfrac{3}{4} \text{ lb}$

9. $3500 \text{ lb} = 3500 \text{ lb} \cdot \dfrac{1 \text{ ton}}{2000 \text{ lb}}$
$= \dfrac{3500 \text{ tons}}{2000}$
$= \dfrac{7}{4} \text{ tons}$
$= 1\dfrac{3}{4} \text{ tons}$

11. $16.25 \text{ lb} = 16.25 \text{ lb} \cdot \dfrac{16 \text{ oz}}{1 \text{ lb}}$
$= 16.25 \cdot 16 \text{ oz}$
$= 260 \text{ oz}$

13. $4.9 \text{ tons} = 4.9 \text{ tons} \cdot \dfrac{2000 \text{ lb}}{1 \text{ ton}}$
$= 4.9 \cdot 2000 \text{ lb}$
$= 9800 \text{ lb}$

15. $4\dfrac{3}{4} \text{ lb} = 4\dfrac{3}{4} \text{ lb} \cdot \dfrac{16 \text{ oz}}{1 \text{ lb}}$
$= \dfrac{19}{4} \cdot 16 \text{ oz}$
$= 19 \cdot 4 \text{ oz}$
$= 76 \text{ oz}$

17. $2950 \text{ lb} = 2950 \text{ lb} \cdot \dfrac{1 \text{ ton}}{2000 \text{ lb}}$
$= \dfrac{2950 \text{ tons}}{2000}$
$= 1.475 \text{ tons}$
$\approx 1.5 \text{ tons}$

19.
$$\begin{array}{r} 34 \text{ lb } 12 \text{ oz} \\ +\ 18 \text{ lb } 14 \text{ oz} \\ \hline 52 \text{ lb } 26 \text{ oz} \end{array} = 52 \text{ lb} + 1 \text{ lb } 10 \text{ oz} = 53 \text{ lb } 10 \text{ oz}$$

21.
$$\begin{array}{r} 6 \text{ tons } 1540 \text{ lb} \\ +\ 2 \text{ tons } \ \ 850 \text{ lb} \\ \hline 8 \text{ tons } 2390 \text{ lb} \end{array} = 8 \text{ tons} + 1 \text{ ton } 390 \text{ lb} = 9 \text{ tons } 390 \text{ lb}$$

23.
$$\begin{array}{r} 5 \text{ tons } 1050 \text{ lb} \\ -\ 2 \text{ tons } \ \ 875 \text{ lb} \\ \hline 3 \text{ tons } \ \ 175 \text{ lb} \end{array}$$

25.
$$\begin{array}{r} 12 \text{ lb } 4 \text{ oz} \\ -\ 3 \text{ lb } 9 \text{ oz} \\ \hline \end{array} = \begin{array}{r} 11 \text{ lb } 20 \text{ oz} \\ -\ 3 \text{ lb } \ \ 9 \text{ oz} \\ \hline 8 \text{ lb } 11 \text{ oz} \end{array}$$

27.
$$\begin{array}{r} 5 \text{ lb } 3 \text{ oz} \\ \times \qquad 6 \\ \hline 30 \text{ lb } 18 \text{ oz} \end{array} = 30 \text{ lb} + 1 \text{ lb } 2 \text{ oz} = 31 \text{ lb } 2 \text{ oz}$$

29.
$$\begin{array}{r} 1 \text{ ton } \quad 700 \text{ lb} \\ 5 \overline{)\ 6 \text{ tons } 1500 \text{ lb}} \\ \underline{-5 \text{ tons}} \qquad\qquad \\ 1 \text{ ton} = 2000 \text{ lb} \\ 3500 \text{ lb} \\ \underline{-\ 3500 \text{ lb}} \\ 0 \end{array}$$

31.
$$\begin{array}{r} 1 \text{ lb } 10 \text{ oz} \\ +\ 3 \text{ lb } 14 \text{ oz} \\ \hline 4 \text{ lb } 24 \text{ oz} \end{array} = 4 \text{ lb} + 1 \text{ lb } 8 \text{ oz} = 5 \text{ lb } 8 \text{ oz}$$

She has 5 lb 8 oz of rice.

33.
$$\begin{array}{r} 64 \text{ lb } \ \ 8 \text{ oz} \\ -\ 28 \text{ lb } 10 \text{ oz} \\ \hline \end{array} = \begin{array}{r} 63 \text{ lb } 24 \text{ oz} \\ -\ 28 \text{ lb } 10 \text{ oz} \\ \hline 35 \text{ lb } 14 \text{ oz} \end{array}$$

His zucchini was 35 lb 14 oz below the record.

35. 4 boxes · 10 packages = 40 total packages
$$\begin{array}{r} 3 \text{ lb } \quad 4 \text{ oz} \\ \times \qquad 40 \\ \hline 120 \text{ lb } 160 \text{ oz} \end{array} = 120 \text{ lb} + 10 \text{ lb} = 130 \text{ lb}$$

4 boxes weigh 130 lb.

37. $\begin{array}{r} 55 \text{ lb } 4 \text{ oz} \\ -\ 2 \text{ lb } 8 \text{ oz} \\ \hline \end{array} = \begin{array}{r} 54 \text{ lb } 20 \text{ oz} \\ -\ 2 \text{ lb } \ 8 \text{ oz} \\ \hline 52 \text{ lb } 12 \text{ oz} \end{array}$

$\begin{array}{r} 52 \text{ lb } 12 \text{ oz} \\ \times \qquad\quad 4 \\ \hline 208 \text{ lb } 48 \text{ oz} \end{array} = 208 \text{ lb} + 3 \text{ lb} = 211 \text{ lb}$

There are 211 lb of pineapple in 4 boxes.

39. $6\frac{3}{4} \text{ oz} \cdot 12 = \frac{27}{4} \text{oz} \cdot 12 = 81 \text{ oz}$

$81 \text{ oz} \cdot \frac{1 \text{ lb}}{16 \text{ oz}} = 5 \text{ lb } 1 \text{ oz}$

A dozen bags will weigh 5 lb 1 oz.

41. To convert grams to kilograms, move the decimal 3 places to the left.
500 g = 0.5 kg

43. To convert grams to milligrams, move the decimal 3 places to the right.
4 g = 4000 mg

45. To convert kilograms to grams, move the decimal 3 places to the right.
25 kg = 25,000 g

47. To convert milligrams to grams, move the decimal 3 places to the left.
48 mg = 0.048 g

49. To convert grams to kilograms, move the decimal 3 places to the left.
6.3 g = 0.0063 kg

51. To convert grams to milligrams, move the decimal 3 places to the right.
15.14 g = 15,140 mg

53. To convert kilograms to grams, move the decimal 3 places to the right.
4.01 kg = 4010 g

55. $\begin{array}{r} 3.8 \text{ mg} \\ +\ 9.7 \text{ mg} \\ \hline 13.5 \text{ mg} \end{array}$

57. 205 mg = 0.205 g or 5.61 g = 5610 mg

$\begin{array}{r} 0.205 \text{ g} \\ +\ 5.610 \text{ g} \\ \hline 5.815 \text{ g} \end{array} = \begin{array}{r} 205 \text{ mg} \\ +\ 5610 \text{ mg} \\ \hline 5815 \text{ mg} \end{array}$

5.815 g or 5815 mg

59. 9 g = 9000 mg or 7150 mg = 7.15 g

$\begin{array}{r} 9000 \text{ mg} \\ -7150 \text{ mg} \\ \hline 1850 \text{ mg} \end{array} = \begin{array}{r} 9.00 \text{ g} \\ -7.15 \text{ g} \\ \hline 1.85 \text{ g} \end{array}$

1850 mg or 1.85 g

61. 1.61 kg = 1610 g or 250 g = 0.25 kg

$\begin{array}{r} 1610 \text{ g} \\ -250 \text{ g} \\ \hline 1360 \text{ g} \end{array} \qquad \begin{array}{r} 1.61 \text{ kg} \\ -0.25 \text{ kg} \\ \hline 1.36 \text{ kg} \end{array}$

63. $\begin{array}{r} 5.2 \text{ kg} \\ \times\ 2.6 \quad \\ \hline 312 \quad \\ 1040 \quad \\ \hline 13.52 \text{ kg} \end{array}$

65. $\begin{array}{r} 2.125 \text{ kg} \\ 8\overline{)\ 17.000 \text{ kg}} \\ \underline{-16} \quad\quad\ \\ 1\ 0 \quad\ \\ \underline{-\ 8} \quad\ \\ 20 \quad \\ \underline{-16} \quad \\ 40 \\ \underline{-40} \\ 0 \end{array}$

67. $\begin{array}{r} 336 \text{ g} \\ \times\ 24 \quad \\ \hline 1344 \quad \\ 6720 \quad \\ \hline 8064 \text{ g} \end{array} = 8.064 \text{ kg}$

24 cans weigh 8.064 kg.

69. $0.09 \text{ g} - 60 \text{ mg} = 90 \text{ mg} - 60 \text{ mg}$
$= 30 \text{ mg}$

The extra-strength tablet contains 30 mg more medication.

71. $0.6 \text{ g} - 350 \text{ mg} = 600 \text{ mg} - 350 \text{ mg}$
$= 250 \text{ mg}$

He can have 250 mg more sodium.

73. $3 \cdot 16 \cdot 3 \text{ mg} = 144 \text{ mg}$

3 cartons contain 144 mg of perservatives.

75. $6.432 \text{ kg} - 12 \cdot 26 \text{ g} = 6.432 \text{ kg} - 312 \text{ g}$
$= 6.432 \text{ kg} - 0.312 \text{ kg}$
$= 6.12 \text{ kg}$

There is 6.12 kg of oatmeal in the carton.

77. $0.3 \text{ kg} + 0.15 \text{ kg} + 400 \text{ g}$
$= 0.3 \text{ kg} + 0.15 \text{ kg} + 0.4 \text{ kg}$
$= 0.85 \text{ kg or } 850 \text{ g}$

The package weighs 0.85 kg or 850 g.

79.
$$\begin{array}{r} 198\text{ g} \\ \underline{12} \\ 396 \\ \underline{1980} \\ 2376\text{ g} \end{array} = 2.376\text{ kg}$$
A dozen bags weigh about 2.38 kg.

81. $\frac{1}{4} = \frac{1 \cdot 25}{4 \cdot 25} = \frac{25}{100} = 0.25$

83. $\frac{4}{25} = \frac{4 \cdot 4}{25 \cdot 4} = \frac{16}{100} = 0.16$

85. $\frac{7}{8} = \frac{7 \cdot 125}{8 \cdot 125} = \frac{875}{1000} = 0.875$

87. Answers may vary.

Section 9.6

Practice Problems

1. $43\text{ pints} = \frac{43\text{ pints}}{1} \cdot \frac{1\text{ qt}}{2\text{ pints}} = \frac{43}{2}\text{ qt} = 21\frac{1}{2}\text{ qt}$

2. $26\text{qt} = \frac{26\text{ qt}}{1} \cdot \frac{4\text{ c}}{1\text{ qt}} = 104\text{ c}$

3.
$$\begin{array}{r} 1\text{ gal }1\text{ qt} \\ -\quad 2\text{ qt} \\ \hline \end{array} \qquad \begin{array}{r} 0\text{ gal }5\text{ qt} \\ -\quad 2\text{ qt} \\ \hline 3\text{ qt} \end{array}$$

4.
$$\begin{array}{r} 2\text{ gal }3\text{ qt} \\ \times \qquad 2 \\ \hline 4\text{ gal }6\text{ qt} \end{array} = 4\text{ gal} + 1\text{ gal }2\text{ qt} = 5\text{ gal }2\text{ qt}$$

5.
$$\begin{array}{r} 3\text{ gal} \qquad 1\text{ pt} \\ 2\overline{)\,6\text{ gal }1\text{ qt}} \\ \underline{-6} \qquad\quad \\ 0 \qquad 1\text{ qt} = 2\text{ pt} \\ \underline{-2\text{ pt}} \\ 0 \end{array}$$

6.
$$\begin{array}{r} 15\text{ gal }3\text{ qt} \\ +\ 4\text{ gal }3\text{ qt} \\ \hline 19\text{ gal }6\text{ qt} \end{array} = 19\text{ gal} + 1\text{ gal }2\text{ qt} = 20\text{ gal }2\text{ qt}$$

7. $2100\text{ ml} = \frac{2100\text{ ml}}{1} \cdot \frac{1\text{ L}}{1000\text{ ml}} = \frac{2100}{1000}\text{ L} = 2.1\text{ L}$

8. To convert decaliters to liters, move the decimal one place to the right.
2.13 dal = 21.3 L

9. 1250 ml = 1.25 L or 2.9 L = 2900 ml
$$\begin{array}{r} 1250\text{ ml} \\ +\ 2900\text{ ml} \\ \hline 4150\text{ ml} \end{array} \qquad \begin{array}{r} 1.25\text{ L} \\ +\ 2.90\text{ L} \\ \hline 4.15\text{ L} \end{array}$$

10.
$$\begin{array}{r} 11.3\text{ L} \\ 13\overline{)\,146.9\text{ L}} \\ \underline{-13}\qquad \\ 16\qquad \\ \underline{-13}\qquad \\ 39\quad \\ \underline{-39}\quad \\ 0\quad \end{array}$$

11.
$$\begin{array}{r} 28.6 \\ \times\ 85 \\ \hline 1430 \\ \underline{22880} \\ 24310 \end{array}$$
2431 L can be pumped in 85 minutes.

Mental Math

1. 2 c = 1 pt

2. 4 c = 2 pt

3. 4 qt = 1 gal

4. 8 qt = 2 gal

5. 2 pt = 1 qt

6. 6 pt = 3 qt

7. 8 fl oz = 1 c

8. 24 fl oz = 3 c

9. 1 pt = 2 c

10. 3 pt = 6 c

11. 1 gal = 4 qt

12. 2 gal = 8 qt

13. No

14. Yes

15. No

16. Yes

Exercise Set 9.6

1. $32 \text{ fl oz} = 32 \text{ fl oz} \cdot \frac{1 \text{ c}}{8 \text{ fl oz}} = \frac{32 \text{ c}}{8} = 4 \text{ c}$

3. $8 \text{ qt} = 8 \text{ qt} \cdot \frac{2 \text{ pt}}{1 \text{ qt}} = 8 \cdot 2 \text{ pt} = 16 \text{ pt}$

5. $10 \text{ qt} = 10 \text{ qt} \cdot \frac{1 \text{ gal}}{4 \text{ qt}} = \frac{10 \text{ gal}}{4} = 2\frac{1}{2} \text{ gal}$

7. $80 \text{ fl oz} = 80 \text{ fl oz} \cdot \frac{1 \text{ pt}}{16 \text{ fl oz}} = \frac{80 \text{ pt}}{16} = 5 \text{ pt}$

9. $2 \text{ qt} = 2 \text{ qt} \cdot \frac{4 \text{ c}}{1 \text{ qt}} = 2 \cdot 4 \text{ c} = 8 \text{ c}$

11.
$$\begin{aligned} 120 \text{ fl oz} &= 120 \text{ fl oz} \cdot \frac{1 \text{ c}}{8 \text{ fl oz}} \cdot \frac{1 \text{ pt}}{2 \text{ c}} \cdot \frac{1 \text{ qt}}{2 \text{ pt}} \\ &= \frac{120 \text{ qt}}{8 \cdot 2 \cdot 2} \\ &= \frac{120 \text{ qt}}{32} \\ &= \frac{15 \text{ qt}}{4} \\ &= 3\frac{3}{4} \text{ qt} \end{aligned}$$

13.
$$\begin{aligned} 6 \text{ gal} &= 6 \text{ gal} \cdot \frac{4 \text{ qt}}{1 \text{ gal}} \cdot \frac{2 \text{ pt}}{1 \text{ qt}} \cdot \frac{2 \text{ c}}{1 \text{ pt}} \cdot \frac{8 \text{ fl oz}}{1 \text{ c}} \\ &= 6 \cdot 4 \cdot 2 \cdot 2 \cdot 8 \text{ fl oz} \\ &= 768 \text{ fl oz} \end{aligned}$$

15. $4\frac{1}{2} \text{ pt} = \frac{9}{2} \text{ pt} \cdot \frac{2 \text{ c}}{1 \text{ pt}} = 9 \text{ c}$

17.
$$\begin{aligned} 2\frac{3}{4} \text{ gal} &= \frac{11}{4} \text{ gal} \cdot \frac{4 \text{ qt}}{1 \text{ gal}} \cdot \frac{2 \text{ pt}}{1 \text{ qt}} \\ &= \frac{11 \cdot 4 \cdot 2 \text{ pt}}{4} \\ &= 22 \text{ pt} \end{aligned}$$

19.
$$\begin{array}{r} 4 \text{ gal } 3 \text{ qt} \\ + \; 5 \text{ gal } 2 \text{ qt} \\ \hline 9 \text{ gal } 5 \text{ qt} \end{array} = 9 \text{ gal} + 1 \text{ gal } 1 \text{ qt} = 10 \text{ gal } 1 \text{ qt}$$

21.
$$\begin{array}{r} 1 \text{ c } \; 5 \text{ fl oz} \\ + \; 2 \text{ c } \; 7 \text{ fl oz} \\ \hline 3 \text{ c } 12 \text{ fl oz} \end{array} = 3 \text{ c} + 1 \text{ c } 4 \text{ fl oz} = 4 \text{ c } 4 \text{ fl oz}$$

23.
$$\begin{array}{r} 3 \text{ gal} \\ - \; 1 \text{ gal } 3 \text{ qt} \\ \hline \end{array} = \begin{array}{r} 2 \text{ gal } 4 \text{ qt} \\ - \; 1 \text{ gal } 3 \text{ qt} \\ \hline 1 \text{ gal } 1 \text{ qt} \end{array}$$

25.
$$\begin{array}{r} 3 \text{ gal } 1 \text{ qt} \\ - \quad 1 \text{ qt } 1 \text{ pt} \\ \hline \end{array} = \begin{array}{r} 2 \text{ gal } 4 \text{ qt } 2 \text{ pt} \\ - \quad 1 \text{ qt } 1 \text{ pt} \\ \hline 2 \text{ gal } 3 \text{ qt } 1 \text{ pt} \end{array}$$

27.
$$\begin{aligned} \begin{array}{r} 1 \text{ pt } 1 \text{ c} \\ \times \quad 3 \\ \hline 3 \text{ pt } 3 \text{ c} \end{array} &= 3 \text{ pt} + 1 \text{ pt } 1 \text{ c} \\ &= 4 \text{ pt } 1 \text{ c} = 2 \text{ qt } 1 \text{ c} \end{aligned}$$

29.
$$\begin{array}{r} 8 \text{ gal } 2 \text{ qt} \\ \times \quad 2 \\ \hline 16 \text{ gal } 4 \text{ qt} \end{array} = 16 \text{ gal} + 1 \text{ gal} = 17 \text{ gal}$$

31.
$$\begin{array}{r} 4 \text{ gal} \quad 3 \text{ qt} \\ 2 \overline{) \; 9 \text{ gal} \quad 2 \text{ qt}} \\ -8 \text{ gal} \qquad \\ \hline 1 \text{ gal} = \underline{4 \text{qt}} \\ 6 \text{ qt} \\ -6 \text{ qt} \\ \hline 0 \quad \end{array}$$

33.
$$\begin{aligned} 1\frac{1}{2} \text{ qt} &= \frac{3}{2} \text{qt} \cdot \frac{2 \text{ pt}}{1 \text{ qt}} \cdot \frac{2 \text{ c}}{1 \text{ qt}} \cdot \frac{8 \text{ fl oz}}{1 \text{ c}} \\ &= \frac{3 \cdot 2 \cdot 2 \cdot 8 \text{ fl oz}}{2} \\ &= 48 \text{ fl oz} \end{aligned}$$

One can holds 48 fl oz.

35.
$$\begin{aligned} 64 \text{ fl oz} &= 64 \text{ fl oz} \cdot \frac{1 \text{ c}}{8 \text{ fl oz}} \cdot \frac{1 \text{ pt}}{2 \text{ c}} \cdot \frac{1 \text{ qt}}{2 \text{ pt}} \\ &= \frac{64 \text{ qt}}{8 \cdot 2 \cdot 2} \\ &= 2 \text{ qt} \end{aligned}$$

Individuals should drink 2 qt of water daily.

37.
$$\begin{array}{r} 5 \text{ pt } 1 \text{ c} \\ + \; 2 \text{ pt } 1 \text{ c} \\ \hline 7 \text{ pt } 2 \text{ c} \end{array} = 7 \text{ pt} + 1 \text{ pt} = 8 \text{ pt} = 4 \text{ qt} = 1 \text{ gal}$$

Yes, the fruit punch can be poured into the container.

39. $\frac{1}{30} \text{ gal} \cdot \frac{4 \text{ qt}}{1 \text{ gal}} \cdot \frac{2 \text{ pt}}{1 \text{ qt}} \cdot \frac{2 \text{ c}}{1 \text{ pt}} \cdot \frac{8 \text{ oz}}{1 \text{ c}} \approx 4.3 \text{ oz}$

41. $12 \text{ fl oz} \cdot 24 = 288 \text{ fl oz}$

$$288 \text{ fl oz} = 288 \text{ fl oz} \cdot \frac{1 \text{ c}}{8 \text{ fl oz}} \cdot \frac{1 \text{ pt}}{2 \text{ c}} \cdot \frac{1 \text{ qt}}{2 \text{ pt}}$$
$$= \frac{288 \text{ qt}}{8 \cdot 2 \cdot 2}$$
$$= 9 \text{ qt}$$

There are 9 quarts in a case of Pepsi.

43. To convert liters to milliliters move the decimal 3 places to the right.
5 L = 5000 ml

45. To convert milliliters to liters, move the decimal 3 places to the left.
4500 ml = 4.5 L

47. To convert liters to kiloliters move the decimal 3 places to the left.
410 L = 0.41 kl

49. To convert milliliters to liters move the decimal 3 places to the left.
64 ml = 0.064 L

51. To convert kiloliters to liters, move the decimal 3 places to the right.
0.16 kl = 160 L

53. To convert liters to milliliters move the decimal 3 places to the right.
3.6 L = 3600 ml

55. To convert liters to kiloliters, move the decimal 3 places to the left.
0.16 L = 0.00016 kl

57.
$$\begin{array}{r} 2.9 \text{ L} \\ +\ 19.6 \text{ L} \\ \hline 22.5 \text{ L} \end{array}$$

59. 2700 ml = 2.7 L or 1.8 L = 1800 ml
$$\begin{array}{rcr} 2.7 \text{ L} & = & 2700 \text{ ml} \\ +\ 1.8 \text{ L} & = & +\ 1800 \text{ ml} \\ \hline 4.5 \text{ L} & \text{or} & 4500 \text{ ml} \end{array}$$

61. 8.6 L = 8600 ml or 190 ml = 0.19 L
$$\begin{array}{rcr} 8600 \text{ ml} & = & 8.60 \text{ L} \\ -190 \text{ ml} & = & -0.19 \text{ L} \\ \hline 8410 \text{ ml} & \text{or} & 8.41 \text{ L} \end{array}$$

63. 11,400 ml = 11.4 L or 0.8 L = 800 ml
$$\begin{array}{rcr} 11.4 \text{ L} & = & 11{,}400 \text{ ml} \\ -0.8 \text{ L} & = & -\ 800 \text{ ml} \\ \hline 10.6 \text{ L} & \text{or} & 10{,}600 \text{ ml} \end{array}$$

65.
$$\begin{array}{r} 480 \text{ ml} \\ \times\ 8 \\ \hline 3840 \text{ ml} \end{array}$$

67. $0.5\overline{)81.2}$
Move decimal points 1 place.
$$\begin{array}{r} 162.4 \\ 5.\overline{)\ 812.0} \\ \underline{-5} \\ 31 \\ \underline{-30} \\ 12 \\ \underline{-10} \\ 20 \\ \underline{-20} \\ 0 \end{array}$$
81.2 L ÷ 0.5 = 162.4 L

69.
$$\begin{array}{rcr} 2 \text{ L} & = & 2.00 \text{ L} \\ -410 \text{ ml} & = & -0.41 \text{ L} \\ \hline & & 1.59 \text{ L} \end{array}$$
1.59 liters remain in the bottle.

71. 354 ml = 0.354 L
$$\begin{array}{lr} \text{gasoline} & 18.600 \text{ L} \\ +\ \text{dry gas} & +\ 0.354 \text{ L} \\ \hline & 18.954 \text{ L} \end{array}$$
There are 18.954 L of gasoline in the tank.

73. $44.3\overline{)\$14.00} \to 443\overline{)\ 140.0000}$
$$\begin{array}{r} 0.3160 \\ 443\overline{)\ 140.0000} \\ \underline{-132\ 9} \\ 7\ 10 \\ \underline{-4\ 43} \\ 2\ 670 \\ \underline{-2\ 658} \\ 120 \end{array}$$
The cost is about \$0.316 per liter.

75.
$$\begin{array}{rcr} 1.89 \text{ L} & = & 1890 \text{ mL} \\ -\ 946 \text{ mL} & = & -\ 946 \text{ mL} \\ \hline & & 944 \text{ mL} \end{array}$$
The larger bottle contains 944 ml more.

77. $0.7 = \frac{7}{10}$

79. $0.03 = \frac{3}{100}$

81. $0.006 = \frac{6}{1000} = \frac{3}{500}$

83. Answers may vary.

85. Each line represents 0.1 cc. B=1.5 cc

87. Each line represents 0.1 cc. D=2.7 cc

89. Each line represents 2u or 0.02 cc. B=54u or 0.54 cc.

91. Each line represents 2u or 0.02 cc. D=86u or 0.86 cc.

Section 9.7

Practice Problems

1. $1.5\text{ cm}\cdot\frac{1\text{ in}}{2.54\text{ cm}}\approx 0.59\text{ in}$

2. $8\text{ oz}\cdot\frac{28.35\text{ g}}{1\text{ oz}}=226.8\text{ g}$

3. $237\text{ ml}\cdot\frac{1\text{ fl oz}}{29.57\text{ ml}}\approx 8\text{ fl oz}$

Exercise Set 9.7

1. $578\text{ ml}\cdot\frac{1\text{ fl oz}}{29.57\text{ ml}}\approx 19.55\text{ fl oz}$

3. $86\text{ in}\cdot\frac{2.54\text{ cm}}{1\text{ in}}\approx 218.44\text{ cm}$

5. $1000\text{ g}\cdot\frac{0.04\text{ oz}}{1\text{ g}}=40\text{ oz}$

7. $93\text{ km}\cdot\frac{0.62\text{ mi}}{1\text{ km}}=57.66\text{ mi}$

9. $14.5\text{ L}\cdot\frac{0.26\text{ gal}}{1\text{ L}}=3.77\text{ gal}$

11. $30\text{ lb}\cdot\frac{1\text{ kg}}{2.20\text{ lb}}\approx 13.64\text{ km}$

13. $10\text{ cm}\cdot\frac{1\text{ in}}{2.54\text{ cm}}\approx 3.94\text{ in}$

15. $70\text{ mi}\cdot\frac{1.61\text{ km}}{1\text{ mi}}=112.7\text{ km per hr}$

17. $200\text{ mg} = 0.2\text{g}\cdot\frac{0.04\text{ oz}}{1\text{ g}}=0.008\text{ oz}$

19. $15\text{ stone}\cdot\frac{14\text{ lb}}{1\text{ stone}}=210\text{ lb} + 10\text{ lb} = 220\text{ lb}$

$220\text{ lb}\cdot\frac{1\text{ kg}}{2.20\text{ lb}}=100\text{ kg}$

Yes, 100 kg is approximately equal to 15 stone 10 pounds.

21. $12\text{ fl oz}\cdot\frac{29.57\text{ ml}}{1\text{ fl oz}}\approx 355\text{ ml}$

Since 335 ml < 380 ml, 380 ml is larger.

23. $3\frac{1}{2}\text{ in} = 3.5\text{ in}\cdot\frac{2.54\text{ cm}}{1\text{ in}}=8.89\text{ cm}\approx 90\text{ mm}$

25. $1.5\text{ lb}-1.25\text{ lb} = 0.25\text{ lb}\cdot\frac{16\text{ oz}}{1\text{ lb}}=4\text{ oz}$

$4\text{ oz}\cdot\frac{28.35\text{ g}}{1\text{ oz}}=113.4\text{ g}$

27. $167\text{ km}\cdot\frac{1\text{ mi}}{1.61\text{ km}}\approx 104\text{ mph}$

29. $8\text{ m}\cdot\frac{3.28\text{ ft}}{1\text{ m}}=26.24\text{ ft}$

31. $4.5\text{ km}\cdot\frac{0.62\text{ mi}}{1\text{ km}}\approx 3\text{ mi}$

33. $24\text{ hr} \div 4 = 6$ doses for 1 day

$6\text{ doses}\cdot 7\text{ days} = 42$ doses for 1 week

$42\text{ doses}\cdot 5\text{ ml} = 210$ ml of medicine is needed

$210\text{ ml}\cdot\frac{1\text{ fl oz}}{29.57\text{ ml}}\approx 7.1\text{ fl oz}$ which is 8 fl oz when rounded up to the next whole flu oz.

35. A

37. B

39. C

41. D

43. D

45. $-6\cdot 4+5\div(-1)=-24+(-5)=-29$

47. $\frac{-10+8}{-10-8}=\frac{-2}{-18}=\frac{1}{9}$

49. $3+5(17-19)-8 = 3+5(-2)-8$
$= 3+(-10)-8$
$= -7-8$
$= -15$

51. $3[(-1+5)\cdot(6-8)] = 3[4(-2)]$
$= 3[-8]$
$= -24$

53. $\text{BSA} = \sqrt{\dfrac{90\times 182}{3600}} \approx 2.13 \text{ sq m}$

55. $40 \text{ in}\cdot\dfrac{2.54 \text{ cm}}{1 \text{ in}} = 101.6 \text{ cm}$
$\text{BSA} = \sqrt{\dfrac{50\times 101.6}{3600}} \approx 1.19 \text{ sq m}$

57. $60 \text{ in}\cdot\dfrac{254 \text{ cm}}{1 \text{ in}} \approx 152 \text{ cm}$
$150 \text{ lb}\cdot\dfrac{0.45 \text{ kg}}{1 \text{ lb}} \approx 68 \text{ kg}$
$\text{BSA} = \sqrt{\dfrac{68\times 152}{3600}} \approx 1.70 \text{ sq m}$

59. $10\cdot 2.13 = 21.3 \text{ mg}$
$12\cdot 2.13 = 25.56 \text{ mg}$
The dosage range would be 21.3 mg - 25.56 mg.

61. $A = lw$ (in meters)
$= 20 \text{ meters}\cdot 40 \text{ meters}$
$= 800 \text{ square meters}$

Convert to feet:
$20 \text{ m}\cdot\dfrac{3.28 \text{ ft}}{1 \text{ m}} = 65.6 \text{ ft}$

$40 \text{ m}\cdot\dfrac{3.28 \text{ ft}}{1 \text{ m}} = 131.2 \text{ ft}$

$A = 65.6 \text{ feet}\cdot 131.2 \text{ feet}$
$= 8606.72 \text{ square feet}$

Section 9.8

Practice Problems

1. $F = \dfrac{9}{5}C+32$
$= \dfrac{9}{5}\cdot 50+32$
$= 90+32$
$= 122$
50°C is 122°F

2. $F = 1.8C+32$
$= 1.8\cdot 18+32$
$= 32.4+32$
$= 64.4$
18°C is 64.4°F

3. $C = \dfrac{5}{9}(F-32)$
$= \dfrac{5}{9}\cdot(86-32)$
$= \dfrac{5}{9}\cdot 54$
$= 30$
86°F is 30°C

4. $C = \dfrac{5}{9}(F-32)$
$= \dfrac{5}{9}\cdot(113-32)$
$= \dfrac{5}{9}\cdot 81$
$= 45$
113°F is 45°C

5. $C = \dfrac{5}{9}(F-32)$
$= \dfrac{5}{9}\cdot(102.8-32)$
$= \dfrac{5}{9}\cdot 70.8$
$= 39.\overline{3}$
102.8°C is approximately 39.3°F

Mental Math

1. Yes

2. No

3. No

4. Yes

5. No

6. No

7. Yes

8. No

Exercise Set 9.8

1. $C = \frac{5}{9}(F - 32)$
$C = \frac{5}{9} \cdot (41 - 32)$
$= \frac{5}{9} \cdot (9)$
$= 5$
$41° F = 5° C$

3. $C = \frac{5}{9}(F - 32)$
$C = \frac{5}{9} \cdot (104 - 32)$
$= \frac{5}{9} \cdot (72)$
$= 5(8)$
$= 40$
$104°F = 40°C$

5. $F = \frac{9}{5}C + 32$
$F = \frac{9}{5} \cdot (115) + 32$
$= 108 + 32$
$= 140$
$60°C = 140°F$

7. $F = \frac{9}{5}C + 32$
$F = \frac{9}{5} \cdot (115) + 32$
$= 9(23) + 32$
$= 207 + 32$
$= 239$
$115°C = 239°F$

9. $C = \frac{5}{9}(F - 32)$
$C = \frac{5}{9} \cdot (62 - 32)$
$= \frac{5}{9} \cdot (30)$
$= \frac{150}{9}$
≈ 16.7
$62°F \approx 16.7°C$

11. $C = \frac{5}{9}(F - 32)$
$C = \frac{5}{9} \cdot (142.1 - 32)$
$= \frac{5}{9} \cdot (110.1)$
$= \frac{550.5}{9}$
≈ 61.2
$142.1°F \approx 61.2°C$

13. $F = 1.8C + 32$
$F = 1.8(92) + 32$
$= 165.6 + 32$
$= 197.6$
$92°C = 197.6°F$

15. $F = 1.8C + 32$
$F = 1.8(16.3) + 32$
$= 29.34 + 32$
$= 61.34$
$16.3°C \approx 61.3°F$

17. $C = \frac{5}{9}(F - 32)$
$= \frac{5}{9}(122 - 32)$
$= \frac{5}{9}(90)$
$= \frac{450}{9}$
$= 50° C$
$122° F = 50° C$

19. $F = 1.8C + 32$
$F = 1.8(27) + 32$
$= 48.6 + 32$
$= 80.6$
$27°C = 80.6°F$

21. $C = \frac{5}{9}(F - 32)$
$C = \frac{5}{9} \cdot (70 - 32)$
$= \frac{5}{9} \cdot (38)$
$= \frac{190}{9}$
≈ 21.1
$70°F \approx 21.1°C$

23. $C = \frac{5}{9}(F - 32)$

$C = \frac{5}{9} \cdot (100.2 - 32)$

$= \frac{5}{9} \cdot (68.2)$

$= \frac{341}{9}$

≈ 37.9

100.2°F ≈ 37.9°C

25. $F = 1.8C + 32$

$F = 1.8 \cdot 118 + 32$

$= 212.4 + 32$

$= 244.4$

118°C = 244.4°F

27. $C = \frac{5}{9}(F - 32)$

$C = \frac{5}{9} \cdot (500 - 32)$

$= \frac{5}{9} \cdot (468)$

$= 5(52)$

$= 260$

500°F = 260°C

29. $C = \frac{5}{9}(F - 32)$

$C = \frac{5}{9} \cdot (864 - 32)$

$= \frac{5}{9} \cdot (832)$

$= \frac{4160}{9}$

≈ 462.2

864°F ≈ 462.2°C

31. $P = 2l + 2w$

$= 2(25 \text{ m}) + 2(6 \text{ m})$

$= 50 \text{ m} + 12 \text{ m}$

$= 62 \text{ m}$

33. $P = 3 \text{ ft} + 3 \text{ ft} + 3 \text{ ft} + 3 \text{ ft} + 3 \text{ ft}$

$= 15 \text{ ft}$

35. $P = 4s$

$= 4 \cdot 2.6 \text{ m}$

$= 10.4 \text{ m}$

37. $C = \frac{5}{9}(F - 32)$

$C = \frac{5}{9} \cdot (9010 - 32)$

$= \frac{5}{9} \cdot (8978)$

$= \frac{44{,}890}{9}$

≈ 4988

9010°F is about 4988°C.

Chapter 9 Review

1. $\angle A$ is a right angle.
2. $\angle B$ is a straight angle.
3. $\angle C$ is an acute angle.
4. $\angle D$ is an obtuse angle.
5. The complement of a 25° angle is 90° − 25° = 65°.
6. The supplement of a 105° angle is 180° − 105° = 75°.
7. The supplement of a 72° angle is 180° − 72° = 108°.
8. The complement of a 1° angle is 90° − 1° = 89°.
9. $\angle x = 90° - 32° = 58°$
10. $\angle x = 180° - 82° = 98°$
11. $\angle x = 105° - 15° = 90°$
12. $\angle x = 45° - 20° = 25°$
13. 47° and 133° are supplementary angles.
14. 47° and 43° are complementary angles.
    58° and 32° are complementary angles.
15. $\angle x$ and the 80° angle are vertical angles, so $\angle x = 80°$. $\angle x$ and $\angle y$ are supplementary angles, so $\angle y = 180° - 80° = 100°$. $\angle y$ and $\angle z$ are vertical angles, so $\angle z = 100°$.

16. $\angle x$ and the 25° angle are supplementary angles, so $\angle x = 180° - 25° = 155°$. $\angle x$ and $\angle y$ are vertical angles, so $\angle y = 155°$. $\angle z$ and the 25° angle are vertical angles, so $\angle z = 25°$.

17. $\angle x$ and the 53° angle are vertical angles, so $\angle x = 53°$. $\angle y$ and the 53° angle are corresponding angles, so $\angle y = 53°$. $\angle y$ and $\angle z$ are supplementary angles, so $\angle z = 180° - 53° = 127°$.

18. $\angle x$ and the 42° angle are vertical angles, so $\angle x = 42°$. $\angle y$ and the 42° angle are corresponding angles, so $\angle y = 42°$. $\angle y$ and $\angle z$ are supplementary angles, so $\angle z = 180° - 42° = 138°$.

19. $108 \text{ in.} = 108 \text{ in.} \cdot \frac{1 \text{ ft}}{12 \text{ in.}} = 9 \text{ ft}$

20. $72 \text{ ft} = 72 \text{ ft} \cdot \frac{1 \text{ yd}}{3 \text{ ft}}$
$= 24 \text{ yd}$

21. $2.5 \text{ mi} = 2.5 \text{ mi} \cdot \frac{5280 \text{ ft}}{1 \text{ mi}} = 13{,}200 \text{ ft}$

22. $6.25 \text{ ft} = 6.25 \text{ ft} \cdot \frac{12 \text{ in.}}{1 \text{ ft}}$
$= 75 \text{ in.}$

23.
$$\begin{array}{r} 17 \\ 3\overline{)52} \\ -3 \\ \hline 22 \\ -21 \\ \hline 1 \end{array}$$
52 ft = 17 yd 1 ft

24.
$$\begin{array}{r} 3 \\ 12\overline{)46} \\ -36 \\ \hline 10 \end{array}$$
46 in. = 3 ft 10 in.

25. 42 m = 4200 cm

26. 82 cm = 820 mm

27. 12.18 mm = 0.01218 m

28. 2.31 m = 0.00231 km

29.
$$\begin{array}{r} 4 \text{ yd } 2 \text{ ft} \\ +\ 16 \text{ yd } 2 \text{ ft} \\ \hline 20 \text{ yd } 4 \text{ ft} \end{array} = 20 \text{ yd} + 1 \text{ yd } 1 \text{ ft}$$
$$= 21 \text{ yd } 1 \text{ ft}$$

30.
$$\begin{array}{r} 12 \text{ ft } 1 \text{ in.} \\ -\ 4 \text{ ft } 8 \text{ in.} \\ \hline \end{array} = \begin{array}{r} 11 \text{ ft } 13 \text{ in.} \\ -\ 4 \text{ ft } \ 8 \text{ in.} \\ \hline 7 \text{ ft } \ 5 \text{ in.} \end{array}$$

31.
$$\begin{array}{r} 8 \text{ ft } 3 \text{ in.} \\ \times \quad 5 \\ \hline 40 \text{ ft } 15 \text{ in.} \end{array} = 40 \text{ ft} + 1 \text{ ft } 3 \text{ in.}$$
$$= 41 \text{ ft } 3 \text{ in.}$$

32.
$$\begin{array}{r} 3 \text{ ft} \quad 8 \text{ in.} \\ 2\overline{)\ 7 \text{ ft} \quad 4 \text{ in.}} \\ -6 \text{ ft} \qquad\quad \\ \hline 1 \text{ ft} = 12 \text{ in.} \\ 16 \text{ in.} \\ -16 \text{ in.} \\ \hline 0 \end{array}$$

33. 8 cm = 80 mm or 15 mm = 1.5 cm
$$\begin{array}{r} 80 \text{ mm} \\ +15 \text{ mm} \\ \hline 95 \text{ mm} \end{array} \qquad \begin{array}{r} 8.0 \text{ cm} \\ +\ 1.5 \text{ cm} \\ \hline 9.5 \text{ cm} \end{array}$$

34. 4 m = 400 cm or 126 cm = 1.26 m
$$\begin{array}{r} 400 \text{ cm} \\ +126 \text{ cm} \\ \hline 526 \text{ cm} \end{array} \qquad \begin{array}{r} 4.00 \text{ m} \\ +\ 1.26 \text{ m} \\ \hline 5.26 \text{ m} \end{array}$$

35. 9.3 km = 9300 m or 183 m = 0.183 km
$$\begin{array}{r} 9300 \text{ m} \\ -183 \text{ m} \\ \hline 9117 \text{ m} \end{array} \qquad \begin{array}{r} 9.300 \text{ km} \\ -\ 0.183 \text{ km} \\ \hline 9.117 \text{ km} \end{array}$$

36. 4100 mm = 4.1 m or 3 m = 3000 mm
$$\begin{array}{r} 4.1 \text{ m} \\ -3.0 \text{ m} \\ \hline 1.1 \text{ m} \end{array} \qquad \begin{array}{r} 4100 \text{ mm} \\ -3000 \text{ mm} \\ \hline 1100 \text{ mm} \end{array}$$

37.
$$\begin{array}{r} 333 \text{ yd } 1 \text{ ft} \\ -\ 163 \text{ yd } 2 \text{ ft} \\ \hline \end{array} \qquad \begin{array}{r} 332 \text{ yd } 4 \text{ ft} \\ -\ 163 \text{ yd } 2 \text{ ft} \\ \hline 169 \text{ yd } 2 \text{ ft} \end{array}$$
169 yards 2 feet of cloth remain.

38.
$$\begin{array}{r} 6 \text{ ft } 4 \text{ in.} \\ \times \quad 20 \\ \hline 120 \text{ ft } 80 \text{ in.} \end{array} = 120 \text{ ft} + 6 \text{ ft } 8 \text{ in.}$$
$$= 126 \text{ ft } 8 \text{ in.}$$
126 feet 8 inches of framing material is needed.

39. The round-trip distance is
$2(217\text{ km}) = 434\text{ km}$.
$\frac{434}{4} = 108.5$
Each must drive 108.5 kilometers.

40. $30\text{ cm} = 0.3\text{ m}$
$$\begin{array}{r} 0.8\text{ m} \\ \times\ 0.3\text{ m} \\ \hline 0.24 \end{array}$$ square meters

41. Perimeter
$= 27\text{ meters} + 17\text{ meters} + 27\text{ meters} + 17\text{ meters}$
$= 88\text{ meters}$

42. $P = a + b + c$
$= 11\text{ centimeters} + 7\text{ centimeters} + 12\text{ centimeters}$
$= 30\text{ centimeters}$

43. The missing lengths are:
10 meters − 7 meters = 3 meters
8 meters − 5 meters = 3 meters
Perimeter = 8 meters + 7 meters + 3 meters + 3 meters + 5 meters + 10 meters
= 36 meters

44. The missing length is: 5 feet + 4 feet + 11 feet = 20 feet
Perimeter = 22 feet + 20 feet + 22 feet + 11 feet + 3 feet + 4 feet + 3 feet + 5 feet
= 90 feet

45. $P = 2l + 2w$
$= 2 \cdot 6\text{ feet} + 2 \cdot 10\text{ feet}$
$= 12\text{ feet} + 20\text{ feet}$
$= 32\text{ feet}$

46. $P = 4s = 4 \cdot 110\text{ feet} = 440\text{ feet}$

47. $C = \pi d$
$= \pi \cdot 1.7\text{ inches}$
$= 1.7\pi\text{ inches}$
$\approx 1.7 \cdot 3.14\text{ inches}$
$= 5.338\text{ inches}$

48. $C = 2\pi r$
$= 2 \cdot \pi \cdot 5\text{ yards}$
$= 10\pi\text{ yards}$
$\approx 10 \cdot 3.14\text{ yards}$
$= 31.4\text{ yards}$

49. $A = \frac{1}{2}(b + B)h$
$= \frac{1}{2} \cdot (12\text{ feet} + 36\text{ feet}) \cdot 10\text{ feet}$
$= 240\text{ square feet}$

50. $A = \frac{1}{2}bh$
$= \frac{1}{2} \cdot 20\text{ meters} \cdot 14\text{ meters}$
$= 140\text{ square meters}$

51. $A = lw$
$= 40\text{ centimeters} \cdot 15\text{ centimeters}$
$= 600\text{ square centimters}$

52. $A = bh$
$= 21\text{ yards} \cdot 9\text{ yards}$
$= 189\text{ square yards}$

53. $A = \pi r^2$
$= \pi \cdot (7\text{ feet})^2$
$= 49\pi\text{ square feet}$
$\approx 49 \cdot 3.14\text{ square feet}$
$= 153.86\text{ square feet}$

54. $A = \pi r^2$
$= \pi \cdot (2\text{ inches})^2$
$= 4\pi\text{ square inches}$
$\approx 4 \cdot 3.14\text{ square inches}$
$= 12.56\text{ square inches}$

55. $A = \frac{1}{2}bh$
$= \frac{1}{2} \cdot 34 \text{ inches} \cdot 7 \text{ inches}$
$= 119 \text{ square inches}$

56.
$A = \frac{1}{2}(b+B)h$
$= \frac{1}{2} \cdot (32 \text{ centimeters} + 64 \text{ centimeters}) \cdot 26 \text{ centimeters}$
$= \frac{1}{2} \cdot 96 \cdot 26 \text{ square centimeters}$
$= 1248 \text{ square centimeters}$

57.

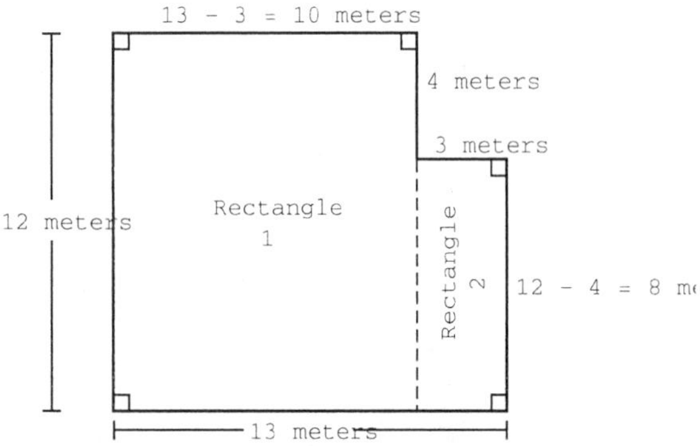

Area of rectangle $1 = 12 \text{ meters} \cdot 10 \text{ meters}$
$= 120 \text{ square meters}$

Area of rectangle $2 = 8 \text{ meters} \cdot 3 \text{ meters}$
$= 24 \text{ square meters}$

Total area $= 120 \text{ square meters} + 24 \text{ square meters}$
$= 144 \text{ square meters}$

58. $A = lw$
$= 36 \text{ feet} \cdot 12 \text{ feet}$
$= 432 \text{ square feet}$

59. $A = lw$
$= 13 \text{ feet} \cdot 10 \text{ feet}$
$= 130 \text{ square feet}$

60. $V = s^3$
$= \left(2\frac{1}{2} \text{ inches}\right)^3$
$= \left(\frac{5}{2} \text{ inches}\right)^3$
$= \frac{125}{8} \text{ or } 15\frac{5}{8} \text{ cubic inches}$

61. $V = lwh$
$= 7 \text{ feet} \cdot 2 \text{ feet} \cdot 6 \text{ feet}$
$= 84 \text{ cubic feet}$

62. $V = \pi r^2 h$
$= \pi \cdot (20 \text{ centimeters})^2 \cdot 50 \text{ centimeters}$
$= 20{,}000\pi \text{ cubic centimeters}$
$\approx 20{,}000 \cdot \frac{22}{7} \text{ cubic centimeters}$
$= 62{,}857\frac{1}{7} \text{ cubic centimeters}$

63. $V = \frac{1}{3}\pi r^2 h$
$= \frac{1}{3} \cdot \pi \cdot \left(5\frac{1}{4} \text{ inches}\right)^2 \cdot 12 \text{ inches}$
$= \frac{1}{3} \cdot \left(\frac{21}{4}\right)^2 \cdot 12 \cdot \pi \text{ cubic inches}$
$= \frac{441}{4}\pi \text{ cubic inches}$
$\approx \frac{441}{4} \cdot \frac{22}{7} \text{ cubic inches}$
$= \frac{693}{2} \text{ or } 346\frac{1}{2} \text{ cubic inches}$

64. $V = \frac{1}{3}s^2 h$
$= \frac{1}{3} \cdot (2 \text{ feet})^2 \cdot 2 \text{ feet}$
$= \frac{1}{3} \cdot 4 \cdot 2 \text{ cubic feet}$
$= \frac{8}{3} \text{ or } 2\frac{2}{3} \text{ cubic feet}$

65. $V = \pi r^2 h$
$= \pi \cdot (3.5 \text{ inches})^2 \cdot 8 \text{ inches}$
$= 98\pi \text{ cubic inches}$
$\approx 98 \cdot 3.14 \text{ cubic inches}$
$= 307.72 \text{ cubic inches}$

66. Volume = $3lwh$

$$= 3 \cdot 2\frac{1}{2} \text{ feet} \cdot 1\frac{1}{2} \text{ feet} \cdot \frac{2}{3} \text{ feet}$$
$$= 3 \cdot \frac{5}{2} \cdot \frac{3}{2} \cdot \frac{2}{3} \text{ cubic feet}$$
$$= \frac{15}{2} \text{ or } 7\frac{1}{2} \text{ cubic feet}$$

67. $V = \pi r^2 h$

$$= \pi \cdot \left(\frac{1 \text{ foot}}{2}\right)^2 \cdot 2 \text{ feet}$$
$$= \frac{1}{4} \cdot 2 \cdot \pi \text{ cubic feet}$$
$$= \frac{1}{2}\pi \text{ or } 0.5\pi \text{ cubic feet}$$

68. $V = lwh$

$$= 15 \text{ feet} \cdot 12 \text{ feet} \cdot 7 \text{ feet}$$
$$= 1260 \text{ cubic feet}$$

69. Volume of first box = $(3 \text{ feet})^3$ = 27 cubic feet

Volume of second box = $(1.2 \text{ feet})^3$ = 1.728 cubic feet

Total volume
= 27 cubic feet + 1.728 cubic feet
= 28.728 cubic feet

70. $66 \text{ oz} = 66 \text{ oz} \cdot \frac{1 \text{ lb}}{16 \text{ oz}} = 4.125 \text{ lb}$

71. $2.3 \text{ tons} = 2.3 \text{ tons} \cdot \frac{2000 \text{ lb}}{1 \text{ ton}} = 4600 \text{ lb}$

72.
```
     3
16)52
  -48
    4
```
52 oz = 3 lb 4 oz

73.
```
         4
2000)8200
    -8000
      200
```
8200 lb = 4 tons 200 lb

74. 1400 mg = 1.4 g

75. 40 kg = 40,000 g

76. 2.1 hg = 21 dag

77. 0.03 mg = 0.0003 dg

78.
```
  6 lb  5 oz        5 lb 21 oz
- 2 lb 12 oz      - 2 lb 12 oz
                    3 lb  9 oz
```

79.
```
  5 tons 1600 lb
+ 4 tons 1200 lb
  9 tons 2800 lb = 9 tons + 1 ton 800 lb
                 = 10 tons 800 lb
```

80.
```
   2 tons   750 lb
3) 6 tons  2250 lb
  -6 tons
   0       2250 lb
          -2250 lb
                 0
```

81.
```
   8 lb  6 oz
×         4
  32 lb 24 oz = 32 lb + 1 lb 8 oz
              = 33 lb 8 oz
```

82. 1300 mg = 1.3 g or 3.6 g = 3600 mg
```
  1.3 g        1300 mg
+ 3.6 g      + 3600 mg
  4.9 g        4900 mg
```

83. 4.8 kg = 4800 g or 4200 g = 4.2 kg
```
  4800 g        4.8 kg
+ 4200 g      + 4.2 kg
  9000 g        9.0 kg = 9 kg
```

84. 9.3 g = 9300 mg or 1200 mg = 1.2 g
```
  9300 mg       9.3 g
- 1200 mg     - 1.2 g
  8100 mg       8.1 g
```

85.
```
  6.3 kg
×   8
 50.4 kg
```

86.
```
  1 lb 12 oz
+ 2 lb  8 oz
  3 lb 20 oz = 3 lb + 1 lb 4 oz
             = 4 lb 4 oz
```
He ordered 4 pounds 4 ounces of candy.

87.
```
   9 tons    1075 lb
4) 38 tons    300 lb
  -36 tons
    2 tons = 4000 lb
             4300 lb
           - 4300 lb
                   0
```
Each township receives 9 tons 1075 pounds of cinders.

88. 450 g = 0.45 kg

$$\begin{array}{r} 8.30\text{ kg} \\ -\,0.45\text{ kg} \\ \hline 7.85\text{ kg} \end{array}$$

She received 7.85 kilograms of flour.

89.

$$\begin{array}{r} 1.1625\text{ kg} \\ 8\overline{)\ 9.3000\text{ kg}} \\ -8\phantom{.0000\text{ kg}} \\ \hline 13\phantom{000\text{ kg}} \\ -\,8\phantom{000\text{ kg}} \\ \hline 50\phantom{00\text{ kg}} \\ -48\phantom{00\text{ kg}} \\ \hline 20\phantom{0\text{ kg}} \\ -16\phantom{0\text{ kg}} \\ \hline 40\phantom{\text{ kg}} \\ -40\phantom{\text{ kg}} \\ \hline 0\phantom{\text{ kg}} \end{array}$$

Each receives 1.1625 kilograms of syrup.

90. $16\text{ pt} = 16\text{ pt}\cdot\frac{1\text{ qt}}{2\text{ pt}} = 8\text{ qt}$

91. $40\text{ fl oz} = 40\text{ fl oz}\cdot\frac{1\text{ c}}{8\text{ fl oz}} = 5\text{ c}$

92. $6.75\text{ gal} = 6.75\text{ gal}\cdot\frac{4\text{ qt}}{1\text{ gal}} = 27\text{ qt}$

93. $8.5\text{ pt} = 8.5\text{ pt}\cdot\frac{2\text{ c}}{1\text{ pt}} = 17\text{ c}$

94.

$$\begin{array}{r} 4 \\ 2\overline{)\ 9} \\ -8 \\ \hline 1 \end{array}$$

9 pt = 4 qt 1 pt

95.

$$\begin{array}{r} 3 \\ 4\overline{)\ 15} \\ -12 \\ \hline 3 \end{array}$$

15 qt = 3 gal 3 qt

96. 3.8 L = 3800 ml

97. 4.2 ml = 0.042 dl

98. 14 hl = 1.4 kl

99. 30.6 L = 3060 cl

100.

$$\begin{array}{r} 1\text{ qt }1\text{ pt} \\ +\ 3\text{ qt }1\text{ pt} \\ \hline 4\text{ qt }2\text{ pt} \end{array} = 4\text{ qt} + 1\text{ qt} = 5\text{ qt} = 1\text{ gal }1\text{ qt}$$

101.

$$\begin{array}{r} 3\text{ gal }2\text{ qt }1\text{ pt} \\ \times\qquad\qquad 2 \\ \hline 6\text{ gal }4\text{ qt }2\text{ pt} \end{array} = 6\text{ gal} + 1\text{ gal} + 1\text{qt} = 7\text{ gal }1\text{ qt}$$

102. 0.946 L = 946 ml or 210 ml = 0.210 L

$$\begin{array}{r} 946\text{ ml} \\ -210\text{ ml} \\ \hline 736\text{ ml} \end{array} \qquad \begin{array}{r} 0.946\text{ L} \\ -\,0.210\text{ L} \\ \hline 0.736\text{ L} \end{array}$$

103. 6.1 L = 6100 ml or 9400 ml = 9.4 L

$$\begin{array}{r} 6100\text{ ml} \\ +9400\text{ ml} \\ \hline 15{,}500\text{ ml} \end{array} \qquad \begin{array}{r} 6.1\text{ L} \\ +9.4\text{ L} \\ \hline 15.5\text{ L} \end{array}$$

104.

$$\begin{array}{r} 4\text{ gal }2\text{ qt} \\ -\ 1\text{ gal }3\text{ qt} \\ \hline \end{array} = \begin{array}{r} 3\text{ gal }6\text{ qt} \\ -\ 1\text{ gal }3\text{ qt} \\ \hline 2\text{ gal }3\text{ qt} \end{array}$$

2 gal 3 qt of tea remains.

105. 1 c 4 fl oz = 8 fl oz + 4 fl oz
= 12 fl oz
12 fl oz ÷ 2 = 6 fl oz
6 fluid ounces of beef broth should be used.

106. 85 ml · 8 · 16 = 10,880 ml = 10.88 L
8 boxes contain 10.88 liters of polish.

107. 6 L + 1300 ml + 2.6 L
= 6 L + 1.3 L + 2.6 L
= 9.9 L
Yes, since 9.9 L < 10 L, it will fit.

108. $7\text{ m}\cdot\frac{3.28\text{ ft}}{1\text{ m}} = 22.96\text{ ft}$

109. $11.5\text{ yd}\cdot\frac{1\text{m}}{1.09\text{ yd}} \approx 10.55\text{ m}$

110. $17.5\text{ L}\cdot\frac{1\text{ gal}}{3.79\text{ L}} \approx 4.62\text{ gal}$

111. $7.8\text{ L}\cdot\frac{1.06\text{ qt}}{1\text{ L}} \approx 8.27\text{ qt}$

112. $15\text{ oz}\cdot\frac{28.35\text{ g}}{1\text{ oz}} = 425.25\text{ g}$

113. $23\text{ lb}\cdot\frac{1\text{ kg}}{2.20\text{ lb}} \approx 10.45\text{ kg}$

114. $100\text{ m}\cdot\frac{1.09\text{ yd}}{1\text{m}} = 109\text{ yd}$

115. $82\text{ kg}\cdot\dfrac{2.20\text{ lb}}{1\text{ kg}}=180.4\text{ lb}$

116. $3\text{ L}\cdot\dfrac{1.06\text{ qt}}{1\text{ L}}=318\text{ qt}$

117. $1.2\text{ mm}=0.12\text{ cm}\cdot\dfrac{1\text{ in}}{2.54\text{ cm}}\cdot 50\approx 2.36\text{ in}$

118. $F=\dfrac{9}{5}\cdot 245+32=441+32=473$

$245°C=473°F$

119.
$$\begin{aligned}F&=\frac{9}{5}\cdot 160+32\\&=288+32\\&=320\end{aligned}$$
$160°C=320°F$

120.
$$\begin{aligned}F&=1.8(42)+32\\&=75.6+32\\&=107.6\end{aligned}$$
$42°C=107.6°F$

121.
$$\begin{aligned}F&=1.8\cdot 86+32\\&=154.8+32\\&=186.8°F\end{aligned}$$
$86°C=186.8°F$

122.
$$\begin{aligned}C&=\frac{5}{9}\cdot(93.2-32)\\&=\frac{5}{9}\cdot 61.2\\&=\frac{306.0}{9}\\&=34\end{aligned}$$
$93.2°F=34°C$

123.
$$\begin{aligned}C&=\frac{5}{9}\cdot(51.8-32)\\&=\frac{5}{9}\cdot 19.8\\&=\frac{99}{9}\\&=11\end{aligned}$$
$51.8°F=11°C$

124.
$$\begin{aligned}C&=\frac{5}{9}\cdot(41.3-32)\\&=\frac{5}{9}\cdot 9.3\\&=\frac{46.5}{9}\\&=5.1\overline{6}\\&\approx 5.2\end{aligned}$$
$41.3°F\approx 5.2°C$

125.
$$\begin{aligned}C&=\frac{5}{9}\cdot(80-32)\\&=\frac{5}{9}\cdot 48\\&=\frac{240}{9}\\&=26.\overline{6}\\&\approx 26.7\end{aligned}$$
$80°F\approx 26.7°C$

126.
$$\begin{aligned}C&=\frac{5}{9}\cdot(35-32)\\&=\frac{5}{9}\cdot 3\\&=\frac{15}{9}\\&=1.\overline{6}\\&\approx 1.7\end{aligned}$$
$35°F\approx 1.7°C$

127.
$$\begin{aligned}F&=\frac{9}{5}\cdot 165+32\\&=297+32\\&=329\end{aligned}$$
$165°C=329°F$

Chapter 9 Test

1. The complement of a 78° angle is $90°-78°=12°$.

2. The supplement of a 124° angle is $180°-124°=56°$.

3. $\angle x=90°-40°=50°$

4. Since $\angle x$ and the 62° angle are supplementary angles, $\angle x=180°-62°=118°$. $\angle y$ and the 62° angle are vertical angles, so $\angle y=62°$. $\angle x$ and $\angle z$ are vertical angles, so $\angle z=118°$.

5. $\angle x$ and the 73° angle are vertical angles, so $\angle x=73°$. $\angle y$ and the 73° angle are corresponding angles, so $\angle y=73°$. $\angle z$ and $\angle y$ are vertical angles, so $\angle z=73°$.

6. $d = 2r$
$d = 2(3.1 \text{ m})$
$d = 6.2 \text{ m}$

7. $r = \frac{1}{2}d$
$r = \frac{1}{2}(20 \text{ in})$
$\text{r} = 10 \text{ in}$

8. $C = 2\pi r$
$= 2 \cdot \pi \cdot 9 \text{ inches}$
$= 18\pi \text{ inches}$
$\approx 18 \cdot 3.14 \text{ inches}$
$= 56.52 \text{ inches}$

$A = \pi r^2$
$= \pi \cdot (9 \text{ inches})^2$
$= 81\pi \text{ square inches}$
$\approx 81 \cdot 3.14 \text{ square inches}$
$= 254.34 \text{ square inches}$

9. $P = 2l + 2w$
$= 2 \cdot 7 \text{ yards} + 2 \cdot 5.3 \text{ yards}$
$= 14 \text{ yards} + 10.6 \text{ yards}$
$= 24.6 \text{ yards}$

$A = lw$
$= 7 \text{ yards} \cdot 5.3 \text{ yards}$
$= 37.1 \text{ square yards}$

10.

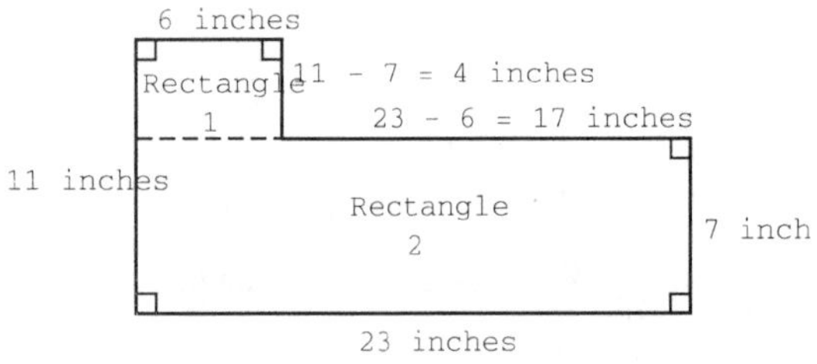

Perimeter = 6 inches + 4 inches + 17 inches + 7 inches + 23 inches + 11 inches
= 68 inches
Area of rectangle 1 = 6 inches · 4 inches
= 24 square inches
Area of rectangle 2 = 7 inches · 23 inches
= 161 square inches
Total area = 161 square inches + 24 square inches
= 185 square inches

11. $V = \pi r^2 h$
$= \pi \cdot (2 \text{ inches})^2 \cdot 5 \text{ inches}$
$= 20\pi$ cubic inches
$\approx 20 \cdot \frac{22}{7}$ cubic inches
$= \frac{440}{7}$ or $62\frac{6}{7}$ cubic inches

12. $V = lwh$
$= 3 \text{ feet} \cdot 5 \text{ feet} \cdot 2 \text{ feet}$
$= 30$ cubic feet

13. $P = 4s = 4 \cdot 4 \text{ inches} = 16 \text{ inches}$

14. $V = lwh$
$= 3 \text{ feet} \cdot 3 \text{ feet} \cdot 2 \text{ feet}$
$= 18$ cubic feet

15. $A = lw$
$= 123.8 \text{ feet} \cdot 80 \text{ feet}$
$= 9904$ square feet

16.
$$\begin{array}{r} 23 \\ 12\overline{)280} \\ -24 \\ \hline 40 \\ -36 \\ \hline 4 \end{array}$$
280 in. = 23 ft 4 in.

17. $2\frac{1}{2} \text{ gal} = \frac{5}{2} \text{ gal} \cdot \frac{4 \text{ qt}}{1 \text{ gal}} = 10 \text{ qt}$

18. $30 \text{ oz} = 30 \text{ oz} \cdot \frac{1 \text{ lb}}{16 \text{ oz}} = 1.875 \text{ lb}$

19. $2.8 \text{ tons} = 2.8 \text{ tons} \cdot \frac{2000 \text{ lb}}{1 \text{ ton}} = 5600 \text{ lb}$

20. 2.4 km = 2400 m

21. 3.6 cm = 36 mm

22. 4.3 dg = 0.43 g

23. 0.83 L = 830 ml

24. $7 \text{ kg} \cdot \frac{2.20 \text{ lb}}{1 \text{ kg}} = 15.4 \text{ lb}$

25. $8.5 \text{ in} \cdot \frac{2.54 \text{ cm}}{1 \text{ in}} = 21.59 \text{ cm}$

26. $C = \frac{5}{9} \cdot (84 - 32)$
$= \frac{5}{9} \cdot 52$
$= \frac{260}{9}$
$= 28.\overline{8}$
≈ 28.9
84°F ≈ 28.9°C

27. $F = 1.8 \cdot 12.6 + 32$
$= 22.68 + 32$
$= 54.68$
12.6°C = 54.7°F

28. $8.4 \text{ m} \cdot \frac{1}{3} = 2.8 \text{ m}$
8.4 m − 2.8 m = 5.6 m
The maples will be 5.6 meters tall after the cutting.

29. 20 gal = 19 gal 4 qt
$$\begin{array}{r} 19 \text{ gal } 4 \text{ qt} \\ -\ 15 \text{ gal } 1 \text{ qt} \\ \hline 4 \text{ gal } 3 \text{ qt} \end{array}$$
4 gal 3 qt of oil remains.

30. 340 cm = 3.4 m
$$\begin{array}{r} 88.0 \text{ m} \\ +\ 3.4 \text{ m} \\ \hline 91.4 \text{ m} \end{array}$$
The span is 91.4 m long.

31.
$$\begin{array}{r} 2 \text{ ft } 9 \text{ in.} \\ \times \qquad 6 \\ \hline 12 \text{ ft } 54 \text{ in.} \end{array} = 12 \text{ ft} + 4 \text{ ft } 6 \text{ in.}$$
$= 16 \text{ ft } 6 \text{ in. or } 16\frac{1}{2} \text{ ft}$

16 ft 6 inches or $16\frac{1}{2}$ feet of material is needed for 6 scarves.

32. $4667 \text{ gal} = \frac{4667}{1} \text{ gal} \cdot \frac{4 \text{ qt}}{1 \text{ gal}} \cdot \frac{2 \text{ pt}}{1 \text{ qt}}$
$= 4667 \cdot 4 \cdot 2 \text{ pt}$
$= 37,336 \text{ pt}$
Thus, 37,336 pints of ice cream were used.

33. $5 \text{ g} \cdot \frac{0.04 \text{ oz}}{1 \text{ g}} = 0.2 \text{ oz}$

34. $5 \text{ gal} \cdot \frac{3.79 \text{ L}}{1 \text{ gal}} = 18.95 \text{ L}$

35. $5\text{ km}\cdot\frac{1\text{ mi}}{1.61\text{ km}}\approx 3.1\text{ mi}$

Cumulative Review

1.
$$\begin{aligned}3a-6&=a+4\\3a-6-a&=a+4-a\\2a-6&=4\\2a-6+6&=4+6\\2a&=10\\\frac{2a}{2}&=\frac{10}{2}\\a&=5\end{aligned}$$

2.
$$\begin{aligned}2x+1&=3x-5\\2x+1-3x&=3x-5-3x\\-x+1&=-5\\-x+1-1&=-5-1\\-x&=-6\\\frac{-x}{-1}&=\frac{-6}{-1}\\x&=6\end{aligned}$$

3.

a. $\left(\frac{2}{5}\right)^4=\left(\frac{2}{5}\right)\left(\frac{2}{5}\right)\left(\frac{2}{5}\right)\left(\frac{2}{5}\right)=\frac{16}{625}$

b. $\left(-\frac{1}{4}\right)^2=\left(-\frac{1}{4}\right)\left(-\frac{1}{4}\right)=\frac{1}{16}$

4.

a. $\left(-\frac{1}{3}\right)^3=\left(-\frac{1}{3}\right)\left(-\frac{1}{3}\right)\left(-\frac{1}{3}\right)=-\frac{1}{27}$

b. $\left(\frac{3}{7}\right)^2=\left(\frac{3}{7}\right)\left(\frac{3}{7}\right)=\frac{9}{49}$

5.
$$\begin{aligned}1\tfrac{4}{5}&=\ \ 1\tfrac{8}{10}\\4&=\ \ 4\\+2\tfrac{1}{2}&=+2\tfrac{5}{10}\\\hline &\ \ \ 7\tfrac{13}{10}=7+1\tfrac{3}{10}=8\tfrac{3}{10}\end{aligned}$$

6.
$$\begin{aligned}2\tfrac{1}{3}&=\ \ 2\tfrac{5}{15}\\4\tfrac{2}{5}&=\ \ 4\tfrac{6}{15}\\+3&=+3\\\hline &\ \ \ 9\tfrac{11}{15}\end{aligned}$$

7.
$$\begin{aligned}&11.1x-6.3+8.9x-4.6\\&=11.1x+8.9x-6.3-4.6\\&=20x-10.9\end{aligned}$$

8.
$$\begin{aligned}&2.5y+3.7-1.3y-1.9\\&=2.5y-1.3y+3.7-1.9\\&=1.2y+1.8\end{aligned}$$

9. $\frac{0.7+1.84}{0.4}=\frac{2.54}{0.4}=6.35$

10. $\frac{0.12+0.96}{0.5}=\frac{1.08}{0.5}=2.16$

11. $0.\overline{7}=0.\overline{7}=\frac{7}{9}$

12. $0.43>0.40=\frac{2}{5}$

13.
$$\begin{aligned}0.5y+2.3&=1.65\\0.5y+2.3-2.3&=1.65-2.3\\0.5y&=-0.65\\\frac{0.5y}{0.5}&=\frac{-0.65}{0.5}\\y&=-1.3\end{aligned}$$

14.
$$\begin{aligned}0.4x-9.3&=2.7\\0.4x-9.3+9.3&=2.7+9.3\\0.4x&=12\\\frac{0.4x}{0.4}&=\frac{12}{0.4}\\x&=30\end{aligned}$$

15. Two sides of the square with the diagonal will form a right triangle, therefore we use the Pythagorean Theorem. The diagonal is C.
$$\begin{aligned}a^2+b^2&=c^2\\300^2+300^2&=c^2\\90,000+90,000&=c^2\\180,000&=c^2\\\sqrt{180,000}&=c\\424&\approx c\end{aligned}$$
The diagonal is 424 feet.

16. The length, width, and diagonal of the rectangle will form a right triangle, so we will use the Pythagorean Theorem. The diagonal is C.

$$\begin{aligned} a^2+b^2 &= c^2 \\ 200^2+125^2 &= c^2 \\ 40,000+15,625 &= c^2 \\ 55,625 &= c^2 \\ \sqrt{55,625} &= c \\ 236 &\approx c \end{aligned}$$

The diagonal is 236 feet.

17. **a.** $\dfrac{\text{width}}{\text{length}}=\dfrac{5}{7}$

b. $\dfrac{\text{length}}{\text{perimeter}}=\dfrac{7}{5+7+5+7}=\dfrac{7}{24}$

18. **a.** $\dfrac{\text{side}}{\text{perimeter}}=\dfrac{9}{9+9+9+9}=\dfrac{9}{36}=\dfrac{1}{4}$

b. $\dfrac{\text{perimeter}}{\text{area}}=\dfrac{36}{9^2}=\dfrac{36}{81}=\dfrac{4}{9}$

19. $\dfrac{10\text{ nails}}{6\text{ feet}}=\dfrac{5\text{ nails}}{3\text{ feet}}$

20. $\dfrac{8\text{ chaperones}}{40\text{ students}}=\dfrac{1\text{ chaperone}}{4\text{ students}}$

21. $$\begin{aligned} \frac{1.6}{1.1} &= \frac{x}{0.3} \\ 1.1x &= 0.48 \\ x &\approx 0.44 \end{aligned}$$

22. $$\begin{aligned} \frac{2.4}{3.5} &= \frac{0.7}{x} \\ 2.4x &= 2.45 \\ x &\approx 1.02 \end{aligned}$$

23. $$\begin{aligned} \frac{4}{25} &= \frac{x}{140} \\ 25x &= 560 \\ x &= 22.4 \end{aligned}$$

The standard dose is 22.4 cc

24. $$\begin{aligned} \frac{2}{3} &= \frac{5}{x} \\ 2x &= 15 \\ x &= 7.5 \end{aligned}$$

7.5 cups of flour is needed

25. $\dfrac{17}{100}=17\%$

26. $\dfrac{17}{100}=17\%$

27. $$\begin{aligned} 13 &= 0.065\cdot x \\ \frac{13}{0.065} &= x \\ 200 &= x \end{aligned}$$

28. $$\begin{aligned} 54 &= 0.045\cdot x \\ \frac{54}{0.045} &= x \\ 1200 &= x \end{aligned}$$

29. $$\begin{aligned} x &= .30\cdot 9 \\ x &= 2.7 \end{aligned}$$

30. $$\begin{aligned} x &= .42\cdot 30 \\ x &= 12.6 \end{aligned}$$

31. $\text{percent increase }=\dfrac{45-34}{34}=\dfrac{11}{34}\approx 32\%$

32. $\text{percent increase }=\dfrac{19-15}{15}=\dfrac{4}{15}\approx 27\%$

33. sales tax $=\$85.50\cdot 0.075=\$6.41$
total price $=\$85.50+\$6.41=\$91.91$

34. sales tax $=\$375\cdot 0.08=\$30$
total price $=\$375+\$30=\$405$

35. $A(-4,2), B(1,2), C(0,1), D(-3,0), E(5,-4)$

36. $A(2,-3), B(-5,0), C(0,4), D(-3,-2)$

37.

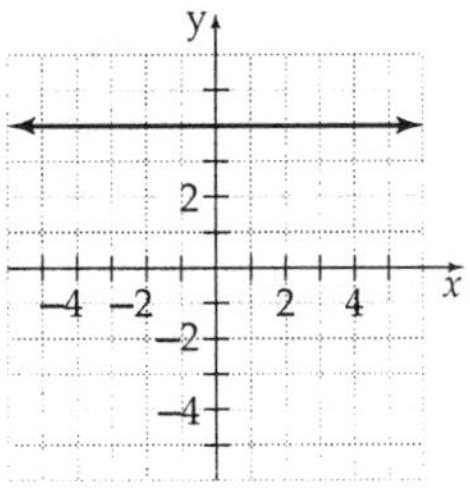

38.

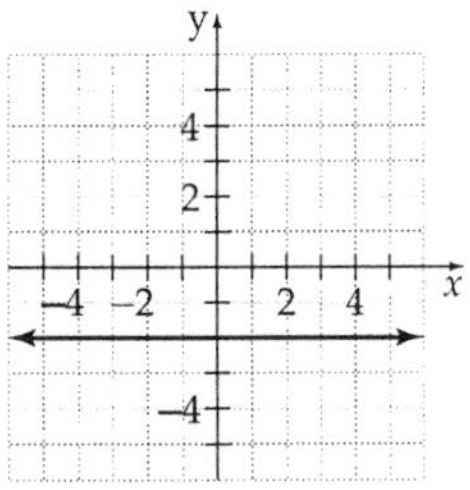

39. Arrange numbers from smallest to largest
25, 54, 56, 57, 60, 71, 98
Median: the middle number which is 57.

40. Arrange numbers from smallest to largest
60, 72, 83, 89, 85
Median: the middle number which is 83.

41. $\frac{\text{number of ways the event can occur}}{\text{number of possible outcomes}} = \frac{1}{4}$

42. $\frac{\text{number of ways the event can occur}}{\text{number of possible outcomes}} = \frac{2}{7}$

43. $90° - 48° = 42°$

44. $180° - 137° = 43°$

45. $8\text{ ft} \cdot \frac{12\text{ in}}{1\text{ ft}} = 96\text{ inches}$

46. $7\text{ yd} \cdot \frac{3\text{ ft}}{1\text{ yd}} = 21\text{ feet}$

47.

$$\begin{array}{rcr} 8\text{ tons } 1000\text{ lb} & = & 7\text{ tons } 3000\text{ lb} \\ -3\text{ tons } 1350\text{ lb} & = & -3\text{ tons } 1350\text{ lb} \\ \hline & & 4\text{ tons } 1650\text{ lb} \end{array}$$

48.

$$\begin{array}{r} 9\text{ lb } 3\text{ oz} \\ +8\text{ lb } 15\text{ oz} \\ \hline 17\text{ lb } 18\text{ oz} \end{array} = 181\text{ lb } 2\text{ oz}$$

49.

$C = \frac{5}{9}(F - 32)$

$C = \frac{5}{9}(59 - 32)$

$C = \frac{135}{9}$

$C = 15$

59° F is equal to 15° C

50.

$C = \frac{5}{9}(86 - 32)$

$C = \frac{270}{9}$

$C = 30$

86° F is equal to 30° C

Chapter 10

Pretest

1. $(7y^2 - 15y + 9) + (-8y + 17)$
$= 7y^2 - 15y - 8y + 9 + 17$
$= 7y^2 - 23y + 26$

2. $(9b - 5) - (-8b + 7) = (9b - 5) + (8b - 7)$
$= 9b + 8b - 5 - 7$
$= 17b - 12$

3. $(2z^4 - z^3 + 5z) - (-3z^4 + 6z^2 + 2z)$
$= (2z^4 - z^3 + 5z) + (3z^4 - 6z^2 - 2z)$
$= 2z^4 + 3z^4 - z^3 - 6z^2 + 5z - 2z$
$= 5z^4 - z^3 - 6z + 3z$

4. $6t^3 - 5t + 18$ when $t = -2$.
$6(-2)^3 - 5(-2) + 18 = 6(-8) + 10 + 18$
$= -48 + 10 + 18$
$= -38 + 18$
$= -20$

5. $9n^6 \cdot 4n^{12} = (9 \cdot 4)(n^6 \cdot n^{12})$
$= 36n^{6+12}$
$= 36n^{18}$

6. $4x \cdot 5x \cdot 6x = (4 \cdot 5 \cdot 6)(x \cdot x \cdot x) = 120x^3$

7. $(t^{18})^3 = t^{18 \cdot 3} = t^{54}$

8. $(3n^2)^4 = 3^4(n^2)^4 = 81n^{2 \cdot 4} = 81n^8$

9. $(3a^2bc^3)^5 \cdot (8ab^4c)^2$
$= 3^5(a^2)^5 b^5 (c^3)^5 \cdot 8^2 a^2 (b^4)^2 c^2$
$= 243a^{10}b^5c^{15} \cdot 64a^2b^8c^2$
$= (243 \cdot 64)(a^{10} \cdot a^2)(b^5 \cdot b^8)(c^{15} \cdot c^2)$
$= 15,552a^{12}b^{13}c^{17}$

10. $2d(9d^4 - 5d^2 + 11)$
$= 2d \cdot 9d^4 - 2d \cdot 5d^2 + 2d \cdot 11$
$= 18d^5 - 10d^3 + 22d$

11. $(x + 6)(x + 3) = x(x + 3) + 6(x + 3)$
$= x \cdot x + x \cdot 3 + 6 \cdot x + 6 \cdot 3$
$= x^2 + 3x + 6x + 18$
$= x^2 + 9x + 18$

12. $(y - 4)(2y + 5) = y(2y + 5) - 4(2y + 5)$
$= y \cdot 2y + y \cdot 5 - 4 \cdot 2y - 4 \cdot 5$
$= 2y^2 + 5y - 8y - 20$
$= 2y^2 - 3y - 20$

13. $(3x - 2)^2 = (3x - 2)(3x - 2)$
$= 3x(3x - 2) - 2(3x - 2)$
$= 3x \cdot 3x - 3x \cdot 2 - 2 \cdot 3x - 2(-2)$
$= 9x^2 - 6x - 6x + 4$
$= 9x^2 - 12x + 4$

14. $(n + 10)(n - 10) = n(n - 10) + 10(n - 10)$
$= n \cdot n - n \cdot 10 + 10 \cdot n - 10 \cdot 10$
$= n^2 - 10n + 10n - 100$
$= n^2 - 100$

15. $(4a + 1)(2a^2 - a + 7)$
$= 4a(2a^2 - a + 7) + 1(2a^2 - a + 7)$
$= 4a \cdot 2a^2 - 4a \cdot a + 4a \cdot 7 + 1 \cdot 2a^2 - 1 \cdot a + 1 \cdot 7$
$= 8a^3 - 4a^2 + 28a + 2a^2 - a + 7$
$= 8a^3 - 2a^2 + 27a + 7$

16. $18 = 2 \cdot 3 \cdot 3$
$45 = 3 \cdot 3 \cdot 5$
$\text{GCF} = 3 \cdot 3 = 9$

17. $y^9 = y^3 \cdot y^6$
$y^3 = y^3 \cdot 1$
$y^8 = y^3 \cdot y^5$
$\text{GCF} = y^3$

18. $6 = 2 \cdot 3$
$14 = 2 \cdot 7$
$18 = 2 \cdot 3 \cdot 3$
$\text{GCF} = 2$
$m^5 = m \cdot m^4$
$m = m \cdot 1$
$m^4 = m \cdot m^3$
$\text{GCF} = m$
GCF of $6m^5$, $14m$, $18m^4 = 2 \cdot m = 2m$

19. $10y^2 = 2 \cdot 5y^2$
$6y = 2 \cdot 3y$
$14 = 2 \cdot 7$
$10y^2 + 6y - 14 = 2 \cdot 5y^2 + 2 \cdot 3y - 2 \cdot 7$
$= 2(5y^2 + 3y - 7)$

20. $8n^6 = 4n^3 \cdot 2n^3$
$12n^5 = 4n^3 \cdot 3n^2$
$20n^3 = 4n^3 \cdot 5$
$8n^6 - 12n^5 + 20n^3$
$= 4n^3 \cdot 2n^3 - 4n^3 \cdot 3n^2 + 4n^3 \cdot 5$
$= 4n^3(2n^3 - 3n^2 + 5)$

Section 10.1

Practice Problems

1. $(2y+7)+(9y-14) = (2y+9y)+(7-14)$
$= (11y)+(-7)$
$= 11y-7$

2. $(5x^2+4x-3)+(x^2-6x)$
$= 5x^2+x^2+4x-6x-3$
$= 6x^2-2x-3$

3. $(7z^2-4.2z+11)+(-9z^2-1.9z+4)$
$= 7z^2-9z^2-4.2z-1.9z+11+4$
$= -2z^2-6.1z+15$

4.
$$\begin{array}{r} 7z^2-4.2z+11 \\ \underline{-\ 9z^2-1.9z+\ 4} \\ -2z^2-6.1z+15 \end{array}$$

5. $-(7y^2+4y-6) = -1(7y^2+4y-6)$
$= -1(7y^2)+(-1)(4y)+(-1)(-6)$
$= -7y^2-4y+6$

6. $(3b-2)-(7b+23) = (3b-2)+(-7b-23)$
$= 3b-7b-2-23$
$= -4b-25$

7. $\left(11x^2+7x+2\right)-\left(15x^2+4x\right)$
$=\left(11x^2+7x+2\right)+\left(-15x^2-4x\right)$
$= 11x^2-15x^2+7x-4x+2$
$= -4x^2+3x+2$

8. $(-4x^2+20x+17)-(3x^2-12x)$
$= (-4x^2+20x+17)+(-3x^2+12x)$
$= -4x^2-3x^2+20x+12x+17$
$= -7x^2+32x+17$

9.
$$\begin{array}{r} -4x^2+20x+17 \\ \underline{-(3x^2-12x)} \end{array} \qquad \begin{array}{r} -4x^2+20x+17 \\ \underline{-3x^2+12x} \\ -7x^2+32x+17 \end{array}$$

10. $2y^3+y^2-6 = 2(3)^3+(3)^2-6$
$= 2(27)+(9)-6$
$= 54+9-6$
$= 57$

11. When $t = 1$ second:
$-16t^2+530 = -16(1)^2+530$
$= -16+530$
$= 514$
The height of the object at 1 second is 514 feet.
When $t = 4$ seconds:
$-16t^2+530 = -16(4)^2+530$
$= -256+530$
$= 274$
The height of the object at 4 seconds is 274 feet.

Exercise Set 10.1

1. $(2x+3)+(-7x-27) = (2x-7x)+(3-27)$
$= -5x+(-24)$
$= -5x-24$

3.
$$\begin{array}{r} -4z^2-6z+1 \\ \underline{+\ -5z^2+4z+5} \\ -9z^2-2z+6 \end{array}$$

5. $(12y-20)+(9y^2+13y-20)$
$= 9y^2+(12y+13y)+(-20-20)$
$= 9y^2+25y-40$

7. $(4.3a^4+5)+(-8.6a^4-2a^2+4)$
$= (4.3a^4-8.6a^4)+(-2a^2)+(5+4)$
$= -4.3a^4-2a^2+9$

9. $(5a-6)-(a+2)$
$= (5a-6)+(-a-2)$
$= (5a-a)+(-6-2)$
$= 4a-8$

11. $(3x^2-2x+1)-(5x^2-6x)$
$= (3x^2-2x+1)+(-5x^2+6x)$
$= (3x^2-5x^2)+(-2x+6x)+1$
$= -2x^2+4x+1$

13. $(10y^2 - 7) - (20y^3 - 2y^2 - 3)$
$= (10y^2 - 7) + (-20y^3 + 2y^2 + 3)$
$= (-20y^3) + (10y^2 + 2y^2) + (-7 + 3)$
$= -20y^3 + 12y^2 - 4$

15.
$$\begin{array}{r} 2x+12 \\ -\ (3x-4) \\ \hline \end{array} \qquad \begin{array}{r} 2x+12 \\ +\ -3x+\ 4 \\ \hline -x+16 \end{array}$$

17.
$$\begin{array}{r} 13y^2-6y-14 \\ -\ (5y^2+4y-\ 6) \\ \hline \end{array} \qquad \begin{array}{r} 13y^2-\ 6y-14 \\ +\ -5y^2-\ 4y+\ 6 \\ \hline 8y^2-10y-\ 8 \end{array}$$

19. $(25x - 5) + (-20x - 7)$
$= (25x - 20x) + (-5 - 7)$
$= 25x - 12$

21. $(4y + 4) - (3y + 8)$
$= (4y + 4) + (-3y - 8)$
$= (4y - 3y) + (4 - 8)$
$= y - 4$

23. $(9x^2 - 6) + (-5x^2 + x - 10)$
$= (9x^2 - 5x^2) + x + (-6 - 10)$
$= 4x^2 + x - 16$

25. $(10x + 4.5) + (-x - 8.6)$
$= (10x - x) + (4.5 - 8.6)$
$= 9x - 4.1$

27. $(12a - 5) - (-3a + 2)$
$= (12a - 5) + (3a - 2)$
$= (12a + 3a) + (-5 - 2)$
$= 15a - 7$

29. $(21y - 4.6) - (36y - 8.2)$
$= (21y - 4.6) + (-36y + 8.2)$
$= (21y - 36y) + (-4.6 + 8.2)$
$= -15y + 3.6$

31. $(18t^2 - 4t + 2) - (-t^2 + 7t - 1)$
$= (18t^2 - 4t + 2) + (t^2 - 7t + 1)$
$= (18t^2 + t^2) + (-4t - 7t) + (2 + 1)$
$= 19t^2 - 11t + 3$

33. $(b^3 - 2b^2 + 10b + 11) + (b^2 - 3b - 12)$
$= b^3 + (-2b^2 + b^2) + (10b - 3b) + (11 - 12)$
$= b^3 - b^2 + 7b - 1$

35. $(b^3 - 2b^2 + 10b + 11) + (b^2 - 3b - 12)$
$= b^3 + (-2b^2 + b^2) + (10b - 3b) + (11 - 12)$
$= b^3 - b^2 + 7b - 1$

37. $\left(3z + \frac{6}{7}\right) - \left(3z - \frac{3}{7}\right) = \left(3z + \frac{6}{7}\right) + \left(-3z + \frac{3}{7}\right)$
$= (3z - 3z) + \left(\frac{6}{7} + \frac{3}{7}\right)$
$= \frac{9}{7}$

39. $-3x + 7$
Let $x = 2$.
$-3(2) + 7 = -6 + 7 = 1$

41. $x^2 - 6x + 3$
Let $x = 2$.
$(2)^2 - 6(2) + 3 = 4 - 12 + 3 = -5$

43. $\frac{3x^2}{2} - 14$
Let $x = 2$.
$\frac{3(2)^2}{2} - 14 = \frac{3 \cdot 4}{2} - 14$
$= \frac{12}{2} - 14$
$= 6 - 14$
$= -8$

45. $2x + 10$
Let $x = 5$.
$2(5) + 10 = 10 + 10 = 20$

47. x^2
Let $x = 5$.
$(5)^2 = 25$

49. $2x^2 + 4x - 20$
Let $x = 5$.
$2(5)^2 + 4(5) - 20 = 2(25) + 20 - 20 = 50$

51. $16t^2$
Let $t = 6$.
$16(6)^2 = 16(36) = 576$
The object falls 576 feet in 6 seconds.

53. $3000 + 20x$
Let $x = 10$.
$3000 + 20(10) = 3000 + 200 = 3200$
It costs \$3200 to manufacture 10 file cabinets.

55. When $t = 3$ seconds:
$$\begin{aligned}1053 - 16t^2 &= 1053 - 16(3)^2\\ &= 1053 - 16 \cdot 9\\ &= 1053 - 144\\ &= 909\end{aligned}$$
The height of the object above the river after 3 seconds is 909 feet.

57. $3^4 = 3 \cdot 3 \cdot 3 \cdot 3 = 81$

59. $(-5)^2 = (-5) \cdot (-5) = 25$

61. $x \cdot x \cdot x = x^3$

63. $2 \cdot 2 \cdot a \cdot a \cdot a \cdot a = 2^2 a^4$

65. $(2x + 1) + (x + 11) + (5x - 10)$
$= (2x + x + 5x) + (1 + 11 - 10)$
$= 8x + 2$
The perimeter is $(8x + 2)$ inches.

67.
$$\begin{aligned}(7x - 10) - (3x + 5) &= (7x - 10) + (-3x - 5)\\ &= (7x - 3x) + (-10 - 5)\\ &= 4x - 15\end{aligned}$$
The unknown length is $(4x - 15)$ units.

69.
$$\begin{array}{r} 3x^2 + \underline{\quad}x - \underline{\quad} \\ + \ \underline{\quad}x^2 - \ 6x + \ 2 \\ \hline 5x^2 + 14x - \ 4 \end{array}$$

$$\begin{bmatrix}(3 + \underline{\quad})x^2 = 5x^2\\ (3 + \underline{2})x^2 = 5x^2\end{bmatrix}$$

$$\begin{bmatrix}(\underline{\quad} - 6)x = 14x\\ (\underline{20} - 6)x = 14x\end{bmatrix}$$

$$\begin{bmatrix}(-\underline{\quad} + 2) = -4\\ (-\underline{6} + 2) = -4\end{bmatrix}$$

$$\begin{array}{r} 3x^2 + \underline{20}x - \underline{6} \\ + \ \underline{2}x^2 - \ 6x + 2 \\ \hline 5x^2 + 14x - 4 \end{array}$$

71. $7a^4 - 6a^2 + 2a - 1$
$= 7(1.2)^4 - 6(1.2)^2 + 2(1.2) - 1$
$= 7(2.0736) - 6(1.44) + 2.4 - 1$
$= 14.5152 - 8.64 + 2.4 - 1$
$= 7.2752$

73. When $t = 8$ seconds:
$$\begin{aligned}1053 - 16t^2 &= 1053 - 16(8)^2\\ &= 1053 - 16 \cdot 64\\ &= 1053 - 1024\\ &= 29\end{aligned}$$
The height of the object above the river after 8 seconds is 29 feet.
When $t = 9$ seconds:
$$\begin{aligned}1053 - 16t^2 &= 1053 - 16(9)^2\\ &= 1053 - 16 \cdot 81\\ &= 1053 - 1296\\ &= -243\end{aligned}$$
The height of the object above the river after 9 seconds is –243 feet. The object hits the water between 8 and 9 seconds.

Section 10.2

Practice Problems

1. $z^4 \cdot z^8 = z^{4+8} = z^{12}$

2.
$$\begin{aligned}7y^5 \cdot 3y^9 &= (7 \cdot 3)(y^5 \cdot y^9)\\ &= 21y^{5+9}\\ &= 21y^{14}\end{aligned}$$

3.
$$\begin{aligned}(-7r^6s^2)(-3r^2s^5) &= (-7 \cdot -3)(r^6 \cdot r^2)(s^2 \cdot s^5)\\ &= 21r^{6+2}s^{2+5}\\ &= 21r^8s^7\end{aligned}$$

4.
$$\begin{aligned}9y^4 \cdot 3y^2 \cdot y &= (9 \cdot 3)(y^4 \cdot y^2 \cdot y^1)\\ &= 27y^{4+2+1}\\ &= 27y^7\end{aligned}$$

5. $(z^3)^{10} = z^{3 \cdot 10} = z^{30}$

6. $(z^4)^5 \cdot (z^3)^7 = z^{20} \cdot z^{21} = z^{20+21} = z^{41}$

7. $(3b)^4 = 3^4b^4 = 81b^4$

8. $(4x^2y^6)^3 = 4^3(x^2)^3(y^6)^3 = 64x^6y^{18}$

9. $(2x^2y^4)^4 \cdot (3x^6y^9)^2$
$= 2^4(x^2)^4(y^4)^4 \cdot 3^2(x^6)^2(y^9)^2$
$= 16x^8y^{16} \cdot 9x^{12}y^{18}$
$= (16 \cdot 9)(x^8 \cdot x^{12})(y^{16} \cdot y^{18})$
$= 144x^{20}y^{34}$

Exercise Set 10.2

1. $x^5 \cdot x^9 = x^{5+9} = x^{14}$

3. $a^6 \cdot a = a^{6+1} = a^7$

5. $3z^3 \cdot 5z^2 = (3 \cdot 5)(z^3 \cdot z^2) = 15z^5$

7. $-4x \cdot 10x = (-4 \cdot 10)(x \cdot x) = -40x^2$

9. $(-5x^2y^3)(-5x^4y) = (-5)(-5)(x^2 \cdot x^4)(y^3 \cdot y)$
$= 25x^6y^4$

11. $(7ab)(4a^4b^5) = (7 \cdot 4)(a \cdot a^4)(b \cdot b^5)$
$= 28a^5b^6$

13. $2x \cdot 3x \cdot 5x = (2 \cdot 3 \cdot 5)(x \cdot x \cdot x) = 30x^3$

15. $a \cdot 4a^{11} \cdot 3a^5 = (4 \cdot 3)(a \cdot a^{11} \cdot a^5) = 12a^{17}$

17. $(x^5)^3 = x^{5 \cdot 3} = x^{15}$

19. $(z^2)^{10} = z^{2 \cdot 10} = z^{20}$

21. $(b^7)^6 \cdot (b^2)^{10} = b^{7 \cdot 6} \cdot b^{2 \cdot 10}$
$= b^{42} \cdot b^{20}$
$= b^{42+20}$
$= b^{62}$

23. $(3a)^4 = 3^4 \cdot a^4 = 81a^4$

25. $(a^{11}b^8)^3 = a^{11 \cdot 3} \cdot b^{8 \cdot 3} = a^{33}b^{24}$

27. $(11x^3y^6)^2 = 11^2(x^3)^2(y^6)^2 = 121x^6y^{12}$

29. $(-3y)(2y^7)^3 = (-3y) \cdot 2^3(y^7)^3$
$= (-3y) \cdot 8y^{21}$
$= (-3)(8)(y^1 \cdot y^{21})$
$= -24y^{22}$

31. $(4xy)^3(2x^3y^5)^2 = 4^3x^3y^3 \cdot 2^2(x^3)^2(y^5)^2$
$= 64x^3y^3 \cdot 4x^6y^{10}$
$= (64 \cdot 4)(x^3 \cdot x^6)(y^3 \cdot y^{10})$
$= 256x^9y^{13}$

33. $7(x - 3) = 7x - 21$

35. $-2(3a + 2b) = -6a - 4b$

37. $9(x + 2y - 3) = 9x + 18y - 27$

39. area $= s^2 = (4x^6)^2 = 4^2(x^6)^2 = 16x^{12}$
The area is $16x^{12}$ square inches.

41. area $= \frac{1}{2} \cdot b \cdot h$
$= \frac{1}{2} \cdot (6a^3b^4) \cdot (4ab)$
$= \left(\frac{1}{2} \cdot 6 \cdot 4\right)(a^3 \cdot a)(b^4 \cdot b)$
$= 12a^4b^5$
The area is $12a^4b^5$ square meters.

43. $(14a^7b^6)^3(9a^6b^3)^4$
$= 14^3(a^7)^3(b^6)^3 \cdot 9^4(a^6)^4(b^3)^4$
$= 2744a^{21}b^{18} \cdot 6561a^{24}b^{12}$
$= (2744 \cdot 6561)(a^{21}a^{24})(b^{18}b^{12})$
$= 18,003,384a^{45}b^{30}$

45. $(8.1x^{10})^5 = 8.1^5(x^{10})^5 = 34,867.84401x^{50}$

47. Answers may vary.

49. $\left(a^{20}b^{10}c^5\right)^5\left(a^9b^{12}\right)^3$
$= \left(a^{20}\right)^5\left(b^{10}\right)^5\left(c^5\right)^5 \cdot \left(a^9\right)^3\left(b^{12}\right)^3$
$= a^{100}b^{50}c^{25} \cdot a^{27}b^{36}$
$= \left(a^{100}a^{27}\right)\left(b^{50}b^{36}\right)c^{25}$
$= a^{127}b^{86}c^{25}$

Integrated Review

1. $(7x + 1) + (-3x - 2) = 7x - 3x + 1 - 2 = 4x - 1$

2. $(14y - 6) + (19y - 2) = 14y + 19y - 6 - 2$
$= 33y - 8$

3. $(7x + 1) - (-3x - 2) = (7x + 1) + (3x + 2)$
$= 7x + 3x + 1 + 2$
$= 10x + 3$

4. $(14y - 6) - (19y - 2) = (14y - 6) + (-19y + 2)$
$= 14y - 19y - 6 + 2$
$= -5y - 4$

5. $(a^3 + 1) + (2a^3 + 5a - 9)$
$= a^3 + 2a^3 + 5a + 1 - 9$
$= 3a^3 + 5a - 8$

6. $(1.2y^2 - 3.6y) + (0.6y^2 + 1.2y - 5.6)$
$= 1.2y^2 + 0.6y^2 - 3.6y + 1.2y - 5.6$
$= 1.8y^2 - 2.4y - 5.6$

7. $(3.5x^2 - 0.5x) - (5.3x^2 - 2.9x + 1.7)$
$= (3.5x^2 - 0.5x) + (-5.3x^2 + 2.9x - 1.7)$
$= 3.5x^2 - 5.3x^2 - 0.5x + 2.9x - 1.7$
$= -1.8x^2 + 2.4x - 1.7$

8. $(2a^3 - 6a^2 + 11) - (6a^3 + 6a^2 + 11)$
$= (2a^3 - 6a^2 + 11) + (-6a^3 - 6a^2 - 11)$
$= 2a^3 - 6a^3 - 6a^2 - 6a^2 + 11 - 11$
$= -4a^3 - 12a^2$

9. $(8x + 1) - (2x - 6) = (8x + 1) + (-2x + 6)$
$= 8x - 2x + 1 + 6$
$= 6x + 7$

10. $(5x^2 + 2x - 10) - (3x^2 - x + 2)$
$= (5x^2 + 2x - 10) + (-3x^2 + x - 2)$
$= 5x^2 - 3x^2 + 2x + x - 10 - 2$
$= 2x^2 + 3x - 12$

11. $2x - 7 = 2(-3) - 7 = -6 - 7 = -13$

12. $x^2 + 5x + 2 = (-3)^2 + 5(-3) + 2$
$= 9 - 15 + 2$
$= -4$

13. $x^7 \cdot x^{11} = x^{7+11} = x^{18}$

14. $x^6 \cdot x^6 = x^{6+6} = x^{12}$

15. $y^3 \cdot y = y^{3+1} = y^4$

16. $a \cdot a^{10} = a^{1+10} = a^{11}$

17. $(x^7)^{11} = x^{7 \cdot 11} = x^{77}$

18. $(x^6)^6 = x^{6 \cdot 6} = x^{36}$

19. $\left(x^3\right)^4 \cdot \left(x^5\right)^6 = x^{3 \cdot 4} \cdot x^{5 \cdot 6}$
$= x^{12} \cdot x^{30}$
$= x^{12+30}$
$= x^{42}$

20. $\left(y^2\right)^9 \cdot \left(y^3\right)^3 = y^{18} \cdot y^9$
$= y^{27}$

21. $(2x)^4 = 2^4 x^4 = 16x^4$

22. $(3y)^3 = 3^3 y^3 = 27y^3$

23. $(-6xy^2)(2xy^5) = (-6 \cdot 2)(x^1 \cdot x^1)(y^2 \cdot y^5)$
$= -12x^{1+1}y^{2+5}$
$= -12x^2y^7$

24. $(-4a^2b^3)(-3ab) = (-4 \cdot -3)(a^2 \cdot a^1)(b^3 \cdot b^1)$
$= 12a^{2+1}b^{3+1}$
$= 12a^3b^4$

25. $(x^9y^5)^4 = (x^9)^4(y^5)^4 = x^{36}y^{20}$

26. $(a^{10}b^{12})^2 = (a^{10})^2(b^{12})^2 = a^{20}b^{24}$

27. $(10x^2y)^2 \cdot (3y) = 10^2(x^2)^2(y)^2 \cdot (3y)$
$= 100x^4y^2 \cdot 3y$
$= 300x^4y^3$

28. $(8y^3z)^2 \cdot (2z^5) = 8^2(y^3)^2(z)^2 \cdot (2z^5)$
$= 64y^6z^2 \cdot 2z^5$
$= 128y^6z^7$

29. $\left(2a^5b\right)^4\left(3a^9b^4\right)^2 = 2^4\left(a^5\right)^4b^4 \cdot 3^2\left(a^9\right)^2\left(b^4\right)^2$
$= 16a^{20}b^4 \cdot 9a^{18}b^8$
$= 144a^{38}b^{12}$

30. $\left(5x^4y^6\right)^3\left(x^2y^2\right)^5 = 5^3\left(x^4\right)^3\left(y^6\right)^3 \cdot \left(x^2\right)^5\left(y^2\right)^5$
$= 125x^{12}y^{18} \cdot x^{10}y^{10}$
$= 125x^{22}y^{38}$

Section 10.3

Practice Problems

1. $3y(7y^2+5)=3y\cdot 7y^2+3y\cdot 5=21y^3+15y$

2. $5r(8r^2-r+11)=5r\cdot 8r^2+5r(-r)+5r\cdot 11$
$=40r^3-5r^2+55r$

3. $(b+7)(b+5)=b(b+5)+7(b+5)$
$=b\cdot b+b\cdot 5+7\cdot b+7\cdot 5$
$=b^2+5b+7b+35$
$=b^2+12b+35$

4. $(5x-1)(5x+4)=5x(5x+4)-1(5x+4)$
$=5x\cdot 5x+5x\cdot 4-1\cdot 5x-1\cdot 4$
$=25x^2+20x-5x-4$
$=25x^2+15x-4$

5. $(6y-1)^2=(6y-1)(6y-1)$
$=6y(6y-1)-1(6y-1)$
$=6y\cdot 6y+6y(-1)-1(6y)-1(-1)$
$=36y^2-6y-6y+1$
$=36y^2-12y+1$

F O I L

6. $10x\cdot x+10x\cdot 3+(-7)(x)+(-7)(3)$
$=10x^2+30x-7x-21$
$=10x^2+23x-21$

7. $(3x+2)^2=(3x+2)(3x+2)$
F O I L
$=3x\cdot 3x+3x\cdot 2+2\cdot 3x\cdot 2\cdot 2$
$=9x^2+6x+6x+4$
$=9x^2+12x+4$

8 $(2x+5)(x^2+4x-1)$
$=2x(x^2+4x-1)+5(x^2+4x-1)$
$=2x\cdot x^2+2x\cdot 4x+2x(-1)+5\cdot x^2+5\cdot 4x+5(-1)$
$=2x^3+8x^2-2x+5x^2+20x-5$
$=2x^3+13x^2+18x-5$

9.
$$\begin{array}{r} x^2+4x-1 \\ 2x+5 \\ \hline 5x^2+20x-5 \\ 2x^3+\ 8x^2-\ 2x \\ \hline 2x^3+13x^2+18x-5 \end{array}$$

Exercise Set 10.3

1. $$\begin{aligned} 3x(9x^2-3) &= 3x\cdot 9x^2+3x\cdot(-3) \\ &= (3\cdot 9)(x\cdot x^2)+(3)(-3)(x) \\ &= 27x^3+(-9x) \\ &= 27x^3-9x \end{aligned}$$

3. $$\begin{aligned} &-5a(4a^2-6a+1) \\ &= (-5a)(4a^2)+(-5a)(-6a)+(-5a)(1) \\ &= (-5)(4)(a\cdot a^2)+(-5)(-6)(a\cdot a)+(-5a) \\ &= -20a^3+30a^2-5a \end{aligned}$$

5. $$\begin{aligned} &7x^2(6x^2-5x+7) \\ &= (7x^2)(6x^2)+(7x^2)(-5x)+(7x^2)(7) \\ &= (7\cdot 6)(x^2\cdot x^2)+(7)(-5)(x^2\cdot x)+(7\cdot 7)x^2 \\ &= 42x^4-35x^3+49x^2 \end{aligned}$$

7. $$\begin{aligned} (x+3)(x+10) &= x(x+10)+3(x+10) \\ &= x\cdot x+x\cdot 10+3\cdot x+3\cdot 10 \\ &= x^2+10x+3x+30 \\ &= x^2+13x+30 \end{aligned}$$

9. $$\begin{aligned} (2x-6)(x+4) &= 2x(x+4)-6(x+4) \\ &= 2x\cdot x+2x\cdot 4-6\cdot x-6\cdot 4 \\ &= 2x^2+8x-6x-24 \\ &= 2x^2+2x-24 \end{aligned}$$

11. $$\begin{aligned} (6a+4)^2 &= (6a+4)(6a+4) \\ &= 6a(6a+4)+4(6a+4) \\ &= 6a\cdot 6a+6a\cdot 4+4\cdot 6a+4\cdot 4 \\ &= 36a^2+24a+24a+16 \\ &= 36a^2+48a+16 \end{aligned}$$

13. $$\begin{aligned} (a+6)(a^2-6a+3) &= a(a^2-6a+3)+6(a^2-6a+3) \\ &= a\cdot a^2+a(-6a)+a\cdot 3+6\cdot a^2+6(-6a)+6\cdot 3 \\ &= a^3-6a^2+3a+6a^2-36a+18 \\ &= a^3-33a+18 \end{aligned}$$

15. $(4x-5)(2x^2+3x-10) = 4x(2x^2+3x-10)-5(2x^2+3x-10)$
$= 4x\cdot 2x^2+4x\cdot 3x+4x(-10)-5\cdot 2x^2-5\cdot 3x-5(-10)$
$= 8x^3+12x^2-40x-10x^2-15x+50$
$= 8x^3+2x^2-55x+50$

17. $(x^3+2x+x^2)(3x+1+x^2) = x^3(3x+1+x^2)+2x(3x+1+x^2)+x^2(3x+1+x^2)$
$= x^3\cdot 3x+x^3\cdot 1+x^3\cdot x^2+2x\cdot 3x+2x\cdot 1+2x\cdot x^2+x^2\cdot 3x+x^2\cdot 1+x^2\cdot x^2$
$= 3x^4+x^3+x^5+6x^2+2x+2x^3+3x^3+x^2+x^4$
$= x^5+4x^4+6x^3+7x^2+2x$

19. $10r(-3r+2) = 10r(-3r)+10r(2)$
$= -30r^2+20r$

21. $-2y^2(3y+y^2-6)$
$= -2y^2\cdot 3y+(-2y^2)\cdot y^2+(-2y^2)(-6)$
$= -6y^3-2y^4+12y^2$

23. $(x+2)(x+12) = x(x+12)+2(x+12)$
$= x\cdot x+x\cdot 12+2\cdot x+2\cdot 12$
$= x^2+12x+2x+24$
$= x^2+14x+24$

25. $(2a+3)(2a-3)$
$= 2a(2a-3)+3(2a-3)$
$= 2a\cdot 2a+2a(-3)+3\cdot 2a+3(-3)$
$= 4a^2-6a+6a-9$
$= 4a^2-9$

27. $(x+5)^2 = (x+5)(x+5)$
$= x(x+5)+5(x+5)$
$= x\cdot x+x\cdot 5+5\cdot x+5\cdot 5$
$= x^2+5x+5x+25$
$= x^2+10x+25$

29. $\left(b+\frac{3}{5}\right)\left(b+\frac{4}{5}\right) = b\left(b+\frac{4}{5}\right)+\frac{3}{5}\left(b+\frac{4}{5}\right)$
$= b^2+\frac{4}{5}b+\frac{3}{5}b+\frac{3}{5}\cdot\frac{4}{5}$
$= b^2+\frac{7}{5}b+\frac{12}{25}$

31. $(6x+1)(x^2+4x+1)$
$= 6x(x^2+4x+1)+1(x^2+4x+1)$
$= 6x^3+24x^2+6x+x^2+4x+1$
$= 6x^3+25x^2+10x+1$

33. $(7x+5)^2 = (7x+5)(7x+5)$
$= 7x(7x+5)+5(7x+5)$
$= 49x^2+35x+35x+25$
$= 49x^2+70x+25$

35. $(2x-1)^2 = (2x-1)(2x-1)$
$= 2x(2x-1)-1(2x-1)$
$= 4x^2-2x-2x+1$
$= 4x^2-4x+1$

37. $(2x^2-3)(4x^3+2x-3)$
$= 2x^2(4x^3+2x-3)-3(4x^3+2x-3)$
$= 8x^5+4x^3-6x^2-12x^3-6x+9$
$= 8x^5-8x^3-6x^2-6x+9$

39.

$$\begin{array}{r} x^3+x^2+x \\ \times \quad x^2+x+1 \\ \hline x^3+x^2+x \\ x^4+x^3+x^2 \quad \\ x^5+x^4+x^3 \quad\quad \\ \hline x^5+2x^4+3x^3+2x^2+x \end{array}$$

41.

$$\begin{array}{r} 2z^2-z+1 \\ \times \quad 5z^2+z-2 \\ \hline -4z^2+2z-2 \\ 2z^3-z^2+z \quad \\ 10z^4-5z^3+5z^2 \quad\quad \\ \hline 10z^4-3z^3 \quad +3z-2 \end{array}$$

43. $50 = 2\cdot5\cdot5 = 2\cdot5^2$

45. $72 = 2\cdot2\cdot2\cdot3\cdot3 = 2^3\cdot3^2$

47. $200 = 2\cdot2\cdot2\cdot5\cdot5 = 2^3\cdot5^2$

49. $(y-6)(y^2+3y+2)$
$= y(y^2+3y+2)-6(y^2+3y+2)$
$= y^3+3y^2+2y-6y^2-18y-12$
$= y^3-3y^2-16y-12$
The area is $(y^3-3y^2-16y-12)$ square feet.

51. $(x^2-1)^2-x^2 = (x^2-1)(x^2-1)-x^2$
$= x^2(x^2-1)-1(x^2-1)-x^2$
$= x^4-x^2-x^2+1-x^2$
$= x^4-3x^2+1$
The area of the shaded figure is (x^4-3x^2+1) square meters.

53. Answers may vary.

Section 10.4

Practice Problems

1. $42 = 2\cdot3\cdot7$
$28 = 2\cdot2\cdot7$
The common prime factors are 2 and 7.
The GCF is $2\cdot7 = 14$.

2. In the list z^7, z^8 and z^1, the smallest exponent to which z is raised is 1. Thus, the GCF is $z^1 = z$.

3. The GCF of 6, 3, and 15 is 3.
The GCF of a^4, a^5, and a^2 is a^2.
Thus, the GCF of $6a^4$, $3a^5$, and $15a^2$ is $3a^2$.

4. The GCF of $10y^7$ and $5y^9$ is $5y^7$.
$10y^7+5y^9 = 5y^7\cdot2+5y^7\cdot y^2$
$= 5y^7(2+y^2)$

5. The GCF of $4z^2-12z+2$ is 2.
$4z^2-12z+2 = 2\cdot2z^2-2\cdot6z+2\cdot1$
$= 2(2z^2-6z+1)$

6. $-3y^2-9y+15x^2$
$= (-3)\cdot y^2+(-3)(3y)+(-3)(-5x^2)$
$= -3(y^2+3y-5x^2)$

Exercise Set 10.4

1. $48 = 2\cdot2\cdot2\cdot2\cdot3$
$15 = 3\cdot5$
GCF = 3

3. $60 = 2\cdot2\cdot3\cdot5$
$72 = 2\cdot2\cdot2\cdot3\cdot3$
GCF = $2\cdot2\cdot3 = 12$

5. $12 = 2\cdot2\cdot3$
$20 = 2\cdot2\cdot5$
$36 = 2\cdot2\cdot3\cdot3$
GCF = $2\cdot2 = 4$

7. $8 = 2 \cdot 2 \cdot 2$
$32 = 2 \cdot 2 \cdot 2 \cdot 2 \cdot 2$
$100 = 2 \cdot 2 \cdot 5 \cdot 5$
$\text{GCF} = 2 \cdot 2 = 4$

9. $y^7 = y^2 \cdot y^5$
$y^2 = y^2$
$y^{10} = y^2 \cdot y^8$
$\text{GCF} = y^2$

11. $a^5 = a^5$
$a^5 = a^5$
$a^5 = a^5$
$\text{GCF} = a^5$

13. $x^3y^2 = x \cdot x^2 \cdot y^2$
$xy^2 = x \cdot y^2$
$x^4y^2 = x \cdot x^3y^2$
$\text{GCF} = x \cdot y^2 = xy^2$

15. $3 = 3$
$5 = 5$
$10 = 2 \cdot 5$
$\text{GCF} = 1$

$x^4 = x \cdot x^3$
$x^7 = x \cdot x^6$
$x = x$
$\text{GCF} = x$

$\text{GCF} = 1 \cdot x = x$

17. $2 = 2$
$14 = 2 \cdot 7$
$18 = 2 \cdot 3 \cdot 3$
$\text{GCF} = 2$

$z^3 = z^3$
$z^5 = z^3 \cdot z^2$
$z^3 = z^3$
$\text{GCF} = z^3$

$\text{GCF} = 2z^3$

19. $3y^2 = 3y \cdot y$
$18y = 3y \cdot 6$
$\text{GCF} = 3y$
$3y^2 + 18y = 3y \cdot y + 3y \cdot 6 = 3y(y+6)$
Check:
$3y(y+a) = 3y \cdot y + 3y \cdot 6 = 3y^2 + 18y$

21. $10a^6 = 5a^6 \cdot 2$
$5a^8 = 5a^6 \cdot a^2$
$\text{GCF} = 5a^6$
$10a^6 - 5a^8 = 5a^6 \cdot 2 - 5a^6 \cdot a^2$
$= 5a^6(2 - a^2)$
Check:
$5a^6(2 - a^2) = 5a^6 \cdot 2 - 5a^6 \cdot a^2$
$= 10a^6 - 5a^8$

23. $4x^3 = 4x \cdot x^2$
$12x^2 = 4x \cdot 3x$
$20x = 4x \cdot 5$
$\text{GCF} = 4x$
$4x^3 + 12x^2 + 20x = 4x \cdot x^2 + 4x \cdot 3x + 4x \cdot 5$
$= 4x(x^2 + 3x + 5)$
Check:
$4x(x^2 + 3x + 5) = 4x \cdot x^2 + 4x \cdot 3x + 4x \cdot 5$
$= 4x^3 + 12x^2 + 20x$

25. $z^7 = z^5 \cdot z^2$
$6z^5 = z^5 \cdot 6$
$\text{GCF} = z^5$
$z^7 - 6z^5 = z^5 \cdot z^2 - z^5 \cdot 6 = z^5(z^2 - 6)$
Check:
$z^5(z^2 - 6) = z^5 \cdot z^2 - z^5 \cdot 6 = z^7 - 6z^5$

27. $35 = 7 \cdot 5$
$14y = 7 \cdot 2y$
$7y^2 = 7 \cdot y^2$
$\text{GCF} = 7$
$-35 + 14y - 7y^2$
$= -7 \cdot 5 + 7 \cdot 2y - 7 \cdot y^2$
$= 7(-5 + 2y - y^2)$ or $-7(5 - 2y + y^2)$
Check:
$7(-5 + 2y - y^2) = 7 \cdot (-5) + 7 \cdot 2y - 7 \cdot y^2$
$= -35 + 14y - 7y^2$

29. $12a^5 = 12a^5$
$36a^6 = 12a^5 \cdot 3a$
$\text{GCF} = 12a^5$
$12a^5 - 36a^6 = 12a^5 \cdot 1 - 12a^5 \cdot 3a$
$= 12a^5(1 - 3a)$
Check:
$12a^5(1 - 3a) = 12a^5 \cdot 1 - 12a^5 \cdot 3a$
$= 12a^5 - 36a$

31. 30% of 120 is what number?
$30\% \cdot 120 = x$
$0.3 \cdot 120 = x$
$36 = x$

33. $80\% = \frac{80}{100} = \frac{4}{5}$

35. $\frac{3}{8} = \frac{x}{100}$
$3 \cdot 100 = 8 \cdot x$
$300 = 8x$
$x = \frac{300}{8} = 37.5$
$\frac{3}{8} = 37.5\%$

37. area on the left: $x \cdot x = x^2$
area on the right: $2 \cdot x = 2x$
total area: $x^2 + 2x$
Notice that $x(x+2) = x^2 + 2x.$

39. Answers may vary.

Chapter 10 Review

1. $(2b+7)+(8b-10) = 2b+7+8b-10$
$= 2b+8b+7-10$
$= 10b-3$

2. $(7s-6)+(14s-9) = 7s-6+14s-9$
$= 7s+14s-6-9$
$= 21s-15$

3. $(3x+0.2)-(4x-2.6) = (3x+0.2)+(-4x+2.6)$
$= 3x-4x+0.2+2.6$
$= -x+2.8$

4. $(10y-6)-(11y+6) = (10y-6)+(-11y-6)$
$= 10y-11y-6-6$
$= -y-12$

5. $(4z^2+6z-1)+(5z-5) = 4z^2+6z+5z-1-5$
$= 4z^2+11z-6$

6. $(17a^3+11a^2+a)+(14a^2-a)$
$= 17a^3+11a^2+14a^2+a-a$
$= 17a^3+25a^2$

7. $\left(9y^2-y+\frac{1}{2}\right)-\left(20y^2-\frac{1}{4}\right)$
$= \left(9y^2-y+\frac{1}{2}\right)+\left(-20y^2+\frac{1}{4}\right)$
$= 9y^2-20y^2-y+\frac{1}{2}+\frac{1}{4}$
$= -11y^2-y+\frac{3}{4}$

8. $(x^2-6x+1)-(x-2) = (x^2-6x+1)+(-x+2)$
$= x^2-6x-x+1+2$
$= x^2-7x+3$

9. $5x^2$ when $x = 3$
$5(3)^2 = 5 \cdot 9 = 45$

10. $2-7x$ when $x = 3$
$2-7(3) = 2-21 = -19$

11. $p = 2(10x-2)+2(3x+16)$
$= 20x-4+6x+32$
$= (26x+28)$ feet

12. $x^{10} \cdot x^{14} = x^{10+14} = x^{24}$

13. $y \cdot y^6 = y^{1+6} = y^7$

14. $4z^2 \cdot 6z^5 = (4 \cdot 6)(z^2 \cdot z^5) = 24z^7$

15. $(-3x^2y)(5xy^4) = (-3 \cdot 5)(x^2 \cdot x)(y \cdot y^4)$
$= -15x^3y^5$

16. $(a^5)^7 = a^{5 \cdot 7} = a^{35}$

17. $(x^2)^4 \cdot (x^{10})^2 = x^{2 \cdot 4} \cdot x^{10 \cdot 2}$
$= x^8 \cdot x^{20}$
$= x^{8+20}$
$= x^{28}$

18. $(9b)^2 = 9^2b^2 = 81b^2$

19. $(a^4b^2c)^5 = (a^4)^5 \cdot (b^2)^5 \cdot (c)^5$
$= a^{20}b^{10}c^5$

20. $(7x)(2x^5)^3 = 7x \cdot 2^3 \cdot (x^5)^3$
$= 7x \cdot 8 \cdot x^{15}$
$= (7 \cdot 8)(x \cdot x^{15})$
$= 56x^{16}$

21. $(3x^6y^5)^3(2x^6y^5)^2$
$= \left(3^3 \cdot (x^6)^3 \cdot (y^5)^3\right) \cdot \left(2^2 \cdot (x^6)^2 \cdot (y^5)^2\right)$
$= (27 \cdot x^{18} \cdot y^{15}) \cdot (4 \cdot x^{12} \cdot y^{10})$
$= (27 \cdot 4)(x^{18} \cdot x^{12})(y^{15} \cdot y^{10})$
$= 108x^{30}y^{25}$

22. area $= s^2 = (9a^7)^2 = 9^2 \cdot (a^7)^2 = 81a^{14}$
The area of the square is $81a^{14}$ square miles.

23. $2a(5a^2 - 6) = 2a \cdot 5a^2 + 2a \cdot (-6) = 10a^3 - 12a$

24. $-3y^2(y^2 - 2y + 1)$
$= -3y^2 \cdot y^2 + (-3y^2)(-2y) + (-3y^2)(1)$
$= -3y^4 + 6y^3 - 3y^2$

25. $(x+2)(x+6) = x(x+6) + 2(x+6)$
$= x^2 + 6x + 2x + 12$
$= x^2 + 8x + 12$

26. $(3x-1)(5x-9) = 3x(5x-9) - 1(5x-9)$
$= 15x^2 - 27x - 5x + 9$
$= 15x^2 - 32x + 9$

27. $(y-5)^2 = (y-5)(y-5)$
$= y(y-5) - 5(y-5)$
$= y^2 - 5y - 5y + 25$
$= y^2 - 10y + 25$

28. $(7a+1)^2 = (7a+1)(7a+1)$
$= 7a(7a+1) + 1(7a+1)$
$= 49a^2 + 7a + 7a + 1$
$= 49a^2 + 14a + 1$

29. $(x+1)(x^2 - 2x + 3)$
$= x(x^2 - 2x + 3) + 1(x^2 - 2x + 3)$
$= x^3 - 2x^2 + 3x + x^2 - 2x + 3$
$= x^3 - x^2 + x + 3$

30. $(4y^2 - 3)(2y^2 + y + 1)$
$= 4y^2(2y^2 + y + 1) - 3(2y^2 + y + 1)$
$= 8y^4 + 4y^3 + 4y^2 - 6y^2 - 3y - 3$
$= 8y^4 + 4y^3 - 2y^2 - 3y - 3$

31.
$$\begin{array}{r} 3z^2 + 2z + 1 \\ \times \qquad z^2 + z + 1 \\ \hline 3z^2 + 2z + 1 \\ 3z^3 + 2z^2 + z \quad \\ 3z^4 + 2z^3 + z^2 \qquad \quad \\ \hline 3z^4 + 5z^3 + 6z^2 + 3z + 1 \end{array}$$

32. $A = lw$
$= (a+6)(a^2 - a + 1)$
$= a(a^2 - a + 1) + 6(a^2 - a + 1)$
$= a^3 - a^2 + a + 6a^2 - 6a + 6$
$= a^3 + 5a^2 - 5a + 6$
The area is $(a^3 + 5a^2 - 5a + 6)$ square centimeters.

33. $20 = 2 \cdot 2 \cdot 5$
$35 = 5 \cdot 7$
GCF = 5

34. $12 = 2 \cdot 2 \cdot 3$
$32 = 2 \cdot 2 \cdot 2 \cdot 2 \cdot 2$
GCF $= 2 \cdot 2 = 4$

35. $24 = 2 \cdot 2 \cdot 2 \cdot 3$
$30 = 2 \cdot 3 \cdot 5$
$60 = 2 \cdot 2 \cdot 3 \cdot 5$
GCF $= 2 \cdot 3 = 6$

36. $10 = 2 \cdot 5$
$20 = 2 \cdot 2 \cdot 5$
$25 = 5 \cdot 5$
GCF = 5

37. $x^3 = x^2 \cdot x$
$x^2 = x^2$
$x^{10} = x^2 \cdot x^8$
GCF $= x^2$

38. $y^{10} = y^7 \cdot y^3$
$y^7 = y^7$
$y^7 = y^7$
GCF $= y^7$

39. $xy^2 = xy \cdot y$
$xy = xy$
$x^3y^3 = xy \cdot x^2y^2$
GCF $= xy$

40. $a^5b^4 = a^5b^2 \cdot b^2$
$a^6b^3 = a^5b^2 \cdot ab$
$a^7b^2 = a^5b^2 \cdot a^2$
GCF $= a^5b^2$

41. $5a^3 = 5a \cdot a^2$
$10a = 5a \cdot 2$
$20a^4 = 5a \cdot 4a^3$
GCF $= 5a$

42. $12y^2z = 4y^2z \cdot 3$
$20y^2z = 4y^2z \cdot 5$
$24y^5z = 4y^2z \cdot 6y^3$
$\text{GCF} = 4y^2z$

43. $2x^2 = 2x \cdot x$
$12x = 2x \cdot 6$
$\text{GCF} = 2x$
$2x^2 + 12x = 2x \cdot x + 2x \cdot 6 = 2x(x+6)$

44. $6a^2 = 6a \cdot a$
$12a = 6a \cdot 2$
$\text{GCF} = 6a$
$6a^2 - 12a = 6a \cdot a - 6a \cdot 2 = 6a(a-2)$

45. $6y^4 = y^4 \cdot 6$
$y^6 = y^4 \cdot y^2$
$\text{GCF} = y^4$
$6y^4 - y^6 = y^4 \cdot 6 - y^4 \cdot y^2 = y^4(6 - y^2)$

46. $7x^2 = 7 \cdot x^2$
$14x = 7 \cdot 2x$
$7 = 7 \cdot 1$
$\text{GCF} = 7$
$$\begin{aligned} 7x^2 - 14x + 7 &= 7 \cdot x^2 - 7 \cdot 2x + 7 \cdot 1 \\ &= 7(x^2 - 2x + 1) \end{aligned}$$

47. $5a^7 = a^3 \cdot 5a^4$
$a^4 = a^3 \cdot a$
$a^3 = a^3 \cdot 1$
$\text{GCF} = a^3$
$$\begin{aligned} 5a^7 - a^4 + a^3 &= a^3 \cdot 5a^4 - a^3 \cdot a + a^3 \cdot 1 \\ &= a^3(5a^4 - a + 1) \end{aligned}$$

48. $10y^6 = 10y \cdot y^5$
$10y = 10y \cdot 1$
$\text{GCF} = 10y$
$10y^6 - 10y = 10y \cdot y^5 - 10 \cdot 1 = 10y(y^5 - 1)$

Chapter 10 Test

1. $$\begin{aligned} (11x-3)+(4x-1) &= (11x+4x)+(-3-1) \\ &= 15x - 4 \end{aligned}$$

2. $$\begin{aligned} (11x-3)-(4x-1) &= (11x-3)+(-4x+1) \\ &= (11x-4x)+(-3+1) \\ &= 7x - 2 \end{aligned}$$

3. $$\begin{aligned} &(1.3y^2+5y)+(2.1y^2-3y-3) \\ &= (1.3y^2+2.1y^2)+(5y-3y)-3 \\ &= 3.4y^2+2y-3 \end{aligned}$$

4. $$\begin{aligned} &(6a^2+2a+1)-(8a^2+a) \\ &= (6a^2+2a+1)+(-8a^2-a) \\ &= (6a^2-8a^2)+(2a-a)+1 \\ &= -2a^2+a+1 \end{aligned}$$

5. $$\begin{aligned} x^2 - 6x + 1 &= (8)^2 - 6(8) + 1 \\ &= 64 - 48 + 1 \\ &= 17 \end{aligned}$$

6. $y^3 \cdot y^{11} = y^{3+11} = y^{14}$

7. $(y^3)^{11} = y^{3 \cdot 11} = y^{33}$

8. $(2x^2)^4 = 2^4(x^2)^4 = 16x^8$

9. $(6a^3)(-2a^7) = (6)(-2)(a^3 \cdot a^7) = -12a^{10}$

10. $$\begin{aligned} (p^6)^7(p^2)^6 &= p^{6\cdot 7} \cdot p^{2\cdot 6} \\ &= p^{42} \cdot p^{12} \\ &= p^{42+12} \\ &= p^{54} \end{aligned}$$

11. $$\begin{aligned} (3a^4b)^2(2ba^4)^3 &= 3^2a^8b^2 \cdot 2^3b^3a^{12} \\ &= (9 \cdot 8)(a^8 \cdot a^{12})(b^2 \cdot b^3) \\ &= 72a^{20}b^5 \end{aligned}$$

12. $$\begin{aligned} 5x(2x^2+1.3) &= 5x \cdot 2x^2 + 5x \cdot 1.3 \\ &= 10x^3 + 6.5x \end{aligned}$$

13. $$\begin{aligned} &-2y(y^3+6y^2-4) \\ &= -2y \cdot y^3 - 2y \cdot 6y^2 - 2y \cdot (-4) \\ &= -2y^4 - 12y^3 + 8y \end{aligned}$$

14. $$\begin{aligned} (x-3)(x+2) &= x(x+2) - 3(x+2) \\ &= x^2 + 2x - 3x - 6 \\ &= x^2 - x - 6 \end{aligned}$$

15. $$\begin{aligned} (5x+2)^2 &= (5x+2)(5x+2) \\ &= 5x(5x+2) + 2(5x+2) \\ &= 25x^2 + 10x + 10x + 4 \\ &= 25x^2 + 20x + 4 \end{aligned}$$

16. $(a+2)(a^2-2a+4)$
$=a(a^2-2a+4)+2(a^2-2a+4)$
$=a^3-2a^2+4a+2a^2-4a+8$
$=a^3+8$

17. area:
$(x+7)(5x-2)=x(5x-2)+7(5x-2)$
$=5x^2-2x+35x-14$
$=5x^2+33x-14$
The area is $(5x^2+33x-14)$ square inches.
perimeter:
$2(2x)+2(5x-2)=4x+10x-4=14x-4$
The perimeter is $(14x-4)$ inches.

18. $45=3\cdot3\cdot5$
$60=2\cdot2\cdot3\cdot5$
$\text{GCF}=3\cdot5=15$

19. $6y^3=3y^3\cdot2$
$9y^5=3y^3\cdot3y^2$
$18y^4=3y^3\cdot6y$
$\text{GCF}=3y^3$

20. $3y^2=3y\cdot y$
$15y=3y\cdot5$
$3y^2-15y=3y\cdot y-3y\cdot5=3y(y-5)$

21. $10a^2=2a\cdot5a$
$12a=2a\cdot6$
$10a^2+12a=2a\cdot5a+2a\cdot6=2a(5a+6)$

22. $6x^2=6\cdot x^2$
$12x=6\cdot2x$
$30=6\cdot5$
$6x^2-12x-30=6\cdot x^2-6\cdot2x-6\cdot5$
$=6(x^2-2x-5)$

23. $7x^6=x^3\cdot7x^3$
$6x^4=x^3\cdot6x$
$x^3=x^3\cdot1$
$7x^6-6x^4+x^3=x^3\cdot7x^3-x^3\cdot6x+x^3\cdot1$
$=x^3(7x^3-6x+1)$

Cumulative Review

1. $A=lw$
$A=(380\text{ miles})(280\text{ miles})$
$A=106,400\text{ square miles}$

2. $21\cdot7=147$
147 pecan trees

3. $1+(-10)+(-8)+9=-9+(-8)+9$
$=-17+9$
$=-8$

4. $-2+(-7)+3+(-4)=-9+3+(-4)$
$=-6+(-4)$
$=-10$

5. $8-15=8+(-15)=-7$

6. $4-7=4+(-7)=-3$

7. $-4-(-5)=-4+5=1$

8. $3-(-2)=3+2=5$

9. $7x=6x+4$
$7x-6x=6x+4-6x$
$x=4$

10. $4x=-2+3x$
$4x-3x=-2+3x-3x$
$x=-2$

11. $\dfrac{8\cdot4}{3x\cdot4}=\dfrac{32}{12x}$

12. $\dfrac{3\cdot4}{2c\cdot4}=\dfrac{12}{8c}$

13.
$$\begin{array}{rcr} 12 & = & 11\frac{7}{7} \\ -8\frac{3}{7} & = & -8\frac{3}{7} \\ \hline & & 3\frac{4}{7} \end{array}$$

14.
$$\begin{array}{rcl} 15 & = & 14\frac{5}{5} \\ -4\frac{2}{5} & = & -4\frac{2}{5} \\ \hline & & 10\frac{3}{5} \end{array}$$

15. Since there is a 3 in the hundredths place, 736.2359 rounded to the nearest tenth is 736.2

16. Since there is a 7 in the hundredths place, 328.174 rounded to the nearest tenth is 328.2.

17.
$$\begin{array}{r} 23.850 \\ +1.604 \\ \hline 25.454 \end{array}$$

18.
$$\begin{array}{r} 12.762 \\ +4.290 \\ \hline 17.052 \end{array}$$

19. $3.7(-9) = -3.33$
$-33.3 = -3.33$ False
-9 is not a solution.

20. $2.8(6) = 16.8$
$16.8 = 16.8$ True
6 is a solution.

21. $\frac{786}{10,000} = 0.0786$

22. $\frac{818}{1000} = 0.818$

23. $\frac{0.12}{10} = 0.012$

24. $\frac{5.03}{100} = 0.0503$

25. $-2(3.8) + 5 = -7.6 + 5 = -2.6$

26. $6(-2.1) - 1 = -12.6 - 1 = -13.6$

27.
$$\begin{array}{r} 3.142 \\ 7\overline{)\,22.000} \\ -21 \\ \hline 10 \\ -7 \\ \hline 30 \\ -28 \\ \hline 20 \\ -14 \\ \hline 6 \end{array}$$

$\frac{22}{7} \approx 3.14$

28.
$$\begin{array}{r} 1.9473 \\ 19\overline{)\,37.0000} \\ -19 \\ \hline 180 \\ -171 \\ \hline 90 \\ -76 \\ \hline 140 \\ -133 \\ \hline 70 \\ -57 \\ \hline 13 \end{array}$$

$\frac{37}{19} \approx 1.947$

29. $\sqrt{\frac{1}{36}} = \frac{1}{6}$

30. $\sqrt{\frac{4}{25}} = \frac{2}{5}$

31. $\frac{x}{69} = \frac{6}{9}$
$9 = 414$
$x = 46$
The tree is 46 feet high.

32. $\frac{1}{2} = \frac{x}{6}$
$2x = 6$
$x = 3$
The fire hydrant is 3 feet high.

33. $1.2 = 30\% \cdot x$

34. $9 = 45\% \cdot x$

35. $x \cdot 50 = 8$

$$x = \frac{8}{50}$$

$$\frac{8}{50} = \frac{16}{100} = 16\%$$

36. $x \cdot 16 = 4$

$$x = \frac{4}{16}$$

$$x = \frac{1}{4}$$

$$\frac{1}{4} = \frac{25}{100} = 25\%$$

37. $31 = 4\% \cdot x$

$$31 = 0.04 \cdot x$$

$$\frac{31}{0.04} = x$$

$$775 = x$$

There are a total of 775 freshmen.

38. $29 = 2\% \cdot x$

$$29 = 0.02 \cdot x$$

$$\frac{29}{0.02} = x$$

$$1450 = x$$

There are 1450 apples in the shipment.

39. $I = PRT$

$$I = (2400)(0.10)\left(\frac{8}{12}\right)$$

$$I = \frac{1920}{12}$$

$$I = 160$$

He paid \$160 in interest.

40.

$$I = (1000)(0.03)\left(\frac{10}{12}\right)$$

$$I = \frac{300}{12}$$

$$I = 25$$

\$25 of interest was earned.

41. One + Two + Three + Four or More
$= 47\% + 15\% + 6\% + 3\% = 71\%$

42. Zero + One + Two
$29\% + 47\% + 15\% = 91\%$

43. $P = 2L + 2W$

$P = 2 \cdot 11$ inches $+ 2 \cdot 3$ inches

$P = 22$ inches $+ 6$ inches

$P = 28$ inches

44. $P = 6$ feet $+ 8$ feet $+ 11$ feet $= 25$ feet

45. $A = bh$

$A = (3.4 \text{ miles})(1.5 \text{ miles})$

$A = 51$ square miles

46.

$$A = \frac{1}{2}bh$$

$$A = \frac{1}{2}(17 \text{ inches})(8 \text{ inches})$$

$A = 68$ square inches

47.

```
  5 lb  9 oz
  ×      6
-------------
30 lb 54 oz = 30 lb + 3 lb 6 oz
                   33 lb 6 oz
```

48.

```
5 tons   700 lb
 ×          3
---------------
5 tons 2100 lb = 5 tons + 1 ton 100 lb
               = 6 tons 100 lb
```

49. 3210 ml = 3.21 L

50. 4321 cl = 43.21 L